W9-AWL-688

MATHEMATICS
ITS MAGIC AND MASTERY

AARON BAKST

THIRD EDITION

D. VAN NOSTRAND COMPANY, INC.

PRINCETON, NEW JERSEY

TORONTO   LONDON   MELBOURNE

TO

SIMON L. RUSKIN

Physician, Scientist, Collaborator

and Friend

Van Nostrand Regional Offices: *New York, Chicago, San Francisco*

D. Van Nostrand Company, Ltd., *London*

D. Van Nostrand Company (Canada), Ltd., *Toronto*

D. Van Nostrand Australia Pty, Ltd., *Melbourne*

Copyright © 1941, 1952, 1967, by D. VAN NOSTRAND COMPANY, INC.

Published simultaneously in Canada by
D. Van Nostrand Company (Canada), Ltd.

*No reproduction in any form of this book, in whole or
in part (except for brief quotation in critical articles
or reviews), may be made without written authorization
from the publisher.*

Library of Congress Catalog Card No. 67-23114

PRINTED IN THE UNITED STATES OF AMERICA

Preface to Third Edition

Dr. Bakst had always believed that his books should be kept up-to-date in the sense of reflecting changing emphases in topics of mathematical interest. In order to continue this policy, this new edition has been prepared by the addition of new material on coordinate systems, on the elementary mathematics of space vehicles, and on the theory of games. It is earnestly to be hoped that this added material will maintain in this volume the broadness of interest and clarity of presentation that have always characterized Dr. Bakst's books.

W. R. M.

Princeton, N. J.
June, 1967

Preface to the Second Edition

Ten years have elapsed since the first edition of this book was presented to those whose interest in mathematics was stronger than the fear of abstract mathematical speculations. If a confession might be in order, the author had fears and trepidations when this book appeared in print. He was uncertain whether his treatment of the subject would meet with some degree of approval. Now that a new edition is projected and presented the author is not gripped by any fears. The reception accorded to this book convinced the author that he was correct in his estimate of the proper approach to mathematics. Mathematics is no more difficult than our everyday thinking. Fundamentally, mathematics is an application of common sense to situations that confront us. And common sense is not a commodity that is exclusive with mathematicians.

Since the publication of the first edition several misprints and errors have been detected. As far as humanly possible, these now have been eliminated. Some of the numerical data have been adjusted so as to bring the book up to date. Also more problems with answers have been added at the ends of chapters.

The author wishes to express his gratitude to the numerous readers of this book. Their encouraging reactions and comments would be music to any author's ears . . . and have been a source of gratification for having produced a novel approach to mathematics which is as fresh now as it was ten years ago.

A. B.

New York City
January 1952

Preface to the First Edition

There was a time when mathematics was regarded as an intricate subject that could be mastered only by the elite of the scholarly world. Fortunately, this day is long passed. We now know that anyone with a taste for figures and an interest in reading can find a vast enjoyment in the symmetry and harmony of basic mathematics and in the solving of mathematical problems.

This book is designed to make mathematics interesting. The science is not treated formally; abstract conceptions and uninteresting and abstruse procedures are completely avoided; yet at the same time the book is sufficiently complete so as to give a broad picture of mathematical fundamentals. Mathematics, in order to be appreciated by those who do not have a flare for the intangible must be seen in the light of its versatility in the various fields of human endeavor. This is very much the central theme of this book.

Although designed for amusement, the book is not restricted merely to novel and tricky and entertaining mathematical stunts. The prevailing trend in books on mathematical amusements published during the last three or four centuries has been in the direction of amusement in mathematics for the sake of the mathematics itself. It is not possible to enumerate all of the books published in this field but the most recent works of Ahrens, Ball, Fourray, Kraitchik, Lucas, Perelman and others rarely consider (excepting Perelman) the applications of mathematics.

In this way, this book differs from the classical treatment of amusement in mathematics and it is hoped that it gives an answer to the reader's quest not only for amusement in mathematics but also for an easily read and clearly understandable discussion of mathematical processes. The material is simply developed. No proofs of any kind are used in the unfolding of the mathematical processes and properties. It is the firm belief of the author that

v

mathematics must be understood to be appreciated and that an understanding of the subject does not require involved theoretical discussions. Those who, after reading this book, care to continue their study of elementary mathematics thoroughly and exhaustibly will find it profitable to refer to the books, "Mathematics for Self Study" by J. E. Thompson, D. Van Nostrand Co., Inc., New York, and "Integrated Mathematics" by John A. Swenson, Edwards Brothers, Ann Arbor, Michigan.

In the compilation of the book the author referred freely to the vast literature on elementary mathematics and on recreations in mathematics. If there is any claim of originality, it is to originality of treatment and method. Otherwise, any similarity to any book published or unpublished is purely accidental and/or coincidental.

A. B.

New York City
May, 1941

Contents

CHAPTER   **PAGE**

1. NUMERALS & NUMERATION   1

   A Notch: Mathematics Is Born—Numeration Arrives, Accompanied by the Tax Collector—The Price-Tag Mystery—The Use of Numerals.

2. SYSTEMS OF NUMERATION   9

   The Strange Case of Dr. X.—Which Is the Easiest?— This Trick Is Honest—The Two-System—How to Mystify Your Friends—The Chinese Knew Their Digits—A Hole in 10,101—The Three-System—The Truth about Dr. X's Golf Scores—Other Systems—Homework Was Never Like This $1 + 1 = 10$—Remember This When That Collector Comes Around: $10 - 1 = 1$ — Sometimes!—How to Multiply and Like It—Short Turns in Long Division—Some Addition and Multiplication Tables You Didn't Find in Grade School—Odd or Even?— Fractions without Denominators.

3. SOME REMARKABLE PROPERTIES OF NUMBERS . . .   31

   Those 'Lucky' and 'Unlucky' Numbers—Number 12: The Ancients' Favorite—Versatile 365—Number 99, the Rapid Calculator—The Game of 999—The Thousand-and-First Parlor Trick—Triple-Play 10,101—The Number 10,001—Tricky 9,999, 99,999, and 999,999—A Puzzler with 111,111—Number Curiosities—The Oddity 123,456,-789—Repeated-Digit Bafflers—Orderly 142,857—Cyclic Handy Men—Some Wit Testers.

4. NUMBER GIANTS   51

   Close-up of a Million—The Long Count—All Is Lost: That Housefly Is Here Again—Pity the Poor Billionaire: A Fifty-Nine-Mile Pile of Bills—You Owe $500—Now, Some Really Big Numbers—Archimedes Counts the Sands—A Cure for Egotists—Timetable for a Tour of the Stars.

5. NUMBER PYGMIES   65

   Some Gigantic Runts—Cosmic Small Fry—The Populous Bacterium—The Other Side of Zero—Where "Split Seconds" Drag.

CHAPTER	PAGE

6. There's Secrecy in Numbers 79

Trlx hoex erfa eeth mpel—Transposition: How to Scramble a Message—More Scrambling: How to Make Cryptography More Cryptic—Befuddling the Foe, or How to Have Fun with the Fifth Column—How to Hide the Key and Keep Your Code from Talking—The Civil War's Secret Weapon: The Grille—Anatomy of a Grille—Behind the Grille: A Little Math—A Full-Dress Grille: The Shape's the Thing—Substitution: Alphabetical and Otherwise—Double Trouble for Code Kibitzers.

7. The Arithmetic of Measurement 102

The Great Pyramid Mystery—What a Little Juggling with Numbers Will Do—So's the National Debt—Nothing's Ever Right—The Turncoat Zero—Rounding Sums: Plus and Minus—Products and Quotients—To Stop Runaway Digits.

8. Simple Calculating Devices 113

This Little Pig Went to Market—A Homemade Calculating Machine—Daughters of Abacus: Suan-pan, Soroban, and Schoty.

9. Rapid Calculations 125

The Astounding Mr. Doe—How to Remember That Telephone Number—Arithmetical Rabbits—Multiplication Made Painless.

10. Problems & Puzzles 134

It's a System—Two-Timing Puzzles—Application of the Three-System—Arithmetic for Sherlock Holmes.

11. How the Number Magician Does It 150

"I Will Now Predict . . ."—The Guessing Game—How To Make Your Own Tricks—If She's Coy about Her Age—Age and Date of Birth, Please.

12. Algebra & Its Numbers 158

It's Hotter than You Think—Both Ways at Once—A Rule for Signs—Multiplication Magic for the Million—Secrets of Some Curiosities.

13. The Algebra of Number Giants and Pygmies . . 171

The Fifth Operation: Making and Mastering Googols—Taxi to the Moon—Jujitsu for Number Giants—Some Puzzling Results—1,900,000,000,000,000,000,000,000,-000,000—Up for Air: $50,000,000,000 Worth—Wood Is Always Burning—Double Strength—Number Giants with a Few Digits.

CHAPTER   PAGE

14. THE GRAMMAR OF ALGEBRA 186

The Heirs' Problem—Beware of the Math-Minded Mother-in-Law!—One for the Relief Administrator—A Rolling Pin Is How Heavy?—Million-Dollar Swap—Help Wanted: One Stag Line, Slightly Used—Men at Work: Fractions Ahead—Proceed at Own Risk—The Erring Speed Cop—An Accountant's Headache—Algebra and Common Sense.

15. ALGEBRA, BOSS OF ARITHMETIC 209

How the Stage Magician Does It—Performing with Three-Place Numbers—Making It Easier—Short-Order —Rapid Extraction of Roots—Less Work, Same Result.

16. ALGEBRA LOOKS AT INSTALMENT BUYING 224

Debt on the Instalment Plan—How to Learn the Price of Money—Advertising Is an Art—What Makes the Instalment Wheels Go 'Round and 'Round—The How-Much Ladder—How to Buy a House on Instalment—The Rich Get Rich, and the Poor Try to Borrow.

17. CHAIN-LETTER ALGEBRA 246

The Silk-Stocking-Bargain Bubble—Dream of an Opium Eater—The Family-Minded Fly—The Arithmetical Plague of Australia—The How-Many-Times Ladder—A Sequence for the Rabbits—A Clever Rat—The Banker's Mathematics.

18. STREAMLINING EVERYDAY COMPUTATION 264

Napier's Escape from Drudgery—Napier's Clue: Addition Is Easier—Number's Common Denominator: The Lowly Logarithm—A Mathematical Rogue's Gallery: Every Number Has Its Fingerprint—What You Pay the Middle-Men—Logarithm Declares a Dividend—Sing a Song of Sixpence—The Roar of a Lion and the Twinkle of a Star—The Algebra of Starlight: 437,000 Full Moons = 1 Bright Midnight—The Trade-in Value of Your Car: $a = A(1 - r)^n$.

19. THE BANKERS' NUMBER—JACK OF ALL TRADES . . . 295

Simple Life—How to Make Money Breed—The Shortest Insurance Policy Ever Written: 'e'—How Fast Your Money Can Grow—How Fast Your Money Can Go—The Mathematics of Slow Death—How Fast Is Slow Death?—The Curves of Growth and Death—The Bankers' Number and Aviation—How Hot is Your Coffee?—The Bankers' Number Gets Around.

CHAPTER   PAGE
20. How to Have Fun With Lady Luck   329

Fickle as the Flip of a Coin—How Good Is a Hunch?—
The 'What' in 'What a Coincidence'—Ten in a Row:
Algebra Hits the Jackpot—Mugwump Math: Head or
Tail?—An Ancient Lullaby: Baby Needs Shoes—What
the 'Odds' Are—How Long Will You Live?—What
Price Life?—Drop a Needle, Pick Up a Probability.

21. The Thinking Machines   354

Hollywood Goes Mathematical—That Good-Movie Formula—Memo for Burglars—Why Robbers Blow Up Safes
—Wisdom by the Turn of a Crank—An Infinity of Nonsense—A Tip for Radio Baritones.

22. Postoffice Mathematics   365

How to Keep out of the Dead-Letter Department: An
Introduction to Relativity—'Somewhere' in Math: A
Game of Chess—Where Einstein Began—Don't Let Rela-
tivity Disturb You: 2 Is Still 2—If All the World Were a
Pancake—This Expanding Universe: Three-Dimensional
Worlds—Geometric Comet: $Y = 6$.

23. New Worlds for Old   377

Totalitarian Utopia: World without Freedom—The In-
hibited Insect—The Perils of Flatland—An Arithmetic
Oddity in a Geometric Dress—Unsquaring the Square—
Surveying in Flatland—"Seeing" Three-Dimensional Pic-
tures—Formula for Creating a World: Algebra +
Imagination.

24. Passport for Geometric Figures   392

Moving Day: It's all Done by Math—Life on a Merry-
Go-Round—Some Points on the Way to Infinity—Baby-
lonian Heritage: 360 Pieces of Circle—How to Run
Around in Distorted Circles—Nature's Favorite: The
Ellipse—Meet the Circle's Fat Friends: Sphere, Hyper-
sphere, and Ellipsoid—This Curve May Kill You: The
Parabola—How to Get Your Geometric Passport—Every
Passport Has Its Picture.

25. Man's Servant—The Triangle   420

Measure Magic—The Triangle: Simple, Eternal, and
Mysterious—The Bases of Comparison—Similar Triangles
and Their Properties—Two Especially Helpful Triangles
—The Triangle as a Superyardstick—How to Measure
Distant Heights—An Instrument for Measuring Any
Height—Measuring Heights with a Mirror—Measuring

CHAPTER   PAGE

Distances between Inaccessible Objects—Measuring be-
tween Two Inaccessible Points—Another Method for
Inaccessible Points—What the Surveyor Does When He
Surveys.

26. THE TRIANGLE—MAN'S MASTER 446

The Triangle Key to Measurement—How to Measure
Angles—Angles and Their Ratios—The Ratio That Does
Everything.

27. CIRCLES, ANGLES, AND AN AGE-OLD PROBLEM . . . 456

The Circle: Sphinx to the Mathematician, Old Saw to the
Carpenter—The Elusive Pi—Taking the Girth of a Circle
—Trig Without Tables—This Lopsided World: Even
Your Best Friend Is Two-Faced—Squaring the Circle.

28. THE MATHEMATICS OF SEEING 469

Can You Trust Your Eyes?—Actual and Apparent Sizes
—The Circle Family: Meet Cousin Chord—Don't Eclipse
the Moon with a Match—How Good Is Your Eyesight?
—The Glass Eye: Sees All, Knows All—The Historical
Eye: Don't Look Now, Boys.

29. THE LOST HORIZON 479

If the Earth Were Flat—How Far Is Faraway?—Seeing Is
Not So Simple—How Far Can You See?—Distance Ob-
servation in Sea Warfare—Reaching Out for the Horizon
—Celestial Illusion: Sunrise and Sunset—The Soaring
Horizon: Another Illusion.

30. THE SHAPE OF THINGS 493

Foundation for a Figure—Tailoring with Straight Lines
and Angles—Three Straight Lines and Three Angles—
Adding Another Line and Angle—Squashing the Rect-
angle—There's Method in Their Math—Math's Trade
Secret Applied to Other Fields—How to Wrap a Circle
—Jumping Off into Infinity.

31. THE SIZE OF THINGS 520

Birth of a World—Measurements in Flatland—Algebra
to the Rescue of Geometry—The Area of a Circle—The
Area of Any Figure.

32. ESCAPE FROM FLATLAND 538

Measuring in Three Dimensions—What's in a Figure?—
The Refugee Returns to His Land of Flight: Flatland
Again—Comes the Revolution: Cones and Pyramids—
Just How Big Is the Earth?—Speaking of Volumes: It's
a Small World—Name Your Figure.

CHAPTER   PAGE
33. How Algebra Serves Geometry   564

200 Men and an Egg—The Lesson of the Shrinking Dime
—Tin-Can Economy—Square vs. Rectangle—Squares, Cir-
cles, and Suds—Sawing Out the Biggest Log—Cutting
Corners from a Triangle, or How to Get the Most Out
of a Garret—How to Make Money in the Box Business
—Nature Study: Why Is a Sphere?—Fashion Your Own
Funnel.

34. Cork-Screw Geometry   585

But the Earth Isn't Flat . . .—Shortest Distances in Three
Dimensions—A Tip for the Spider—How to Know Your
Way around a Prism—Journey across a Pyramid—Points
about a Glass—It All Depends on Your Direction—The
Screw: Industry Spirals Up Its Stairway—Coming around
the Cone: Helix, the Spiral Screw—The Shortest Route
on Earth.

35. Mathematics, Interpreter of the Universe   . . .   609

Railroading among the Stars—Portrait of a Timetable—
Timing Straight-Line Motion—The Algebra of Speed
—Speed on the Curves—Why Don't We Fly Off into
Space?—What Makes the Universe Hang Together?—
The Democracy of a Tumble—A Multiplication Table
for Physical Relations—What Came First, the Chicken
or the Egg?—Flatfoot to the Universe: Gravitation.

36. The Firing Squad & Mathematics   641

What Happens When You Pull the Trigger?—How
Strong Is a Bullet?—You May Not Hit the Target, but
You'll Get a Kick out of This—The Path of a Bullet—
Big Bertha's Secret—Aerial Artillery: Bigger than
Bertha—The Algebra of a Fired Shell—Bertha's Shell and
Johnny's Top—Out of the Firing Pan into the Fire—The
Gun's Angle of Elevation—How to Determine the Firing
Angle—If You Want to Hit Your Target, Don't Aim
at It.

37. Of Math & Magic   678

Computing Is Believing—How a Locomotive Takes a
Drink—Gaining Weight on a Merry-Go-Round—The
Cheapest Way Around the World: Go East, Old Man—
The 'Human Cannon Ball'—Want to Break a Record?
Don't Go to Berlin!—The 'Devil's Ride' or Looping the
Loop—Stepping on Your Brakes—The Hammer and
Anvil Circus Act—The Engineer's Dilemma—Gravitation
and Flirtation—Getting the Moon Rocket Started.

CHAPTER   PAGE

38. WHERE ARE YOU? 705

Your Address in Two Numbers—Rectangular Cartesian Coordinates—Polar Coordinates in the Plane—Spherical Polar Coordinates—Celestial Coordinates—Other Coordinate Systems—Use of Coordinate Systems—Staying in Orbit—How Fast Must You Go?

39. PLAYING TO WIN 730

Two-Person Zero-Sum Game—Saddle Points—Mixed Strategies—2 × N Games—3 × 3 Games—Other Games

APPENDIX 757

1. Signs and Symbols Used in This Book.

I. Algebra

2. Addition of Signed Numbers—3. Multiplication and Division of Signed Numbers—4. Multiplication of Polynomials—5. Division of Polynomials by a Monomial—6. Some Formulas for the Multiplication of Polynomials—7. Fundamental Property of Fractions—8. Addition and Subtraction of Fractions—9. Multiplication of Fractions—10. Division of Fractions—11. Proportion—12. Some Results of a Proportion—13. The Arithmetic Mean—14. Raising to a Power—15. Extraction of Roots—16. The Sign of the Root—17. Special Properties of Powers and Roots—18. Operations with Powers and Roots—19. Extraction of Square Roots of Numbers—20. Arithmetic Progressions—21. Geometric Progressions—22. Logarithms—23. Raising of a Binomial to a Power—24. Equations of the First Degree in One Unknown—25. Rules for the Solution of Equations of the First Degree in One Unknown—26. Systems of Equations of the First Degree in Two Unknowns—27. Quadratic Equations—28. Formulas for the Roots of Quadratic Equations—29. The Test for the Roots of a Quadratic Equation—30. The Properties of the Roots of a Quadratic Equation.

II. Geometry

31. Lines and Angles—32. Triangles—33. Parallel Lines—34. Quadrangles—35. The Altitude, the Angle Bisector and the Median of a Triangle—36. Four Remarkable Points in a Triangle—37. Formulas Associated with Triangles—38. Formulas for the Areas of Polygons—39. The Circle—40. Two Circles—41. The Circumference

and Area of a Circle—42. Regular Polygons—43. Polyhedra—44. Formulas for the Areas of the Surfaces and
the Volumes of Polyhedra.

III. Trigonometry

45. Trigonometric Ratios of an Acute Angle—46. Some
Special Values of Trigonometric Ratios—47. Formulas
for the Solution of Right Triangles—48. Fundamental
Formulas of Trigonometry—49. Solution of Triangles.

IV. Tables

A. Table of Logarithms of Numbers—B. Table of
Squares of Numbers—C. Table of Square Roots of
Numbers—D. Tables of Trigonometric Ratios.

V. Approximate Formulas for Simplified Computation

Answers to Problems 823

Index 835

≅ 1 ≅

Numerals & Numeration

A Notch: Mathematics Is Born

Somewhere back in the early days of humankind a hairy hand hesitatingly notched a tree to record a kill, or the suns of his journeying. Later, some Stone Age Einstein may have formulated the theory of the notch to keep track of his flock—each scratch (or notch) upon a piece of wood corresponding to one animal and the total scratches therefore equaling the total flock. In some such unprofessorial way man took his first plunge into the mathematical world and came up with a revolutionary concept—how to count. For when man learned how to count, he acquired a scientific tool with which he could break up the universe into its component units and thus master the size and shape of things.

Some of us, however, are still stuck in the notch. Peasants in many countries have made little improvement upon the ancient shepherd's theory. And this is also true of modern city dwellers, although few realize it. Suppose you receive a bill and wish to compare the items enumerated with those you ordered and received. To be certain that each item is accounted for, you make a check mark beside it on the bill to indicate that the charge is correct. If there are several purchases of the same kind, you may place two or more check marks.

In "modern, scientific" office work, too, especially in bookkeeping when individual objects are counted, it is a common practice to record similar individual items by writing a short vertical stroke (the notch again) for each. Thus:

/ denotes 1 object
// denotes 2 objects
/// denotes 3 objects
//// denotes 4 objects
///// denotes 5 objects

To avoid confusion, when a fifth object is counted, it is often recorded (or, in technical terms, *tabulated*) by a cross stroke, thus: ////.
This method of crossing out facilitates further counting.

The method of writing the fifth stroke horizontally, however, is not universally accepted. Recording may be done by vertical strokes until nine objects are counted (/////////), and, when a tenth is added, by another vertical stroke or by a horizontal stroke (////////).

When all the objects have been checked off it is easy to rewrite in numerical form the results of the work-sheet tabulation. Thus, if we have

Chairs   ////   ////   ////   ////   ///
Tables   ////   ////   ////   //
Beds   ////   ////   ////

we can write

23 chairs
17 tables
14 beds

Notice that every //// represents five objects. Thus, the procedure of the rewriting is as follows:

4 times 5 = 20, and 20 plus 3 = 23
3 times 5 = 15, and 15 plus 2 = 17
2 times 5 = 10, and 10 plus 4 = 14

The same objects might have been recorded as follows:

Chairs   /////////   /////////   ///
Tables   /////////   ////////
Beds   ////////   ////

However, the tabulation by four vertical strokes and one horizontal is preferable, because the fewer strokes, the less the chance of a mistake.

Numeration Arrives, Accompanied by the Tax Collector

The art of recording numbers, or *numeration*, was invented to meet the needs of a society more complex than our ancient herdsman's. The numbers now in use, however, are—if the age of civilization is considered—of comparatively recent origin. These numerals (0, 1, 2, 3, 4, 5, 6, 7, 8, and 9) have been in common use for not more than a thousand years. They are known as Hindu-Arabic figures, because they originated in India and were introduced to Europe by the Arabs.

Before their introduction, sums were done in various ways, all lengthy. For example, in Russia under the Tatar occupation (during the thirteenth and fourteenth centuries) receipts for taxes collected by Tatar officials were of this form:

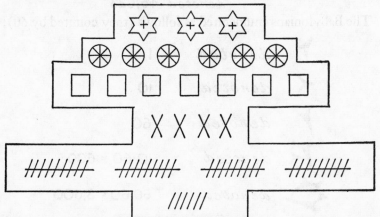

This recorded the payments of the *iasak* (the Tatar word for taxes) of 3,674 rubles and 46 kopecks (1 ruble equals 100 kopecks). Thus:

✡	*denoted*	1,000 RUBLES
⊕	*denoted*	100 RUBLES
☐	*denoted*	10 RUBLES
X	*denoted*	1 RUBLE
₶₶₶₶₶₶	*denoted*	10 KOPECKS
¡	*denoted*	1 KOPECK

The border drawn around the numerals on the receipt was prescribed by law on the optimistic theory that it would tend to prevent additions or other finagling. The symbols for the numerals enabled the people, who by and large could neither read nor write, to keep records of their payments.

This way of writing numbers was used (in a variety of forms) by many ancient peoples. For example, the Egyptians wrote their numbers this way:

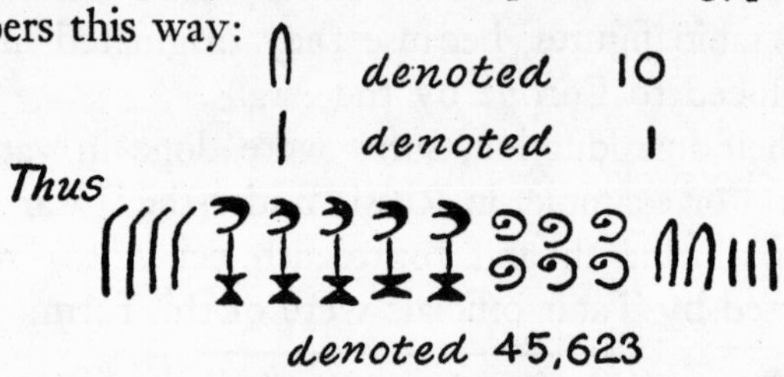

$\cap$ *denoted*   10

$|$ *denoted*   1

Thus

$||||\ ????? \ \vartheta\vartheta\vartheta \ \cap\cap|||$

denoted 45,623

The Babylonians enumerated as follows (they counted by 60):

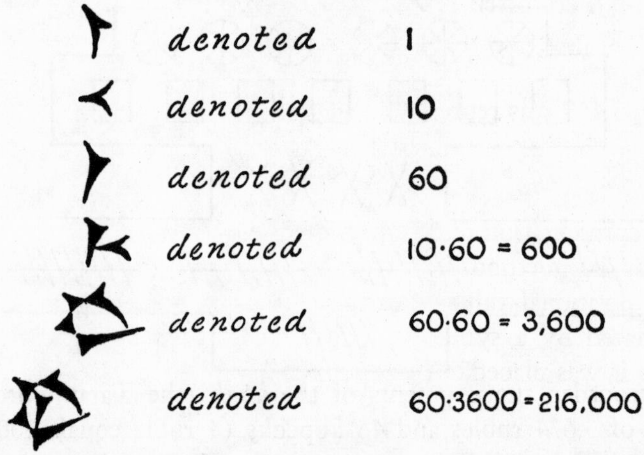

Υ	*denoted*	1
$\prec$	*denoted*	10
Υ	*denoted*	60
K	*denoted*	10·60 = 600
$\triangleleft$	*denoted*	60·60 = 3,600
$\mathbb{D}$	*denoted*	60·3600 = 216,000

The symbol method is retained today in the system of Roman numerals. These were in widespread use in Europe until about the fifteenth or sixteenth century. With their equivalents, they are:

I   denotes 1
V   denotes 5
X   denotes 10
L   denotes 50
C   denotes 100
D   denotes 500
M   denotes 1,000

Thus 1940 when written in Roman numerals is MCMXL (the C before M denotes that CM is 900, and the X before L denotes that XL is 40).

The Chinese, up to the thirteenth century of our era, employed bamboo (and sometimes ivory) sticks for numeration and counting as well as calculation. To represent the nine digits these sticks were arranged in the following manner:

│	‖	‖‖	‖‖‖	‖‖‖‖	T	T	T	T
1	2	3	4	5	6	7	8	9

Sometimes the sticks were placed horizontally:

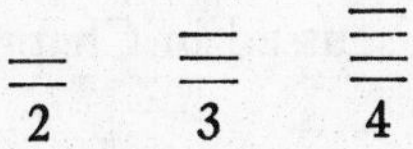

═	≡	≣
2	3	4

Four was represented also by two crossed sticks, as ✕, and 6, 7, 8, and 9 were often represented as follows:

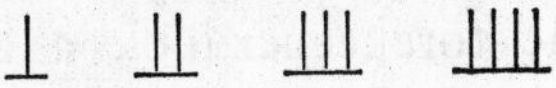

⊥   ⊥⊥   ⊥⊥⊥   ⊥⊥⊥⊥

Thus 63,459 was represented as

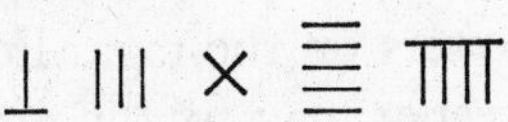

⊥ ‖‖ ✕ ≡ T

The representation of numbers by these sticks was similar to the present-day method of writing numbers, that is, the digits were given positional value as in the decimal system. The zero was designated by a symbol which indicated the absence of units where it was placed. Thus 800,540 was represented as

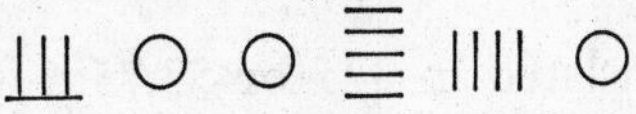

‖‖ ○ ○ ≡ ‖‖‖ ○

Modifications of the above symbols, as shown below, are used extensively nowadays in Chinese business deals:

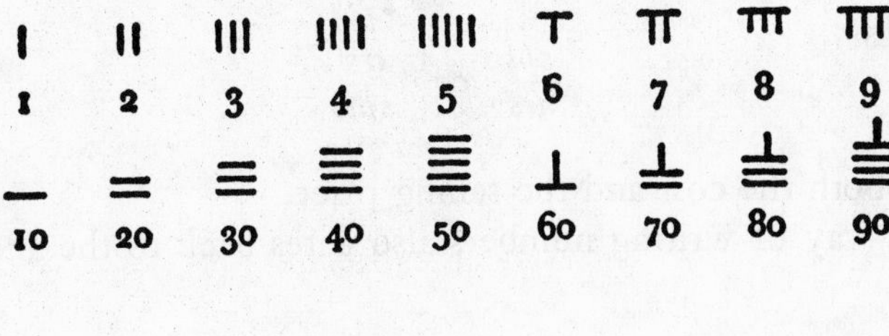

│	‖	‖‖	‖‖‖	‖‖‖‖	T	T	T	T
1	2	3	4	5	6	7	8	9
─	═	≡	≣	≣	⊥	⊥	⊥	⊥
10	20	30	40	50	60	70	80	90

The symbols for 10, 100, 1,000, and 10,000 were discarded, and the decimal system, with the positional value as employed by us, is used.

For printing, the Chinese use the following symbols:

一 二 三 四 五
1   2   3   4   5

六 七 八 九 十
6   7   8   9   10

About 5,000 years ago the Chinese used a different number system. This will be discussed in Chapter 2.

The Price-Tag Mystery

Often when you make a purchase, particularly in a small shop, you may note that the storekeeper looks at a cryptic marking on the tag before telling you the price. If you buy, he will make certain that the mark is erased so that you can't learn the secret.

Usually there are letters on the tag. For example, there may be *nrs*, and the storekeeper may fix the price at $5.98. There is no mystery, however. As a rule, the merchant selects a ten-letter word in which no letter is repeated, say "manuscript," and assigns each letter a number:

$$m \quad a \quad n \quad u \quad s \quad c \quad r \quad i \quad p \quad t$$
$$1 \quad 2 \quad 3 \quad 4 \quad 5 \quad 6 \quad 7 \quad 8 \quad 9 \quad 0$$

Then *nrs* is translated in 375 or $3.75. This storekeeper recorded the cost of the object to him. If he had wanted to record the selling price, he would have written *spi*. In variations of this procedure, two numbers may be written as a fraction

$$\frac{spi}{nrs} \quad \text{or} \quad \frac{nrs}{spi}$$

telling both the cost and the selling price.

This way of writing numbers also dates back to the ancients.

The Greeks and the Hebrews used their alphabets in writing numbers.

A′   B′   Γ′   Δ′   E′   F′   Z′   H′   Θ′
1   2   3   4   5   6   7   8   9

י ט ח ז ו ה ד ג ב א
10 9 8 7 6 5 4 3 2 1

The Use of Numerals

Besides counting, numerals denote the ordered arrangement of objects, as 1st, 2d, 3d, 10th, 12th, etc.

In libraries books are catalogued according to *the decimal system of classification*. Under this system a specified book will have the same number in any library.

Every field of knowledge is assigned a number, and the numerals in the number of the book disclose its general field and its subclassification. Under this internationally accepted principle the major classes are numbered:

0—Works of general nature
1—Philosophy
2—Religion
3—Social sciences, law
4—Languages, the science of language
5—Physical and natural sciences, mathematics
6—Applied sciences (medical, technology, agriculture, etc.)
7—Arts
8—Literature
9—History, geography, biography

When a book is given a number, its first digit indicates one of the ten enumerated fields. Every book on history will have as its first digit 9, every book on medical subjects 6, every book on mathematics 5.

Each general class is divided into ten subclasses. The numbers assigned to the subclasses are made up of two digits each, the first digit denoting the class and the second the subclass. Thus, books on physical and natural sciences and mathematics are subdivided as follows:

50—Books of general nature
51—Mathematics
52—Astronomy, geodesy
53—Physics, theoretical mechanics
54—Chemistry, mineralogy
55—Geology
56—Paleontology
57—Biology, anthropology
58—Botany
59—Zoology

Each subclass is subdivided into smaller subclasses. Thus the books on mathematics (51) are denoted by three-digit numbers:

510—Books of general nature
511—Arithmetic
512—Algebra
513—Geometry, etc.

Every small subclass may be divided again to avoid confusion in the locations of special books. On the library shelves the books are arranged according to numbers, those having the first three digits the same being placed alphabetically according to authors. By this method any owner of a library, however large or small it may be, can arrange his books to be found or replaced at a moment's notice. In libraries with hundreds of thousands of volumes, numbers will run up to six or seven digits. Library-goers can find what they want with a minimum of effort once they know the secret—in the librarians' language, *cataloguing*.

⊕ 2 ⊕

Systems of Numeration

The Strange Case of Dr. X

An eccentric mathematician, when he died, left a stack of unpublished papers. When his friends were sorting them they came across the following statement:

"I graduated from college when I was 44 years old. A year later, I, a 100-year-old young man, married a 34-year-old young girl. Since the difference in our ages was only 11 years, we had many common interests and hopes. A few years later we had a family of 10 children. I had a college job, and my salary was $1,300 a month. One-tenth of my salary went for the support of my parents. However, the balance of $1,120 was more than sufficient for us to live on comfortably."

Just a screwball? We shall see.

First, we note there are only numbers with the digits 0, 1, 2, 3, and 4. Moreover, when 1 is added to 44 we get 100. Then Dr. X must have used some system of numeration other than ours. In the decimal system when 1 is added to 99 we get 100. In the system that Dr. X used, 4 does the work of 9, that is, $1 + 4 = 10$. Just as 10 is not a digit in the decimal system, 5 is not a digit in Dr. X's system, 5 being written as 10.

The decimal system is based on the principle that the digits have different values according to position. The farthest position on the right of a whole number (or *integer*, as it is usually

9

called) is the place of the units. The position to the left of the units has a value ten times as large. The next position to the left is that of the hundreds, which has a value ten times as large again. On the left of the hundreds is the position of the thousands, then the ten-thousands, the hundred-thousands, millions, and so on. In other words, in the decimal system the value of each position, moving to the left, is ten times that of the preceding position Thus, 46,537 is composed of

four ten-thousands,	or	40,000
six thousands,	or	6,000
five hundreds,	or	500
three tens,	or	30
seven units,	or	7
Total		46,537

In the five-system of numeration (the one used by Dr. X) only the digits 0, 1, 2, 3, and 4 are used, and the consecutive values of the positions, from right to left, are multiples of five by fives. On the right is the position of the units. Next on the left is the position of the *fives*. Then come the five-fives, or *twenty-fives*; then the *one hundred and twenty-fives*, then the *six hundred and twenty-fives*, and so on.

Applying the five-system to the autobiography of Dr. X,

$$44 \text{ is } 4 \cdot 5 \ + 4 = 24$$
$$100 \text{ is } 1 \cdot 25 + 0 \cdot 5 + 0 = 25$$
$$34 \text{ is } 3 \cdot 5 \ + 4 = 19$$
$$11 \text{ is } 1 \cdot 5 \ + 1 = 6$$
$$10 \text{ is } 1 \cdot 5 \ + 0 = 5$$
$$1,300 \text{ is } 1 \cdot 125 + 3 \cdot 25 + 0 \cdot 5 + 0 = 200$$
$$\tfrac{1}{10} \text{ is } \frac{1}{1 \cdot 5 + 0} = \tfrac{1}{5}$$
$$1,120 \text{ is } 1 \cdot 125 + 1 \cdot 25 + 2 \cdot 5 + 0 = 160$$

Thus the puzzler may be translated as follows:

"I graduated from college when I was 24 years old. A year later, I, a 25-year-old young man, married a 19-year-old young girl. Since the difference in our ages was only 6 years, we had many common interests and hopes. A few years later we had a family of 5 children. I had a college job, and my salary was $200 a month.   One-fifth of my salary went for the support of my parents.   However, the balance of $160 was more than sufficient for us to live on comfortably."

Before examining the various other systems of numeration and their properties, it is interesting to note that in any system, the number that denotes the system is not used as a digit.   For example, in the ten-system (the decimal system), 10 is not used as a digit, nor is 5 in the five-system.   In a theoretical twenty-four-system, 24 would not be a digit either.

Which Is the Easiest?

The simplicity of a system of numeration is conditioned by several factors.   First, consider the number symbols that must be used.   A 24-system, for instance, would require twenty-four symbols—would you call that simple?   The other extreme would be a system with only one symbol—the notch or *unitary* system described in Chapter 1.   This would be just as bad, but in a different way.   To write a number, say 47, you would have to jot down forty-seven strokes.   You can see how cumbersome addition, subtraction, multiplication, and division would become. For example, 19 · 23 would require nineteen strokes written out twenty-three times—and then just try to count them!   Bear in mind, too, that in a system other than the decimal the names for numbers in the decimal system cannot be used.   New names must be found for all the various numbers and positions.   In the unitary system a name for 211 probably would be longer than the space occupied by 211 tally-marks.

This Trick Is Honest

Many parlor tricks are based on the fact that the observer pays too little attention, and that the hand is quicker than the eye. But here is one, based on a method of numeration, that involves no deception.

Place nine small envelopes and $5.11 in small change on a table. Distribute the money in the envelopes and then announce that you can hand over any sum up to $5.11 without counting the money. Some one names \$3.46, and you hand him certain envelopes. He counts the money and finds that

1 envelope contains	\$2.56
1 envelope contains	0.64
1 envelope contains	0.16
1 envelope contains	0.08
1 envelope contains	0.02
Total	\$3.46

To vary the trick, add 89 cents in a tenth envelope and say that you can now produce, without counting, any sum named up to \$6. \$5.69 is named, and you again hand over five envelopes. This time your friend finds

1 envelope contains	\$2.56
1 envelope contains	1.28
1 envelope contains	0.64
1 envelope contains	0.32
1 envelope contains	0.89
Total	\$5.69

Asked for your secret, you can say with a superior air that the trick is based on the two-system of numeration.

The Two-System

In the two-system only two digits are used, 0 and 1. The digits in this system, as in all others except the unitary, have positional value. The place on the right is that of the units, the place next to its left is that of the *twos*, then the two-twos or the *fours*, then the *eights, sixteens, thirty-twos, sixty-fours*, etc. The first 10 numbers are as follows:

$$
\begin{array}{lll}
1 & \text{is} & 1 \\
10 & \text{is} & 2, \quad \text{or} \quad 1 \cdot 2 + 0 \\
11 & \text{is} & 3, \quad \text{or} \quad 1 \cdot 2 + 1 \\
100 & \text{is} & 4, \quad \text{or} \quad 1 \cdot 4 + 0 \cdot 2 + 0 \\
101 & \text{is} & 5, \quad \text{or} \quad 1 \cdot 4 + 0 \cdot 2 + 1 \\
110 & \text{is} & 6, \quad \text{or} \quad 1 \cdot 4 + 1 \cdot 2 + 0 \\
111 & \text{is} & 7, \quad \text{or} \quad 1 \cdot 4 + 1 \cdot 2 + 1 \\
1000 & \text{is} & 8, \quad \text{or} \quad 1 \cdot 8 + 0 \cdot 4 + 0 \cdot 2 + 0 \\
1001 & \text{is} & 9, \quad \text{or} \quad 1 \cdot 8 - 0 \cdot 4 + 0 \cdot 2 + 1 \\
1010 & \text{is} & 10, \quad \text{or} \quad 1 \cdot 8 + 0 \cdot 4 + 1 \cdot 2 + 0 \\
\end{array}
$$

Thus, 1,111,111 would be

$$1 \cdot 64 + 1 \cdot 32 + 1 \cdot 16 + 1 \cdot 8 + 1 \cdot 4 + 1 \cdot 2 + 1,$$

or 127.

Here is the way to translate a number from the decimal system to the two-system. Divide the decimal-system number by 2, and note the remainder. Divide the quotient by 2, and again note the remainder. Divide the quotient obtained from the second division by 2; note the remainder. Continue this process until the last quotient is 1. Write this quotient and all the remainders in reverse order, that is, from right to left. Thus, the last quotient becomes the digit on the extreme left; next comes the last remainder, then the preceding remainder, and so on, so that the last digit on the right is the remainder obtained from the first division by 2.

For example, 29 is translated into the two-system as follows:

$$29 \div 2 = 14 \cdot 2 + 1$$
$$14 \div 2 = 7 \cdot 2 + 0$$
$$7 \div 2 = 3 \cdot 2 + 1$$
$$3 \div 2 = 1 \cdot 2 + 1$$

Then 29 in the two-system is 11,101. Checking this result,

$$11,101 = 1 + 0 \cdot 2 + 1 \cdot 4 + 1 \cdot 8 + 1 \cdot 16 = 29.$$

The division may be written in a simpler form:

```
  29 | 2
   1 | 14 | 2
        0 |  7 | 2
             1 |  3 | 2
                  1 |  1
```

In this scheme the remainders and the last quotient are in italics.

Another number, 672, is translated into the two-system as follows:

```
 672 | 2
   0 | 336 | 2
         0 | 168 | 2
               0 |  84 | 2
                     0 |  42 | 2
                           0 |  21 | 2
                                 1 |  10 | 2
                                       0 |   5 | 2
                                             1 |   2 | 2
                                                   0 |   1
```

The result is 1,010,100,000.

Among other things, the two-system is important because of its ready adaptability to code writing.   (See Chapter 6.)

How to Mystify Your Friends

In the two-system the respective values of the digit places, from right to left, are 1, 2, 4, 8, 16, 32, 64, 128, 256, etc. And

$$1 + 2 + 4 + 8 + 16 + 32 + 64 + 128 + 256 = 511$$

or exactly the amount of money distributed among the nine envelopes in the trick.   To pick out the envelopes containing $3.46 exactly, translate 346 from the decimal system to the two-system.   This is 101,011,010, or

$$1 \cdot 256 + 1 \cdot 64 + 1 \cdot 16 + 1 \cdot 8 + 1 \cdot 2$$

This may be done mentally.   Note the remainders obtained by the division by 2, and remember that these remainders denote the digit places in increasing order of magnitude as the division by 2 progresses.

Arrange the envelopes in the following order:

1st	2d	3d	4th	5th	6th	7th	8th	9th
$2.56	$1.28	$0.64	$0.32	$0.16	$0.08	$0.04	$0.02	$0.01

Now, taking $4.35 as the requested sum, translate it into the two-system, picking up an envelope for each 1 that appears in the two-system figures:

$$435 \div 2 = 217 + \text{remainder } 1 \cdot \text{Pick up envelope 9.}$$
$$217 \div 2 = 108 + \text{remainder } 1 \cdot \text{Pick up envelope 8.}$$
$$108 \div 2 = 54$$
$$54 \div 2 = 27$$
$$27 \div 2 = 13 + \text{remainder } 1 \cdot \text{Pick up envelope 5.}$$
$$13 \div 2 = 6 + \text{remainder } 1 \cdot \text{Pick up envelope 4.}$$
$$6 \div 2 = 3$$
$$3 \div 2 = 1 + \text{remainder } 1 \cdot \text{Pick up envelopes 2 and 1.}$$

Perform an abracadabra or two and hand your friend the envelopes.   They contain $0.01, $0.02, $0.16, $0.32, $1.28, and $2.56, or a total of $4.35.

The variation involving larger sums is easy. When the amount is greater than $5.11 but less than $10.23 (because the place value to the left of 512 in the two-system is 1,024), subtract $5.11 from it (in this case it is $6.00) and place the difference in a tenth envelope. Then if a number greater than $5.11 is asked for, subtract the sum in the tenth envelope (in this case $0.89) from the number named and then translate the difference into the two-system. The tenth envelope thus will be one of those picked up.

The Chinese Knew Their Digits

About 5,000 years ago the Chinese employed the two-system of numeration. *Je-Kim* (The Book of Combinations), written by the Chinese philosopher and legislator Fo-Hi, contains a table of sixty-three line figures, as shown below, which was deciphered by the German mathematician Leibnitz as a representation of the two-system.

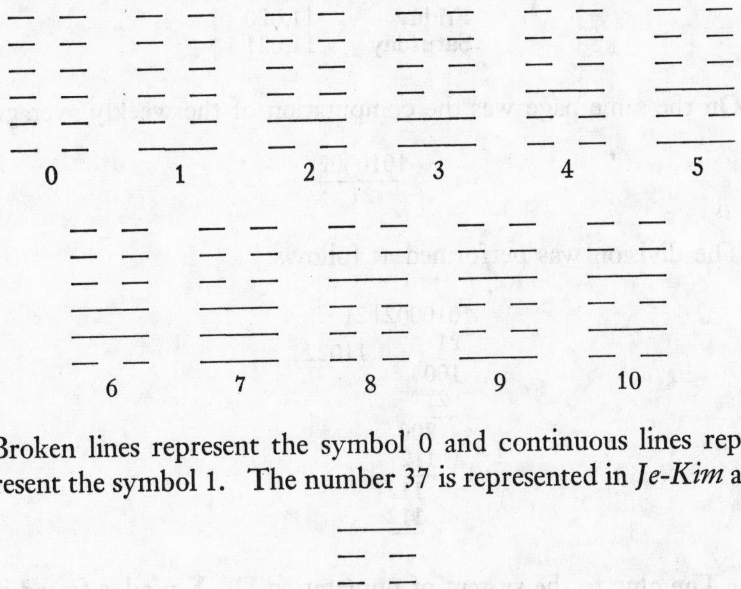

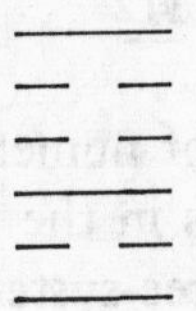

Broken lines represent the symbol 0 and continuous lines represent the symbol 1. The number 37 is represented in *Je-Kim* as and 63 is represented as

$$\begin{array}{c}
\rule{3em}{0.5pt} \\[-2pt]
\rule{3em}{0.5pt} \\[-2pt]
\rule{3em}{0.5pt} \\[-2pt]
\rule{3em}{0.5pt} \\[-2pt]
\rule{3em}{0.5pt} \\[-2pt]
\rule{3em}{0.5pt}
\end{array}$$

which corresponds to writing 37 as 100,101 and 63 as 111,111.

A Hole in 10,101

Among the papers of the eccentric Dr. X were found records of his golf scores. He kept records of all his golf matches, and weekly averages too. One weekly record read this way:

Sunday	11,011
Monday	11,101
Tuesday	11,111
Wednesday	11,001
Thursday	11,120
Friday	11,020
Saturday	11,021

On the same page was the computation of the weekly average:

$$\frac{1010002}{21}$$

The division was performed as follows:

$$\begin{array}{r|l}
1010002 & 21 \\
\underline{21} & \quad 11022 \\
100 & \\
\underline{21} & \\
200 & \\
\underline{112} & \\
112 & \\
\underline{112} & \\
\end{array}$$

The clue to the system of numeration Dr. X used is found in his computations as well as in the denominator of the fraction. He apparently used the three-system.

The Three-System

In the three-system three digits are used, 0, 1, and 2. The place on the right is the place of the units; next on the left come the *threes*, then the three-threes or the *nines*, then the *twenty-sevens*, the *eighty-ones*, *two hundred and forty-threes*, and so on.

The first ten numbers when written in the three-system are:

$$
\begin{array}{llll}
1 & \text{is} & 1 & \\
2 & \text{is} & 2 & \\
10 & \text{is} & 3, & \text{or} \quad 1 \cdot 3 + 0 \\
11 & \text{is} & 4, & \text{or} \quad 1 \cdot 3 + 1 \\
12 & \text{is} & 5, & \text{or} \quad 1 \cdot 3 + 2 \\
20 & \text{is} & 6, & \text{or} \quad 2 \cdot 3 + 0 \\
21 & \text{is} & 7, & \text{or} \quad 2 \cdot 3 + 1 \\
22 & \text{is} & 8, & \text{or} \quad 2 \cdot 3 + 2 \\
100 & \text{is} & 9, & \text{or} \quad 1 \cdot 9 + 0 \cdot 3 + 0 \\
101 & \text{is} & 10, & \text{or} \quad 1 \cdot 9 + 0 \cdot 3 + 1.
\end{array}
$$

The number 1,212 in the three-system corresponds to 50 in the decimal system. This can be checked as follows:

$$1 \cdot 27 + 2 \cdot 9 + 1 \cdot 3 + 2 = 27 + 18 + 3 + 2 = 50$$

The number 12,120 in the three-system corresponds to 150 in the decimal system.

Numbers can be translated from the decimal system to the three-system by dividing by 3 and is continued until the last quotient is either 1 or 2. For example

$$
\begin{array}{r|l}
269 & 3 \\
\hline
2 & \begin{array}{r|l} 89 & 3 \\ \hline 2 & \begin{array}{r|l} 29 & 3 \\ \hline 2 & \begin{array}{r|l} 9 & 3 \\ \hline 0 & \begin{array}{r|l} 3 & 3 \\ \hline 0 & 1 \end{array} \end{array} \end{array} \end{array}
\end{array}
$$

Thus, 269 in the three-system is 100,222.

The Truth about Dr. X's Golf Scores

Now that we know something about his system of numeration, we can decipher the sad story of Dr. X's golf. No wonder he preferred to hide it.

The daily scores were:

Sunday	112
Monday	118
Tuesday	121
Wednesday	109
Thursday	123
Friday	114
Saturday	115

The weekly average, then, was

$$\frac{812}{7} = 116$$

Other Systems

The five-system was the one employed in the autobiography of Dr. X. Digits used are 0, 1, 2, 3, and 4. On the right are the units, then the *fives*, the *twenty-fives*, the *one hundred and twenty-fives*, etc. The first ten numbers in the five-system are:

1	is	1		
2	is	2		
3	is	3		
4	is	4		
10	is	5,	or	$1 \cdot 5 + 0$
11	is	6,	or	$1 \cdot 5 + 1$
12	is	7,	or	$1 \cdot 5 + 2$
13	is	8,	or	$1 \cdot 5 + 3$
14	is	9,	or	$1 \cdot 5 + 4$
20	is	10,	or	$2 \cdot 5 + 0$

The higher the numerical value of the system, of course, the more digits are used. For the eleven-system an eleventh numeral must be invented; for the twelve-system, two additional numerals. Thus, in the twelve-system the digit for 10 may be designated by t and the digit for 11 by e.

Translation of a number, say 100,644, into the twelve-system is done as follows:

$$
\begin{array}{r|r}
100644 & 12 \\ \hline
0 & 8387 \;|\; 12 \\
& 11 \;|\; 698 \;|\; 12 \\
& & 2 \;|\; 58 \;|\; 12 \\
& & & 10 \;|\; 4
\end{array}
$$

and the number is 4*t*2*e*0.

In the twelve-system, right to left, are the units, the *twelves*, *one hundred and forty-fours*, and so forth.

Homework Was Never Like This: 1 + 1 = 10

School training makes simple arithmetical operations so mechanical that they must be analyzed closely in order to apply them to systems of numeration other than the decimal.

Take addition, for instance. In totaling a column of figures (starting on the right, of course), if a number greater than 10 is obtained, the units are recorded and the remaining numbers (denoting the tens) are *carried* to the next column. To add 639, 472, and 593, the process is as follows:

$$639$$
$$472$$
$$593$$

$$9 + 2 + 3 = 14. \quad \text{Record } 4 \text{ and carry } 1.$$
$$1 + 3 + 7 + 9 = 20. \quad \text{Record } 0 \text{ and carry } 2.$$
$$2 + 6 + 4 + 5 = 17. \quad \text{Record } 17.$$

The sum is then 1,704.

The principle of *carrying* holds for other systems of numeration. *But remember that the number that represents the system has no numeral for itself—it is always written as 10.*

Here is the way to add two (or more) numbers, say 1,101 and 111, in the two-system:

$$1,101$$
$$111$$

$$1 + 1 = 10. \quad \text{Write } 0 \text{ and carry } 1.$$
$$1 + 0 + 1 = 10. \quad \text{Write } 0 \text{ and carry } 1.$$
$$1 + 1 + 1 = 11. \quad \text{Write } 1 \text{ and carry } 1.$$
$$1 + 1 = 10. \quad \text{Write } 10.$$

Therefore the sum is 10,100.

The addition can be checked by the decimal system. The number 1,101 corresponds to 13, and 111 corresponds to 7. $13 + 7 = 20$, and 20 in the two-system is therefore 10,100.

Numbers in the three-system are added in the same way.
Thus:

$$2,122$$
$$212$$
$$121$$

$1 + 2 + 2 = 12.$ Write   *2* and carry 1.
$1 + 2 + 1 + 2 = 20.$ Write   *0* and carry 2.
$2 + 1 + 2 + 1 = 20.$ Write   *0* and carry 2.
$2 + 2 = 11.$ Write *11*.

and the sum is 11,002.

The check shows that 2,122 corresponds to 71 in the decimal system, 212 corresponds to 23, and 121 corresponds to 16.
$71 + 23 + 16 = 110$, and 110 is 11,002 in the three-system.

Below are examples of addition in various systems:

Four-System	*Five-System*	*Six-System*
3231	4312	45312
133	432	5423
312	243	355
11002	11042	55534

Seven-System	*Eight-System*	*Nine-System*
56543	64753	784521
3635	2567	63677
216	471	2467
64030	70233	861776

Twelve-System
5e4t2e0
4ett2t
ettee
6548019

The reader may check the sums by the decimal system.

Remember This When That Collector Comes Around:
    10 − 1 = 1 —Sometimes!

In subtraction, the method of *borrowing* will be used. An analysis of the decimal-system technique may be helpful. Suppose 17 is to be subtracted from 42. Since 7 cannot be subtracted from 2, 1 is borrowed from 4 (actually 10 from 40): 7 from 12, then, gives 5; finally, 1 from 3 (not 4) is 2, and the answer is 25.

It should be remembered that, in each system of numeration, the number corresponding to the number of the system is the one borrowed. In the seven-system, 7 is borrowed; in the twelve-system, 12 is borrowed.

To subtract 1,101 from 101,011 in the two-system, proceed as follows:

$$\begin{array}{r} \overset{\cdot\,\cdot\,\cdot}{101011} \\ \underline{1101} \\ 11110 \end{array}$$

Dots are placed over the fourth, fifth, and sixth digits from the right in the upper number (the minuend) to indicate that 10 (which corresponds to 2 in the decimal system) was borrowed from each. Since $1 + 1 = 10$ in the two system, $10 - 1 = 1$. The result of the subtraction may be checked by addition in the two-system. Thus:

$$\begin{array}{r} 11110 \\ \underline{+1101} \\ 101011 \end{array}$$

Below are examples of subtraction in various systems:

Three-System	*Four-System*	*Five-System*
$\overset{\cdot\,\cdot\,\cdot}{}$	$\overset{\cdot\,\cdot\,\cdot\,\cdot}{}$	$\overset{\cdot\,\cdot\,\cdot\,\cdot}{}$
22110	312023	43420
1202	33231	3442
20201	212132	34423

Six-System	*Seven-System*	*Eight-System*
$\overset{\cdot\,\cdot\,\cdot}{}$	$\overset{\cdot\,\cdot\,\cdot\,\cdot\,\cdot}{}$	$\overset{\cdot\,\cdot\,\cdot\,\cdot}{}$
452050	31611012	12472
43443	4256261	6777
404203	24321421	3473

Nine-System	*Twelve-System*
$\overset{\cdot\,\cdot\,\cdot\,\cdot}{}$	$\overset{\cdot\,\cdot}{}$
73421	9tet2te
8678	ettet0
63632	8e0e30e

The results may be checked by addition or by the decimal system.

How to Multiply and Like It

Multiplication is performed the same way in all systems of numeration. In systems other than the decimal the chief difficulty is a tendency to think in terms of the decimal system. To avoid this, remember that the number denoting the system is always written as 10. The multiplication tables given in this chapter also will be useful.

Multiplication in the two-system is so easy that it bears out the statement that this is the simplest of all systems. As you know, there are only two digits, 0 and 1, and multiplication by 1 naturally results in the same number. Thus:

$$
\begin{array}{r}
10011 \\
101 \\
\hline
10011 \\
10011 \\
\hline
1011111
\end{array}
$$

The product of two numbers in the three-system is obtained as follows:

$$
\begin{array}{r}
112 \\
221 \\
\hline
112 \\
1001 \\
1001 \\
\hline
110222
\end{array}
$$

The multiplication by 1 results in the original number 112. Multiplying 112 by 2 is done this way:

$2 \cdot 2 = 11,$ Write 1 and carry 1.
$2 \cdot 1 = 2,$ and $2 + 1 = 10.$ Write 0 and carry 1.
$2 \cdot 1 = 2,$ and $2 + 1 = 10.$ Write 10.

The product, therefore, is 1,001.

Below are examples of multiplication:

Four-System	Five-System	Six-System
3312	3414	45531
213	344	1054
23202	30221	315404
3312	30221	405335
13230	21302	45531
2111322	3013131	54344154

Seven-System	Eight-System	Nine-System
64625	576732	8867
562	4567	487
162553	5170366	68724
551322	4371434	78702
453364	3572502	38801
54345503	2773550	4856844
	3424125126	

Twelve-System

```
       ette
        tet
      9e112
      te001
      9e112
     ttt0322
```

Multiplication in the twelve-system is performed as follows (using the decimal system for illustration):

$t \cdot e = 110 = 9 \cdot 12 + 2.$		Write 2 and carry 9.
$t \cdot t = 100,$	$100 + 9 = 109 = 9 \cdot 12 + 1.$	Write 1 and carry 9.
$t \cdot t = 100,$	$100 + 9 = 109 = 9 \cdot 12 + 1.$	Write 1 and carry 9.
$t \cdot e = 110,$	$110 + 9 = 119 = 9 \cdot 12 + 11.$	Write $9e$.

Short Turns in Long Division

Division, too, follows the same pattern in all systems of numeration. The reader is advised to go back over the sections on subtraction and multiplication before proceeding. Below are examples of division:

Two-System

```
11011011 | 111
  111      11111
 1101
  111
 1100
  111
 1011
  111
 1001
  111
   10
```

Thus, $11{,}011{,}011 \div 111 = 11111 \cdot 111 + \dfrac{10}{111}.$

Three-System

$$\begin{array}{r|l} 2122 & 12 \\ \underline{12} & 112 \\ 22 \\ \underline{12} \\ 102 \\ \underline{101} \\ 1 \end{array}$$

Thus, $2,122 \div 12 = 112 \cdot 12 + 1.$

Four-System

$$\begin{array}{r|l} 33210 & 213 \\ \underline{213} & 121 \\ 1131 \\ 1032 \\ \underline{330} \\ 213 \\ \underline{111} \end{array}$$

Note that in the last example, when 1,131 was divided by 213, 2 was chosen as a quotient; 3 was not chosen because from inspection $3 \cdot 2 = 12$, and the first two digits of 1,131 are 11. Thus, 3 would have been too large.

Five-System

$$\begin{array}{r|l} 43214 & 123 \\ \underline{424} & 302 \\ 314 \\ \underline{301} \\ 13 \end{array}$$

Some Addition and Multiplication Tables You Didn't Find in Grade School

Operations with numbers in the various systems of numeration are simplified by addition and multiplication tables, similar to the decimal-system tables taught in one form or another to all grade-school pupils. Below are some of the tables.

TWO-SYSTEM TABLES

Addition

0	1
1	10

Multiplication

$1 \cdot 1 = 1$

To find the sum or product of two numbers take one number in the first column and one number in the first row. Where the column and row intersect is the required number. Thus, $0 + 1 = 1$, $1 + 1 = 10$. This principle applies to all the tables.

THREE-SYSTEM TABLES

Addition

0	1	2
1	2	10
2	10	11

Multiplication

1	2
2	11

FOUR-SYSTEM TABLES

Addition

0	1	2	3
1	2	3	10
2	3	10	11
3	10	11	12

Multiplication

1	2	3
2	10	12
3	12	21

FIVE-SYSTEM TABLES

Addition

0	1	2	3	4
1	2	3	4	10
2	3	4	10	11
3	4	10	11	12
4	10	11	12	13

Multiplication

1	2	3	4
2	4	11	13
3	11	14	22
4	13	22	31

SIX-SYSTEM TABLES

Addition

0	1	2	3	4	5
1	2	3	4	5	10
2	3	4	5	10	11
3	4	5	10	11	12
4	5	10	11	12	13
5	10	11	12	13	14

Multiplication

1	2	3	4	5
2	4	10	12	14
3	10	13	20	23
4	12	20	24	32
5	14	23	32	41

SEVEN - SYSTEM TABLES

Addition

0	1	2	3	4	5	6
1	2	3	4	5	6	10
2	3	4	5	6	10	11
3	4	5	6	10	11	12
4	5	6	10	11	12	13
5	6	10	11	12	13	14
6	10	11	12	13	14	15

Multiplication

1	2	3	4	5	6
2	4	6	11	13	15
3	6	12	15	21	24
4	11	15	22	26	33
5	13	21	26	34	42
6	15	24	33	42	51

EIGHT - SYSTEM TABLES

Addition

0	1	2	3	4	5	6	7
1	2	3	4	5	6	7	10
2	3	4	5	6	7	10	11
3	4	5	6	7	10	11	12
4	5	6	7	10	11	12	13
5	6	7	10	11	12	13	14
6	7	10	11	12	13	14	15
7	10	11	12	13	14	15	16

Multiplication

1	2	3	4	5	6	7
2	4	6	10	12	14	16
3	6	11	14	17	22	25
4	10	14	20	24	30	34
5	12	17	24	31	36	43
6	14	22	30	36	44	52
7	16	25	34	43	52	61

NINE - SYSTEM TABLES

Addition

0	1	2	3	4	5	6	7	8
1	2	3	4	5	6	7	8	10
2	3	4	5	6	7	8	10	11
3	4	5	6	7	8	10	11	12
4	5	6	7	8	10	11	12	13
5	6	7	8	10	11	12	13	14
6	7	8	10	11	12	13	14	15
7	8	10	11	12	13	14	15	16
8	10	11	12	13	14	15	16	17

Multiplication

1	2	3	4	5	6	7	8
2	4	6	8	11	13	15	17
3	6	10	13	16	20	23	26
4	8	13	17	22	26	31	35
5	11	16	22	27	33	38	44
6	13	20	26	33	40	46	53
7	15	23	31	38	46	54	62
8	17	26	35	44	53	62	71

TWELVE - SYSTEM

Addition

0	1	2	3	4	5	6	7	8	9	t	e
1	2	3	4	5	6	7	8	9	t	e	10
2	3	4	5	6	7	8	9	t	e	10	11
3	4	5	6	7	8	9	t	e	10	11	12
4	5	6	7	8	9	t	e	10	11	12	13
5	6	7	8	9	t	e	10	11	12	13	14
6	7	8	9	t	e	10	11	12	13	14	15
7	8	9	t	e	10	11	12	13	14	15	16
8	9	t	e	10	11	12	13	14	15	16	17
9	t	e	10	11	12	13	14	15	16	17	18
t	e	10	11	12	13	14	15	16	17	18	19
e	10	11	12	13	14	15	16	17	18	19	1t

Multiplication

1	2	3	4	5	6	7	8	9	t	e
2	4	6	8	t	10	12	14	16	18	1t
3	6	9	10	13	16	19	20	23	26	29
4	8	10	14	18	20	24	28	30	34	38
5	t	13	18	21	26	2e	34	39	42	47
6	10	16	20	26	30	36	40	46	50	56
7	12	19	24	2e	36	41	48	53	5t	65
8	14	20	28	34	40	48	54	60	68	74
9	16	23	30	39	46	53	60	69	76	83
t	18	26	34	42	50	5t	68	76	84	92
e	1t	29	38	47	56	65	74	83	92	t1

Odd or Even?

Is 12 an even number or is it odd? Is 37 an odd number or is it even?

In the decimal system the test for odd and even numbers, that is, for divisibility by 2, is simple. If the last digit on the right is even (zero is considered even), the number is even. Otherwise the number is not divisible by 2, and so is odd.

But suppose that 12 is written in the four-system. Is it odd or even? Suppose that 37 is written in the eight-system. Is it odd or even?

The test for the divisibility by 2 of numbers in systems of numeration with even bases, such as the 2, 4, 6, 8, 10, and 12 systems, is the same as that used in the decimal system. If the last digit on the right is even, the number is even; otherwise it is odd.

Thus 12, in the four-system, is divisible by 2, $(12 \div 2 = 3)$ and is even, and 37, in the eight-system, is not divisible by 2, $(37 \div 2 = 17 + \frac{1}{2})$ and is odd.

The test in systems with odd bases is as follows: if the sum of the digits of the number is even, then the number is even; otherwise it is odd.

Thus 12, in the three-system, is not divisible by 2, $(12 \div 2 = 2 + \frac{1}{2})$ and is odd, and 37, in the nine-system, is divisible by 2, $(37 \div 2 = 18)$ and is even.

While on the topic of the divisibility of numbers, it may be mentioned that the divisibility test of *casting out nines* used in the decimal system has its counterpart in other systems. In the decimal system $9 = 10 - 1$, that is, the base number diminished by 1. The same test by casting out *the base diminished by 1* holds good in other systems. Thus, to determine whether a number in the seven-system is divisible by 6, *cast out sixes.* If the sum of the digits is divisible by 6, the number is divisible by 6; otherwise it is not. For example, 54,324 in the seven-system is divisible by 6, because in the seven-system

$$5 + 4 + 3 + 2 + 4 = 24$$

and 24 is divisible by 6, since $2 + 4 = 6$.

Don't be fooled by the 5 in systems other than the decimal. Is 135 divisible by 5? In the decimal and in the five-system it is. But is 135 divisible by 5 in the six-system? In the six-system 5 is the base diminished by 1. The sum of the digits of 135 (in the six-system) is 13, and 13 is not divisible by 5. Is 135 divisible by 5 in the eight-system? To find out, translate 135 into the decimal system. If the number thus obtained is divisible by 5, then 135 in the eight-system is divisible by 5; otherwise it is not. When translated 135 is 93, which is not divisible by 5; hence 135 in the eight-system is not divisible by 5.

Fractions without Denominators

The principle used in writing decimal fractions in the decimal system may be applied to other systems. Thus 1.3 in the six-system is 1 3/6, or 1 1/2, which is 1.5 in the decimal system. Two-ninths in the nine-system is written as 0.2.

In the six-system 1.24 can be translated into an improper fraction (a fraction with a denominator) as follows:

$$1.24 = 1 + \tfrac{2}{6} + \tfrac{4}{36} = 1 + \tfrac{1}{3} + \tfrac{1}{9} = 1\tfrac{4}{9} = \tfrac{13}{9}$$

PROBLEMS

1. In what system of numeration has the following addition been performed?

$$
\begin{array}{r}
642 \\
4534 \\
55023 \\
\hline
63532
\end{array}
$$

2. In what system of numeration has the following subtraction been performed?

$$
\begin{array}{r}
21306 \\
3427 \\
\hline
16768
\end{array}
$$

3. In what system of numeration has the following multiplication been performed?

$$
\begin{array}{r}
443 \\
312 \\
\hline
1330 \\
443 \\
2213 \\
\hline
231500
\end{array}
$$

4. In what system of numeration has the following division been performed?

$$
\begin{array}{r|l}
2340324 & \underline{312} \\
\underline{2303} & 4102 \\
323 & \\
\underline{312} & \\
1124 & \\
\underline{1124} & \\
\end{array}
$$

5. Write 473 in all the systems of numeration from the two-system to the twelve-system, inclusive.

6. Take the number 120,433.

a) What are its equivalents in the decimal system if this number were written in all the other systems from the five-system to the twelve-system, inclusive?

b) State whether this number is odd or even in the six-system and when it is written in the seven-system. Do not translate it into the decimal system.

c) If it is written in the eight-system, is it divisible by 8 without leaving a remainder?

7. Translate the twelve-system number *tee* into the five-system. [Answer: 22,313]

8. Subtract (in the twelve-system) *tt,ttt* from *ee,eee* and state the result in the ten-system. [Answer: 22,621]

9. Perform the following addition

$$
\begin{array}{r}
46.35 \\
12.63 \\
\end{array}
$$

when the numbers are written in (*a*) the seven-system, (*b*) the nine-system. [Answers: (*a*) 62.31, (*b*) 60.08]

10. Perform the following multiplication

$$
\begin{array}{r}
4,444 \\
\underline{444} \\
\end{array}
$$

when the numbers are written in (*a*) the seven-system, (*b*) the eight-system. [Answers: (*a*) 3,046,362, (*b*) 2,466,420]

Some Remarkable Properties
of Numbers

Those 'Lucky' and 'Unlucky' Numbers

Since the earliest times particular numbers have had a strange
fascination. Certain ones have been believed to be endowed
with mysterious qualities, and even nowadays many believe that
everyone has "lucky" and "unlucky" numbers. An astonish-
ingly large group of people are convinced that 13 especially is
very unlucky; this superstition is so generally rooted that in
many office buildings the thirteenth floor is numbered 12A.
And Friday the Thirteenth is almost National Hoodoo Day.

Actually, of course, there is nothing supernatural in numbers.
Each does possess certain properties, but they are purely mathematical. These properties are intriguing, however, and princi-
pally because few ordinarily suspect their existence. Now we
shall examine some of the more remarkable examples, many of
which are employed by persons who perform tricks with rapid
calculation and with number puzzles. We may consider first
the numbers 2, 5, and 9.

We have met 2 before. It is an even number in all systems of
numeration, and the two-system itself is the simplest of all, being
especially useful therefore in code writing.

The number 5 has no unusual mathematical properties but, for
some unknown reason, many persons have a considerable preference for it. People generally, when asked to estimate length,
weight, age, etc., automatically give a number that will end either

31

in a 5 or 0. Scientists have made studies of these preferences as evidenced in the giving of ages and find that most of us choose to give numbers that end in 0. The next preference is those that end in 5. The first ten digits as they appear in the order of their general preference as endings are 0, 5, 8, 2, 3, 7, 6, 4, 9, 1. This sequence was checked many times in varying experiments, such as estimating lengths, weights, heights, and so on.

Number 12: The Ancients' Favorite

The number 12 was for a long time a rival of the number 10 as the base of the numeration system. There were twelve tribes in Israel, named for the twelve sons of Jacob, and there were the twelve Apostles. Nowadays we use 12 very often as a unit of measure: There are twelve months in a year, twelve inches in a foot, twelve in a dozen, twenty-four (twice 12) hours in a day, and in Great Britain there are twelve pence in a shilling.

In ancient Babylon 12 was at one time the base of the system of numeration; later on, it was replaced by 60 (five times 12). Subsequently in almost all lands the base 12 was replaced by 10, and our system of numeration became decimal (probably because we have ten fingers on our hands, and the first steps in counting were performed on the fingers). However, 12 has been retained in our everyday counting such as, for further example, 5 times 12, or 60, minutes in an hour and 60 seconds in a minute. We even have a name (gross) for twelve dozen, and in the twelve-system, as we already know, 144 is written as 100.

We use the decimal system in our calculations but it is not, however, as convenient as the twelve-system. For example, 10 is divisible by 2, 5, and 10 only, while 12 is divisible by 2, 3, 4, 6, and 12. Thus, while 10 has three divisors, 12 has five. A number that ends in zero when written in the twelve-system is divisible by at least 2, 3, 4, 6, and 12. In the decimal system a number that ends in zero is divisible by at least 2 and 5, and naturally is inconvenient when 1/2, 1/3, 1/4, 1/6, and 1/12 of a number are to be obtained as a whole number. Thus, in the decimal system 1/3 of 10 is not a whole number, and 10/3 when represented as a mixed decimal fraction (3.333) is unending. In the twelve-system, however, 1/3 of 10 (we should remember that 10 in the twelve-system corresponds to 12 in the decimal system) is 4 and 1/6 is 2, while in the decimal system the latter is 1.6666 . . . , and its decimal part is unending.

A number in the decimal system ending in two zeros is divisible by at least 2, 4, 5, 10, 25, 50, and 100. A number in the twelve-system when it ends in two zeros (it should be remembered that 100 in the twelve-system corresponds to 144 in the decimal system) is divisible by at least 2, 3, 4, 6, 8, 9, 12, 16, 18, 24, 36, 48, 72, and 144. Thus in the decimal system a number that ends in two zeros has at least eight divisors, while in the twelve-system it has at least fourteen.

In the decimal system only fractions whose denominators are multiples of 2 and 5 (or both) can be expressed exactly as ending decimal fractions. For example, 1/2 = 0.5, 1/4 = 0.25, 1/5 = 0.2, 1/8 = 0.125, 1/10 = 0.1, 1/20 = 0.05, and so on. In the twelve-system all the fractions whose denominators are multiples of 3 or 2 (or both) can be represented exactly as ending fractions which are written in the same manner as the fractions in the decimal system. Thus: 1/2 = 0.6, 1/3 = 0.4, 1/4 = 0.3, 1/6 = 0.2, 1/8 = 0.16, 1/9 = 0.14, 1/12 = 0.1, 1/16 = 0.09, 1/18 = 0.08, 1/24 = 0.06, 1/36 = 0.04, 1/48 = 0.03, 1/72 = 0.02, and 1/144 = 0.01.

The foregoing, however, should not be interpreted as a superiority of the twelve-system in that a number which is not exactly divisible, say by 9, in the decimal system will be exactly divisible by 9 in the twelve-system. This would be a wrong interpretation. Suppose, for instance, that we have a box with pebbles. If we can divide these pebbles into 9 heaps, each containing an equal number of pebbles, the number of the pebbles will be exactly divisible by 9 regardless of the system of numeration used for writing of the number. The advantage of the twelve-system is that in it the divisibility by 6 or by 72 may be easily detected (the number must end at least by one zero for 6 and by at least two zeros for 72) and that we obtain more whole numbers as quotients than in the decimal system.

Versatile 365

This is the number of days in a year that is not a leap year. When 365 is divided by 7 we obtain a remainder 1; so in a year there are 52 weeks and one day over. But the remarkable property of 365 is that

$$365 = 10 \cdot 10 + 11 \cdot 11 + 12 \cdot 12$$

Indeed,

$$10 \cdot 10 + 11 \cdot 11 + 12 \cdot 12 = 100 + 121 + 144 = 365$$

Moreover,

$$365 = 13 \cdot 13 + 14 \cdot 14 \text{ or } 169 + 196 = 365$$

The only five consecutive positive numbers which have this peculiar property associated with 365 are 10, 11, 12, 13, and 14.

Number 99, the Rapid Calculator

Number 99 is interesting in that by its help we may perform rapid multiplication of two-place numbers. We will now develop a method for doing this.

Suppose we examine the product of 64 and 99. We know that $64 \cdot 99 = 6,336$. Observe that $63 + 36 = 99$. This may be explained as $99 = 100 - 1$.

Then

$$64 \cdot 99 = 64(100 - 1) = 6,400 - 64 = 6,336$$

This holds for any two-place numbers. For example,

$$15 \cdot 99 = 1,485$$
$$36 \cdot 99 = 3,564$$

or

$$99 \cdot 99 = 9,801$$

The rule for this multiplication is then:

Diminish the number by 1 and write to the right of it the difference between 99 and this diminished number.

Moreover, $99 = 3 \cdot 3 \cdot 11$. If we remember this property we can write a four-place number such that it will be divisible by 11 without a remainder. In such numbers we may consider two parts consisting of two-place numbers, as in 4,653 we have 46 and 53. The sum of these two-place numbers must be equal to 99. Thus, if we take some two-place number, 73 for example, and subtract it from 99, we obtain 26. Write this difference to the right of 73. This number, 7,326, is divisible by 11 exactly.

The Game of 999

In the same way we multiply two-place numbers by 99 we can perform multiplications of three-place numbers by 999. Suppose that we want to obtain the product of 637 and 999. We have that $637 \cdot 999 = 636,363$. Observe that $636 + 363 = 999$. This may be explained as $999 = 1000 - 1$. Then

$$637 \cdot 999 = 637 \, (1,000 - 1) = 637,000 - 637 = 636,363$$

This holds for any three-place numbers. For example,

$$377 \cdot 999 = 376,623, \text{ or } 999 \cdot 999 = 998,001$$

The rule is:

Diminish the number by 1, subtract the diminished number from 999, and write this difference to the right of the diminished number.

Moreover, 999 possesses another unusual property:

$$999 = 9 \cdot 111 = 3 \cdot 3 \cdot 3 \cdot 37$$

If we remember this property we can write at once a six-place number that is exactly divisible by 37. In such a number there are two parts, each of three digits. If each part is considered as a three-place number, then the sum of these two must always be equal to 999. In other words, we take some three-place number, 537 for example, and subtract it from 999. We write the difference, 462, either to its left or to its right and the resulting numbers, 537,462 and 462,537, are both divisible by 37. Thus

$$537,462 = 14,526 \cdot 37 \text{ and } 462,537 = 12,501 \cdot 37$$

A simple arithmetical game may be played if you know this property of 999. You may ask someone to write secretly a three-place number, diminish it by 1 and subtract it from 999. Then you will ask that the difference thus obtained be written to the right of the original number (but the difference must be written as a three-place number; that is, if you took 963 the other number must be written as 036). Then you may ask another person to divide this six-place number by 27. The quotient is then handed to a third person with the request to divide it by 37, assurance that the division will be performed without remainder. After the division you may take the slip with the quotient and, without looking at it, hand it to the person who made the original selection and announce that this is the number. Those not familiar with the property of 999 will be completely mystified.

The Thousand-and-First Parlor Trick

The number 1,001 is probably best associated with the famous Arabian tales of Scheherazade, but it has other claims on our interest here. If we want to multiply a three-place number by 1,001 we need not perform multiplication; just write the number twice, and there is the answer. For example,

$$643 \cdot 1,001 = 643,643$$

because

$$1,001 = 1,000 + 1$$

Interesting, too, is the fact that as $1,001 = 7 \cdot 11 \cdot 13$, any three-place number written twice so that it becomes a six-place number is divisible by 7, 11, and 13. This property allows us another variation on our number trick.

We ask someone to write a three-place number and repeat it, so that it becomes a six-place number—this and subsequent operations, of course, being kept concealed from us. The slip is handed to a second person with the request to divide it by, say, 11. The quotient then is given to a third person with the request to divide it by 7, and the new quotient to a fourth person to divide by 13. The result is then the original three-place number.

Triple-Play 10,101

Multiplication of any two-place number by 10,101 requires writing of that number three times. Thus

$$56 \cdot 10,101 = 565,656$$

because

$$10,101 = 10,000 + 100 + 1$$

and

$$56 \cdot 10,101 = 56 \, (10,000 + 100 + 1) = 560,000 + 5,600 + 56 = 565,656$$

Likewise,

$$48 \cdot 10,101 = 484,848 \text{ and } 92 \cdot 10,101 = 929,292$$

However, an interesting property of 10,101 is that it equals $3 \cdot 7 \cdot 13 \cdot 37$. This leads us to the conclusion that any six-place number consisting of two digits repeated three times as in the foregoing is divisible by 3, 7, 13, and 37, and that there will be no remainders after these divisions. Thus we have another number trick, performed in the same manner as 1,001, except that, of course, a two-place number must be repeated thrice to provide a six-place number, and the numbers 3, 7, 13, and 37 must be used in the divisions. As a variation the divisions may be performed with, consecutively, 21, 13, and 37; 3, 91, and 37; 7, 39, and 37 and 7, 13, and 111, as these are combinations in product form of the four numbers, 3, 7, 13, and 37.

The Number 10,001

The peculiar property of 10,001, as far as its multiplication of any four-place number is concerned, is now clear: the product will be an eight-place number in which the digits of the four-place number are repeated; for example,

$$5,892 \cdot 10,001 = 58,925,892$$

Since

$$10,001 = 73 \cdot 137$$

our trick may be done with a repeated four-place number and 73 and 137 as the dividing numbers.

Tricky, 9,999, 99,999, and 999,999

Multiplications of a four-place number by 9,999, of a five-place number by 99,999, and of a six-place number by 999,999, are performed in the same manner as the multiplication of a three-place number by 999.

We note that

$$9,999 = 10,000 - 1$$
$$99,999 = 100,000 - 1$$

and

$$999,999 = 1,000,000 - 1$$

Thus when a four-place number is multiplied by 9,999, with, for example, 6,473 as the four-place number, we actually perform the following operation:

$$6,473 \cdot 9,999 = 6,473\,(10,000 - 1) = 64,730,000 - 6,473 =$$
$$64,723,527$$

We observe that $6,472 + 3,527 = 9,999$. We now have the rule for the multiplication of a four-place number by 9,999: We diminish the number by 1 and to the right of the remainder write the difference between 9,999 and this diminished number. A number trick similar to those above may be added to our repertory.

Multiplication of a five-place number by 99,999 is done in the same way as a four-place number by 9,999. The resulting number trick follows the usual pattern.

A Puzzler with 111,111

It will be recalled that multiplication of three-place numbers by 1,001 results in the writing of this number twice, and immediately note that 111,111 must have 1,001 as a factor. Thus $111,111 = 111 \cdot 1,001$, but $111 = 3 \cdot 37$, and $1,001 = 7 \cdot 11 \cdot 13$. Therefore

$$111,111 = 3 \cdot 7 \cdot 11 \cdot 13 \cdot 37$$

This property of 111,111 provides a different trick: Someone is asked to write a digit, any from 1 to 9 inclusive, six times in succession as a six-place number. Then others (one at a time) are asked to divide by 3, 7, 11, 13, and 37, and finally the last quotient is handed to the first person with the remark that this is the digit originally set down. As a variation of division by 3, 7, 11, 13, and 37, product-combinations of these numbers may be offered. For example, 21, 11, 13, and 37; 33, 7, 13, and 37; 39, 7, 11, and 37; 111, 7, 11, and 13; 3, 77, 13, and 37; and 3, 11, 91, and 37.

Number Curiosities

Here are some curious results, but the reader will find little difficulty now in explaining them as all are based on the multiplication rules earlier described:

$$9 \cdot 9 = 81$$
$$99 \cdot 99 = 9801$$
$$999 \cdot 999 = 998001$$
$$9999 \cdot 9999 = 99980001$$
$$99999 \cdot 99999 = 9999800001$$
$$999999 \cdot 999999 = 999998000001$$
$$9999999 \cdot 9999999 = 99999980000001$$

Is this oddity clear? If not, turn to the pages where the multiplications by 999, 9,999, and 99,999 are described.

Here are some more interesting results:

$$999999 \cdot 2 = 1999998$$
$$999999 \cdot 3 = 2999997$$
$$999999 \cdot 4 = 3999996$$
$$999999 \cdot 5 = 4999995$$
$$999999 \cdot 6 = 5999994$$
$$999999 \cdot 7 = 6999993$$
$$999999 \cdot 8 = 7999992$$
$$999999 \cdot 9 = 8999991$$

We now may modify the rules for the multiplications by 99, 999, 9,999, 99,999, 999,999, etc. Earlier in these rules we limited ourselves to numbers with the same number of places as these factors. However, the rules given may be modified so that the total of places in the numbers simply does not exceed the total number of those in the factors 99, 999, etc. This modification is possible because where a number has two places and the other factor is, say, 99,999, by means of writing three zeros to the left of the two-place number we have a five-place number for our purposes. Thus,

$$38 \cdot 99{,}999 = 3{,}799{,}962$$

This explains the foregoing table of products. We may write

$$3 \cdot 999{,}999 = 000{,}003 \cdot 999{,}999 = 2{,}999{,}997$$

Some number curiosities display a regularity, easily explained, in the order in which the digits appear. Consider these products and sums:

$$
\begin{aligned}
1 \cdot 9 + 2 &= 11 \\
12 \cdot 9 + 3 &= 111 \\
123 \cdot 9 + 4 &= 1111 \\
1234 \cdot 9 + 5 &= 11111 \\
12345 \cdot 9 + 6 &= 111111 \\
123456 \cdot 9 + 7 &= 1111111 \\
1234567 \cdot 9 + 8 &= 11111111 \\
12345678 \cdot 9 + 9 &= 111111111
\end{aligned}
$$

Let us examine in detail one of these, for example,

$$12{,}345 \cdot 9 + 6 = 111{,}111$$

This may be rewritten as

$$12{,}345 \, (10 - 1) + 6 = 123{,}450 + 6 - 12{,}345 = 123{,}456 - 12{,}345$$

But

$$123{,}456 - 12{,}345 = 111{,}111$$

because

$$6 - 5 = 1, \; 5 - 4 = 1, \; 4 - 3 = 1, \; 3 - 2 = 1, \text{ and } 2 - 1 = 1$$

Thus when we multiply one of the numbers in the column by 9 and add a number represented by a digit that follows (in order of numeration) the last digit on the extreme right of the number, we actually obtain another number in which the digits are all 1's. For example.

$$1234 \cdot 9 + 5 = 1234 \, (10 - 1) + 5 = 12340 + 5 - 1234 = 11111$$

Here is another set of number products and sums that displays odd regularity:

$$1 \cdot 8 + 1 = 9$$
$$12 \cdot 8 + 2 = 98$$
$$123 \cdot 8 + 3 = 987$$
$$1234 \cdot 8 + 4 = 9876$$
$$12345 \cdot 8 + 5 = 98765$$
$$123456 \cdot 8 + 6 = 987654$$
$$1234567 \cdot 8 + 7 = 9876543$$
$$12345678 \cdot 8 + 8 = 98765432$$
$$123456789 \cdot 8 + 9 = 987654321$$

This regularity may be explained if we consider that

$$123456 \cdot 8 + 6 = 987654$$

that $8 = 9 - 1$, and that $6 = 7 - 1$. Then

$$123456 \cdot 8 + 6 = 123456 \, (9 - 1) + (7 - 1) = 123456 \cdot 9 + 7 - 123456 - 1$$

But $123456 \cdot 9 + 7 = 1111111$ (this was obtained in the first table of products and sums), and $123456 + 1 = 123457$. Then

$$123456 \cdot 8 + 6 = 1111111 - 123457$$

This subtraction may be represented as:

$$1,000,000 - 100,000 = 900000$$
$$100,000 - 20,000 = 80000$$
$$10,000 - 3,000 = 7000$$
$$1,000 - 400 = 600$$
$$100 - 50 = 50$$
$$11 - 7 = 4$$

Thus $1111111 - 123457 = 987654$. This explains why the numbers on the right of the second table have their digits in the descending order of numeration. The reader will find no special difficulty in checking any other expression in the first table and convincing himself that there is nothing mysterious in the regularity displayed in the second.

Consider this table of products and sums:

$$9 \cdot 9 + 7 = 88$$
$$98 \cdot 9 + 6 = 888$$
$$987 \cdot 9 + 5 = 8888$$
$$9876 \cdot 9 + 4 = 88888$$
$$98765 \cdot 9 + 3 = 888888$$
$$987654 \cdot 9 + 2 = 8888888$$
$$9876543 \cdot 9 + 1 = 88888888$$
$$98765432 \cdot 9 + 0 = 888888888$$

Let us examine one of these expressions, for example,

$$987,654 \cdot 9 + 2 = 8,888,888$$

From the first table we have that

$$123456 \cdot 9 + 7 = 1,111,111$$

Multiply both sides of the last expression by 8; we have then 8,888,888. But from the second table we have that

$$123,456 \cdot 8 + 6 = 987,654$$

Then

$$123,456 \cdot 8 = 987,654 - 6 = 987,648$$

and

$$8,888,888 = 987,648 \cdot 9 + (7 \cdot 8)$$

But

$$(7 \cdot 8) = 56 = 54 + 2 = 6 \cdot 9 + 2$$

Then

$$8,888,888 = 987,648 \cdot 9 + 6 \cdot 9 + 2 = (987,648 + 6)9 + 2$$

Finally

$$8,888,888 = 987,654 \cdot 9 + 2$$

If the reader will follow this analysis, he will find no difficulty in checking every expression in the foregoing table, and explaining the properties of regularity as displayed in the three tables.

Let us examine the last line of the first table of products and sums, that is,

$$12,345,678 \cdot 9 + 9 = 111,111,111$$

This expression can be rewritten as

$$12,345,678 \cdot 9 + 9 = (12,345,678 + 1)9 = 12,345,679 \cdot 9 = 111,111,111$$

Now if we recall that $2 \cdot 9 = 18$, $3 \cdot 9 = 27$, $4 \cdot 9 = 36$, $5 \cdot 9 = 45$, $6 \cdot 9 = 54$, $7 \cdot 9 = 63$, $8 \cdot 9 = 72$, $9 \cdot 9 = 81$, we obtain the following table:

$$12345679 \cdot 9 = 111111111$$
$$12345679 \cdot 18 = 222222222$$
$$12345679 \cdot 27 = 333333333$$
$$12345679 \cdot 36 = 444444444$$
$$12345679 \cdot 45 = 555555555$$
$$12345679 \cdot 54 = 666666666$$
$$12345679 \cdot 63 = 777777777$$
$$12345679 \cdot 72 = 888888888$$
$$12345679 \cdot 81 = 999999999$$

The Oddity 123,456,789

This number possesses some unusually distinctive properties. Let us write it backwards and perform this subtraction:

$$
\begin{array}{r}
987654321 \\
-\,123456789 \\
\hline
864197532
\end{array}
$$

The difference is made up of the same nine nonrepetitive digits. Moreover, if we multiply 123,456,789 by a number less than 10 that is not a multiple of 3 we obtain:

$$123456789 \cdot 2 = 246913578$$
$$123456789 \cdot 4 = 493827156$$
$$123456789 \cdot 5 = 617283945$$
$$123456789 \cdot 7 = 864197523$$
$$123456789 \cdot 8 = 987654312$$

Also note that

$$987654321 - (123456789 \cdot 8) = 987654321 - 987654312 = 9$$

The sequence of the digits 123456789 may be obtained by multiplying 111,111,111 by itself:

$$
\begin{array}{r}
111111111 \\
111111111 \\
\hline
111111111 \\
111111111 \\
111111111 \\
111111111 \\
111111111 \\
111111111 \\
111111111 \\
111111111 \\
111111111 \\
\hline
12345678987654321
\end{array}
$$

However, this arrangement of digits in the ascending and then descending order is present also in the product of numbers composed of several repeated digits 1, when these numbers are multiplied by themselves. Thus

$$11 \cdot 11 = 121$$
$$111 \cdot 111 = 12321$$
$$1111 \cdot 1111 = 1234321$$
$$11111 \cdot 11111 = 123454321$$
$$111111 \cdot 111111 = 12345654321$$
$$1111111 \cdot 1111111 = 1234567654321$$
$$11111111 \cdot 11111111 = 123456787654321$$
$$111111111 \cdot 111111111 = 12345678987654321$$

Repeated-Digit Bafflers

Here is an interesting property of numbers written with the repeated digits:

$$(111 \cdot 111) - 10(11 \cdot 11) = 11111$$
$$(1111 \cdot 1111) - 10(111 \cdot 111) = 1111111$$
$$(11111 \cdot 11111) - 10(1111 \cdot 1111) = 111111111$$
$$(111111 \cdot 111111) - 10(11111 \cdot 11111) = 11111111111$$
$$(1111111 \cdot 1111111) - 10(111111 \cdot 111111) = 1111111111111$$
$$(11111111 \cdot 11111111) - 10(1111111 \cdot 1111111) = 111111111111111$$
$$(111111111 \cdot 111111111) - 10(11111111 \cdot 11111111) = 11111111111111111$$

Will this property hold for any number composed of the repeated digits 1? The reader should not fail to see that the second term (the one that should be subtracted) represents a number with one digit less that is multiplied by itself. Here is a relationship that is known to be true. The first number contains 18 digits 1 repeated:

$$(111111111111111111 \cdot 111111111111111111) - 10(11111111111111111 \cdot 11111111111111111) =$$
$$= 1111111111111111111111111111111111111$$

The reader may check this at his leisure. However, as a more simple exercise he may check the following:

$$(1111111111 \cdot 1111111111) - 10(111111111 \cdot 111111111) = 111111111111111111$$

This expression, when the products are obtained, is

$$\begin{array}{r} 1234567900987654321 \\ - \ 123456789876543210 \\ \hline 1111111111111111111 \end{array}$$

For extension of the trick with 111,111, here are some numbers written with the repeated digits 1 and their respective factors:

$$111 = 3 \cdot 37$$
$$1111 = 11 \cdot 101$$
$$11111 = 41 \cdot 271$$
$$111111 = 3 \cdot 7 \cdot 11 \cdot 13 \cdot 37$$
$$1111111 = 239 \cdot 4649$$
$$11111111 = 11 \cdot 73 \cdot 101 \cdot 137$$
$$111111111 = 9 \cdot 37 \cdot 333,667$$
$$1111111111 = 11 \cdot 41 \cdot 271 \cdot 9091$$
$$11111111111 = 21,649 \cdot 513,239$$
$$111111111111 = 3 \cdot 7 \cdot 11 \cdot 13 \cdot 37 \cdot 101 \cdot 9901$$
$$1111111111111 = 53 \cdot 79 \cdot 265,371,653$$
$$11111111111111 = 11 \cdot 239 \cdot 4649 \cdot 909,091$$
$$111111111111111 = 3 \cdot 31 \cdot 37 \cdot 41 \cdot 271 \cdot 2,906,161$$
$$1111111111111111 = 11 \cdot 17 \cdot 73 \cdot 101 \cdot 137 \cdot 5,882,353$$
$$11111111111111111 = 2,071,723 \cdot 5,363,222,357$$
$$111111111111111111 = 7 \cdot 9 \cdot 11 \cdot 13 \cdot 19 \cdot 37 \cdot 52,579 \cdot 333,667$$

Orderly 142,857

The best way to learn the properties and the nature of 142,857 is to perform some multiplications with it:

$$142,857 \cdot 1 = 142,857$$
$$142,857 \cdot 2 = 285,714$$
$$142,857 \cdot 3 = 428,571$$
$$142,857 \cdot 4 = 571,428$$
$$142,857 \cdot 5 = 714,285$$
$$142,857 \cdot 6 = 857,142$$
$$142,857 \cdot 7 = 999,999$$

Inspection of the first six products reveals that the order of the digits is always preserved. Thus when we want to obtain the product of 142,857 and 4, we note that this product must have 8 as its last digit on the extreme right because $7 \cdot 4 = 28$. Then the digits 57 are transposed to the extreme left, and the remaining digits 1428 are written to the right of 57.

Now we may consider the nature of this number. Let us center our attention on the product $142,857 \cdot 7 = 999,999$. We then can write

$$\frac{142,857}{999,999} = \frac{1}{7}$$

Let us write 1/7 as a decimal fraction. By long division we obtain 1/7 = 0.142857 142857 142857. . . . Thus we have found that 142,857 represents the repeating part of an unending decimal fraction, known as a "periodic fraction," and 142,857 is known as the "period" of this fraction. Thus we can clear up the mystery of the regular order of the digits in the products of 142,857 by 1, 2, 3, 4, 5, and 6. When we multiply 142,857, say by 4, we may think of this product as 4/7. Now, if we transform 4/7 into a decimal fraction, we note that 4 is one of the remainders obtained when we transformed 1/7 into a decimal fraction. Naturally the same remainders must be obtained and in the same order, but they must begin with some other digit, and not 1, as in the case of 1/7. This means that when a fraction with a denominator 7, but with a numerator other than 1, is transformed into a decimal fraction we obtain the same period, except that some of the digits of 142,857 will be transposed to the right. When we multiply 142,857 by 7 we should obtain 1, but since the fraction 1/7 is represented as an unending repeating decimal fraction, we take for 1/7 the fraction 0.142,857 which is less than 1/7, and thus we obtain for our product 0.999999. . . .

Let us examine 142,758 more closely. If we break up this six-digit number into two parts, we have 142 and 857. But note that

$$142 + 857 = 999$$

In other words, if we recall what was stated in this chapter respecting 999, we may consider 142,857 as a product. Now

$$143 \cdot 999 = 142,857$$

But $143 = 11 \cdot 13$. Moreover, we should recall also that $1,001 = 7 \cdot 11 \cdot 13$. Then

$$142,857 \cdot 7 = 143 \cdot 999 \cdot 7 = 7 \cdot 11 \cdot 13 \cdot 999 = 1,001 \cdot 999 = 999,999$$

Now, let us consider the product

$$142,857 \cdot 8 = 142,857 \cdot 7 + 142,857 = 999,999 + 142,857$$

But $999,999 = 1,000,000 - 1$. Then

$$142,857 \cdot 8 = 1,000,000 + 142,857 - 1 = 1,142,857 - 1 = 1,142,856$$

This number differs from 142,857 in that it has an extra digit 1 on its left and the last digit (7) is diminished by 1. Similarly we may obtain the product

$$142,857 \cdot 12 = 142,857 \cdot 7 + 142,857 \cdot 5 = 999,999 + 714,285$$

Finally, we have

$$142,857 \cdot 12 = 1,000,000 + 714,285 - 1 = 1,714,284$$

Let us obtain one more product before we arrive at the rule for the multiplication of 142,857 by any number; $142,857 \cdot 25 = (142,857 \cdot 7)3 + 142,857 \cdot 4 = 999,999 \cdot 3 + 571,428$, and

$$142,857 \cdot 25 = (1,000,000 - 1)3 + 571,428 = 3,000,000 + 571,428 - 3 = 3,571,425$$

We observe that the first digit in this product is the quotient of the division of 25 by 7, and this quotient (which in this case is 3) is subtracted from the product of the remainder of the division of 25 by 7 (4) by 142,857. This product is written to the left of the quotient of the division of 25 by 7.

Then the rule for the multiplication of 142,857 by any number is as follows: Divide the second number by 7 and write its quotient to the left of the product. To the right of this quotient is written the product of 142,857 and of the remainder of the division of the second number by 7. Finally, the quotient of the division (which is written on the left) is subtracted from the extreme right of the number thus written. For example, the product of 142,857 and 543 is obtained thus: $543 = 77 \cdot 7 + 4$; therefore

$$142,857 \cdot 543 = 77,571,428 - 77 = 77,571,351$$

If the second number is exactly divisible by 7 as, for example, 91, then the quotient is diminished by 1, and to the left of the diminished quotient we write the product of 142,857 and of 7, that is 999,999, and from the number thus written we subtract the diminished quotient. Thus

$$142,857 \cdot 91 = 12,999,999 - 12 = 12,999,987$$

Cyclic Handy Men

Our 142,857 is part of a family of numbers possessing properties amenable to rapid multiplication. Another such number is 0,588,235,294,117,647. That the zero is necessary is evident from this table of products:

$$
\begin{aligned}
0,588,235,294,117,647 \cdot \ 2 &= 1,176,470,588,235,294 \\
0,588,235,294,117,647 . \ 3 &= 1,764,705,882,352,941 \\
0,588,235,294,117,647 \cdot \ 4 &= 2,352,941,176,470,588 \\
0,588,235,294,117,647 \cdot \ 5 &= 2,941,176,470,588,235 \\
0,588,235,294,117,647 \cdot \ 6 &= 3,529,411,764,705,882 \\
0,588,235,294,117,647 \cdot \ 7 &= 4,117,647,058,823,529 \\
0,588,235,294,117,647 \cdot \ 8 &= 4,705,882,352,941,176 \\
0,588,235,294,117,647 \cdot \ 9 &= 5,294,117,647,058,823 \\
0,588,235,294,117,647 \cdot 10 &= 5,882,352,941,176,470 \\
0,588,235,294,117,647 \cdot 11 &= 6,470,588,235,294,117 \\
0,588,235,294,117,647 \cdot 12 &= 7,058,823,529,411,764 \\
0,588,235,294,117,647 \cdot 13 &= 7,647,058,823,529,411 \\
0,588,235,294,117,647 \cdot 14 &= 8,235,294,117,647,058 \\
0,588,235,294,117,647 \cdot 15 &= 8,823,529,411,764,705 \\
0,588,235,294,117,647 \cdot 16 &= 9,411,764,705,882,352 \\
0,588,235,294,117,647 \cdot 17 &= 9,999,999,999,999,999
\end{aligned}
$$

The reader may now guess (and correctly) that our 0,588,-235,294,117,647 is the period of the fraction 1/17 when it is translated into a repeating decimal fraction. However, not every fraction so translated will give a period that is expressed by a number possessing the same property as 142,857. Note that 142,857 contains six digits and originated from the fraction 1/7, and that 0,588,235,294,117,647 contains 16 digits and also originated from 1/17. Only those fractions that yield periods containing one less digit than the number in the denominator of the fraction lead to numbers that possess the properties described by us above. Such fractions include 1/7, 1/17, 1/19, 1/23, 1/29 and an infinity of similar combinations. The fraction 1/13 does not lead to such a period, however.

Some Wit Testers

The following problem is an interesting exercise: Write a certain number (you may use the signs +, ·, and ÷) by using all the digits (0, 1, 2, 3, 4, 5, 6, 7, 8, and 9) but every digit once only. Thus 9 may be written as

$$\frac{97,524}{10,836}, \quad \frac{95,823}{10,647}, \quad \frac{95,742}{10,638}, \quad \frac{75,249}{08,361}, \quad \frac{58,239}{06,471}, \quad \frac{57,429}{06,381}$$

Are there any other possible ways of writing 9 in the same manner? How about writing some other number, say 7, or 8, or 6?

Writing of 100 may be done by means of the digits 1, 2, 3, 4, 5, 6, 7, 8, and 9, as

$$97 + \frac{5+3}{8} + \frac{6}{4} + \frac{1}{2}$$

or

$$75 + 24 + \tfrac{9}{18} + \tfrac{3}{6}$$

$$975 + 4 + \tfrac{16}{28} + \tfrac{3}{7}.$$

$$98 + 1 + \tfrac{27}{54} + \tfrac{3}{6}, \qquad\qquad 91 + 8 + \tfrac{27}{54} + \tfrac{3}{6},$$

$$94 + 5 + \tfrac{38}{76} + \tfrac{1}{2}, \qquad\qquad 95 + 4 + \tfrac{38}{76} + \tfrac{11}{2},$$

$$1 + 95 + 3 + \tfrac{4}{28} + \tfrac{6}{7}, \qquad\qquad 1 + 93 + 5 + \tfrac{4}{28} + \tfrac{6}{7},$$

$$91 + 3 + 5 + \tfrac{4}{28} + \tfrac{6}{7},$$

$$57 + 42 + \tfrac{9}{18} + \tfrac{3}{6}, \qquad\qquad 52 + 47 + \tfrac{9}{18} + \tfrac{3}{6},$$

$$3\tfrac{69258}{714}, \quad 81\tfrac{5643}{297}, \quad 81\tfrac{7524}{396}, \quad 82\tfrac{3546}{197}, \quad 91\tfrac{5742}{638},$$

$$91\tfrac{67254}{836}, \quad 91\tfrac{5823}{647}, \quad 94\tfrac{1578}{265}, \quad 96\tfrac{2148}{537}, \quad 96\tfrac{1428}{357}, \quad 96\tfrac{1752}{438}.$$

Also 100 may be written as follows:

$$1 + 2 + 3 + 4 + 5 + 6 + 7 + (8 \cdot 9),$$
$$1 + (2 \cdot 3) + (4 \cdot 5) - 6 + 7 + (8 \cdot 9),$$
$$1 + (2 \cdot 3) + 4 + 5 + 67 + 8 + 9,$$
$$(1 \cdot 2) + 34 + 56 + 7 - 8 + 9,$$
$$-(1 \cdot 2) - 3 - 4 - 5 + (6 \cdot 7) + (8 \cdot 9),$$
$$12 + 3 - 4 + 5 + 67 + 8 + 9,$$
$$12 - 3 - 4 + 5 - 6 + 7 + 89,$$
$$123 + 4 - 5 + 67 - 89,$$
$$123 + 45 - 67 + 8 - 9,$$
$$123 - 45 - 67 + 89,$$
$$123 - 4 - 5 - 6 - 7 + 8 - 9,$$
$$(1 + 2 - 3 - 4)(5 - 6 - 7 - 8 - 9)$$

Here are some products in which every digit from 1 to 9 inclusive appears once only:

$$4 \cdot 1,738 = 6,952 \qquad 4 \cdot 1,963 = 7,852$$
$$12 \cdot \quad 483 = 5,796 \qquad 18 \cdot \quad 297 = 5,346$$
$$27 \cdot \quad 198 = 5,346 \qquad 28 \cdot \quad 157 = 4,396$$
$$39 \cdot \quad 186 = 7,254 \qquad 42 \cdot \quad 138 = 5,796$$

A few more curious properties of numbers:

Take any two-place number, write it backward, and add these two numbers. Do the same to the sum thus obtained and add the two numbers again. This process can be repeated until at some stage the sum reads exactly the same from left to right and from right to left. For instance, with 16 we have

$$16 + 61 = 77; \ 29 + 92 = 121;$$

$$69 + 96 = 165; \ 165 + 561 = 726; \ 726 + 627 = 1,353; \ 1,353 + 3,531 = 4,884$$

These three-place numbers are divisible by the product of their respective digits: 111, 112, 115, 128, 132, 135, 144, 175, 212, 216, 224, 312, 315, 384, 432, 612, 624, 672, 735, and 816.

And here is an interesting property of fractions:

$$\frac{47,591 - 47}{99,990} = \frac{47,591,591 - 47}{99,999,900} = \frac{47,591,591 - 47,591}{99,900,000}$$

PROBLEMS

1. Write 1,000 by using eight 8's.
2. Write 24 by using three 8's.
3. Write 24 by using any three identical digits.
4. Write 30 by using three 5's.
5. Write 1 by using all the ten digits (each digit to be used once only).
6. Write 10 with five 9's.
7. Write 100 with five identical digits (five 1's, or five 3's, etc.).
8. Write 100 by using four 9's.

+ 4 +

Number Giants

Close-up of a Million

Nowadays there is a great deal of familiar talk about big numbers such as millions and billions, but we rarely stop to think exactly what these terms signify. A million does seem a mere trifle when the cost of running our government runs into billions a year, when the cost of a single battleship is fifty millions, and when the cost of sending our children to school is about 5,000 millions a year. As a point of fact, however, "a million" is still only a casual acquaintance to us. If you really visualize a million, you have a bigger and better imagination than most.

If the walking step of a man is 1 yard, it would take about a million steps to carry him from Washington, D. C., to Portland, Maine, or from New York City to Cleveland provided, of course, he didn't give up and hop the fast freight.

If you don't like walking, however, and still want to gain some notion of a million, try to write a million strokes with a pencil. Suppose you make one stroke a second; it will take you about 278 hours, or 11 days and 14 hours of nonstop writing. If you work only 8 hours a day (Sundays and holidays included), it will take you at least 34 days and 4 hours. And this is only a million.

The word million is just a little more than four hundred years old. It first appeared in Italy about 1500, eight years after Columbus discovered America. Since then only about 232 million minutes have elapsed, there being about 526,000 minutes in a year.

Can we visualize, for example, the yearly crop of corn in the United States? It is about 2,500 millions of bushels a year. Can we imagine the quantity of coal that is mined in this country daily, about one and a half million tons a day; or the iron and steel output in this country, about a million tons of iron and one and a half million tons of steel a week?

PROBLEMS

1. How many five-ton trucks would it require to cart away the yearly production of coal in the United States?

2. A bushel of corn weighs about 56 pounds. One ton is equal to 2,000 pounds. How many five-ton trucks would it require to cart away the yearly crop of corn in the United States?

3. If a man, on the average, walks three miles a day, how long would it take him to cover a million feet? (A mile is 5,280 feet.)

The Long Count

How long would it take to count a million objects if it takes a second to count one object? There are 60 seconds in a minute and 60 minutes in an hour, thus 3,600 seconds in an hour. Then there are $\frac{1,000,000}{3,600}$ hours in a million seconds. This is approximately equal to 278 hours, or 11 days and 14 hours of nonstop counting.

Suppose that only 8 hours a day are spent on the counting. Under these circumstances only $(60 \cdot 60 \cdot 8) = 28,800$ objects would be counted. In ten days only 288,000 objects would be counted, just a little over one-fourth of the objects. The entire million objects would be counted in 34 days and 4 hours, provided you work like a clock and give up both Sundays and holidays.

PROBLEMS

4. A man smokes, on the average, a pack of cigarettes a day (a pack contains 20 cigarettes). How long would it take him to smoke a million cigarettes?

5. The United States imports about 80 million pounds of tea

yearly. If it takes 1 pound of tea to make 100 cups, and there are about 50 million persons in this country who drink tea, how many cups of tea a year does one person consume in one year?

6. There are about 25 million milch cows in the United States. A cow yields about 4 gallons of milk a day. How many pints of milk are produced daily in this country?

All Is Lost: That Housefly Is Here Again

When we want to say something is very thin, we say that it has the breadth of a hair. The average thickness of a human hair, we know, is about three-thousandths of an inch.

Suppose the breadth of a hair is increased one million times; what would be its width? Would it be as wide as a fist, or as wide as a door? This answer is startling, as we shall see after we have performed the simple computation

$$0.003 \text{ inch } 1,000,000 = 3,000 \text{ inches} = 250 \text{ feet}$$

A human hair, its breadth increased a million times, would be wider than an average city block!

A common housefly is a nuisance even though only 0.3 inch long. If its length were increased a million times it would be 25,000 feet, almost five miles, long. We would really have a problem of national defense then.

A six-foot man, if his height were increased a million times, would be about 1,136 miles tall. If he could lie down with his feet resting in Chicago, his head would just about reach Galveston, Texas.

We mentioned that the daily production of coal in this country is about one and a half million tons a day. A cubic foot of coal weighs about 90 pounds. There are 2,000 pounds in a ton. Thus a ton of coal is

$$\frac{2000}{90} \text{ cubic feet} = \frac{200}{9} \text{ cubic feet}$$

and 1,500,000 tons of coal are

$$\frac{200 \cdot 1500000}{9} \text{ cubic feet} = \frac{200 \cdot 500000}{3} \text{ cubic feet}$$

$$= 33,333,333 \text{ cubic feet}$$

The yearly production of coal is 365 times as large. In a cubic mile there are (5,280·5,280·5,280) cubic feet. Then in cubic miles the yearly production of coal is

$$\frac{33333333 \cdot 365}{(5280 \cdot 5280 \cdot 5280)} \text{ cubic mile} = 0.083 \text{ cubic mile}$$

A cube of this size will be about 2,300 feet long, 2,300 feet wide, and 2,300 feet high.

If a million men were placed in one line shoulder to shoulder the line would stretch out about 155 miles.

A book of about 700 pages of small type contains about one million letters.

A million days is about equal to 2,700 years. Thus since the Birth of Christ a million days has not elapsed.

One million dots of the size of the period on this page, when placed in one line close one to another, will occupy a line about 328 feet long.

A million nickels (5 cent coins) placed in one line will stretch 68,800 feet, or about 13 miles.

PROBLEMS

7. The diameter of an ordinary pocket watch is about 1.5 inches. What would be its diameter if it were increased one million times? How large would be the hour number if originally it were 1/8 inch long?

8. A mosquito is about 3/8 inch long. How big would be one a million times enlarged?

9. A thimble of water weighs about a gram. What would be the weight of a million thimbles of water?

10. The diameter of a 50-watt electric bulb is about 2.5 inches. What would be the length covered by a million bulbs?

11. *Gone With the Wind* sold about 1,500,000 copies. If this book is about 2 inches thick, and if all sold were stacked in one column, how tall would such a column be?

Pity the Poor Billionaire: A Fifty-Nine-Mile Pile of Bills

So a million is a fair-sized number, but huge as it is it does not satisfy the requirements of modern life. We need larger numbers, numbers almost beyond imagination.

The next unit larger than a million is a billion, or one thousand millions, in figures 1,000,000,000.

In science even a billion is not always large enough. Scientists use next a number that exceeds a billion a thousand times. The name for this unit is a trillion (1,000,000,000,000). However, even this number is sometimes not large enough for the physicist or astronomer. In fact, these scientists long ago gave up the idea of making such units and developed, with the help of mathematics, a method of writing large numbers in a very compact form. For the present, however, we shall try to be satisfied with a billion.

In some of the European countries this billion has another name, "milliard." This word came into use after the Franco-Prussian war of 1871, when France was compelled to pay to Germany 5,000,000,000 francs for reparations.

To grasp the magnitude of a billion, let us consider a few examples:

A package of 100 one-dollar bills is about 3/8 inch thick. A billion bills stacked in one column would be about 59.3 miles high.

At 10:40 o'clock on April 29, 1902, a billion minutes have elapsed since the beginning of our era.

In one cubic meter there are 1,000,000,000 cubic millimeters. If these cubic millimeters were stacked up in a column they would tower up 1,000 kilometers.

A billion objects, if one were counted each second, could be counted in about 31.7 years provided the teller worked on a non-stop shift day and night, weekday, and holiday.

That housefly, if its length were increased a billion times, would be larger than the moon.

A six-foot man, given a magic billion-expanding pill could, if he were standing on the earth, allow the moon to pass between his legs just about his knees. The height of such a man would be greater than the diameter of the sun.

12. The diameter of an ordinary pocket watch is about 1.5 inches. What would be the diameter of a watch a billion times as large? What would be the length of an hour number on such a watch if on an ordinary watch it is about 1/8 inch long?

13. If the average weight of a pair of shoes is about 1.5 pounds, what would be the weight of a pair worn by a man whose height was increased a billion times?

14. If the length of a human head is about 10 inches, what would be its length for a man whose height was expanded a billion times?

You Owe $1,735

We have considered a few spectacular and grotesque cases where very large numbers were employed, but realize that the magnitude of these numbers figures realistically as well in our daily routine life. Let us consider just a few cases:

The total debt of the United States Government is, at the moment, about 260 billion dollars. This means that if this debt were equally distributed among every man, woman, and child in this country, everyone would have to pay about $1,735 to wipe it out.

The cost of running the United States Government is now about seventy billion dollars a year; if this cost were equally distributed among the population, everyone would have to pay $475 a year to keep the government operating.

The assessed valuation of land and real property of Manhattan Island in New York City is eight billion dollars. There are 14,211 acres of land on Manhattan (one acre is equal to 6,272, 240 square inches). The length of a one-dollar bill is 6 inches, and its width is 2.5 inches. Thus the area of a one-dollar bill is (2.5·6) square inches = 15 square inches. The total area of Manhattan Island is 14,211·6,272,240 square inches. If the entire island were covered completely with dollar bills, the value of the money would not be equal to the assessed valuation, eight billion dollars. This can be seen from the following:

The area covered by eight billion one-dollar bills is

15·8,000,000,000 square inches = 120,000,000,000 square inches

and the area of Manhattan Island is

$$14,211·6,272,240 = 89,134,602,640 \text{ square inches}$$

Then

$$120,000,000,000 - 89,134,602,640 = 30,865,397,360$$

Therefore the area covered by the dollar bills exceeds the area of Manhattan Island by 30,865,397,360 square inches, or

$$\frac{120,000,000,000}{14,211·6,272,240} = 1.34 \ldots \text{ times}$$

The yearly production of cigarettes in this country is about 350 billions. A cigarette usually is 2.75 inches long. If these cigarettes were laid out lengthwise in one line, it would stretch fifteen million miles. This distance is about twenty times as large as the diameter of the sun. The line of the cigarettes could be wound around the equator of the earth 600 times.

PROBLEMS

15. The average production of apples in the United States is about 150,000,000 bushels a year. A bushel of apples weighs 50 pounds. How many pounds of apples are produced in a year in this country?

16. It was found that 84.1 per cent of an apple is water. How much water is there in the yearly crop of apples in this country?

17. The reported consumption of gasoline in 1940 in the United States was 22,685,056,000 gallons. The average tax rate for that year was 3.96 cents a gallon. How much was collected by all the states in gasoline taxes in 1940?

Now, Some Really Big Numbers

But it is the scientists who deal in really large numbers, numbers such that a billion to them is the same as 1, and even less, is to a billion. We note that a billion is written as 1 with nine zeros. Since it is inconvenient to write, as well as to read and to evaluate readily when all the zeros are written, scientists make use of a mathematical method for a simple and compact writing of a large number. We shall now see how this is done.

When a number is multiplied by itself it is written as, say, 10·10. However, we may write this in another way, to indicate that a given number was taken as a product twice. For this purpose we write the number and, on the right just above it, we write a small 2, provided that we agree to interpret this 2 as an indicator of this repeated multiplication. Thus 10·10 is written as 10^2. We may continue this method of writing and extend this principle to the cases when a number is multiplied by itself more than twice. Thus 10·10·10 is written as 10^3, 10·10·10·10·10 as 10^5, and so on.

Now we observe that when 10 is multiplied by itself we obtain 100, or a 1 with two zeros to its right; when multiplied by itself three times we get 1,000, with three zeros, and when multiplied by itself five times, we obtain 100,000, or 1 with five zeros on its right. Thus we note that the number that is the indicator of how many times 10 is multiplied by itself and the number of zeros written to the left of the 1 are always the same.

We then can reverse the process, and instead of writing 100,-000,000 we may write 10^8. A billion (1,000,000,000) is then written as 10^9. Now if we need a number larger than a billion, instead of writing additional zeros on the right we increase the indicator, which is known as the "exponent." Thus a trillion is 10^{12}, a quadrillion is 10^{15}, and so on. It is easily observable that actually there is no need to give special names to the various units, since there is very little importance in the name. One glance at the exponent of the 10 is sufficient to gather all the information needed. Moreover, numbers that are larger than a billion are really inconceivable, except that they convey some information as to magnitude. If a number is written with twenty-five zeros, the addition of one, two or more zeros on its right will not add much to our comprehension of the actual magnitude, unless we use some other means for its interpretation.

Moreover, once we command this method, we may go on writing such large numbers indefinitely, obtaining still larger numbers. So, there just isn't any "largest" number, as will be now illustrated.

PROBLEMS

18. New York City in 1939 consumed on the average $1.002 \cdot 10^9$ gallons of water daily. How much was consumed in a year?

19. If the population of New York City in 1939 was $7.6 \cdot 10^6$, what was the average daily consumption of water for one man in 1939?

20. If the population of the United States in 1950 was estimated as $150 \cdot 10^6$, and the average consumption of water a day is about the amount that a New Yorker consumes in a day, how much water was consumed in the United States in a day during 1950?

Archimedes Counts the Sands

We read in the Old Testament that the Lord promised to Abraham that his descendants would be as numerous as the grains of sand on the seashore. This poetical expression was in great vogue with the ancient writers, but the job of counting the number of grains, not only on the seashore but in the entire universe if it were filled with the finest sand to the firmament of the fixed stars, was actually tackled by a Greek mathematician, Archimedes, who lived in Syracuse on the island of Sicily in the third century B.C. In a later chapter we shall repeat his calculations but here, we shall be content with stating his result; he arrived at a number that does not exceed

1,000,000,000,000,000,000,000,000,000,000,000,000,000,000,000,000,000,000,000,000,000

or in our modern scientific writing, 10^{63}.

To state a number with sixty-three zeros to the right of the 1, Archimedes was compelled to develop his own system of numbers. We must bear in mind that the Greeks did not have our method of writing numbers; they used their alphabet, every letter of which was assigned a numerical value. Moreover, for as large a number as 10,000 the Greeks had a special name, "myriad."

Archimedes' first step was to arrange numbers in classes. In the first class the unit was 1, and he counted until he reached a myriad of myriads, 100,000,000, or 10^8 as we would write it.

Within this number he considered the first class completed and began to build up the second class, which also consisted of a myriad of myriads. The part of 1 in the second class is played by 10^8. Thus he counted a myriad of myriads of 10^8 (he called the 10^8 an "octade"). This led to a number with sixteen zeros, that is, to 10^{16}. This number he called the second octade. The third octade was a number with twenty-four zeros, 10^{24}. We observe that for every octade he added 8 to the exponent of 10. He continued to build up numbers in this way until he had an octade of octades; that is, he had in the exponent of 10 an 8 multiplied by 10^8. In our method of writing this number would be

$$10^{8 \cdot 10^8},$$

or $10^{800,000,000}$, or a number that begins with a 1 and has to its right 800 million zeros. All these numbers, according to Archimedes, constitute the "first period." But he did not stop here. He now took

$$10^{8 \cdot 10^8}$$

and considered it as the 1 of the second period. Then

the first octade of the second period   is $10^{8 \cdot 10^8 + 8}$

the second octade of the second period is $10^{8 \cdot 10^8 + 16}$

the third octade of the second period is $10^{8 \cdot 10^8 + 24}$

and so on until the octade of the second period is

$$10^{8 \cdot 10^8} \ (10^{8 \cdot 10^8}) \quad \text{or} \quad 10^{2 \cdot 8 \cdot 10^8}$$

and this number closes the second period, as well as becoming the 1 of the third period. Archimedes proceeded in the same manner until he built up the number

$$10^{10 \cdot 8 \cdot 10^8}$$

This is $10^{8,000,000,000}$, or a 1 with eight billion zeros to the right of the 1. Archimedes did not have to stop even there, he could continue to build up the numbers indefinitely. The number $10^{8,000,000,000}$ has no real meaning to us. It is so large that no one will ever have a chance to put it to practical use. And that, in these days of numeration-minded science, indicates a pretty sizable figure.

Let us consider a simple problem that may help us to grasp the scope of Archimedes' numbers. Let us write with three 9's the largest possible number. Some may think 999 is the number, but they are most mistaken. The answer is

$$9^{9^9}$$

This means that 9 is multiplied by itself 9^9 or $9 \cdot 9 \cdot 9 \cdot 9 \cdot 9 \cdot 9 \cdot 9 \cdot 9 \cdot 9$ times. But 9^9 is not such a small number. The reader may try to multiply 9 by itself 9 times. This product is 387,420,489. Then

$$9^{9^9}$$

is $9^{387,420,489}$, and this means that 9 must be multiplied by itself 387,420,489 times. This would require almost four hundred million multiplications.

How large is this number written with only three 9's? Not as large as the number that Archimedes has obtained, but nobody has ever calculated it. It is so large that if written on a strip of paper, allowing 200 digits to every foot, it would require 350 miles of paper, and the strip could be stretched between Cleveland and Chicago. If someone knew this number and would set out to write it down at the rate of one digit a second, it would take him 11 years and 8 months of steady uninterrupted writing. However, we have partial information concerning the number; it begins with the digits 428,124,773,175,747,048,036,987,118, and ends with 89. What is between these digits no one knows. This number has 369,693,100 digits.

PROBLEMS

21. Which is larger, 10^{myriad} or $myriad^{10}$?
22. Express as 10 with an indicator (exponent) an $octade^{myriad}$.

A Cure for Egotists

If we find it difficult to visualize large numbers when they refer to objects, it is no wonder that most of us fail to grasp fully the meaning of large numbers in terms of time. Have we ever considered how old our earth is? Can we comprehend the age of our solar system? We think it striking when a man lives more than one hundred years. We consider mankind very old (our civilization and recorded history is about 6,000 years old) but is of course new-born in comparison with other life on this globe.

We know that human beings roamed certain areas about 50,000 years ago, but the birth of the earth took place at least two billion years ago (and this estimate is very conservative), and the birth of the sun at least five billion years ago. Only about five hundred million years ago the earth was cooled sufficiently to create rock deposits. That time is known as the Cambrian period, and life in very primitive forms was evident then. Compare five hundred million years with seventy years, a ripe old age in the life of a man.

Suppose we imagine a line fifty feet long. This represents the age of the sun. The age of the earth then will be occupied by a twenty-foot portion, and the five hundred million years will be taken up by five feet. The age of humans, even if we allow 200,000 years for this period, will take up only about 0.024 inch. One would need a magnifying glass to see so small a line. The last 6,000 years of the history of mankind will need only about 0.001 inch. To see this small speck we would have to use a fairly good microscope. The average life of man, if we take it as seventy years, would require only 0.00001 inch.

Compare then the life of man with the life of the sun.

PROBLEMS

23. The average heartbeat of a man is about seventy-five times a minute. How many heartbeats are there in a life of seventy years?

24. According to the findings of physicists the sun loses in weight, owing to the emission of energy, about $4 \cdot 10^6$ tons of its mass every minute. How much has the sun lost during the last 5,000 years?

25. Sound travels at the rate of about 1,100 feet a second. Radio waves travel at the rate of about 186,000 miles a second. A radio performance is broadcast from a concert hall 250 feet long. One person sits at the wall opposite the stage of the hall (which is in New York City), and another person sits near his radio set in Los Angeles, California. Who of these two will hear the performance first?

Timetable for a Tour of the Stars

If we take an automobile trip of a thousand miles, we spend a lot of time getting ready. A trip across the country is something to worry about and, if everything goes well, to brag about; a trip around the world, is a real feat. However, let us compare these distances with some in space:

The nearest neighbor of the earth is the moon, about 240,000 miles away. An airplane at 300 miles an hour would travel 800 hours from the earth to reach the moon; that is, 33 days of non-stop flight.

Light travels at approximately 186,000 miles a second. This means that it takes light just about one and one-third seconds to reach the earth from the moon. And what about the sun?

The sun is about 93,000,000 miles from the earth. Our airplane would have to travel 465,000 hours, or about 53 years, to reach the sun. How much gasoline and oil would such a trip require?

It takes light, however, about 8 1/2 minutes to reach the earth from the sun. This means that when we are looking at the sun, we do not see it as it is at the moment but as it was 8 1/2 minutes ago.

The nearest star, our next neighbor outside our own solar system, is so far away that astronomers have invented another yardstick for measuring distances—the light-year, or the distance traversed by light (at the rate of 186,000 miles a second) in 365 days. This distance is

$$186,000 \cdot 60 \cdot 60 \cdot 24 \cdot 365 \text{ miles} = \text{about } 6,000,000,000,000 \text{ miles}$$

or, as we would write, $6 \cdot 10^{12}$ (6,000 billion) miles. In the case of the nearest star this distance is equal to 4.3 years, or about $3 \cdot 10^{13}$ miles. An airplane trip to the nearest star would take about seven million years.

But we have considered only the nearest star. Astronomers recently announced that they had photographed universes of stars so distant that it takes light at least two hundred million years to reach the earth. This distance is about 10^{21} miles. How long would it take an airplane to reach this universe?

While we are flying around in space we may as well note that our sun, and thus ourselves also, belong to a star universe, the Milky Way. There are hundreds of millions of stars, some bigger, some smaller, and some about the same size as the sun, in this Milky Way. Our island universe is shaped like a watch. It measures between 200,000 and 300,000 light-years across and is about 50,000 light-years in thickness. We are located a fourth of the way from the center of this big disk. Thus the dimensions of the Milky Way are

across 1,000,000,000,000,000,000 miles

and

thick 300,000,000,000,000,000 miles

Compare these distances with the earth's diameter, which is about 8,000 miles, or with the sun's, about 800,000 miles. Or, you may contrast the Milky Way mileage to that supposedly longish trip from the earth to the sun, about 93,000,000 miles.

PROBLEMS

26. The earth goes around the sun at approximately 19 miles a second. How great a distance was covered by the earth during the last 5,000 years?

27. The sun travels in space at approximately 19 miles a second. Suppose that the sun is five billion years old and that the rate of travel has not changed during this time. How great a distance was covered by the sun during this time?

28. A rifle bullet leaves the muzzle of a rifle with a speed of about 600 feet a second. If the distance from the earth to the sun is about 93,000,000 miles, how long would it take the bullet to reach the surface of the sun?

= 5 =

Number Pygmies

Some Gigantic Runts

How small is "small"? We have noted as one conception the familiar "hair's breadth," actually three-thousandths of an inch. In the aircraft and automobile industries manufacturers pride themselves that some parts are measured to a ten-thousandth of an inch; if they achieve a hundred-thousandth it is advertised as an almost impossible feat. Though apparently "small," even these proportions bulk large in the world of the very small.

We think of a hair's breadth as tiny because we ordinarily judge the magnitude of objects by our unaided senses. Our senses, however, are extremely crude: we do not see certain magnitudes because we cannot see all the waves that constitute light, nor can we hear all the waves that constitute sound. Until the microscope was invented we had no suspicion of the existence of bacteria, and even the most powerful microscope is sometimes inadequate to detect the virus of the common cold, or the living creature that causes infantile paralysis.

Place a hair under a microscope that magnifies a thousand times and it will appear as though it were three inches thick. Under the same microscope the virus of the common cold is invisible. Now think of comparing the magnitude of this virus with the breadth of a hair: We do not know the exact size of the virus; we only know that it is vastly smaller than our previous hair's breadth extreme. But still it is not the smallest object in this world. It is impossible to answer the question: How small is small? as it is to define: How large is large? We have seen that even though almost incredibly large magnitudes may be created, we still can think of numbers yet larger, although they may have no definite meaning. In this chapter we shall repeat the procedure of the last, but in reverse; we shall seek out not giants but pygmies. Some of these pygmies will be giants among themselves, but we shall delve deeply into the land of the small, the smaller, and the smallest . . . if we ever attain the last.

We shall have to appeal now to more advanced science for examples of "very small" objects and shall express the numerical values of the pygmies by a method similar to that of evaluating the giants. We recall that with large numbers we resorted to a special way of writing the products of 10 by themselves; we denoted by a number-indicator (or exponent) written on the right, just above the 10, the number of times 10 was multiplied by itself. Thus:

10,000,000	is written as	10^7
1,000,000	is written as	10^6
100,000	is written as	10^5
10,000	is written as	10^4
1,000	is written as	10^3
100	is written as	10^2
10	is written as	10^1

Now we shall resort to a simple analogy. When we write the positive numbers in the decreasing order, we finally reach zero and, if we continue, must write the negative number. Thus we have

$$\cdots, 8, 7, 6, 5, 4, 3, 2, 1, 0, -1, -2, -3, -4, -5, -6, -7, \cdots$$

This table of the products of 10, if continued in the decreasing order, should have as its next member 1, and the exponent of 10 should be zero. Then the next member should be 1/10, or 0.1, and the exponent of 10 should be -1. The next member should be 1/100, or 0.01, and the exponent should be -2. We then complete the table as follows.

$$1 \quad \text{is written as} \quad 10^0$$

$$\frac{1}{10} \quad \text{or} \quad 0.1 \quad \text{is written as} \quad 10^{-1}$$

$$\frac{1}{100} \quad \text{or} \quad 0.01 \quad \text{is written as} \quad 10^{-2}$$

$$\frac{1}{1000} \quad \text{or} \quad 0.001 \quad \text{is written as} \quad 10^{-3}$$

$$\frac{1}{10,000} \quad \text{or} \quad 0.0001 \quad \text{is written as} \quad 10^{-4}$$

$$\frac{1}{100,000} \quad \text{or} \quad 0.00001 \quad \text{is written as} \quad 10^{-5}, \text{etc.}$$

Multiplication of the numbers written in this manner should offer no difficulty. The indicators (exponents) show how many zeros there are in the products of 10, and when two such numbers (each a product of 10 by itself several times) are multiplied, the indicators of the zeros are added. Thus, $10^4 \cdot 10^3 = 10,000 \cdot 1,000 = 10,000,000 = 10^7$. When the exponents are negative, the same rule holds. Thus $1/10,000 \cdot 1/1,000 = 1/10,000,000$. But the same number can be written as $10^{-4} \cdot 10^{-3} = 10^{-7}$.

PROBLEMS

1. The radius of the earth's sphere is about 4,000 miles. If this radius were diminished one billion times, how would it compare with the breadth of a hair?

2. How many times larger is the distance from the earth to the sun than the radius of the earth's sphere?

3. The radius of the sun is about 400,000 miles. The volumes of two spheres are to one another as the cubes of their radii. What part of the sun's volume is the volume of the earth's sphere?

4. The largest known star has a radius of about 690,000,000 miles. What part of the volume of this star is the volume of the sun?

5. The distance from the sun to the outermost planet Pluto is, on the average, about 4,500,000,000 miles. What part of this distance is the length of the diameter of the earth?

Cosmic Small Fry

What is the smallest unit of measure now in science? In the world of pygmy numbers scientists employ the metric system and we shall do likewise. To clarify the relation between the metric system and the system used in our everyday activities, here are some of the equivalents:

$$1 \text{ kilometer} = 0.621 \text{ mile, approximately}$$
$$1 \text{ meter} = 3.281 \text{ feet, approximately}$$
$$1 \text{ centimeter} = 0.394 \text{ inch, approximately}$$
$$1 \text{ millimeter} = 0.0394 \text{ inch, approximately}$$

In the metric system all the units are obtained by multiplying a smaller unit by products of 10, or by dividing a larger unit by products of 10. Thus:

$$1 \text{ kilometer} = 1,000 \text{ meters}$$
$$1 \text{ meter} = 100 \text{ centimeters} = 1,000 \text{ millimeters}$$
$$1 \text{ centimeter} = 10 \text{ millimeters}$$
$$1 \text{ millimeter} = 1,000 \text{ microns}$$
$$1 \ x = 1/10,000,000 \text{ of a micron}$$

Every human being carries within himself a number giant— the blood. It contains red corpuscles, tiny bodies each like a circular disk somewhat flattened at the center and about 0.007 millimeter in diameter and 0.002 millimeter thick. In a drop of blood (1 cubic millimeter) there are about 5,000,000 of these corpuscles, and an average adult has about 3,500,000 cubic millimeters of blood. A simple calculation shows that an average adult has in his system

$$5,000,000 \cdot 3,500,000 = 5 \cdot 10^6 \cdot 35 \cdot 10^5 = 175 \cdot 10^{11} \text{ red corpuscles}$$

If all these corpuscles were strung out in a single chain, its length would be

$$175 \cdot 10^{11} \cdot 7 \cdot 10^{-3} \text{ millimeters} = 1,225 \cdot 10^8 \text{ millimeters}$$

But there are 10^3 millimeters in a meter and 10^3 meters in a kilometer. That is, there are 10^6 millimeters in a kilometer; thus our chain is

$$\frac{1,225 \cdot 10^8}{10^6} = 122,500 \text{ kilometers}$$

This chain could be wound around the earth's equator three times and over.

The population of the world is about $2 \cdot 10^9$ people. Thus, if all the red corpuscles of the entire population were strung out in a single chain, it would be

$$1,225 \cdot 10^2 \cdot 2 \cdot 10^9 = 25 \cdot 10^{13} \text{ kilometers, approximately}$$

or about

$$25 \cdot 0.6 \cdot 10^{13} = 15 \cdot 10^{13} \text{ miles}$$

This distance would extend seven and a half times farther than the nearest star, and light would require about twenty-six years to traverse it.

Thus a pygmy blood corpuscle can give rise to a mathematical giant, and is itself a giant in comparison with some other objects of the universe. Suppose a corpuscle should be increased in diameter a million times: its diameter would then be

$$7 \cdot 10^{-3} \cdot 10^6 = 7,000 \text{ millimeters} = 7 \text{ meters}$$

or about thirty feet in length.

But in chemistry and physics there is a unit of substance called a molecule. A molecule can be broken up into the component substances which form the atom, and atoms can be broken up into their components, too. Suppose we take an atom and increase its diameter a million times. It still will be not greater than the period at the end of this sentence. Compare this with thirty feet, and indeed our corpuscle is a giant.

Let us take a glass of water and learn something more about number pygmies. A molecule of water consists of three atoms. Two of these are hydrogen atoms and one an oxygen atom. We may represent the molecule schematically as in this drawing:

The large circle may represent the oxygen atom and the two small circles the hydrogen atoms of a molecule of water although, of course, the drawing does not depict an actual water molecule or assume that the atoms are small spheres of different sizes.

The diameter of a molecule of water is

$$28 \cdot 10^{-9} = \frac{28}{1,000,000,000} \text{ centimeter}$$

The volume of a molecule of water is $115 \cdot 10^{-25}$ cubic centimeter, or

$$\frac{115}{10,000,000,000,000,000,000,000,000} \text{ cubic centimeter}$$

These numbers are much smaller than those associated with the measurement of the blood corpuscle.

A gram of water (which measures 1 cubic centimeter) contains about $34 \cdot 10^{21}$ molecules of water. A glass of water contains about 400 grams and thus contains

$$400 \cdot 34 \cdot 10^{21} = 136 \cdot 10^{23} \text{ molecules}$$

Now, how many molecules of water are there in all the oceans? It is estimated that this water occupies about $15 \cdot 10^8$ cubic kilometers. First, we shall have to calculate how many cubic centimeters there are in a cubic kilometer: 1 kilometer $= 1,000$ meters, and 1 meter $= 100$ centimeters. Then 1 kilometer $= 100,000$ centimeters, or 10^5 centimeters, and 1 cubic kilometer $= 10^5 \cdot 10^5 \cdot 10^5$ cubic centimeters $= 10^{15}$ cubic centimeters. Then

$$15 \cdot 10^8 \text{ cubic kilometers} = 15 \cdot 10^8 \cdot 10^{15} = 15 \cdot 10^{23} \text{ cubic}$$
$$\text{centimeters}$$

Finally we have the answer: In all the oceans there are about

$$34 \cdot 10^{21} \cdot 15 \cdot 10^{23} = 51 \cdot 10^{45} \text{ molecules}$$

Let us examine how large a giant we have obtained now. To comprehend its magnitude we shall examine just one drop of water. A drop weighs about a tenth of a gram, and its volume is about 0.33 cubic centimeter. Thus in one drop of water there are

$$34 \cdot 10^{21} \cdot 33 \cdot 10^{-2} = 1,122 \cdot 10^{19}$$

or in round numbers, about 10^{22} molecules. The diameter of a molecule of water is about $28 \cdot 10^{-9}$ centimeter. If all the molecules of a drop were strung out in a single chain, its length would be

$$28 \cdot 10^{-9} \cdot 1,122 \cdot 10^{19} = 31,416 \cdot 10^{10}$$

or $3 \cdot 10^{14}$ centimeters, or $3 \cdot 10^{12}$ meters, or $3 \cdot 10^9$ kilometers.

How great is this distance? It takes light one second to traverse 300,000 kilometers ($3 \cdot 10^5$ kilometers). Thus light would traverse the distance in

$$\frac{3 \cdot 10^9}{3 \cdot 10^5} = 10,000 \text{ seconds}$$

or in about 166 2/3 minutes, just about twenty times the time it takes light to travel from the sun to the earth. In other words, the molecules of one drop of water, if strung out in a single chain, would reach twenty times the distance from the earth to the sun. And this is only for one drop; how about the molecules of the water in all the oceans?

They would, if in a single chain, cover about $51 \cdot 10^{45} \cdot 28 \cdot 10^{-9}$ centimeters, or about $143 \cdot 10^{37}$ centimeters, or, in round figures, $15 \cdot 10^{38}$ centimeters, or $15 \cdot 10^{36}$ meters, or $15 \cdot 10^{33}$ kilometers. Light would cover this distance in

$$\frac{15 \cdot 10^{33}}{3 \cdot 10^5} = 5 \cdot 10^{28} \text{ seconds}$$

There are $60 \cdot 60 \cdot 24 \cdot 365 = 31,536,000$ seconds in a year. Let us take the round number 32,000,000, or $32 \cdot 10^6$. Then $2 \cdot 10^{31}$ seconds is about

$$\frac{5 \cdot 10^{28}}{32 \cdot 10^6} = 15 \cdot 10^{20} \text{ years}$$

or 1,500,000,000,000,000,000,000 years.

The most distant island universe known is only 200,000,000 light years away. Our chain of molecules stretches out

$$\frac{15 \cdot 10^{20}}{2 \cdot 10^8}$$

or about 7,500,000,000,000 times farther. The diameter of our universe is probably much smaller than this distance.

6. There are about $51 \cdot 10^{45}$ molecules of water in all the oceans. Suppose that the radius of our universe is a billion light-years. The volume of the sphere with that radius is obtained by translating a light-year into miles, and multiplying this by a billion, and finally cubing this number. This cubed result is multiplied by $1.33 \cdot 3.14$ or 4.18. If all these molecules were evenly distributed in such a sphere, how much space would be allotted to one molecule?

7. How many molecules (see Problem 6) may be found in a cubic mile of water?

8. What would be the weight of water in a cubic mile (see Problems 6 and 7)?

9. The radius of the earth's sphere is about 4,000 miles. If the blood of all the human beings were evenly distributed in a sphere of the size of the earth, how many red blood corpuscles would be allotted to every cubic mile?

10. How much space would be required for one blood corpuscle of one man under the conditions of Problem 6?

The Populous Bacterium

The smallest living thing that can be detected under a microscope is a bacterium. Bacteria are of different sizes, but let us consider the smallest of all that can be seen. Its diameter is about $2 \cdot 10^{-5}$ centimeter, much larger than that of a molecule of water. It is

$$\frac{2 \cdot 10^{-5}}{28 \cdot 10^{-9}} = 700$$

or about seven hundred times larger than the diameter of a molecule of water. But this margin is so large that no present microscope can detect a molecule. The volume of the bacterium is then $700 \cdot 700 \cdot 700$ or about 343,000,000 times as large as that of a molecule; in other words, a bacterium can contain in itself 343,-000,000 molecules of water. Thus there can be in a bacterium so many molecules of water that their number will be about two and a half times the population of the United States. This is not much of a number when we compare it with some of the numbers we have obtained before. But . . .

Molecules are made up of smaller things—atoms, which are in turn made up of electrons and a few other substances which are of little interest to us in this discussion. Physicists compute the weight of an electron to be about $9 \cdot 10^{-27}$ gram. The number of electrons in a gram depends on the substance under consideration, because different substances (that is, their atoms) have different numbers of electrons. Thus a hydrogen atom has 1 electron, an oxygen atom has 16, and an atom of the heaviest known element, uranium, has 238. In other words, the number of electrons in an atom is closely related to the weight of a substance. We shall recall that Archimedes computed the number of grains of sand in the universe. Let us compute the number of electrons in the universe, as we now conceive it, if every bit of space were filled with atoms of uranium.

We shall assume first that the universe is a sphere whose radius is the distance that is traversed by light in 1,000,000,000 (or 10^9) years. This is five times as great as the distance to the farthest known island universe. Light traverses 300,000 (or $3 \cdot 10^5$) kilometers in a second, and we have calculated that there are about $32 \cdot 10^6$ seconds in a year. Then our radius is

$$3 \cdot 10^5 \cdot 32 \cdot 10^6 \cdot 10^9 = 96 \cdot 10^{20}$$

or, in round numbers, 10^{22} kilometers.

The volume of a sphere of this size is about $4 \cdot 10^{66}$ cubic kilometers. There are 10,000 centimeters in a kilometer and $10^5 \cdot 10^5 \cdot 10^5$ cubic centimeters in a cubic kilometer. Then our sphere will contain $4 \cdot 10^{66} \cdot 10^{15}$ or $4 \cdot 10^{81}$ cubic centimeters.

There are about 10^{22} atoms of uranium in a cubic centimeter, and since each atom of uranium has 238 electrons, there are about $238 \cdot 10^{22}$ electrons in a cubic centimeter of uranium. Then the total number of electrons in our sphere would be

$$238 \cdot 10^{22} \cdot 4 \cdot 10^{81} = 1,472 \cdot 10^{103}$$

or, in round numbers, about 10^{106} electrons. This is a number with 106 zeros to the right of the 1. Actually, it has been computed that there are not more than 10^{83} electrons in the entire universe. As you see, there is still plenty of elbow room between the stars.

A Columbia University professor, Dr. Edward Kasner, has invented a special name for the number 10^{100}. He calls it "goo-

gol," and he has a name, too, for a number larger than googol.
The number 10^{googol}, that is, a 1 with googol zeros to its right, is
called "googolplex." Thus, a googol is merely

$$10,000,000,000,000,000,000,000,000,000,000,$$
$$000,000,000,000,000,000,000,000,000,000,000,$$
$$000,000,000,000,000,000,000,000,000,000,000$$

A googolplex, however, has that many zeros to the right of 1. A
number to think about when you are lying awake on a hot night.

PROBLEMS

11. If there were 10^{83} electrons in the universe, and we assume the
radius of the universe to be a billion light-years (see Problem 6 in
the preceding section), and if all the electrons were evenly distributed, how much space would be allotted to one electron?
12. How many electrons would be found in one cubic mile?
13. What would be the weight of the electrons found in one cubic
mile under the conditions of Problem 12?
14. How many googols are there in 10^{myriad}?
15. Which is larger: (1) googol^{googol} or myriad^{myriad};
                       (2) googol^{googol} or 9^{9^9};
                       (3) googolplex^{googol} or googol^{googolplex}?
16. After you have answered Problem 15, state by how many
times one number is larger than the other.
17. Write googolplex^{googolplex} in terms of 10 and 100.

The Other Side of Zero

In the preceding chapter we posed the problem of writing the
largest possible number with three 9's and we wrote it as

$$9^{9^9}$$

We also learned that this number had 369,693,100 digits. Likewise, in the preceding section, we wrote a number considerably
larger, the googolplex. This number has googol + 1 digits and
is really a macrogiant (or supergiant). Now let us invert our
procedure. We learned something about very small numbers,
but is there a limit beyond which we find only zero? Is there a
smallest number?

Small numbers are usually written as fractions. Suppose that we write the fraction

$$\frac{1}{9^{9^9}}$$

This is equal to

$$\frac{1}{9^{387420489}}$$

The same may be done with the googolplex. Then, we have

$$\frac{1}{10^{googol}}$$

or, if we employ the scientific method of writing, we have $10^{-googol}$. This decimal fraction will have googol -1 zeros after the decimal point, and to their right there will be a 1.

Have we reached the limit? Certainly not. With a flip of the brain we can call up a number such as $googol^{googol}$, that is, a googol multiplied by itself a googol times. And from this we may readily obtain the fraction

$$\frac{1}{googol^{googol}}$$

which may be also written as

$$googol^{-googol}$$

How many digits are there in a $googol^{googol}$? Even if we could say, we could still go farther and write a much larger number:

$$googol^{googol^{googol}}$$

and also the fraction

$$googol^{-\left(googol^{googol}\right)}$$

All these numbers, large or small, are beyond any possible application. But still larger and smaller numbers may always be obtained, although their writing is just a pastime; neither the largest nor the smallest number can ever be set down.

Where "Split Seconds" Drag

It has happened to the best of us. You have forgotten your toothbrush or neglected to say good-by to Aunt Minna, and since then traffic has been just one big red light. You dash through the station and catch your train (we hope) in that last "split second." No doubt the margin of safety seemed painfully small when you clambered aboard, but exactly how long was that split second? Is it a half, a tenth, or a thousandth of a second? Of course, a thousandth of a second is too fleeting a period for our physical senses to detect, but in these fast-spinning days it is actually too much of a moment for us to ignore.

For instance, suppose a train travels at 50 miles an hour; in one-thousandth of a second the train will go

$$\frac{50 \cdot 5,280 \cdot 12}{1,000 \cdot 60 \cdot 60} = 0.88 \text{ inch}$$

more than 3/4 of an inch.

Sounds travel in air about 13 inches in one-thousandth of a second. A mosquito flaps its wings once in 1/1,000 of a second. The earth travels around the sun at the rate of 19 miles a second; in 1/1,000 of a second it moves forward about 100 feet. The sun traverses space at the same rate. Radio signals travel at the rate of light, about 186,000 miles a second, and in 1/1,000 of a second covers about 186 miles—from Chicago to Indianapolis, for example.

Thus we see that 1/1,000 of a second is not such a small interval. Suppose therefore we try a smaller one: Let us see how brief one-millionth of a second is. Light travels at the rate of 300,000 kilometers a second, and in one-millionth of a second passes through 0.3 kilometer, or 300 meters, approximately equal to 984 feet. This is just a little less than the distance covered by sound in a second. Thus we see that something does happen in a millionth of a second; physicists, in fact, were dissatisfied for some time with such a "long" interval.

The light waves which produce the red effect in our vision vibrate at the rate of about 400,000,000,000,000, or $4 \cdot 10^{14}$, a second. Thus in one-millionth of a second about 400,000,000 waves enter our eyes, or one wave enters in $\dfrac{1}{400,000,000,000,000}$ of a second. The millionth of a second is a long time in comparison with this interval, but we must remember that the red light waves are not the shortest. Certain X-rays are more frequent and some are sixty times as frequent; that is, one wave enters at the rate of $\dfrac{1}{25,000,000,000,000,000}$ of a second.

And these X-rays are not the shortest, either. The recently discovered cosmic rays are considerably shorter. Perhaps soon will be discovered other rays whose period of vibration will be a micro-pigmy in comparison with that of the cosmic rays. Even among pygmies we must distinguish between giant-pygmies and micro-pygmies.

So, we perceive the magnitude of an object or of a number is a relative notion. In comparison with the earth's sphere a pea is a pygmy, but in comparison with the molecule of water a pea is a giant. As a matter of fact, the relation of a pea to the earth's sphere is the same as the relation of a molecule of water to the pea. We may have then the proportion:

$$\frac{\text{the earth's sphere}}{\text{pea}} = \frac{\text{pea}}{\text{molecule}}$$

For years we were ignorant of the structure of matter. Nowadays we know that atoms, which are the smallest individual distinct particles that possess the properties of the respective elements, are not simple in their structure. Atoms are miniature solar systems in which the electrons play the part of the planets, and the nucleus corresponds to the sun. Moreover, an electron is 1,850 times smaller in weight than the molecule of hydrogen. To compare a speck of dust with an electron would be almost an impossibility. But if we compare a speck of dust with an atom, and an atom with an electron, we may have the proportion

$$\frac{\text{electron}}{\text{atom}} = \frac{\text{atom}}{\text{a speck of dust}}$$

According to this proportion, an atom is then about 250,000 times larger in diameter than an electron.

We may then construct the following size scheme in which the next object is about 250,000 times larger in diameter than the preceding one:

> Electron
> Atom
> A speck of dust
> An average home
> The earth's sphere
> The solar system (now, it is twice the size)
> The distance to the Polar Star
> The Milky Way

PROBLEMS

18. Light travels at approximately 186,000 miles a second. If the red-producing waves of light vibrate $4 \cdot 10^{14}$ times a second, what is the length of one wave in inches?

19. How many waves of the red-producing light are there in one foot?

20. How many vibrations of the red-producing light will there be in the distance covered by light coming from the farthest known island universe, some 200,000,000 light-years away?

21. On page 60 we stated a number which was obtained by Archimedes:

$$10^{8,000,000,000}.$$

An average page contains 2,500 letters. Suppose that this number of Archimedes is to be printed. Allowing 400 pages to a book, how many books will be required for the printing of this number? [Answer: $10^{7,999,999,994}$ books]

22. If a book weighs 2 pounds, what would be the weight in tons of the books which are required for the printing of the number in problem 21? [Answer: $10^{7,999,999,991}$ tons]

23. How many 100-car freight trains will be required to haul the books in problem 22? One freight car usually carries 50 tons. [Answer: $2 \cdot 10^{7,999,999,987}$ freight trains]

24. If the length of a 100-car freight train is one mile how far (in light years) will the trains in problem 23 stretch? [Answer: $3 \cdot 10^{7,999,999,974}$ light years]

÷ 6 ÷

There's Secrecy in Numbers

Trlx hoex erfa eetb mpel

This is the message that shook Europe for one hundred days.
Had it been intercepted and read, the course of history might
have been different. But this message reached its destination,
and Napoleon Bonaparte was able to land safely in Marseille
while his enemies were napping.

Naturally, such an important message had to be so disguised
that only a few trusted persons could read it. Messages that
are written in such a concealed manner are said to be "in code,"
and the process of reading coded messages is known as "decoding."

In order to decode a message the secret of its arrangement or
the "key" of the code must be known. This is the same key
which is used by a person when he translates his message into a
coded one.

Generally, the key of a code is a secret which is closely
guarded by the sender as well as the recipient of the coded
message. However, sometimes the secret of the code may be
discovered through observation and reflection. Let us take the
above message,

Trlx hoex erfa eetb mpel

We observe that the entire message was broken up into five
groups of four letters each. This alone does not give us a clue.
However, we note that the first letter of each group, if removed

from the coded message and written all together *T h e e m*, may mean something. This may be an important clue. Consequently, we try the same thing with the second letters of the groups. We obtain *r o r e p*. If we examine the combination of these five letters closely we may observe that the reversal of their order yields *p e r o r*. Thus the first two trials yielded *The emperor*. The third set of letters gives *l e f t e*, and the fourth set of letters, which is again written backwards, is *x x a b l*. Reversing the order of the fourth set of letters yields *l b a x x*. Now, assembling our findings, we have

The emperor left Elba xx.

What the x's at the end of the message mean is not clear to us. They may denote something very secret. On the other hand, they might have been added simply to bring the total number of letters in the message to twenty (which is a multiple of four, the number of letters in each group of the coded message). This is a common procedure as will be shown presently.

There are many reasons why people send messages in concealed forms. In some cases the reason may be quite legitimate, in other cases, sinister. Coded messages may be used by spies to transmit reports to their employers or by criminals and plotters to communicate with their accomplices. On the other hand, governments use secret codes for communication between their legal agents so that messages may be read only by those for whom they are intended. Armies and navies of all countries have secret codes which are guarded day and night and which are known only to trusted officials. Telegraph companies use special codes for transmitting commercial messages in order to save money; their codes are not secret and may be obtained or inspected in any office of these companies.

There are many methods for writing coded messages. Some of them are very simple and may be easily decoded. Others have now become extremely complex. The decoding of a secret message from some government agent, for instance, may be a tremendous task. The entire secret of a coded message lies in the manner an intelligible message is rewritten so that it becomes unintelligible. If the correct instructions for coding and decoding are available, deciphering may prove comparatively simple. But if the code key is not known, even a Dick Tracy may be baffled for a clue. Should the key be discovered, however, the entire code naturally becomes valueless. Because of this danger of discovery, governments are continually revising their codes.

There are two main methods of code writing. One consists of using the same letters as they appear in the original message, but changing their relative positions in a definitely prearranged manner. In other words, the letters of the message are carefully scrambled. The system used in this scrambling is the secret of the code. This method of code writing is known as *transposition*. The other method of code writing consists of the replacement of the letters of the original message by other letters (according to a certain definite system). This method is known as *substitution*.

Transposition: How to Scramble a Message

Suppose we have the following message:

Queen Mary left with a cargo of airplanes today.

To transmit this message in code a rectangle with as many squares in it as there are letters in the message will be selected. If the number of letters in the message is such that we cannot obtain a rectangle with that many squares, the nearest in size (but larger) rectangle is selected. The few extra squares may be filled with dummy letters if desired. Now since the number of letters in the message is 39, we may select a rectangle with 40 squares in it. Into each square we shall fit one and only one letter. Our rectangle may have 8 columns and 5 rows or 10 columns and 4 rows, but we shall illustrate the process of coding by considering a rectangle with 8 columns and 5 rows. Generally, the first line (row) of letters is written from left to right, the second line (row) in reverse, that is, from right to left; the third again from left to right, the fourth in reverse, and so on. However, we may start writing the first column from right to left and reverse the order for each alternating row, the choice of the order being a part of the key. We have then

```
Q u e e n M a r
t i w t f e l y
h a c a r g o o
n a l p r i a f
e s t o x d a y
```

The letter *x* is a dummy letter.

The coded message is then written by columns as follows:

Qthne uiaas ewclt etapo nfrrx megid aloaa ryofy.

The message *The emperor left Elba* is transcribed in code as follows. As this message contains 18 letters, we add two dummy letters to it to make a rectangle of 20 squares. We choose a 4-row, 5-column rectangle and proceed with the rewriting as follows:

```
T h e e m
r o r e p
l e f t e
x x a b l
```

Thus the coded message

Trlx hoex erfa eetb mpel

To read off coded messages of this type, put the letters in the original order. Then if you know the key of the code you will find no difficulty in arranging the coded message in the proper columns and rows. If you do not know the key, you had better roll up your sleeves and dig in for a long winter night. For there is no ready rule for the discovery of the key of the code, other than close scrutiny and hard thinking. There are certain clues in almost every coded message, however,—as well as an occasional false alarm.

```
T h e e m p
e l r o r e
f t e l b a
```

The first lead that should be analyzed is the way in which the letters are grouped. In the last coded message the letters were grouped by three. This suggests the possibility of three horizontal rows and six vertical columns.

Tef hlt ere eol mrb pea

The second lead is usually obtained from close study of the coded message, especially with regard to the position of certain letters. We may note that the first letters *T h e e m p* form a certain sequence which has some suggestion of making sense. Then the second sequence, *e r o r l e* (written backwards), is immediately obtained. Combining the first and second sequences, we have *The emperor le*. Such a result is extremely encouraging, because it convinces us that we are on the right track. Then for the third sequence we obtain *f t e l b a*, and thus the message is decoded.

However, not all coded messages are decoded so easily. Codes would be of little value if they were. The coding of a message has as its natural aim the attainment of such a disguise as to make decoding almost impossible.

More Scrambling: How to Make Cryptography More Cryptic

The coded messages in the preceding section are, from the point of view of cryptography (the science of writing messages in code and deciphering them), very simple. For an experienced cryptographer the decoding of such messages is child's play. In order to conceal the coded messages the system of transposition allows further complication by means of several variations in the system of coding. We shall examine a few of these variations.

The first variation discards the writing of the message by starting with the first left column. Instead of this we start with the last column on the right. Let us write in code the message *The emperor left Elba* by using three rows and six columns; this will eliminate the necessity of two dummy letters. We then have

```
T  h  e  e  m  p
e  l  r  o  r  e
f  t  e  l  b  a
```

and the coded message is *pea mrb eol ere hlt tef.*

However, the decoding of this message still presents no difficulty. If the method that was described in the preceding section fails to yield results, it is applied backwards, so to speak. We start from the right and take one letter from each group. We thus obtain the same sequence of letters that was derived in the preceding section, that is, *t h e e m p*, *e r o r l e*, and *f t e l b a*.

A second variation usually introduces sufficient concealment to preclude the discovery of the code, unless the person who decodes the message (assuming that the key is not known to him) is an expert cryptographer. For this variation, after the message has been written in a certain number of rows we begin the transcription by starting with the upper right-hand corner. As a rule the message is written in groups of letters so that each group contains more letters than there are rows. Thus

```
T h e e m p
e l r o r e
f t e l b a
```

is transcribed as follows: *peab rmeo lere hltf et* or *peabr meole rehlt fet*.

The message *Queen Mary left with a cargo of airplanes today* may be rewritten by using six letters in each group:

```
Q u e e n M a r
t i w t f e l y
h a c a r g o o
n a l p r i a f
e s t o x d a y
```

Thus we have *ryofya aoladi gemxrr fnopat etlcwe saaiue nhtq*. Note that in this method of transcribing we start in the upper right-hand corner and go down in the first column, but in the second column we go up, in the third column we go down again, and so on.

The same procedure applies for seven or more letters.

In order to prevent any additional chance of the number of rows and columns being discovered it is advisable not to use dummy letters. Thus the Queen Mary message may be put in code as follows (we shall now use 4 rows and 10 columns):

```
Q  u  e  e  n  M  a  r  y  l
a  c  a  h  t  i  w  t  f  e
r  g  o  o  f  a  i  r  p  l
y  a  d  o  t  s  e  n  a
```

Grouping, we have

lelan pfyrt resiw amiat oftne hodao aeucg yraq

or, if we use six letters

lelanp fyrtre siwami atoftn ehodao aeucgy raq

The advantage of this variation in the method of coding lies in the fact that the person who sends the coded messages may vary the number of letters in the groups of different messages. He thus has the opportunity to vary the number of the columns and rows and the number of letters in the groups. The person who receives the message and who knows the number of rows and columns (this is the key of the code) needs to count the total number of letters in the message and divide this number by the number of the key; the remainder after this division will give the number of letters in the last row. Thus, in the above message there are 39 letters, the key is 10, and the last row contains 9 letters. The last column then contains three letters. It should be noted that the *last* column is on the left of the rectangle. This process is continued column by column until the message is completely deciphered.

Befuddling the Foe, or How to Have Fun with the Fifth Column

The coded messages discussed heretofore can be deciphered, although not without a certain amount of ingenuity and experience. But this is not enough. Any code whose key is fairly discoverable is not a desirable code. Naturally, a more complicated code is demanded. The user of a transposition code then resorts to a transposition within the rectangle. Instead of proceeding directly from one column to its neighbor, the code key is made more complex by scrambling up the order of the columns. Such a procedure makes the discovery of the key almost an impossibility. We shall examine this method of coding in detail.

Let us return to the message *The emperor left Elba*. For the purpose of coding we wrote the letters in a rectangle as follows:

```
1  2  3  4  5  6
T  h  e  e  m  p
e  l  r  o  r  e
f  t  e  l  b  a
```

Now, instead of following the regular procedure of writing the message in groups of three starting either with the first column on the left or the last column on the right, that is, following the order of the columns 1-2-3-4-5-6 or 6-5-4-3-2-1 we select a different order, say 4-1-6-2-5-3. The coded message then is

eol tef pea hlt mrb ere.

The code thus has an additional element in its key, the order of the columns 4-1-6-2-5-3. Decoding such a message, if its key is not known, is a very difficult affair. No general plan of attack can be devised; discovery of the key is a hit or miss proposition. When code messages are sent according to this method of scrambling the columns, the sender as well as the recipient may be certain that a fifth columnist will have a hard time trying to deliver the original message to the enemy. However, an expert cryptographer who makes a specialty of deciphering secret messages will be able to decode this type of message, as well as messages written in even more complicated codes based on the procedure described above.

To decipher a coded message of the scrambled-column type the order in which the columns have been taken must be known. The order of the columns is, as stated above, a part of the key of the code. However, this arrangement need not be permanent for all the messages. The order may be changed with each message, that is, the sender of coded messages is free to choose any order of columns he wishes, provided he somehow informs the recipient of his selection. Thus, this part of the key may become a part of the message. Presently we shall discuss a system which will enable the sender of a coded message to transmit this part of the key in code form.

The decoding of a message of the above type presents no difficulties when the recipient has the key. Suppose the coded message is

nfrrx uiaas aloaa ewclt megid etapo ryofy qthne

and the additional key is

5-2-7-3-6-4-8-1

First, we rearrange the groups so that their original order is restored. Thus we obtain

qthne uiaas ewclt etapo nfrrx megid aloaa ryofy

Then we rewrite the groups of letters in columns:

```
q  u  e  e  n  m  a  r
t  i  w  t  f  e  l  y
h  a  c  a  r  g  o  o
n  a  l  p  r  i  a  f
e  s  t  o  x  d  a  y
```

Thus, we have our message, *Queen Mary left with a cargo of airplanes today.*

The columns may also be scrambled up when the coded message is to contain groups of letters with more (or less) letters than the number of letters in each column. For example, if we decide to code the Queen Mary in six-letter groups without the use of a dummy letter (to make deciphering more difficult), and if the key for scrambling up the columns is 2-6-1-8-5-7-4-3, we have

```
1  2  3  4  5  6  7  8
Q  u  e  e  n  M  a  r
t  i  w  t  f  e  l  y
h  a  c  a  r  g  o  o
n  a  l  p  r  i  a  f
e  s  t  o  d  a  y
```

The coded message is then

uiaasa igemqt hnefoy rnfrrd yaolae tapotl cwe

The decoding of this message proceeds in essentially the same fashion as described in this section. However, if the complete key is not available, only an expert decoder may finally succeed in unraveling the original message. And the chances are that he will have more than one headache.

How to Hide the Key and Keep Your Code from Talking

As stated in the preceding section, scrambling up the order of the columns of a coded message greatly insures against the possibility of a code being deciphered by anyone who intercepts a coded message. Moreover, the sender of a coded message need not always use the same order for the rearranged columns. He may select any order at random, provided he has some definite means of letting his recipient know what order he has used. If this order were mentioned directly in the message, however, the sender would be giving away his secret. Therefore, he must resort to more devious means of stating his information. This may be accomplished by giving the order of the columns in a number system other than the decimal.

To facilitate the coding of the key arrangement of the columns, especially if the number of columns is greater than 5, it is best to break up the rectangle into two parts and work on each part in the same manner as it was described above. Let us illustrate this procedure by again coding the Queen Mary message:

1	*2*	*3*	*4*	*1*	*2*	*3*	*4*
Q	u	e	e	n	M	a	r
t	i	w	t	f	e	l	y
h	a	c	a	r	g	o	o
n	a	l	p	r	i	a	f
e	s	t	o	d	a	y	

We may choose the following order: 4-2-1-3, 3-4-1-2. The coded message (if it is written in groups of six letters) is as follows

etapos aaiuqt hnetlc wealoa yfoyrn frrdai gem

To conceal the numbers 4,213-3,412, we may assume that they are in the 5-system and that their equivalents in the decimal system are 558 and 482, respectively. Thus the key in code may be written as 558-5-482, where the middle 5 may indicate the numeration system. Others may write this as 558-5-76, provided that there is an understanding between the correspondents that the smaller number represents the difference. This key may be still further concealed. Instead of the numbers 4,213 and 3,412 we may write 3,102 and 2,301, then, using the 3-system, we have 210-3-178, or, if we wish 210-3-32.

The recipient of the message must translate these numbers back into the numeration system indicated by the middle number. Naturally, if there is a definite understanding concerning the numeration system which the correspondents will use, this middle number may be omitted (and this will make it even more difficult for an enemy to find the key to your code). After the correct number has been obtained—for example, 4,213-3,412— the recipient of the message writes it out as follows:

$$1-2-3-4-5-6-7-8$$
$$4-2-1-3-3-4-1-2$$

Therefore the arrangement of the column is

$$4-2-1-3-7-8-5-6$$

The Civil War's Secret Weapon: The Grille

The grille, a variation of transposition code writing, was in wide use during the Civil War, but for some reason it has been discarded for more complicated code systems. Nowadays the requirements of code writing are such that the system must be complicated in its transcription of the message as well as in its concealment of the secret of the code. No doubt, experience demonstrated that the use of the grille was not satisfactory from one of these viewpoints, and hence it was discarded. However, the grille system guards well the secret of the code, as we shall see shortly.

The principle is simple. The grille itself is of square form and has little squares ruled on it, an equal number being on each side. One-fourth of these squares are perforated according to a definite plan, and the message is written through these perforations on a specially ruled squared paper. Since only one-fourth of the squares of the grill are perforated, only one-fourth of the message can be written. But, the arrangement of the perforations is such that if the grille is turned one-fourth of the way clockwise or counterclockwise (the direction of turning is a part of the code) another fourth of the message can be written through the perforations, and the part that was previously written is covered up. Then after the second fourth of the message is written, the grille is turned again one-fourth of the way *in the same direction*, and the third fourth of the message is written. Finally, the grille is again turned one-fourth of the way *in the same direction*, everything that was previously written is covered up, and the fourth and final part of the message is written. Thus, while the grille is kept in four different positions the entire message is written, but the individual letters of the entire message are located in different, widely distant places, so that the entire message is scrambled up. Only the person who has a copy of the grille that was used in the process of the coding of the message can decode it.

The size of a grille depends on the number of the letters in a given message. But since a grille is always of square form and must have an equal number of ruled squares on each side, the total number of ruled squares in the grille will not necessarily be equal to the number of letters in the message. To determine the size of the grille, select a grille with a total number of ruled squares either equal to the number of letters in the message, or, if this is impossible, select a grille whose total number of ruled squares in the grille exceeds the number of letters in the message.

For example, if the number of letters in the message is thirty-six, then the grille will have six ruled squares on each of its sides. If the number of letters in the message is fifty-nine, the grille must have sixty-four ruled squares, that is, eight ruled squares on each side. In other words, the square grille must contain a squared number of ruled squares. Each ruled square of the grille is designed for one and only one letter of the message. Later on we shall also have examples of grilles which allow the writing of more than one letter in each perforation. At present, however, we shall confine our discussion to grilles which allow the writing of only one letter in each perforation.

Let us transcribe the following message:

Transport leaving with convoy taking northern route now

The total number of letters in the message is forty-eight. Therefore, the grille should have forty-nine ruled squares, twelve of which (that is, one-fourth) are perforated.

The paper on which the message is to be inscribed is also ruled and is of the same size as the grille. Likewise, it should be noted that the central square, that is, the square in the fourth row and the fourth column of the grille, is not perforated. If this square were perforated, it would always be in the same place and would thus expose the same square on the writing paper four times. Such repetition would be disad-

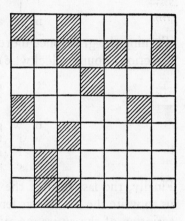

vantageous in the transcription of the message, since the principle of the construction of a grille is that the perforations be made in such a manner that every square of the writing paper be exposed once and once only. The reader will, no doubt, have observed that only in grilles with odd-number squares will there be a centrally located square which should not be perforated. Thus in a grille with 36, 64, 100, or 144 squares there will be no centrally located square.

With the forty-nine-square grille ready we proceed with the transcription of our message. We place the grille on the ruled writing paper and write the first fourth of our message as follows:

```
        t       r
            a     n   s
                p
        o             r
              t
       l
       e    a
```

Turning the grille one quarter of the way counterclockwise we inscribe the next twelve letters:

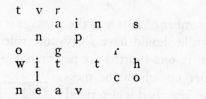

```
t  v  r
      a  i  n        s
      n     p
o     g           í
w  i  t     t        h
l              c  o
n  e  a  v
```

Turning the grille once more one-quarter of the way in the same direction (counterclockwise) we inscribe the next twelve letters:

```
t  v  r        o  y
      a  i  n  n  s
      n     p  o
o  w  g           r  t
w  i  t  a     t     h
k  l  i     n  c  o
n  e  a  v  g     n
```

Finally, the last turn of the grille in the same direction enables us to write the last twelve letters, and thus we complete the transcription of the entire message.

```
t  v  t  o  o  y  r
t  h  a  i  n  n  s
e  n  r  p  o  n  r
o  w  g  x  o  r  t
w  i  t  a  t  u  h
k  l  i  t  n  c  o
n  e  a  v  g  e  a
```

Note that in the central square (the one that was never exposed through a perforation) we inserted a dummy letter *x* (any other letter may do).

Anatomy of a Grille

As stated above, a grille may contain any number of cells provided this number is a perfect square (that is, a number which is obtained by multiplying an integer by itself, as, for example, $4 \cdot 4 = 16$, $5 \cdot 5 = 25$, etc.).

The method of perforating the necessary number of the cells is comparatively simple. We shall describe it in detail.

When a message has been composed it is necessary to count the number of letters. Then for the number of the cells in a grille we take the nearest perfect square that exceeds the number of letters in the message, unless of course the number of the letters is a perfect square. If odd, it is not necessary to delete one letter in the message because the central cell of the grille is not perforated. When the entire message, with the exception of the last letter, is transcribed, this last letter is then written in the vacant central square. Naturally, the extra unfilled squares on the writing paper will have to be filled with dummy letters in order that every square of the writing paper is filled.

In the two drawings above there are eighty-one and sixty-four cells, respectively. The rows of cells are drawn so as to show a border effect. Then the cells are numbered as shown in the drawings, and only one set of numbers (from 1 up) is crossed out in each border. This tends to prevent a perforated cell from exposing the same square two or more times. The cells that have been crossed out are to be perforated, and after all the perforations have been made the grille is ready for use. A careful inspection of the number of the crossed-out cells forming same border will reveal that one-fourth of the cells are crossed out. Thus, in an eighty-one-cell grille only twenty cells will be perforated, and in a sixty-four-cell grille only sixteen cells will be perforated.

Generally, almost any code secret may be discovered by a specialist; but even in the case of a small grille, say of sixty-four cells, the possible combinations of perforation patterns are so numerous that even a notorious international spy would have little chance of stumbling across the original pattern (unless, of course, he used his wiles to spirit away a copy of the original).

To decode a message written by grille, the recipient simply places the grille over the message and in four operations (turns of the grille) obtains the four different parts of the message.

However, should you fear the cunning of your fifth column's master-mind you may further scramble up the grille-coded message by means of any of the methods of transposition described in the preceding sections. Naturally, this complicates the key of the code. But, as already pointed out, nowadays a simple code is almost useless. Simple codes belong to the good old days when spying was left to a few honest traitors or pleasantly seductive Mata Haris and had not yet mushroomed into a foul-fighting underground army.

Behind the Grille: A Little Math

For protection, a scheme may be devised so that neither the sender nor the recipient of coded messages need keep ready-made grilles on hand. The arrangement of the perforated cells of a grille may be so concealed that once a grille has been used by the sender or the recipient of a message, the grille may be immediately destroyed, and when the need for a grille arises again a new one may be constructed. As will be shown below, the secret of the perforation pattern may be written in the form of a code, which thus becomes the key to the grille.

Let us denote every perforated cell of a grille by 1 and every other cell by 0. Thus the arrangement of the grille on page 91 may be represented as follows:

```
1010000
0010101
0001000
1000010
0010000
0100000
0110000
```

If we discard the zeros to the left of 1 in each number we have

$$
\begin{aligned}
&1010000 \\
&10101 \\
&1000 \\
&1000010 \\
&10000 \\
&100000 \\
&110000
\end{aligned}
$$

Let us suppose that these numbers are not numbers written in the decimal system of numeration but in some other, say the two-system. Then their equivalents in the decimal system are 80, 21, 8, 66, 16, 32, 48. These numbers may be easily translated back into the two-system of numeration. Thus, the person who uses a grille may safely destroy his instrument, provided he has the key to it. Moreover, the sender of a coded message may vary the arrangement of the perforations of the grille that he uses. When he sends a message, he must include in it the key of the grille that he used for the transcription of his message. He need not be confined to the two-system. He may use the three-, four-, five-, or any other system, provided the recipient of the message is properly informed of the system used. When the recipient begins to decode the message, he first decodes the key to the grille, then reconstructs the grille itself so that he can proceed with the decoding of the actual message itself.

For example, suppose that the key is 759, 81, 244, 27, 2,433, 280, 3, 2,187. Also suppose that by some definite prearrangement the recipient of the coded message was informed that the sender used the three-system. Then the recipient of the message will have no difficulty in obtaining the equivalents of these in the three-system. They are

$$
\begin{aligned}
&1001010 \\
&10000 \\
&1000001 \\
&1000 \\
&10100010 \\
&1010101 \\
&10 \\
&10000000
\end{aligned}
$$

They represent the sixty-four-cell grille shown on page 93:

```
01001010
00010000
01000001
00001000
10100010
01010101
00000010
10000000
```

A Full-Dress Grille: The Shape's the Thing

A grille may be used not only for writing one letter in each square. We may construct a grille such that in each space that is exposed through the perforations of the grille a predetermined (but constant for a given message) number of letters may be written. Accordingly, 2, 3, 4, etc., letters may be written in every space exposed by a perforation. Such a grille will be rectangular instead of square but will be constructed according to the same principles as the square grille and will contain a perfect square number of cells, one-fourth of which will be perforated. A grille of this type is shown below.

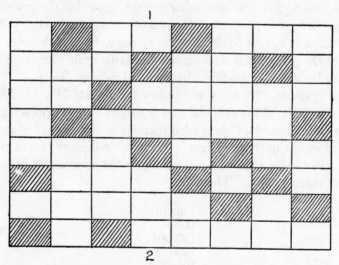

This grille is used in the following manner: After the first fourth of the message is transcribed, the grille is reversed so that the lower edge (marked 2) is now uppermost. The second fourth of the message is then transcribed. After the second fourth of the message is recorded the grille is *turned over* face downward and is used again twice in the same manner as described above. In each position after the first the grille covers everything that has been already recorded. In other words, every rectangle on the writing paper is exposed once and once only.

Rectangular-grille procedure is somewhat different from square-grille procedure. The rectangular grille is turned over, and the cells are perforated in such a manner that in every row or column there are no cells equidistant from the edges of the rectangle. Thus if cell 2 in the third row is perforated, then cell 7 in this row should not be perforated. Moreover cell 2 in the third row is also cell 3 in the second column. Hence cell 6 in the second column must not be perforated. This restriction on perforations thus prevents the possibility that any part of the writing paper will be exposed through a perforation more than once.

Let us take the rectangular grille shown on page 96, and, using groups of three letters, transcribe the following message:

Ruins of an ancient buried Indian city, which evidently flourished before the Spanish conquest 400 years ago, have been discovered by laborers on a ranch near San Augustin. Hundreds of stone idols have been found intact.

In the transcription we shall write out all numerals as words. Thus "400" will become "four hundred."

The position of the grille inscribes one-fourth of the message as follows:

```
    rui              nso
              fan            anc
          ien
    tbu                            rie
              din       dia
    nci           ty,       whi
                      che          vid
    ent       lyf
```

The second position allows the inscription of the second fourth of the message:

	rui			*nso*	*lou*		*ris*
hed		*bef*	*fan*			*anc*	
	ore	*ien*	*the*				*spa*
	tbu	*nis*		*hco*			*rie*
nqu			*din*		*dia*	*est*	
nci				*ty,*	*fou*	*whi*	
	rhu			*ndr*	*che*		*vid*
ent		*lyf*	*edy*			*ear*	

The third position enables us to transcribe the third fourth of the message:

	rui		*sag*	*nso*	*lou*	*o, h*	*ris*
hed	*ave*	*bef*	*fan*	*bee*		*anc*	
	ore	*ien*	*the*		*ndi*		*spa*
sco	*tbu*	*nis*		*hco*		*ver*	*rie*
nqu		*edb*	*din*	*yla*	*dia*	*est*	
nci	*bor*		*ers*	*ty,*	*fou*	*whi*	*ona*
ran	*rhu*	*chn*		*ndr*	*che*		*vid*
ent		*lyf*	*edy*		*ear*	*ear*	*san*

The fourth position of the grille permits the completion of the transcription of the message. Thus we have

aug	*rui*	*ust*	*sag*	*nso*	*lou*	*o, h*	*ris*
hed	*ave*	*bef*	*fan*	*bee*	*in.*	*anc*	*hun*
dre	*ore*	*ien*	*the*	*dso*	*ndi*	*fst*	*spa*
sco	*tbu*	*nis*	*one*	*hco*	*ido*	*ver*	*rie*
nqu	*lsh*	*edb*	*din*	*yla*	*dia*	*est*	*ave*
nci	*bor*	*bee*	*ers*	*ty,*	*fou*	*whi*	*ona*
ran	*rhu*	*chn*	*nfo*	*ndr*	*che*	*und*	*vid*
ent	*int*	*lyf*	*edy*	*act*	*ear*	*ear*	*san*

Decoding the message by means of the grille is simply a reversal of the above process. The grille is placed over the message in the same four positions, each position thus decoding one-fourth of the message.

Substitution, Alphabetical and Otherwise

The method of substitution is based on replacement of the letters of a given message by the letters of any alphabet, or by any symbols which may be chosen at will for this purpose. The method of substitution, generally in a very complicated form, has a wide use in code writing today. For the sake of simplicity, however, we shall only make use here of our alphabet of twenty-six letters.

The simplest form of substitution, and this form illustrates the principle of the method, consists of the direct substitution of a certain letter for another letter of the alphabet. Thus the key for this kind of code writing consists of two lines. The upper line, generally, is the original alphabet, and the lower line is the substitution alphabet. The arrangement of the letters in the substitution alphabet may vary; the selection of this arrangement is entirely arbitrary.

Here is an example of a substitution code:

```
a b c d e f g h i j k l m n o p q r s t u v w x y z
q x p a k o c m z u s w b r f l j e y i d t n g h v
```

When a message is written in code, every letter of the message is replaced by the letter that corresponds to it in the substitution code. Thus the message *We are ready to destroy plans* is transcribed in code as follows:

nk qek ekqah if akyiefy lwqry.

However, this process of substitution does not conceal the message sufficiently well. In order to conceal the message further, the message may be transcribed by the method of transposition, so that the original order of the letters is scrambled up. We may proceed as follows. There are twenty-four letters in the message. We may use four rows and six columns, and then transcribe by groups of five. Then, we have

```
w e a r e r
o t y d a e
d e s t r o
s n a l p y
```

Therefore, starting from the upper corner on the right, we have

reoyp raerd tlasy aeten sdow.

By means of the above substitution code, the message is

ekfhl eqkea iwqyh qkikr yafn.

Even if a message were written in the manner described above, it would be a dead giveaway for any experienced cryptographer. Code writers would never think of using such uncomplex procedure.

Since there is no restriction on the possible arrangement of letters in the substitution code, the number of substitution codes possible is enormous. Consequently, there is almost no chance that any two persons, except the sender and the recipient of the coded message, will possess the same substitution code, though expert cryptographers may, by devious methods, succeed in unearthing the key.

Double Trouble for Code Kibitzers

To safeguard the code used in the transcription of a message a combination of the transposition and substitution systems is effective. Codes that are based on this principle are favorites of governments and their various departments. We shall look at a simple type of this combination code and see what is the basis of this political favoritism.

Suppose that a message is transcribed by the method of transposition. It may contain several groups of letters each containing a definite number of these letters. For every group a separate substitution alphabet is designed. Thus, for

reoyp   raerd   tlasy   aeten   sdow,

the transcription of the message *We are ready to destroy plans* given in the preceding section, we must have five substitution codes, as, for example,

	a	b	c	d	e	f	g	h	i	j	k	l	m	n	o	p	q	r	s	t	u	v	w	x	y	z
1	p	j	w	z	o	t	k	r	v	x	c	g	a	s	y	e	h	d	l	a	n	b	f	m	q	i
2	g	m	z	q	s	v	y	l	p	r	a	t	x	f	b	u	e	c	o	w	d	h	i	l	j	k
3	r	h	o	n	z	p	j	a	u	f	s	d	t	i	v	g	k	x	e	y	m	l	c	w	p	b
4	v	t	i	k	a	w	c	s	z	b	v	o	y	f	m	d	x	l	u	q	h	j	r	g	n	p
5	o	u	y	w	j	l	d	v	q	s	z	g	i	x	k	m	b	h	n	f	a	r	e	p	c	t

Thus the first line is used for transcription by substitution of the first group of five letters, the second line for the second group of

five letters, the third line for the third group of five letters, and
so on. The message is then transcribed as follows:

doyqe   cgscq   ydrep   vaqaf   nwke

For messages with a larger number of letter groups there
should be as many substitution alphabets as there are groups.

If the recipient of a message is in possession of the code, he
will find no difficulty in its decoding. As far as the spy or
saboteur who intercepts the message is concerned, the sender
may as well have the key. For unless the interceptor is an X-ray-
eyed cryptographer, all his spying has been just so much cheating
at solitaire.

*The Arithmetic of
Measurement*

The Great Pyramid Mystery

On the sands of Egypt not far from the banks of the Nile
there is a tall stone structure several thousand years old. King-
doms rise and fall, nations are born and disappear; generation
after generation passes by, but it still stands, a monument to the
skill and industry of a nation (and its slaves), and an enigma
that to this moment baffles our modern sciences. The secret of
its design and the nature of the ancient tools capable of constructing a pile of such stupendous size remain a mystery that
may never be unraveled.

The Great Pyramid, or the Pyramid of Cheops as it is called,
is a magnificent figure rising about 486 feet. From the stand-
point of engineering it would be a creditable achievement of
any architect of the twentieth century. No one knows how the
architects of ancient Egypt were able to cut huge blocks of sand-
stone tens of miles away and move them to the site. It took
more than twenty years, and more than 200,000 men laboring
constantly, to erect this tomb for the Pharaoh Cheops. Prior to
its actual building ten years were spent in the construction of
roads over which the stones were dragged from the quarries.

Nowadays before any building is erected plans are drawn by
engineers. But those who have studied the Great Pyramid have
been disappointed from the start; the Egyptian engineers left no
plans for posterity.

What amazed most of the scientists was the simplicity of the Great Pyramid form. Its base was a square; its faces were triangles with two equal sides (we call them isosceles triangles). As simple a figure as this, they reasoned, to serve as a tomb of one of the greatest Pharaohs? There must be something hidden in the meaning of this pyramid. And they found something. The entrance to the pyramid was on the northern side, and it was so slanted that from it the Polar star could be seen. Whether the priests of Egypt used this pyramid for an astronomical observatory or the facing of this entrance was just a coincidence we do not know. However, this was taken as a clue: No doubt, thought some of the scientists, construction of the pyramid and its measurements had something to do with astronomy and mathematics. After all, the priests of Egypt were so skillful as astronomers that they computed the year as of 365 1/4 days, and we still use this crude figure in our modern life.

What a Little Juggling with Numbers Will Do

The scientists had another clue. The Greek historian Herodotus mentioned that the priests of Egypt told him the pyramid was constructed according to a peculiar rule of proportion.

For example, the area of the square that may be constructed with the altitude of the pyramid as a side is equal to the area of every face triangle. Later calculations confirmed this and the supposition that there must be some mathematical meaning in the structure had its first confirmation. So the scientists began to seek other relationships, and their conclusions were so astonishing that volumes have been written about the Great Pyramid of Cheops.

If we add the lengths of the base sides of the pyramid we obtain 3,055.16 feet. Double the size of its height and we obtain

$$(2 \cdot 486.23) = 972.46 \text{ feet}$$

Divide 3,055.16 by 972.46, and we get

$$\frac{3055.16}{972.46} = 3.1416\cdots$$

This number, 3.1416, is one of the most significant in mathematics: It represents the ratio of the circumference of a circle to its diameter. However, this number, represented by the Greek letter *pi*, π, can never be calculated exactly. The value 3.1416 was determined thousands of years later. The Egyptians never calculated π so well. The best value of π that the Egyptians knew was 3.16. But the results just obtained by means of multiplication and division would seem to compel us to revise our notions about Egyptian mathematics. We shall see whether we should revise them.

But this is not all in the mystery of the pyramid. If we translate its height in terms of the mile, we obtain

$$\frac{486.23}{5280} = 0.0921 \text{ mile}$$

Multiply 0.0921 mile by 1,000,000,000 and we obtain 92,100,000 miles, which is an approximate distance of the earth from the sun. Thus the height of the pyramid had something to do with astronomy. Moreover, the Egyptian priests knew considerably more about astronomy than we generally thought they knew. According to our knowledge, the distance from the earth to the sun was first correctly computed in the eighteenth century, several thousand years later. Shall we revise our notions about the astronomical knowledge, too, of ancient Egypt?

To conclude this analysis of the Great Pyramid the scientists searched for more startling facts, and reported they had found them. The average diameter of the earth is about 7,913.333 miles, or

$$7,913.333 \cdot 5,280 \text{ feet} = 41,792,398.24 \text{ feet}$$

Divide this by 20,000,000, and we obtain about 2.09 feet. Now if we divide one side of the base of the pyramid (763.79 feet) by the length of the year, 365.2422 days, we obtain

$$\frac{763.79}{365.2422} = 2.09 \text{ feet}$$

which is 1/20,000,000 of the average diameter of the earth. We are led to think that the Egyptian priests knew more about astronomy, the year, and the diameter of the earth than we ever suspected.

So's the National Debt

These examples are only a few of the numerical jugglings so successfully performed by the Great Pyramid enthusiasts. The results are very convincing on their face value, but are the data, or the numbers used in the computations, basically reliable? A result of any computation is only as authentic (provided everything else is correct, especially the reasoning employed in the process) as the numbers used. Let us test the scientists' numbers:

All these represented measurements of the pyramid were made some time after the middle of the ninetenth century, more than 3,000 years after it was built. Much can and does happen to a building in thirty centuries. Rain, wind, the sun, and other forces of nature constantly erode it; the stones certainly have been much worn. Who can guess to what extent the original dimensions of the pyramid have been reduced?

Further, the dimensions were measured to hundredths and thousandths of a foot. Even if such fine measurements could be cited to justify the scientists' contentions, could any one accept their basic usefulness, since they could not comprehend the original dimensions? The answer is emphatically no; one could accept, at most, the measurements to feet, discarding the fractions of a foot. Thus the dimensions that should have been used in the computations are the earlier-noted whole numbers, 3,055 and 486 feet. And who would vouch that the Egyptian priests had instruments that could measure as minutely as ours today? Measurements to a hundredth of a foot, particularly those outdoors and concerned with height and distance, require the extremely precise instruments used by modern surveyors. Any concession that the Egyptians could have even approximated these is making a great allowance.

Now, in this light, let us repeat the computations, but first we must state an important principle related to the nature of numbers obtained as the result of measurements: When two such numbers are either multiplied or divided, the results cannot contain more reliable digits than the numbers with the least number of digits.

If we suppose that the numbers 3,055 and 972 are made up of reliable digits, then the quotient

$$\frac{3055}{972} = 3.143\cdots$$

has only three reliable digits. But we must remember that 3,055 and 972 do not represent the measurements of the dimensions the pyramid as it was at least three thousand years ago; in other words, even the result 3.14 would be insufficient as a basis for crediting the Egyptian priests with great advances in mathematics.

The reasoning of the scientists that the length of the base of the pyramid was related to the length of the year and the radius of the earth is based both on ignorance of the nature of the numbers they used and on flimsy coincidence. Anyone who just tries to play with numbers but ignores what they represent may arrive at results even more startling than those obtained by these scientists. We might, if we wished, follow their procedure and claim that the height of the pyramid represented a certain portion of the national debt of the United States on a certain date, because

$$\frac{486}{48,600,000,000} = 0.000000001$$

Only the very credulous would accept this type of reasoning.

So the error in the Great Pyramid "discoveries" was twofold: (1) The investigators accepted certain numbers as representing measurements when the numbers were much too good to be true; and (2) they were not familiar with the nature of the numbers they used when computing certain results, and applied to them the rules of ordinary arithmetic. The arithmetic of measurement differs. In ordinary arithmetic results of the calculations must contain all the digits, while in the arithmetic-of-measurement numbers (or, as they are also known, approximate numbers) results of the computations must contain only the digits that are reliable. Had the scientists known something about the arithmetic of approximate numbers they would never have created the myth about the Egyptian priests.

Nothing's Ever Right

All measurements are subject to certain limitations over which no one has control, because measurement is an operation depending upon several factors. These are:

a) We make use of a certain unit of measure that is commonly agreed upon. In this country this unit of measure is

> *i*. for length....... a foot
> *ii*. for weight....... a pound
> *iii*. for time......... an hour.

In most of the European countries the unit of measure is based on the metric system and is

> *i*. for length....... a meter
> *ii*. for weight....... a gram
> *iii*. for time......... a second

The unit, whether the metric or the English (as we call our system of measures), is a man-made unit. Standards of units are usually prepared by special agencies, and the instruments of measurement represent copies of these standards. A copy is generally not an exact representation of the standard, and thus a certain deviation or error is present. Even if attempts are made to correct for these errors, complete correction is impossible.

b) Atmospheric conditions, such as temperature and humidity, cause some variations in the instruments of measurement. And here, also, complete correction is impossible.

These factors may be important only for measurements in scientific and industrial laboratories, but there are other factors:

c) No person can be certain that his application of an instrument of measurement is exact. Slight errors may be caused by carelessness, poor eyesight, slips, and so on.

d) Generally when a measurement is performed, a situation such as this arises: Suppose that a certain length is measured with a yardstick. The measure thus obtained is 25 5/8 inches, but a portion less than 1/8 inch of the object is left over. We may write the numerical value of the measure as 25 5/8 ?/16 inches as we cannot gauge the sixteenths. If we had a more precise instrument we could learn this measure, but then there might remain a portion still smaller than 1/16 inch. This process may be continued indefinitely; in other words, an object cannot be measured exactly, however precise an instrument may be used.

Thus numbers representing measurements are never exact, unless we have the result of a count of some objects and we therefore call them approximate numbers. Moreover, the amount that is usually left over and does not enter in the numerical statement of the measurement is always less than a half of the last unit in terms of which the measurement is stated.

How the arithmetic operations with approximate, or measurement, numbers differ from the ordinary operations with exact numbers may be further seen in the following example:

Suppose a rectangular plot measures 43 by 39 feet and we wish to know its area. The area is expressed by the product of the two measures, and if 43 and 39 were exact, the product would be 1,677. But the two numbers are only approximate: 43 may represent a length a little greater or a little smaller than 43, and the same is true of 39. Thus we may write the two numbers as $43x$ and $39x$. Let us perform their multiplication:

$$
\begin{array}{r}
43.x \\
39.x \\
\hline
xxx \\
387x \\
129x \\
\hline
167xxx
\end{array}
$$

The product is then $167x.xx$. The unit's digit is not reliable (the x denoting a digit that is not reliable) because we have $x + 7 + x$, which is a sum of three numbers, two of which are not reliable. But the sum $x + 7 + x$ may give a number greater than 10, and thus the digit in the ten's place (the third digit of $167x.xx$) may become not reliable also. Thus the only reliable digits are the first two, and the correct way of writing the product is 1,700. The area is thus 1,700 square feet. How many tens and single square feet there are, we do not know. It would have been misleading to write the product as 1,677 because we were not certain of 77, and it would put faith on certain numbers that have no value at all.

Thus when we employ approximate numbers we must not keep all the digits in the final numerical result, but must discard those that are not reliable. This process of discarding unreliable digits is called "rounding digits" and the digits that are reliable are called "significant digits."

The Turncoat Zero

In a number obtained from measurement all the digits are significant except the zero, but the zero may be significant (*a*) if it is located between two significant digits as, for example, in 20.5 inches; (*b*) if it is located after the decimal point to indicate that it represents a performed measurement, as 14.0 feet; and (*c*) if it is at the end of a number and its significance is stated, as 240 pounds correct to a pound.

Zeros are not significant if their position is on the left in a decimal fraction. For example, in 0.0123 mile the zeros are not significant.

Nonsignificant digits should always be discarded by the process known as "rounding digits," the rules of which are:

a) If the first digit to be dropped is less than 5 just discard the digits. If the discarded digits are to the left of the decimal point, write zeros instead of digits, and these zeros will not be significant.

b) If the first digit to be dropped is 5 or greater than 5 increase by 1 the last digit that is left and follow the rule for replacing the dropped digits by zeros as stated in (*a*).

Thus 98,456 is rounded to: 98,460, 98,500, 98,000, and 6.4583 is rounded to: 6.458, 6.46, 6.5.

PROBLEMS

1. Round 3.14159 to four significant digits.
2. Round 365.22427 to five significant digits.
3. Round 1567.83 to three significant digits.

Rounding Sums: Plus and Minus

When numbers that represent measurement are to be added or subtracted, the only rule is that all the numbers should be expressed in the same denominations of the units. This means that if one number is expressed correct to tenths and others to hundredths, thousandths, and so on, all the numbers should be expressed in tenths, and this will require that those numbers that are not expressed to tenths (the tenth being the highest unit) should be rounded. This rule in brief requires the reduction of all the numbers to one unit; for example, if we have the approximate numbers 34.578, 15.3067, and 5.18, the addition is performed thus:

$$34.58$$
$$15.31$$
$$\underline{5.18}$$
$$55.07$$

In subtraction we apply the same process; for example, the difference between 87.6453 and 23.94 is obtained:

$$87.65$$
$$\underline{-23.94}$$
$$63.71$$

The reason for this rule is obvious. We recall that when a number represents a measurement correct to ten-thousandths, it contains more information than one correct to hundredths. When such two numbers are added or subtracted, the lack of the information in one will be carried over into the sum or the difference. This lack leads to uncertain, or nonsignificant, digits. But, since only significant digits should be employed in the numerical statement of a measurement, to eliminate the work with nonsignificant digits we round the number that contains more information than we require, so that the two (or more) numbers have identical information.

PROBLEMS

4. How much fencing will it require to enclose a rectangular plot 100.7 feet long and 43 feet wide?

5. Add the following approximate numbers: 47.136, 873.65, and 1.4631.

6. By how much does the length of the plot in Problem 4 exceed the width?

Products and Quotients

The rule for multiplication and division of approximate numbers, or those obtained as results of measurements, is as follows: The product (or the quotient) of two approximate numbers should contain the same number of significant digits as one of the numbers involved with the least number of significant digits. If one of the numbers involved contains two or more significant digits than the other, it must be rounded so that it contains only one extra significant digit. The reason: this extra digit often contributes to a more refined result. For example, $47 \cdot 8.6 = 404.2$, which is rounded to 400 (the last zero is not significant).

But, suppose that the 47 were obtained from rounding 47.4. By keeping the last 4 (the one after the decimal place) we have $47.4 \cdot 8.6 = 407.64$, which is rounded to 410 (the last zero is not significant). Notice that the product is correct to two significant digits, because 8.6 correct to two significant digits.

The division is performed in the same manner. Thus $47 \div 8.6 = 0.546$, which is rounded to 0.55, while $47.4 \div 8.6 = 0.551$, which is also rounded to 0.55. But in the latter example the result is closer to 0.55 than in the first, which is an assurance that 0.55 is the best result we can expect. It should be remembered that in division the process should be carried to one more digit than is to be kept, so that a final rounding may be possible.

PROBLEMS

7. What is the area of the plot in Problem 4, preceding section?
8. How many times larger than the width is the length of the rectangular plot in Problem 4?

To Stop Runaway Digits

The foregoing rules for operations with approximate numbers refer to the final results. Very often, however, the result is obtained only after several additions, subtractions, multiplications, and divisions have been performed. Thus, we may have intermediate numerical results. If the above rules are rigidly applied to the intermediate numerical results, many significant digits may often be lost. To avoid this, the following rule is set forth:

a) Before the actual numerical work is begun, the approximate numbers should be inspected, and the number of significant digits in each should be noted. The final result will contain the same number of significant digits as the number with the fewest significant digits.

b) All the intermediate numerical results should contain at least one more digit than it is expected to keep in the final result. This will refine the result and provide for its rounding.

Consider this example:
$$\frac{3.75 \cdot 89.34}{23.9 \cdot 0.75}$$

We note that 0.75 has two significant digits. Thus the final result should also have two significant digits. Thus:

$3.75 \cdot 89.34 = 235.0250$ which is rounded to 235

$23.9 \cdot 0.75 = 17.925$ which is rounded to 17.9

$235 : 17.9 = 13.1$

and this is rounded to two significant digits. The final result is therefore 13.

PROBLEMS

9. Perform with the approximate numbers the indicated computations:
$$\frac{56.4 \cdot 8.905}{37.6}$$

10. Perform with the approximate numbers the indicated computations:
$$\frac{11.42 \cdot 6.73}{1.302 \cdot 5.64}$$

±8±

Simple Calculating Devices

This Little Pig Went to Market

From the earliest days of the race men have been counting on their hands in a fashion called "finger reckoning." The method is simple, and we usually employ it instinctively, merely bending down a finger as we count off an object. With sufficient skill we may count easily up to 25 on our ten fingers by this means. As we count off five objects we bend a finger on the hand not used for the single counting. After an additional five objects have been counted off, another finger is bent, and this is continued up to 25 objects.

Some Indian tribes in South and Central America have made use not only of their fingers but their toes, too, giving rise to the system of numeration on the base of 20. No doubt all groups at some stage of their civilization counted the same way; a modern remnant of toe-counting is still much alive in our nursery tale of the two little pigs. In English we even have a special name for twenty—"score."

Few, however, suspect that our fingers may be "handy" not only for counting but for multiplications as well. Not all multiplications can be performed by the fingers, but some, such as by nine, are easily handled.

To illustrate multiplication by 9 we may write the multiplication table by 9 in which the tens and the units are separated:

Factors	Tens	Units
1·9	0	9
2·9	1	8
3·9	2	7
4·9	3	6
5·9	4	5
6·9	5	4
7·9	6	3
8·9	7	2
9·9	8	1
10·9	9	0

The sum of the digits in each product is 9. Thus $0 + 9 = 9$, $1 + 8 = 9$, $2 + 7 = 9$, etc. Moreover, in each product the numbers of the tens is less by 1 than the number multiplied by 9. Thus when we have $3·9 = 27$, $2 = 3 - 1$, $6·9 = 54$, $5 = 6 - 1$.

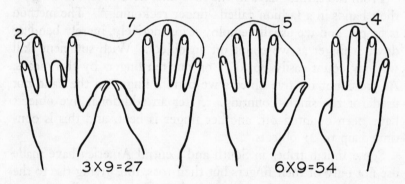

$3 \times 9 = 27$ $6 \times 9 = 54$

Now we have a clue as to how to multiply by 9 by means of our ten fingers. Place the hands on a table with the fingers flat. Suppose that we want the product 4·9. We bend in the fourth finger of the left hand (counting from left); then to the left of the bent finger we have 3 fingers, and to its right 6 fingers, and the product is 36. The following table will show the respective positions of the fingers during the multiplications (for our purposes we shall number the fingers starting with the small finger on the left hand, as first, to tenth):

Factors	Fingers to Left of Bent Finger	Finger Bent	Fingers to Right of Bent Finger
1·9	None	First	9
2·9	1	Second	8
3·9	2	Third	7
4·9	3	Fourth	6
5·9	4	Fifth	5
6·9	5	Sixth	4
7·9	6	Seventh	3
8·9	7	Eighth	2
9·9	8	Ninth	1
10·9	9	Tenth	None

The use of the fingers for multiplication by 9 need not be limited to the first ten numbers. We cannot in this way obtain the product of 11 and 9, but it is found more easily mentally.

Let us write the products of the numbers from 12 to 20 by 9. All these have 1 as their first digit on the left, and this should be kept in mind.

Factors	Hundreds	Tens	Units
12·9	1	0	8
13·9	1	1	7
14·9	1	2	6
15·9	1	3	5
16·9	1	4	4
17·9	1	5	3
18·9	1	6	2
19·9	1	7	1
20·9	1	8	0

We observe that the sum of the digits that are in the places of the tens and of the units is in each case 8. This gives us a clue as to how to multiply by 9 any number between 12 and 20 inclusive; first we proceed exactly as in the multiplication by 9 of the first ten numbers. Suppose we wish to obtain the product 16·9. We bend the sixth finger (the thumb of the right hand). This leaves open five fingers on the left hand and four on the right. Since the product 16·9 has as its first digit 1, we allow one finger on the left for this digit. Thus we are left with four fingers on the left and four fingers on the right. The product then is 144.

The following shows the positions of the fingers during the multiplication and how to read the results:

Factors	Fingers to Left of Bent Finger for		Finger Bent	Finger to Right of Bent Finger for
	Hundreds	Tens		Units
12·9	1	None	Second	8
13·9	1	1	Third	7
14·9	1	2	Fourth	6
15·9	1	3	Fifth	5
16·9	1	4	Sixth	4
17·9	1	5	Seventh	3
18·9	1	6	Eighth	2
19·9	1	7	Ninth	1
20·9	1	8	Tenth	None

14 X 9 =126

25 X 9 =225

34 X 9 =306

38 X 9 =342

A Homemade Calculating Machine

Multiplication and division are tedious processes, especially when large numbers are involved. Calculating machines, however, are expensive. A substitute apparatus, so simple that anyone can construct it of sturdy paper, is a set of Napier's Rods (or "bones") that simplifies multiplication and division of large numbers. A set is shown here:

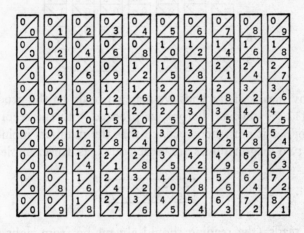

These rods are actually ten strips on which the products of the first ten numbers by one of the numbers from 0 to 9 inclusive are given. Each rod is thus a multiplication table of the first ten numbers by a certain number. Since the rods are glued together, and since many copies of the same rod can be made, we may arrange them in any desired order to obtain the products of any given number (large or small) by the first nine numbers, 1, 2, 3, 4, 5, 6, 7, 8, and 9.

Thus if we have 6,830,112, for example, we select the rods in which, in the lower right-hand corner, the numbers 6, 8, 3, 0, 1, 1, and 2 appear. We then arrange these rods in the order of the digits in the given number, so that the numbers in the second line (below the zeros) read 6,830,112. This arrangement of the rods is:

1	0/6	0/8	0/3	0/0	0/1	0/1	0/2
2	1/2	1/6	0/6	0/0	0/2	0/2	0/4
3	1/8	2/4	0/9	0/0	0/3	0/3	0/6
4	2/4	3/2	1/2	0/0	0/4	0/4	0/8
5	3/0	4/0	1/5	0/0	0/5	0/5	1/0
6	3/6	4/8	1/8	0/0	0/6	0/6	1/2
7	4/2	5/6	2/1	0/0	0/7	0/7	1/4
8	4/8	6/4	2/4	0/0	0/8	0/8	1/6
9	5/4	7/2	2/7	0/0	0/9	0/9	1/8

Thus by means of the rods we may write down the products of 6,830,112. However, before we proceed with the recording of the product it must be explained that the numbers included between two diagonal lines are to be added, as, for example:

2/8	2/5	1/4	0/7

which reads (the reading should always be from right to left) as 30,647. The products then are:

$$6,830,112 \cdot 1 = 6,830,112$$
$$6,830,112 \cdot 2 = 13,660,224$$
$$6,830,112 \cdot 3 = 20,490,336$$
$$6,830,112 \cdot 4 = 27,320,448$$
$$6,830,112 \cdot 5 = 34,150,560$$
$$6,830,112 \cdot 6 = 40,980,672$$
$$6,830,112 \cdot 7 = 47,810,784$$
$$6,830,112 \cdot 8 = 54,640,896$$
$$6,830,112 \cdot 9 = 61,471,008$$

It should be noted that in certain cases the sums obtained in the same diagonals were greater than 10. In these the digit in the place of the tens was transposed to the next place on the left of the number read off, the procedure generally used in addition and known as the "carrying" of a number into the next column on the left.

Thus one setting of Napier's Rods gives us a multiplication table of any number by all the one-digit numbers from 1 to 9 inclusive but here its independent utility ends. If we have to multiply one large number by another, we can obtain all the partial products by means of the rods, but these must be recorded on paper and added. However, the rods reduce the possibility of mistakes in multiplication, because the process is largely mechanized, and lessens fatigue, especially when very large numbers are to be multiplied.

The rods were introduced by John Napier, a Scottish mathematician (1550–1617) in his book *Rhabdologia*. Since then many have attempted to improve the apparatus, which does have certain original deficiencies: First, the "carrying" is not mechanized (this is attainable in calculating machines only); secondly, before proceeding with multiplication it is necessary to select strips with the proper rods; and, finally, the rods are separate, loose strips of paper or cardboard, which makes handling inconvenient.

The second and third deficiencies of Napier's Rods, however, can be remedied by a handy little multiplication-and-division device constructed as follows: Each strip (or rod) is prepared in ten copies. Thus we have 100 strips, every ten of which are exactly alike, or, actually, ten sets of Napier's Rods. Each set is collated in a stack so that the products of 9 are on the bottom of the set, the products of 0 on the top, and all the other strips arranged to make the order 0, 1, 2, 3, 4, 5, 6, 7, 8, and 9. On the top of each strip there should be left a small extra piece, on which the number of the strip should be written. Moreover, the strips should be cut so that those with the products of 0 are the shortest, and the others graduated upward in length. Thus, when they are placed on top of each other, the number of every strip may be seen.

These strips should then be arranged in ten sets of ten each, one alongside another; glued at their lower ends to a permanent

cover (a small notebook is preferable), and the apparatus is ready
for use, as shown below.

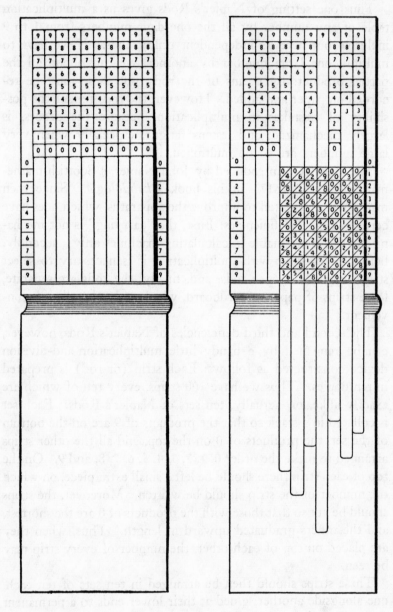

On top of the apparatus we have ten strips showing the products of 0. If we bend these strips over we find beneath them ten strips with the products of 1. Underneath these are ten strips with the products of 2, and so on down to the ten with the products of 9.

To multiply we simply bend over the strips that cover the rods on which appear the products of the digits that make up that number. The drawing on page 120 shows the apparatus set for the products of 4,629,031. On the border are the numbers from 0 to 9 inclusive to facilitate the locating of the proper products.

For division, set the apparatus for the divisor. Thus we obtain the products of this divisor by all the numbers from 0 to 9 inclusive. Then division is reduced to subtraction, which should be performed on paper. For example, to divide 68,305,983 by 3,942, we set the apparatus on 3,942. The consecutive digits of the quotient will be obtained in the same manner as in the process of long division. However, the actual multiplication is not performed because the respective products are given by the arranged rods.

Daughters of Abacus: Suan-pan, Soroban, and Schoty

There are many other such inexpensive calculating devices. The ancient Greeks and Romans counted by means of pebbles, placed on a plaque ruled to contain several compartments, each having a definite place value. Thus numbers were represented on the plaque in the same way as we write them nowadays. This instrument was generally known as the abacus. Variations of the type of abacus we are about to consider are widely used even today in Russia, Japan, and China. The Russians call it "Schoty," the Japanese call it "Soroban," and the Chinese "Suan-pan." The construction of all is the same in principle; they consist of frames on which are strung several wires, each with a definite number of beads. The Schoty has ten beads on each wire, with the numbers represented as if written in the decimal system. Addition is performed on the Schoty by sliding down the required number of beads, and subtraction by sliding them up. Remembering that a number on the Schoty is represented by beads, we have 4,538 recorded as follows:

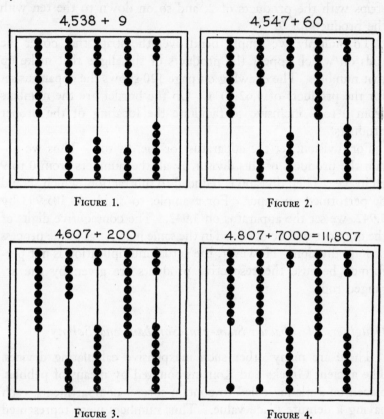

4,538 + 9

FIGURE 1.

4,547+60

FIGURE 2.

4,607 + 200

FIGURE 3.

4.807+7000 = 11,807

FIGURE 4.

Addition of two numbers on the Schoty resembles addition in the decimal system. Thus $4,538 + 7,269$ is performed as illustrated in the following diagrams: Figure 1 shows the adding of $8 + 9 = 17$. Thus one bead is slid upward on the first wire (for the units), and one bead on the second wire (for the tens) is brought down. Figure 2 shows the addition of $4 + 6 = 10$. Four beads are slid upward, and 1 bead is brought down on the third wire (for the hundreds). Figure 3 shows the addition of $2 + 6 = 8$. Two beads are slid down on the third wire. Figure 4 shows the addition of $4 + 7 = 11$. Three beads are slid upward on the fourth wire (for the thousands), and one bead is brought down on the fifth wire (for the ten thousands). Thus, the sum is 11,807.

The Suan-pan also is a frame on which several wires are strung. About two-thirds of the way from its lower edge is a bar dividing the frame into two compartments. In the lower compartment there are five beads on every wire, and in the upper, two beads to a wire. On all wires five beads in the lower portion are equivalent to one on the same wire in the upper. Thus when five beads on the same wire are slid down, they must be slid back upward, and one bead in the upper portion on the same wire must be slid down, as on the Suan-pan the counting is carried out by fives, that is, two fives make ten. In all other respects, the calculation on the Suan-pan is similar to that on the Schoty, except that in the upper portion the beads are slid down, and in the lower portion are slid upward. There is a similarity, too, between the principle of the Suan-pan and the Chinese numerals illustrated in Chapter 1. These numerals are:

I	II	III	IIII	IIIII	T̅	T̅T̅	T̅T̅T̅	T̅T̅T̅T̅
1	2	3	4	5	6	7	8	9

Notice that the numerals for 6, 7, 8, and 9 suggest the method of representing numbers on the Suan-pan, the upper bar on the numeral corresponding to the bead in its upper portion. This drawing of the Suan-pan shows the recording of 1,234,567,890.

The following self-explanatory diagrams illustrate the steps in the addition of 4,358 and 7,269, with both numbers recorded on the same Suan-pan to clarify the illustration. The dotted line through every diagram denotes the divisions of the device.

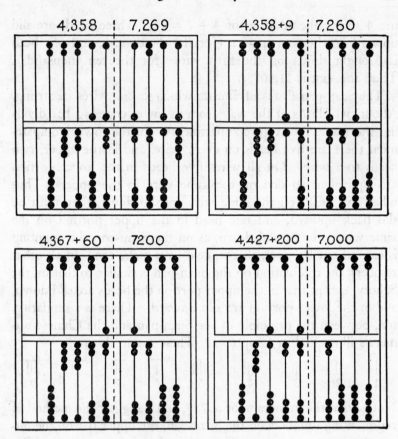

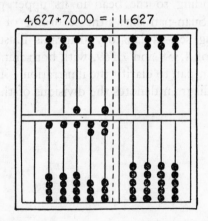

≡ 9 ≡

Rapid Calculations

The Astounding Mr. Doe

Now and then newspapers tell of some "lightning calculator" who astounds audiences with complex mental additions, multiplications, divisions, and other numerical feats. A typical report may read:

"Last night in the Town Hall, Mr. John Richards Doe astonished an audience of 2,000 with feats of near-magic. With lightning speed, he added columns of large numbers that were read off to him by members of the audience while he stood with his back to a blackboard. An assistant steadily recorded these numbers on the board while a volunteer from the crowd performed the operations on a calculating machine. No sooner was a string of ten eight-place numbers dictated to Mr. Doe than he dictated the sum to his assistant. The announcement at the calculating machine that the sum was correct brought loud applause."

Lightning calculators have been known to every generation for at least the last 150 years, mystifying their audiences no less than does Mr. Doe. Mathematicians, psychologists, and scientists in other fields have tried to discover whether some have a prodigious genius or just "secrets," but if the calculators really have exclusive methods they still have not been disclosed. As a rule, however, it would seem extremely doubtful that they do have any; for mathematics is a science in which no secret can be kept—sooner or later someone will discover it. Moreover, if there are generally workable methods for lightning calculation, mathematicians will develop them.

125

We need not interest ourselves with the careers of particular lightning calculators, but if the reader wishes he may learn about them in Russell Ball's book, *Mathematical Recreations and Essays*, Macmillan, (New York, 1940). What really is phenomenal about every one of them is their almost incredible memories, for numbers especially. Lightning calculators apparently must be born with a peculiar knack for numeration.

Any calculator, however, may improve his techniques by perennial practice, and his memory by studied concentration. He may then perform multiplications of six-place numbers as easily as most of us multiply 2 and 2.

Once in a while, however, there appear performers with feats that do involve secrets, but these are not "natural" lightning calculators. They know a few tricks, but for every trick there is a solution. Stage magicians say the hand is quicker than the eye, but the inner eye of mathematics, although it may be slower than the hand of the magician, is endlessly resourceful, and inevitably will sift the tricksters from the real lightning calculators. The trick generally is like a mystery story; the master detective-mathematician needs only a few clues to solve it. So little more can be said of the true lightning calculators than that they are freaks. Much, however, can be said of the tricksters, and in this chapter we will unravel some of their secrets.

How to Remember That Telephone Number

The author once asked a friend his telephone number. It was 4231, and the friend remarked that it was easy to remember, since it was made up of the first four digits. Then, he said, $4 - 2 = 2$, and $3 - 1 = 2$. Also, $4 - 3 = 1$, and $2 - 1 = 1$. Thus, for a four-place number the friend gave five clues. However, these would lead to a wrong-number epidemic if they were examined in this way:

Take the first four digits. They are arranged so that the difference between the digits in the first and second places is 2, and the difference between those in the third and fourth places is also 2. The difference between the digits in the first and third places is 1, and that between the digits in the second and fourth places is also 1. A person with a very poor memory, especially if in a hurry, might call 1324.

Suppose that the original number were 6857. Thus the first clue, that the number is made up of the first four digits, is removed. Reconstruction of the number by this method would be an almost hopeless task for a person in a hurry. The reader may wish, as a diversion, to write all possible numbers such a person might try before the right one would be stumbled upon.

There are other schemes for remembering numbers, schemes supposedly used by lightning calculators, but their worth is very doubtful. According to one scheme each digit has a letter, generally a consonant, assigned to it, as, for example:

b	c	d	f	g	h	j	k	l	m
1	2	3	4	5	6	7	8	9	0
n	p	q	r	s	t	v	w	x	z

To remember a number in this way, it is suggested that we form words in which the digits are represented by consonants, while the vowels are not considered as having any value at all. Thus we may have for the first numbers:

boo	cue	ad	rah	gay	tea	vie	we	lay
1	2	3	4	5	6	7	8	9

Similarly for two-digit numbers we may have:

ban	cap	dad	far	gas	the	java	week	lax
11	22	33	44	55	66	77	88	99

A magician may develop considerable skill in memorizing numbers according to this method, but it becomes considerably involved when ten or more place numbers must be remembered.

Arithmetical Rabbits

Whenever a stage magician decides really to amaze his audience, especially if just additions and multiplications become boring, he will throw out a challenge he can in a flash tell ages, in number of days. This is a variation of lightning calculation and anyone, after short practice, can perform it with the speed of the best stage magician.

Suppose you are thirty-two years old. The number of the days is 365·32, and the multiplication may be performed as follows: We note that 730 = 365·2. Then, instead of 365·32, we perform the multiplication 730·16. The multiplication 73·16 may be performed according to the method of cross-multiplication. It is:

$$
\begin{array}{lll}
& 3\cdot 6 = 18. & \text{Keep 8 and remember} \quad 1 \\
7\cdot 6 + 1\cdot 3 = 45, \quad 45 + 1 = 46. & \text{Keep 6 and remember} \quad 4 \\
7\cdot 1 = 7, \quad 7 + 4 = 11. & \text{The last digits are} \quad 11
\end{array}
$$

Therefore the product is 1,168. Since we omitted the zero we now restore it, and the number of days in thirty-two years is 11,680. Leap years must be accounted for also: Divide 32 by 4, add the 8 to 11,680, and the answer is 11,688 days. Moreover, if the magician wishes to crown this performance he may volunteer to extend his answer to the very day, and ask your birthday. The number of days in the fraction of a year is so easily obtainable that we need not dwell on it.

If your age is an odd number, this should offer no difficulty, either. The magician increases or decreases this number by 1. In either case he will thus have an even number, and then, after his multiplications have been completed, he either subtracts or adds 365.

Another favorite stunt is to tell how many seconds there are in a person's age. However, this one is limited to even years. The procedure follows:

The magician divides the number of years by 2. Half of the original number is multiplied by 63, and the other half by 72. The second product is written to the right of the first, but that only three digits of the second product are to the right of the first product. If the second product has four digits, the first digit on the left of this product is added to the last digit on the right of the first product. Thus, if the first product is 1,008, and the second is 1,152, then the procedure of joining the two is

$$
\begin{array}{r}
1008 \\
1152 \\
\hline
1009152
\end{array}
$$

To this result three zeros are added on the right, and the answer is obtained. To the result, however, it is necessary to add the seconds of the additional days in the leap years. The given number of years is divided by 4, and the quotient is multiplied by the number of seconds in a day, as $24 \cdot 60 \cdot 60$. But even here a short-cut is possible. The number of the years is multiplied by 216 and two zeros are written to the right of the product.

Suppose that the age is twenty-six. Then $26 \div 2 = 13$, and 13 is multiplied by 63 and 72. The reason for this divided multiplication is as follows:

$$365 \cdot 24 \cdot 60 \cdot 60 = 31,536,000$$

the number of seconds in a year. Then, disregarding for the time being the zeros,

$$26 \cdot 31,536 = 26 \cdot 31,500 + 26 \cdot 36 = 13 \cdot 63,000 + 13 \cdot 72$$

Then,

$$
\begin{array}{r}
13 \cdot 63,000 = 819,000 \\
13 \cdot 72 = 936 \\
\hline
13 \cdot 63,072 = 819,936
\end{array}
$$

The correction for the leap years is obtained in this way: $26 \cdot 216 = 13 \cdot 432 = 5,616$. Therefore, the required result is

$$
\begin{array}{r}
819936000 \\
561600 \\
\hline
820497600
\end{array}
$$

If the age is thirty-two, we have:

$$
\begin{array}{r}
16 \cdot 63,000 = 1,008,000 \\
16 \cdot 72 = 1,152 \\
\hline
16 \cdot 63,072 = 1,009,152
\end{array}
$$

The correction for the leap years is obtained as follows:

$$32 \cdot 216 = 16 \cdot 432 = 8 \cdot 864 = 4 \cdot 1,728 = 2 \cdot 3,456 = 6,912$$

The final result is thus

$$
\begin{array}{r}
1009152000 \\
691200 \\
\hline
1009843200
\end{array}
$$

Practice will enable anyone to perform these stunts, and those not initiated in their mysteries will be astounded at the prowess of the calculator.

Multiplication Made Painless

Suppose that we have two two-place numbers, both very close to 100; for example, 94 and 88. To find the product 94·88 we first obtain the complements of these numbers to 100. They are:

	Number	*Complement*
Multiplicand	94	6
Multiplier	88	12

Obtain the difference between a factor and the complement of the other factor. Thus

$$94 - 12 = 82, \quad \text{and} \quad 88 - 6 = 82$$

This difference represents the first two digits of the product. Then obtain the product of the complements:

$$6 \cdot 12 = 72$$

the last two digits of the 94·88 product. Write the two sets of digits consecutively, 8,272, and this is the product of 94 and 88.

The correctness of this may be checked either by the actual multiplication or as follows:

$$
\begin{array}{rl}
94 \cdot 88 = & (82 + 12)88 = 82 \cdot 88 + 12 \cdot 88 \\
82 \cdot 88 = & 82(100 - 12) = 8{,}200 - 12 \cdot 82 \\
12 \cdot 88 = & 12(82 + 6) = 12 \cdot 6 + 12 \cdot 82 \\
\hline
94 \cdot 88 = & 8{,}200 + 72 = 8{,}272
\end{array}
$$

When the product of the complements is greater than 100, the same rule holds. The complement is added to the difference of one factor and complement of the other factor, after this difference is multiplied by 100. For example, the product of 73 and 79 is obtained as follows:

Number	73	79
Complement	27	21

The difference between a factor and the complement of the other factor is 52, and the product of 27 and 21 is 567. Then the product of 73 and 79 is

$$
\begin{array}{r}
5200 \\
567 \\
\hline
5767
\end{array}
$$

The same principle holds when the product of two three-place numbers is obtained. For example, let us obtain the product of 989 and 993. We have

Number	989	993
Complement	11	7

The difference between one factor and complement of the other factor is 982, and the product of the complements is 77. Then the product of the two three-place numbers, 989 and 993, is 982,077.

The correctness of this rule may be checked either by multiplying the two numbers or by performing the following operation:

$$
\begin{array}{lll}
989 \cdot 993 = (982 + 7)993 & = 982 \cdot 993 + 7 \cdot 993 \\
982 \cdot 993 = 982(1,000 - 7) & = 982,000 - 7 \cdot 982 \\
7 \cdot 993 = 7(11 + 982) & = \quad\quad 7 \cdot 11 + 7 \cdot 982 \\
\hline
989 \cdot 993 = & 982,000 + 77 = 982,077
\end{array}
$$

It should be noted that 77 should be written as a three-place number, that is, as 077.

The product of 983 and 965 is obtained according to this rule as follows:

Number	983	965
Complement	17	35

The difference between one factor and the complement of the other factor is 948, and the product of the two complements is

$$17 \cdot 35 = 595$$

The product is then 948,595. Thus the difference between one factor and the complement of the other factor represents the first three digits of the product, and the product of the two complements represents the last three digits. When these two sets of digits are written consecutively, the product of the two three-place numbers is obtained.

If the product of the two complements is greater than 1,000, the same rule holds; that is, the complement is added to the difference between one factor and the complement of the other factor after three zeros are written to the right of this difference. Thus, the product of 943 and 927 is obtained:

Number.	943	927
Complement.	57	73

The difference between one factor and the complement of the other factor is 870. The product of the two complements is 4,161. The product is then:

$$\begin{array}{r} 870000 \\ 4161 \\ \hline 874161 \end{array}$$

Another method of multiplying two three-place numbers (these need not be close to 1,000) follows. The reader will observe that the total product is obtained by means of the consecutive addition of the partial products. Let us obtain the product of 463 and 582. We have 463·582:

Partial Products		*Consecutive Sums*
500·463 =		231,500
80·400 =	32,000	263,500
80· 60 =	4,800	268,300
80· 3 =	240	268,540
2·400 =	800	269,340
2· 60 =	120	269,460
2· 3 =	6	269,466

With practice such multiplications may be performed mentally and with comparative rapidity. Certain other multiplications may be performed almost at a glance, if the calculator is familiar with the properties of numbers. Some of these are:

a) Multiplication by 5. Since $5 = 10 \div 2$, it is best to multiply a number by 10 (which means the writing of a zero to the right of the number) and to divide it by two. Thus

$$43 \cdot 5 = \quad 430 \div 2 = \quad 215$$

or

$$786 \cdot 5 = 7,860 \div 2 = 3,930$$

b) Multiplication by 15. Since $15 = 10 \cdot 1\frac{1}{2}$, we may multiply the number by 10 (that is, write 0 on the right of the number) and then multiply it by $1\frac{1}{2}$. Or, the number may be first multiplied by $1\frac{1}{2}$ and then a zero may be written on its right. For example,

$$72 \cdot 15 = 720 \cdot 1\frac{1}{2} = 1,080$$

or

$$72 \cdot 15 = 72 \cdot 1\frac{1}{2} \cdot 10 = 108 \cdot 10 = 1,080$$

c) Multiplication by 25. Since $25 = 100 \div 4$, we may multiply the number by 100 (that is, write two zeros on the right of the number) and then divide by 4. Or the number may be divided by 4, and then multiplied by 100. For example,

$$112 \cdot 25 = 11200 \div 4 = 2,800$$

or

$$112 \cdot 25 = (112 \div 4) \cdot 100 = 28 \cdot 100 = 2,800$$

d) Multiplication by 125. Since $125 = 1,000 \div 8$, we may multiply the number by 1,000 (that is, write three zeros on its right) and then divide the number by 8. Or, we first divide the number by 8 and then multiply it by 1,000. For example,

$$144 \cdot 125 = 144,000 \div 8 = 18,000$$

or

$$144 \cdot 125 = (144 \div 8) \cdot 1,000 = 18 \cdot 1,000 = 18,000$$

All these multiplications may be performed mentally if the methods are reasonably well practiced.

Problems & Puzzles

It's a System

Most newspapers and many magazines regularly offer as a pastime problems and puzzles in arithmetic that generally baffle those unfamiliar with the peculiar properties of certain numbers. To the initiated, the problem or puzzle is as clear as day; here is a method for the solution of all of them and anyone can master it provided . . .

a) He reads the problem carefully and understands it.

b) He sees clearly all the implications, since arithmetic problems or puzzles are usually so constructed and worded that they switch attention away from the main theme.

c) Before attempting any solution, he lays out a definite plan of procedure. Hit or miss methods and guessing will rarely succeed.

d) He does not think that there is "a trick" to the problem or puzzle. If all the known methods fail and no solution is found, then there must be something that just escaped attention. Think of a trick only as the last resort.

e) He analyzes the problem as a whole to determine whether it fits into a definite scheme or a definite pattern, a point we shall examine further.

Let us consider, for example, a problem that recently appeared in a newspaper. It has to do with an addition of numbers when the digits are replaced by letters. In the sum each letter represents a distinct digit; find the numbers:

$$
\begin{array}{r}
H\ O\ C\ U\ S \\
P\ O\ C\ U\ S \\
\hline
P\ R\ E\ S\ T\ O
\end{array}
$$

134

In the statement of the problem it was not said whether these words represent whole numbers or decimal fractions. Therefore we must assume two possible solutions, one for whole numbers and one for decimal fractions.

Let us attempt to solve the problem for whole numbers first. Notice that the sum represents a six-digit number, hence P must be equal to 1. We then have

$$
\begin{array}{cccccc}
 & H & O & C & U & S \\
 & 1 & O & C & U & S \\
\hline
1 & R & E & S & T & O \\
\end{array}
$$

Since all the letters represent distinct digits, S cannot be equal to zero. If it were, $S + S$ would be equal to zero, and this is impossible, because S and O would be both equal to zero, and this is excluded in the statement of the problem. Nor can S be equal to 1, because P is equal to 1. Thus we are left with eight more digits to consider, and from this stage on we must test each possible digit until we arrive at a solution.

Suppose we let $S = 2$. Then $S + S = O = 4$, and $O + O = E = 8$. Moreover, $C + C = S = 2$. But this would make C equal to 1, and this is impossible (P is equal to 1). Hence $C = 6$ and $C + C = 6 + 6 = 12$. This will make E equal to $1 + 4 + 4 = 9$. But if we now turn to $H + 1 = R$, we note that in order that $H + 1$ be a two-digit number, when O is equal to 4, H must be equal to 9. But this is not possible, because E is equal to 9. Thus our first effort fails us and we must try again. But now we know that H may be equal either to 9 or to 8 (when O is greater than 5, and a 1 is carried from the column with the O's).

So we continue this method of trial by assigning values to S until we find the solution is $S = 6$. We proceed as follows:

$$
\begin{array}{cccccc}
 & 9 & 2 & 8 &   & 6 \\
 & H & O & C & U & S \\
 & P & O & C & U & S \\
 & 1 & 2 & 8 &   & 6 \\
\hline
P & R & E & S & T & O \\
1 & 0 & 5 & 6 &   & 2 \\
\end{array}
$$

Thus far we have used up the digits 0, 1, 2, 5, 6, 8, and 9. The only digits left unused are 3, 4, and 7. If we assign U the value

3, we have $U + U = 3 + 3 = 6$, but a 1 is carried from the column of the *S*'s, and this makes *T* equal to 7. Thus the correct solution is

$$
\begin{array}{r}
92836 \\
12836 \\
\hline
105672
\end{array}
$$

If we take $P = O$, the correct solutions are

$$
\begin{array}{r}
0.16978 \\
0.06978 \\
\hline
0.23856
\end{array}
\qquad
\begin{array}{r}
0.18479 \\
0.08479 \\
\hline
0.26958
\end{array}
\qquad
\begin{array}{r}
0.28479 \\
0.08479 \\
\hline
0.36958
\end{array}
$$

As an exercise in this type of problem the reader may try his head at the following:

$$
\begin{array}{r}
S \quad E \quad N \quad D \\
M \quad O \quad R \quad E \\
\hline
M \quad O \quad N \quad E \quad Y
\end{array}
$$

This problem is subject to the same restrictions: every letter represents a distinct digit and the same letters represent the same digits.

A certain type of problem requires particularly careful analysis because it is a tongue twister. For example, the following problem was proposed by Caliban [Hubert Phillips' book *Question Time*, Farrar and Rinehart (New York, 1938)]:

"Which would cost more: half a dozen dozen oysters at a dozen shillings the half-dozen, or a dozen dozen oysters at a half a dozen shillings the dozen?"

A step-by-step solution should present no difficulty at all, although reading of the problem may flabbergast anyone. Here is the "slow-motion" solution:

A half a dozen dozen is ½ (144) = 72.
A dozen shillings the half a dozen is 12 for 6, or 24 for a dozen.
A dozen dozen is 144.
A half a dozen shillings the dozen is 6 for a dozen.

Therefore the first cost 24·6 shillings, or 12·12 shillings, and the second cost 6·12 shillings.

Solve the following additions:

1. $\begin{array}{r} a\ b\ c\ d \\ e\ b\ c\ d \\ \hline f\ c\ d\ b\ a \end{array}$ 2. $\begin{array}{r} a\ b\ c\ d \\ e\ b\ c\ d \\ \hline c\ d\ b\ a \end{array}$ 3. $\begin{array}{r} a\ b\ c\ d\ e \\ f\ b\ c\ d\ e \\ \hline k\ e\ b\ c\ a \end{array}$ 4. $\begin{array}{r} a\ b\ c\ d\ e \\ f\ b\ c\ d\ e \\ \hline k\ e\ d\ a\ b\ c \end{array}$

Two-Timing Puzzles

In Chapter 2 we observed that the two-system of numeration is the only one that enables us to express any number as a sum of the powers of 2, since in it there are only two digits, 1 and 0. By means of this system many interesting puzzling problems may be constructed. In this section we shall discuss a few of them.

a) How to Guess the Number of Hidden Objects. This stunt may be performed with any number of objects, preferably more than 50 small items such as matches and coins. Hand a friend a box of matches (some of them should be removed, so there need be no suspicion that the number was prearranged). Ask the friend to take any number of matches from the box, making certain that you do not know the number. Then instruct him that while you step out of the room or turn your back, he should take the remaining matches out of the box and divide them into equal halves. One half should be returned to the box, and the other half stacked up. If the number of matches taken out of the box is odd, there will be one extra match. This should be placed to the left of the stack. The matches in the stack should again be divided into two equal parts, one of which should be returned to the box and the other half placed in a stack to the left of the first stack, just below that extra one match obtained after the first division. If the first stack is odd, there will be another match, and this should be placed to the left of the second stack, in the same manner as was the first extra match. This process should be repeated until one match is returned to the box and one match is left on the table, this latter to be placed to the left of the last stack in the same manner as were all the extra matches. All the places where the stacks of matches were originally put should be covered by small pieces of a paper, a piece for each stack. After all the places are covered, the extra matches should be located just above, in front of their respective papers. After this is done you may look at the pieces of paper and the extra matches, and at a glance tell how many matches there were in the box. What is the secret?

Let us take, for example, fifty-nine matches. The first division will produce two stacks of twenty-nine matches each and one extra match; twenty-nine matches are returned to the box, the other twenty-nine are stacked on the table and the extra match is placed in front of it. Then the twenty-nine matches in the stack are divided into two equal parts of fourteen matches each; fourteen matches are returned to the box and the other fourteen are stacked below the extra match that is left over. Then the fourteen matches are divided into two equal parts of seven each, and the seven matches are returned to the box while the other seven are stacked to the left of the place where the fourteen matches were stacked. Then the seven matches are divided into two equal parts of three each, one left over match. Three matches are returned to the box and three are stacked to the left of the place where the seven were stacked, and the extra match is put in front and just above the place where the three matches are. Finally, the three matches are again divided into two parts of one match each and one extra match is left. One match is returned to the box and the extra one is placed as before. The last match thus left on the table is removed to the left of its original position, just as if it were an extra match. Numerically the entire process may be described as follows:

We take fifty-nine matches. These are divided into two stacks of twenty-nine each. The first stack has twenty-nine matches and one extra match in front of it, and these are divided into two parts of fourteen each. Thus the first stack is removed from its place and the place emptied. The second stack has fourteen matches and one extra match in front of it. The fourteen matches are divided into two equal parts of seven each. Thus the second stack is removed from its place, and the place emptied. The third stack has seven matches, and these are divided into two equal parts of three each; the third stack is removed from its place, and the place emptied. The three matches are divided into two equal parts of one match each. Thus the fourth stack is removed from its place and the place is emptied, but in front of it there is an extra match. Finally the last two matches are placed in front of the two places to the left, one match in front of each place. If we denote the empty places by zeros, the matches in front of the other places by one, we have the following set up of the stacks:

Sixth	Fifth	Fourth	Third	Second	First
1	1	1	0	1	1

Their values are:

32	16	8	(4)	2	1

Thus we have
$$32 + 16 + 8 + 2 + 1 = 59$$

the number of the matches that were in the box. So we see that the places of the extra matches and the pieces of the paper tell a complete story in numbers.

b) How to Guess a Number between Numbers. On page 140 is shown a table of six columns of numbers.

Hand this table to someone and ask him to think of a number 1 to 63. Then ask him to tell you in which of the columns his number is located. Suppose he tells you it is in the 1st, 5th, and 6th columns. You tell him his number is 49.

The table is so arranged that the columns have these values:

Column 1........	1	Column 4.......	8
Column 2........	2	Column 5.......	16
Column 3........	4	Column 6.......	32

Thus, when a number is in the 1st, 5th, and 6th columns it is obtained as the sum of the values of these columns. Thus $1 + 16 + 32 = 49$. To guess the number it is not necessary to consult the table after you are told in which columns it is located. However it is necessary to remember the values of the respective columns.

6	5	4	3	2	1
32	16	8	4	2	1
33	17	9	5	3	3
34	18	10	6	6	5
35	19	11	7	7	7
36	20	12	12	10	9
37	21	13	13	11	11
38	22	14	14	14	13
39	23	15	15	15	15
40	24	24	20	18	17
41	25	25	21	19	19
42	26	26	22	22	21
43	27	27	23	23	23
44	28	28	28	26	25
45	29	29	29	27	27
46	30	30	30	30	29
47	31	31	31	31	31
48	48	40	36	34	33
49	49	41	37	35	35
50	50	42	38	38	37
51	51	43	39	39	39
52	52	44	44	42	41
53	53	45	45	43	43
54	54	46	46	46	45
55	55	47	47	47	47
56	56	56	52	50	49
57	57	57	53	51	51
58	58	58	54	54	53
59	59	59	55	55	55
60	60	60	60	58	57
61	61	61	61	59	59
62	62	62	62	62	61
63	63	63	63	63	63

The secret of the table lies in the nature of the two-system of numeration, that any number may be obtained (or represented) as the sum of powers of 2. The columns are arranged according to a definite scheme which conforms to the nature of the two-system of numeration. In column 1 are all the numbers (expressed in the two-system) whose last digit on the extreme right is 1. Column 2 contains all the numbers whose second digit from the right is 1 (it is immaterial what the other digits in these numbers are). Column 3 contains all the numbers whose third digit from the right is 1. Column 4 contains all the digits whose fourth digit from the right is 1. If you wish you may construct a table with seven columns, enabling you to guess numbers up to 127.

c) How to Guess a Combination Number. By means of the foregoing table we may solve another problem, which has a more practical nature. Suppose a storekeeper plans to buy some weights for his balance scales. What weights and how many should he buy so he may weigh up to 63 pounds, and at the same time spend the least money in this purchase?

The table contains all the numbers from 1 to 63 inclusive, and the values of the columns represent the respective weights. To determine the combination of weights for a certain use we simply consult the table: thus for 24 pounds we use a 16-pound and an 8-pound weight. For 31 pounds we use 16-, 8-, 4-, 2-, and 1-pound weights. It should be noted that for every requirement the weights are combined in only one way. Thus, to weigh 63 pounds, the storekeeper must buy six weights, 32-, 16-, 8-, 4-, 2-, and 1-pound values.

Application of the Three-System

Problems of weight may be presented in many variations. In this section we shall not impose the condition, even assumed, of the addition of weights; the weights may be placed on either side of the scale balance. However, we shall restrict the number of weights to 4 and their total value to 40 pounds, in whole pounds.

This problem is solved by the three-system of numeration. Weights that will satisfy the conditions are 1-, 3-, 9-, and 27-pound values, as it will be noted that $1 + 3 + 9 + 27 = 40$.

Since in the three-system of numeration there are in use three digits, 0, 1, and 2, and we are allowed to have only four weights, straight addition of the weights cannot lead to a complete solution. If we were allowed to use a pair of weights of each denomination we could not only solve the problem under the restriction of addition, but could weigh up to 80 pounds. However, since there is no restriction as to addition, subtraction enables us to solve the problem completely. The following table shows the various combinations of weights for the problem, but it should be noted again that only whole pounds can be weighed by this method, fractions not being considered.

Weight	Balance		Weight	Balance	
	Right Side	Left Side		Right Side	Left Side
1	1	0	21	27+3	9
2	3	1	22	27+3+1	9
3	3	0	23	27	3+1
4	3+1	0	24	27	3
5	9	3+1	25	27+1	3
6	9	3	26	27	1
7	9+1	3	27	27	0
8	9	1	28	27+1	0
9	9	0	29	27+3	1
10	9+1	0	30	27+3	0
11	9+3	1	31	27+3+1	0
12	9+3	0	32	27+9	3+1
13	9+3+1	0	33	27+9	3
14	27	9+3+1	34	27+9+1	3
15	27	9+3	35	27+9	1
16	27+1	9+3	36	27+9	0
17	27	9+1	37	27+9+1	0
18	27	9	38	27+9+3	1
19	27+1	9	39	27+9+3	0
20	27+3	9+1	40	27+9+3+1	0

Those numbers that are in the "left side" column are actually negative. Thus this problem suggests a novel method of writing numbers in the three-system of numeration by means of only two digits, 0 and 1.

Arithmetic for Sherlock Holmes

This type of problem appears under several guises. Sometimes the problem is associated with the restoration of destroyed or

partly destroyed records, and solution requires careful analysis
of the possible results of the operations. Here are some typical
problems in each of the fundamental arithmetic operations:

  a) *Addition*. Restore the missing digits in these problems:

(1)	(2)	(3)
6 ? 4 9	? 8 7	? 6 2
? 2 4 ?	3 ? 1	3 9 4 ?
─────────	5 6 ?	? 8 ? 7
? 5 9 ? 9	─────────	───────────
	? 3 ? 0	? 3 3 1 2

The solutions are:

Problem 1.   Since 9 + ? = 9, the digit must be 0.   Then 4 +
4 = 8, and the digit is therefore 8.   Likewise, in ? + 2 = 9 the
digit must be 7, and in 6 + ? = ?5 the digit to the left of 5 must
be 1, and the digit in the second row must be 9.   Thus, the restored numbers are

$$
\begin{array}{r}
6\ 7\ 4\ 9 \\
9\ 2\ 4\ 0 \\
\hline
1\ 5\ 9\ 8\ 9
\end{array}
$$

Problem 2.   As 7 + 1 + ? = 10, the missing digit must be 2.
In 1 + 8 + ? + 6 = ? note that we thus have 15 + ? = ?.   We
must consider the next column on the left.   In it we have
? + 3 + 5 = 13 (it cannot be 23).   Thus if we assign values for
the digit in the second row and the second column to be 5 or
greater (5, 6, 7, 8, 9) we shall have 15 + 5 = 20, 15 + 6 = 21,
15 + 7 = 22, 15 + 8 = 23, and 15 + 9 = 24.   But this will make
the digit in the first row and the first column equal to 3 because
2 is carried over.   If we make the digit in the second row and
second column less than 5, the digit in the first row and the first
column will be 4, because 1 is carried over.

  Thus, the restored digits are (there are several solutions possible in this case):

487	487	487	487	487		387	387	387	387	387
301	311	321	331	341		351	361	371	381	391
562	562	562	562	562		562	562	562	562	562
1,350	1,360	1,370	1,380	1,390		1,300	1,310	1,320	1,330	1,340

We may conclude that whenever there are two, or more than two, digits missing in one column there cannot be a unique (that is, one and only one) solution. In this problem there were two digits missing in one column and we obtained ten solutions.

Problem 3. The solution of this problem is

$$
\begin{array}{r}
562 \\
3,943 \\
8,807 \\
\hline
13,312
\end{array}
$$

The detailed solution is left to the reader as an exercise.

b) *Subtraction.* Restore the missing digits in these problems:

(1)	(2)
_4 ? 6 ?	_? 3 ? 2
? 0 ? 3	? 9 ?
2, 1 6 8	5, 7 4 9

Both are solved in the same manner. We shall show the step-by-step solution of Problem 1, that of Problem 2 is left to the reader as an exercise.

Problem 1. Since $3 + 8 = 11$, the missing digit is 1. But we should remember that a 1 was borrowed from the 6. Then, as $? + 6 = 15$, the missing digit is 9. Here also we should remember that a 1 was borrowed from the missing digit in the column on the left. Likewise, in both $0 + 1 = ? - 1$ and $? + 2 = 4$ the missing digit is 2.

The restored digits are put in their respective places, and we have

$$
\begin{array}{r}
-\,4,261 \\
2,093 \\
\hline
2,168
\end{array}
$$

The solution of Problem 2 is

$$
\begin{array}{r}
-\,6,342 \\
593 \\
\hline
5,749
\end{array}
$$

∓

c) *Multiplication*.   The problem below illustrates the restoring of digits in the case of multiplication:

$$
\begin{array}{r}
4\ ?\ 6 \\
?\ 4\ ? \\
\hline
?\ ?\ 2 \\
?\ ?\ 0\ 4 \\
?\ ?\ ?\ ? \\
\hline
1\ 4\ 5,6\ 9\ 2
\end{array}
$$

The first partial product (??2) can be restored at once.   We note that ? + 4 = 9.   Thus we conclude that the digit in the tens' place is 5.   We have then ?52.   This leads to the conclusion that the first factor is 426, and the digit in the units' place in the second factor is 2 (because 2·6 = 12, and 7 cannot be in that place because 7 times 4?6 will give a four-place number, while we have a three-place number).   Thus the first partial product is 852.   This allows us to restore the digit in the units' place of the third partial product; 8 + 0 + ? = 16, and this digit is 8.   Since we know the first factor (426) the second partial product is 1,704.   Restoration of the digit in the hundreds' place of the second factor as well as of the third partial product is as follows: We note that the digit in the thousands' place of the third partial product is 1 (the first digit of the total sum is 1). Thus the second factor must be 3 (3·6 = 18, and 8·6 = 48, but 8 is too large, because 8·426 = 3,408).   The third partial product is therefore 1,278.   Finally, the restored multiplication problem is

$$
\begin{array}{r}
426 \\
342 \\
\hline
852 \\
1704 \\
1278 \\
\hline
145692
\end{array}
$$

d) *Division*.   The problems in division are somewhat more complicated, but their solution, if done slowly and if the methods for solution of addition, multiplication, and subtraction problems

are mastered, should offer no special difficulties. Let us consider
the following problem:

```
2 ? 1 ? 7 | 2 ?
  ? 0 ?    ￢￢￢
  ￢￢￢     ? 6 ?
  1 8 ?
  ? ? 4
  ￢￢￢
    ? 7
    ? 7
    ￢￢
```

The first step in the solution is to consider the subtraction

```
2 ? 1
? 0 ?
￢￢￢
  1 8
```

By means of the method developed for subtraction we obtain

$$221$$
$$203$$
$$\overline{18}$$

The fact that 203 is an odd number leads to the conclusion that
the divisor 2? is odd, and the first digit of the quotient is also odd
(the product of two odd numbers is odd). Now let us consider
the last subtraction

```
? 7
? 7
￢￢
```

The numeral 7 in the units' place of a product is obtained if we
have the factor combinations of factors $1 \cdot 7 = 7$ and $3 \cdot 9 = 27$.
Thus the quotient must be 29, and the digit in the units' place
of the quotient must be 3. The quotient cannot be 23, and the
digit in the units' place 9 because $23 \cdot 9 = 207$. The divisor cannot be 27, because $27 \cdot 9 = 243$, and we have for the first partial
product only 203. Thus the division process is now as follows:

```
2 2 1 ? 7 | 2 9
2 0 3     ￢￢￢
￢￢￢      7 ? 3
  1 8 ?
  ? ? 4
  ￢￢￢
    8 7
    8 7
    ￢￢
```

To restore second partial product we observe that $4 + 8 = 12$.
Then the second subtraction is

$$\begin{array}{r} 1 \ 8 \ 2 \\ 1 \ 7 \ 4 \\ \hline 8 \end{array}$$

Thus the second digit of the quotient is

$$\frac{174}{29} = 6$$

and the reconstructed division is

$$\begin{array}{r|l} 22127 & \underline{\ 29} \\ 203 & 763 \\ \cline{1-1} 182 & \\ 174 & \\ \cline{1-1} 87 & \\ 87 & \end{array}$$

Construction of problems of this type is simple. An arithmetic operation is performed on a set of numbers, and then certain digits are deleted. Instead of the deleted numbers, question marks or some other symbols are written, and the problem is ready for a mathematical detective. Care must be exercised, however, that deletion of the digits does not introduce the possibility of several solutions. It was earlier pointed out that in the case of addition several deleted digits in the same column will not yield a unique solution. However, in multiplication this restriction is not absolutely necessary, because there are other conditions associated with the problem and adherence to these conditions eliminates generally the chance of several solutions.

Thus if we choose an addition

$$\begin{array}{r} 739 \\ 563 \\ 847 \\ \hline 2,149 \end{array}$$

it may be turned into a problem with missing digits such as

$$\begin{array}{r} 7 \ ? \ 9 \\ 5 \ 6 \ ? \\ ? \ 4 \ 7 \\ \hline 2,1 \ 4 \ 9 \end{array}$$

For division this

```
298291 | 43
258      6937
───
402
387
───
159
129
───
301
301
───
```

may be presented as:

```
2 ? 8 ? 9 ?  | 4 ?
2 5 ?          ? 9 ? 7
───
  ? 0 ?
  3 ? 7
  ───
    ? 5 9
    ? ? ?
    ───
      3 ? ?
      3 ? ?
      ───
```

There may be other variations, and the reader may find it interesting to try to formulate more problems based on this division.

Construction of problems of this type, it is seen, thus presents no special difficulty, their solution requires thorough investigation of all the elements (partial products, partial sums, differences, and quotients). Every clue must be thoroughly tested on all the separate phases of the problem and followed up; if there is a clue that a certain digit may satisfy the requirements of the problem, this digit should be tested on all the partial products (or sums, or differences). Only when there is absolute certainty that such a digit does not fail in any single case can it be accepted as a part of the general solution.

On the other hand, when a problem is constructed, it may be worthwhile to obtain all the possible variations. For example, consider the following problem in division:

```
7955 | 37
74     215
──
55
37
──
185
185
──
```

∓

It may be offered in at least the following variations:

```
7 ? 5 ?   | ? 7        ? 9 ? 5
? 4         ? 1 ?      ? 4
─────     ─────      ─────
  5 5                   5 ?
  ? ?                   3 ?
─────                 ─────
? ? ?                 ? 8 5
? ? ?                 ? 8 5
```

Thus, with a little practice, the reader will find it a fascinating diversion to construct his own puzzlers.

PROBLEMS

Restore the missing digits in the following problems:

```
5.      5 ? 2 ?     6.      4 ? ? 3      7.      5 ? 4 ?
     +  ? 4 ? 2          + ? ? 1 4 ?          ? 4 5 ? 8
     ─────────          ───────────          6 ? 2 5 9
        9 3 2 9          ? ? 3 7 6 8          ─────────
                                              9 4 1 9 6
```

```
8.      ? 4 2 ?     9.       ? ? ? 3     10.     _ ? 3 ? 2
        6 4 ? 8 3           ? 2 4 7 6           ? 1 ?
      ? 7 2 4 ? 2           ? 8 9 2 3 ?         ─────────
      ───────────         ? 7 6 3 4 2 1         4 9 3 9
      ? ? ? 6 9 0 2        ─────────────
                           ? ? 7 4 7 5 4 5
```

```
11.     _ ? 6 ? 5    12.        3 ? 9     13.        ? 6 ?
          ? 1 ?                  6 ?                  ? ? 5
        ─────────              ─────                ? 8 ? 0
          8 0 0                ? 9 ?                6 ? ? 6
                            2 ? ? ?                 3 ? ? ?
                            ─────────             ─────────
                            ? ? ? ? ?             3 ? 9 ? ? 0
```

```
14.  2 ? 7 ? 5 ? 5  | ? 4 ?
     ? 5 7 ?          4 ? 1 ?
     ─────────      ───────
       ? 0 2 5
       1 ? ? ?
       ─────────
         ? 6 ?
         ? ? ?
         ─────────
         3 ? 1 5
         3 ? 1 5
```

11

How the Number Magician
Does it

"I Will Now Predict . . ."

The trick next described is a standby with some stage magicians in flabbergasting audiences. The performer usually asks a spectator to write a large number, a very large one. Then he announces that he will ask someone else to write another number, but first he will write down the sum of the first number, the number that is yet to be written, and one that he will write again. As a rule, he does not write the predicted sum on the blackboard but on a piece of paper and hands it to a member of the audience "for safekeeping."

Suppose that the first spectator wrote on the blackboard 7,438,412. The magician writes 17,438,411, and this is the sum he predicted. The demonstration proceeds like this:

One of the audience wrote..............	7,438,412
Another wrote.......................	3,946,289
The magician writes...................	6,053,710
The sum is...........................	17,438,411

The reader will observe that the sum of the numbers written by the second member of the audience and by the magician is 9,999,999. The total is thus the sum of 7,438,412 and 9,999,999, or 7,438,412 and 10,000,000 — 1, which can be written before any other numbers, that is, the second and third, are written. Thus there is nothing wonderful or magical in the entire procedure.

Very often the magician varies this stunt by offering to predict the sum of many more numbers, but he then reserves the right to write an equal number of addends after the first is written down, and provides that one number must be written first by someone in the audience. For every addend then written down (and he specifies how many will be written) he writes a number which completes that addend to 9,999 . . . , to as many places as there are in the largest addend. For every two addends, one from the audience and one his own, he adds to the first number 1,000 . . . — 1, a very simple matter. This illustrates the procedure:

The first one from the audience wrote....	7,647,318
The second wrote.....................	50,896
The third wrote......................	1,376,982
The magician wrote...................	9,949,103
The magician wrote...................	8,623,017
The sum predicted by him.............	27,647,316

Naturally, he sets another restriction. After the first number is written down, no other number must have more places than this. A number with more places would wreck his stunt, because he cannot predict a sum of such numbers.

The Guessing Game

The stunt of guessing numbers is based on the performance of certain arithmetic operations, and there are many schemes for its performance. For example:

a) Choose a number. Multiply it by 2. Add 4 to the product and divide the sum by 2. Add 7 to the quotient and multiply the resultant sum by 8. Subtract 12 from this product. Then divide the difference by 4, subtract 11 from the quotient, and announce the result.

If you will subtract 4 from the announced result and divide the difference by 2, you will know the number that was taken. For example, suppose that the number is 9. Then

$$9 \cdot 2 = 18, \ 18 + 4 = 22, \ 22 \div 2 = 11, \ 7 + 11 = 18$$
$$18 \cdot 8 = 144, \ 144 - 12 = 132, \ 132 \div 4 = 33, \ \text{and} \ \ 33 - 11 = 22$$
$$\text{Then} \qquad 22 - 4 = 18, \ \ \text{and} \ \ 18 \div 2 = 9$$

b) Multiply any number by 2 and add 18. Multiply the sum by 2, then subtract 36. Announce your result.

If you will divide the announced result by 4 you will obtain the number that was taken. Suppose the number is 13. Then

$$13 \cdot 2 = 26, 26 + 18 = 44, 44 \cdot 2 = 88, \quad \text{and} \quad 88 - 36 = 52$$

Then

$$52 \div 4 = 13$$

c) Add 2 to a number, multiply the sum by 3, then subtract 4. Now multiply the difference by 3 and add the original number to the last product. Announce the result.

If you subtract 6 from the announced result and divide the difference by 10, you will obtain the number taken. Suppose the number is 15. We perform the indicated operations:

$$15 + 2 = 17, 17 \cdot 3 = 51, 51 - 4 = 47, 47 \cdot 3 = 141,$$

and

$$141 + 15 = 156$$

Then we find

$$156 - 6 = 150, \quad \text{and} \quad 150 \div 10 = 15$$

d) Take a small number, never greater than 996. Multiply it by 37, add 111 to it and multiply the sum by 27. Announce the result.

If you complete the result to the nearest thousand, take the number of the thousands and subtract from it 3, you obtain the number taken. Suppose the number is 7. Then

$$7 \cdot 37 = 259; \quad 259 + 111 = 370; \quad 370 \cdot 27 = 9,990$$

Then 9,990 is completed to 10,000, and the number of the thousands is 10. Therefore we have

$$10 - 3 = 7$$

e) Multiply a number by one that is greater by 2. Add 5 to the product and announce the result.

If you subtract 4 from the announced result you will obtain a number that is a perfect square (a product of a number by itself).

Taking the square root of this difference and diminishing it by 1, you will obtain the original number. Suppose the number is 3. Then

$$3 \cdot 5 = 15, \quad \text{and} \quad 15 + 5 = 20$$

Since

$$20 - 4 = 16, \quad \text{and} \quad 16 = 4 \cdot 4$$

we have

$$4 - 1 = 3$$

How To Make Your Own Tricks

The method of writing a letter to indicate that it represents any number allows generalization and at the same time permits the compact expression of an arithmetical rule that is stated in words. Thus, for example, if we say: "Take a number, multiply it by 3, and divide the sum by 2," we can write it as $[(n)3] \div 2$. We use here a tacit agreement concerning the parentheses and brackets. Generally the first operation is performed on the expression enclosed in the parentheses ( ). Then the result thus obtained, which is enclosed in brackets [ ] is subject to the consecutive operation. At times we may need further symbols to indicate that additional operations are to be performed. We then use figurate brackets { }.

We shall now introduce a term to be much used hereafter:

When we operate with numbers alone and perform the operations of addition, subtraction, multiplication, and division, we call these operations "arithmetic," but when we make use of letters to indicate numbers these same operations are called "algebraic."

The process of devising schemes for number tricks involves the following steps:

a) After a number is selected (in general it is represented by a letter, say *n*), a series of operations are to be consecutively performed with it.

b) The operations should be so selected that the final result is of the nature desired for the particular trick.

To illustrate these processes in detail let us develop a scheme for a number trick that will enable us to predict the result of some operations with an unknown number. Suppose this number is n. We shall perform these operations:

Add 23 to the number . . . . $n + 23$
Multiply the obtained sum by 3 . . $(n + 23)3$
(Note that up to this moment the unknown number is thus trebled.)
Subtract 40 from the product . . . . $(n + 23)3 - 40$
Multiply the difference by 5 . . . . . $[(n + 23)3 - 40]5$

By this time the unknown number is multiplied by 15. Thus to eliminate this unknown number we must subtract 15 times the original number from this product. We have then

$$[(n + 23)3 - 40]5 - 15n = [3n + 69 - 40]5 - 15n$$

and finally,

$$15n + 5 \cdot 29 - 15n = 145$$

Thus, whatever operations may have been performed with a number totally unknown to you, the final numerical result is 145.

Some schemes may not contain total elimination of the unknown number. The unknown number, or some multiple of it, may be left in the final numerical result. But when such a scheme is used the performer must announce his final result. The following example will illustrate this procedure, but it should be remembered that selection of the operations and of the auxiliary numbers introduced are selected at will by the person who devises the scheme. Let the number be n.

Add 12 to the number . . . . $n + 12$
Multiply the sum by 12 . . . . $(n + 12)12$
Subtract 84 from the product . . . . $(n + 12)12 - 84$

(Note that 84 is a multiple of 12.)

Divide the result by 4 . . . . $[(n + 12)12 - 84] \div 4$
Add 6 to quotient . . . . $[(n + 12)12 - 84] \div 4 + 6$
Multiply the sum by 2 . . . . $\{[(n + 12)12 - 84] \div 4 + 6\}2$
Subtract the original number and 25 from this product . . . .
$$\{[(n + 12)12 - 84] \div 4 + 6\}2 - (n + 25)$$

By this time the person who performs the operations in accordance with the given instructions has almost lost track of all the numerical work that he has done, and is asked to tell his final numerical result. In fact, he will tell that this result, according to the algebraic operations, is as follows:

$$\{[12n + 144 - 84] : 4 + 6\}2 - n - 25 =$$
$$\{3n + 15 + 6\}2 - n - 25 = 6n + 42 - n - 25, \text{ or } 5n + 17$$

Thus, if 17 is subtracted from this final numerical result, and the difference is divided by 5, the unknown number is obtained. For example, suppose the number is 11. Then obtained in succession are 11, 23, 276, 192, 48, 54, 108, 72. If we subtract 17 from 72 we obtain 55, and 55 when divided by 5 gives 11.

Below are the schemes, or as they are usually called in algebra the "formulas," for the number tricks that were described in the preceding section.

a) $[\{[(2n + 4) \div 2] + 7\}8 - 12] \div 4 - 11 = 2n + 4$
b) $(2n + 18)2 - 36 = 4n$
c) $[(n + 2)3 - 4]3 + n = 10n + 6$
d) $(37n + 111)27 = 999n + 3 \cdot 999 = 999(n + 3)$
e) $n(n + 2) + 5 = n^2 + 2n + 1 + 4 = (n + 1)^2 + 4$

With knowledge of the basic arithmetic operations, these formulas should be self-explanatory. A word, however, about formula (d): If n is not greater than 996, $n + 3$ does not exceed 999, and the announced result does not exceed 1,000. This property explains why the final result must be completed to the nearest thousand, and the number of the thousands gives the unknown number.

If She's Coy about Her Age

This, to learn about ages, is a very intriguing stunt similar in nature to the guessing of a number earlier described. You merely ask a person to follow your instructions and perform certain operations. After these have been performed, you are told of a final numerical result and from it obtain all the information needed. The progressive operations are:

a) Multiply the number of the month of birth by 100.
b) To this product add the date of the month.
c) Multiply this sum by 2.
d) Add 8 to this product.

e)   Multiply the sum by 5.
f)   Add 4 to the product.
g)   Multiply the sum by 10.
h)   Add 4 to the product.
i)   Add to the sum the age, and announce the result.

If you subtract 444 from the announced final numerical result you will have a certain number. Group the digits in this number by two, counting from right to left. The first two digits from the right will give the age. We hope she's younger than you thought. The second two digits from the right will give the date of the month. Finally, the remaining digit (or digits) will give the month.

Let us consider this example: Suppose a woman's actual age is 34, and her date of birth is November 25. The number of the month is then 11. The foregoing operations yield the following results:

a)   Multiply the number of the month of birth by 100 . . . . . . $11 \cdot 100 = 1,100$
b)   To this product add the date of the month . . . . $1,100 + 25 = 1,125$
c)   Multiply this sum by 2 . . . . $1,125 \cdot 2 = 2,250$
d)   Add 8 to the product . . . . $2,250 + 8 = 2,258$
e)   Multiply the sum by 5 . . . . $2,258 \cdot 5 = 11,290$
f)   Add 4 to the product . . . . $11,290 + 4 = 11,294$
g)   Multiply the sum by 10 . . . . $11,294 \cdot 10 = 112,940$
h)   Add 4 to the product . . . . $112,940 + 4 = 112,944$
i)   Add to the sum the age . . . . $112,944 + 34 = 112,978$

The number 112,978 is given to you. You subtract 444 and obtain
$$112,978 - 444 = 112,534$$

By grouping the digits of this number by two from right to left you obtain 11, 25, and 34. You may then announce quietly that the date of birth is November 25, and that the young woman certainly doesn't look her 34 years.

Age and Date of Birth, Please

Guessing the age and the date of birth of the person who performs the numerical operations according to instruction is just another variation on the number tricks.   In this case, however, instead of one number, three are guessed simultaneously.

The formula for this trick is

$$\{[(100m+d)2+8]5+4\}10+4+a = 10000m+100d+a+444$$

where m is the number of the month, d, the date of the month, and a, the age of the person who performs the numerical operations.   Note that in this trick the numbers to be guessed are taken in the order m, d, and a, but this is not absolutely necessary.   Thus, if we begin with the age, multiply it by 100, and add to it the number of the month, and at the final stage the number of the month, we actually make use of the following formula:

$$\{[(100a+d)2+8]5+4\}10+4+m = 10000a+100d+m+444$$

The possible sequences of these numbers are m, d, a; m, a, d; d, a, m; d, m, a; a, d, m; a, m, d.   The number 444 in the formula is used to conceal the apparently obvious numerical result.

Other schemes for the same stunt are possible.   Their construction, however, should always have as its final goal a number of the form $10000a + 100d + m +$ some number.   A possible variation of the sequence of a, d, m is

$$\{[(200a+2d)2+3]5+3\}5+5+m = 10000a+100d+m+95$$

Note that the numbers by which the successive sums are multiplied are selected so that we obtain 10,000, 100, and 1 as the factors.

≠ 12 ≠

≠ 12 ≠
Algebra & Its Numbers

It's Hotter than You Think

In simple arithmetic processes, addition, multiplication, subtraction, and division—we have made use of numbers with only one property, that of quantity. One number has been larger or smaller than another, or two numbers have been equal, and no other properties were either assumed or assigned. Now we shall consider an important property that enables us to widen our understanding and use of numbers.

In many situations when we measure a certain object or a situation of an object, especially when these are under continuous change (whether we can detect it with our senses or have indirect knowledge of the presence of this change) the values obtained run through a series of numbers. Take, for example, the measuring of temperature. On every thermometer we have a point known as zero, and at times the temperature is "below zero." Now let us see exactly what the numbers that are below the zero and the numbers that are above may represent. Let us use in our discussion not our everyday thermometer, the Fahrenheit, which indicates the freezing point at 32 degrees above zero and the boiling point of water at 212 degrees above zero, but the Centigrade thermometer, on which the freezing point is indicated by zero and the boiling point of water by 100 degrees.

Now, when it is extremely cold we know that the temperature is below zero (on the Fahrenheit thermometer this will be indicated by some number below 32 degrees). We have a common notion (not totally correct, however) that cold and heat are opposites. Even if we assume that this notion is correct (and it will help us in drawing the analogy for numbers that we need) we may arrive at the conclusion that the numbers below the zero on the Centigrade thermometer differ from those above it. We have arrived at one conclusion, but we go further.

If we denote the property of the numbers that are above the zero as "positive," then the numbers below it are opposite in nature, and we may call their property "negative." We must understand, however, that this is only an agreement traditionally accepted without any foundation for the method of choice; the numbers might be denoted as black and white, good and bad, or as any other combination of opposites.

This simple endowment of numbers with the property of being positive or negative doubles, so to speak, the amount of numbers that are in use. And in the use of spoken and written language, mathematics thus add two adjectives: "plus" for positive and "minus" for negative. Moreover, since symbols often replace words and long expressions, two are used to denote these two types of numbers: "+," which denotes also the operation of addition, to identify positive numbers, and "−," which also indicates the operation of subtraction, for negative numbers. Thus, $+25$ denotes a positive 25, and $−25$ a negative 25.

However, very often we do not care whether the number is positive or negative; we are interested only in its magnitude or, as we say in mathematical language, its numerical or *"absolute,"* value. Then the number is enclosed in two vertical bars as $|25|$.

As to our reservation concerning the terms "cold" and "heat": we are exceedingly vague when we say merely that an object is cold or hot. On a freezing day, water from a faucet may seem to be very warm, while water of the same temperature may seem refreshingly cold on a day in July; in other words, our notions of hot and cold are relative. However, it is possible to say precisely which object is colder and which is hotter, but for this purpose we must make use of a measure of temperature known as the "absolute." According to physical science there is a temperature, that of the space between stars, which is just a trifle higher than the lowest possible temperature. This lowest possible temperature ("possible" should be thought of as the lowest that can be obtained in laboratory experiments) is about 274 degrees below zero Centigrade. Now, since we have made the agreement concerning the nature of such numbers, we may write it as −274 degrees Centigrade. This is known as the "absolute zero." Thus the zero on the Centigrade thermometer is 274 degrees absolute, and the boiling temperature of water 374 degrees absolute. Thus we may as well cease talking about cold and hot objects, but talk of hot only. The least hot object will have a temperature that is about 0 degree absolute, or −274 degrees Centigrade, and the hottest object may run a temperature of millions in degrees, as the interiors of stars.

PROBLEMS

1. The absolute zero temperature is taken as −274 degrees Centigrade. What is the absolute temperature of boiling water (+100 degrees Centigrade)?

2. The temperature scale in common use in this country (except in scientific work) is the Fahrenheit. On this scale the freezing point is +32° F ("F" for Fahrenheit), and the boiling point of water is +212° F. How many Fahrenheit degrees are equivalent to 100° C ("C" for Centigrade)?

3. From the result of Problem 2 obtain the relation between a Fahrenheit degree and a Centigrade degree.

4. The formula for translating Fahrenheit readings into Centigrade readings is $5/9 (F° − 32°) = C°$. What is the Centigrade reading when the Fahrenheit reading is 112°?

5. The formula for translating Centigrade readings into Farhenheit readings is $F° = 9/5 C° + 32°$. What is the Fahrenheit reading when the Centigrade reading is 72°?

6. What is the Fahrenheit value for the absolute zero temperature (−274° C)?

Both Ways at Once

If we borrow the method of representing numbers on a thermometer, we may obtain a visual or, as we call it, graphic representation. We may take a straight line (again, this is only a

convenient medium; there are other methods) on which we denote one point as the zero point. Then, if the line is horizontal
to the right of this zero point, at equally spaced intervals we
mark off points which may be numbered consecutively, and to
the left of the zero point we similarly mark off points. But to
the right we reserve the portion of the line for positive numbers,
and to the left for negative numbers. This is shown as:

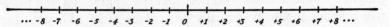

If the line were slanted or vertical, the general agreement is to
reserve the line above the zero point for positive numbers and
below for negative numbers.

Thus, whenever we have problems in which two directions
are involved (these may be up and down, forward and backward, right and left, increase and decrease, gain and loss, income
and expenditure, purchase and sale) we may use positive and
negative numbers for proper representation.

A Rule for Signs

All the work with these two types of numbers is performed
in the same manner as in arithmetic, but special attention must
be given to their respective signs.

The addition and subtraction of these numbers is performed in
such a manner that the negative sign (the minus) denotes subtraction. An illustration: if a man walks a mile north and then
walks back two miles south, he walked $+1$ mile and -2 miles.
He will be, from the starting point, $[(+1) + (-2)]$ miles; that
is, he will be $(+1 - 2)$ or -1 mile, or 1 mile south from the
starting place. However, he actually walked three miles, and if
we recall the notion concerning the absolute value of a number,
we may immediately obtain this result. He actually walked
$|+1| + |-2| = 1 + 2 = 3$ miles. Thus addition of the two
types of numbers is performed with the understanding that a
negative number is subject to subtraction (from the arithmetic
point of view).

Now, since the addition of a negative number actually means subtraction, what is meant by the subtraction of a negative number? Let us recall what was said about the notion of a negative number, and we may extend the notion of positive and negative to the operations of addition and subtraction. It immediately suggests that the negative of addition is subtraction. Then, if the addition of a negative number is actually performed by subtraction, it is reasonable to expect that the subtraction of a negative number should be actually performed as an addition. Let us consider this example: A man has no money and a debt of $50. To liquidate the debt and have $50 in cash on hand he must earn a certain amount. Now we may consider the operation of liquidation as negative, to be denoted by the minus sign $(-)$. Having a debt also may be considered as negative. Then the operation of clearing the $50 debt may be denoted as $-(-50)$, while the earning of a cash balance of $50 will be denoted by $+50$. Thus the total amount of the money that he will have to earn is $[(+50) - (-50)]$. But we know that in order to wipe out the debt and have a cash balance of $50 he must earn $100. In other words

$$[(+50) - (-50)] = 50 + 50 = 100$$

Thus we have this rule: The subtraction of a negative number results in the addition of the same number with its sign changed. In other words, the sign of a negative number that is to be subtracted is reversed; the number is made positive and is then added. The same rule, when applied to the subtraction of expressions enclosed in parentheses, is: When operations on the expressions enclosed in parentheses are performed, every sign of the members of the expressions (numbers and letters) is reversed, and then the operations are performed according to the new signs. For example

$$3a+6b+52-(2a-3b+47)=3a+6b+52-2a+3b-47=a+9b+5$$

Multiplication may be interpreted as repeated addition, as

$$3 \cdot 4 = 3 + 3 + 3 + 3 = 12$$

then the rule of signs for the product of two positives and for the product of a positive and negative number is simple—the product of two positive numbers is positive, and the product of a positive and a negative number is negative. Thus

$$3(-4) = -4 + (-4) + (-4) = -4 - 4 - 4 = -12$$

To arrive at a rule for the product of two negative numbers let us suppose that a city provides in its budget that every person on relief is to receive three dollars a day. Suppose eight unemployed left the city and were stricken off the relief rolls. The finances of the city then are affected as a result of this action. Let us analyze the situation from the mathematical point of view. Every single daily city expenditure of three dollars is actually −3 dollars, because this amount must be subtracted from the city's cash. Moving into a city may be thought of as a positive (+) operation, and leaving is then a negative operation (−). So the eight men who have left may be represented as −8 men. But, since eight have left, the city will be saving $3 \cdot 8 = 24$ dollars a day, and, since the operation of saving is opposite to spending, it may be represented by a positive sign. Then $(-3)(-8) = +24$, and we have the rule of signs for the product of two negative numbers:

The product of two negative numbers is positive.

The division of negative numbers, either a positive by a negative or conversely, or of a negative by a negative may be interpreted as the multiplication of two numbers, one of which is a fraction with 1 as a numerator. Thus the same rules that are applied to the multiplication of numbers are applied to division: $+8 \div (-2) = -4$, and $(-12) \div (-3) = +4$.

PROBLEMS

7. What is the Fahrenheit reading when the Centigrade reading is −45°?

8. What is the Centigrade reading when the Fahrenheit reading is −63°?

9. What is the Centigrade reading when the absolute temperature is −278° F?

10. What is the Fahrenheit reading when the absolute temperature is 171°C?

Multiplication Magic for the Million

Some stage magicians, we may recall, amaze audiences with feats of rapid multiplication of two- to even six-place numbers. Just a simple algebraic manipulation, however, can demonstrate that such stunts are within the command of anybody. For example take the multiplication $985 \cdot 985$. It may be performed as follows:

$$985 \cdot 985 = (985 + 15)(985 - 15) + 15^2 = 1{,}000 \cdot 970 + 225 = 970{,}225$$

Actually this method represents a very common algebraic procedure:

$$a \cdot a = a^2 = (a+b)(a-b) + b^2 = a^2 - ab + ab - b^2 + b^2 = (a^2 - b^2) + b^2$$

Thus, when a number that is very close to 1,000 (or 100, 10,000, etc.) is to be multiplied by itself, the multiplication can be performed quickly as follows: Obtain the complement of this number to, say, 1,000. Subtract this complement from the number. Then multiply the complement by itself and add the product to the difference just obtained after this difference has been multiplied by 1,000. The following examples illustrate this method:

$$83 \cdot 83 = 100 \cdot 66 + 289 = 6{,}600 + 289 = 6{,}889$$
$$9{,}976 \cdot 9{,}976 = 10{,}000 \cdot 9{,}952 + 576 = 99{,}520{,}000 + 576 = 99{,}520{,}576$$

In algebra we have a simplified way of writing of a product of a number by itself. We used this mathematical shorthand above when we wrote $a \cdot a = a^2$, $4 \cdot 4 = 4^2$. Use of this property in the relationship $(a + b)(a - b) = a^2 - b^2$ is very helpful when squares of numbers are to be calculated. For example:

$$16^2 = (16 + 4)(16 - 4) + 4^2 = 20 \cdot 12 + 16 = 240 + 16 = 256$$
$$39^2 = (39 + 1)(39 - 1) + 1^2 = 40 \cdot 38 + 1 = 1{,}520 + 1 = 1{,}521$$
$$72^2 = (72 + 2)(72 - 2) + 2^2 = 74 \cdot 70 + 4 = 5{,}180 + 4 = 5{,}184$$
$$87^2 = (87 + 3)(87 - 3) + 3^2 = 90 \cdot 84 + 9 = 7{,}560 + 9 = 7{,}569$$

In each case we use the relationship

$$a^2 = (a + b)(a - b) + b^2$$

in which we make either $(a + b)$ or $(a - b)$ a multiple of 10. If the digit of the units is to be examined, it is either smaller or greater than or equal to 5. If this digit is smaller than 5, we make $(a - b)$ a multiple of 10 (see 72^2 in the table). If the digit is greater than 5, we make $(a + b)$ a multiple of 10. If the digit is equal to 5, there is still a more simple procedure, which will be developed presently.

Let us recall an example of the type given in Chapter 9. Suppose we have the multiplication $983 \cdot 989$; we showed that it may be performed thus

Number.............. 983   989
Complement to 1,000..   17   11

Then $983 - 11 = 972$, and $989 - 17 = 972$. Also $17 \cdot 11 = 187$, and writing 187 to the right of 972 we obtain the product

$$983 \cdot 989 = 972,187.$$

This process may be explained as

$$983 \cdot 989 = (1,000 - 17)(1,000 - 11)$$

But

$$(1,000 - 17)(1,000 - 11) = 1,000 \cdot 1,000 - 1,000 \cdot 11 - 1,000 \cdot 17 + 17 \cdot 11$$

Let us consider the first three products on the right of the equality sign. We have

$$1,000 \cdot 1,000 - 1,000 \cdot 11 - 1,000 \cdot 17 = 1,000(1,000 - 11) - 1,000 \cdot 17$$

or these three terms are finally equal to

$$1,000 \cdot 989 - 1,000 \cdot 17 = 1,000(989 - 17) = 1,000 \cdot 972$$

Thus we have that

$$983 \cdot 989 = 1,000 \cdot 972 + 17 \cdot 11 = 972,000 + 187 = 972,187$$

Now let us consider the method of squaring a number; that is, the calculation of n^2, when the number ends on 5. Suppose that we have 65 a two-place number although, as it will be seen, the rule can be extended for a number with as many places as desired. It can be written as $6 \cdot 10 + 5$. Then

$$(6 \cdot 10 + 5)^2 = (6 \cdot 10 + 5)(6 \cdot 10 + 5)$$

Performing the multiplication we have:

$$6 \cdot 6 \cdot 100 + 6 \cdot 10 \cdot 5 + 6 \cdot 10 \cdot 5 + 25$$

If we consider the first three terms of the product we have

$$6 \cdot 6 \cdot 100 + 6 \cdot 10 \cdot 5 + 6 \cdot 10 \cdot 5 = 100 \cdot 6 \cdot 6 + 100 \cdot 6$$

and this is equal to

$$100 \cdot 6(6 + 1) = 100 \cdot 6 \cdot 7$$

Finally,

$$65^2 = 100 \cdot 6 \cdot 7 + 25 = 4{,}200 + 25 = 4{,}225$$

Note that we took the number of the tens and multiplied by a number that is 1 larger, and then wrote 25 to the right of the product thus obtained. Let us see whether this is a rule that will always hold. Suppose that our number is $10a + 5$ (where a is either a digit or any number).

$$(10a + 5)^2 = (10a + 5)(10a + 5) =$$
$$100a^2 + 50a + 50a + 25 = 100a^2 + 100a + 25$$

and we finally obtain

$$(10a + 5)^2 = 100a(a + 1) + 25$$

This confirms the rule just obtained and illustrates another result that is very important in algebra:

$$(a + b)^2 = (a + b)(a + b) = a^2 + ab + ab + b^2 = a^2 + 2ab + b^2$$

Later we shall discuss this result in detail. A similar result is obtained for $(a - b)^2$. Thus

$$(a - b)^2 = (a - b)(a - b) = a^2 - ab - ab + b^2 = a^2 - 2ab + b^2$$

Secrets of Some Curiosities

Let us recall the relation, obtained in the preceding section,

$$a^2 - b^2 = (a + b)(a - b)$$

By means of this we may obtain some very striking number curiosities.

Let us select two numbers such that their sum is 11 and their difference is 1. Two such numbers are 5 and 6. Then

$$6^2 - 5^2 = 36 - 25 = 11$$

Now, it happens that

$$56^2 - 45^2 = 1111$$
$$556^2 - 445^2 = 111111$$
$$5556^2 - 4445^2 = 11111111$$
$$55556^2 - 44445^2 = 1111111111$$
$$555556^2 - 444445^2 = 111111111111$$
$$5555556^2 - 4444445^2 = 11111111111111$$
$$\cdots\cdots\cdots\cdots\cdots\cdots$$

and it is possible to prove that

$$(555\cdots56)^2 - (444\cdots45)^2 = 111\cdots11$$

so that if $(555 \ldots 56)$ and $(444 \ldots 45)$ each have a certain equal number of digits, $(111 \ldots 11)$ will have twice as many digits. Let us see whether this is correct.

We observe that

$$56 + 45 = 101 \quad \text{and} \quad 56 - 45 = 11$$
$$556 + 445 = 1001 \quad \text{and} \quad 556 - 445 = 111$$
$$5556 + 4445 = 10001 \quad \text{and} \quad 5556 - 4445 = 1111$$
$$55556 + 44445 = 100001 \quad \text{and} \quad 55556 - 44445 = 11111$$
$$\cdots\cdots\cdots\cdots\cdots\cdots$$

In each case multiplication of the respective sum and difference produces a product that consists of a series of 1. The number of these digits 1 is always twice the number of the digits in either of the other numbers squared.

Let us take two numbers, 7 and 4, whose sum is 11 and difference is 3. Then $7^2 - 4^2 = 49 - 16 = 33$. We can also have here the following relations:

$$57^2 - 54^2 = 333$$
$$557^2 - 554^2 = 3333$$
$$5557^2 - 5554^2 = 33333$$
$$55557^2 - 55554^2 = 333333$$
$$555557^2 - 555554^2 = 3333333$$
$$5555557^2 - 5555554^2 = 33333333$$
$$\cdots\cdots\cdots\cdots\cdots\cdots$$

and it is possible to prove that

$$(555\ldots57)^2 - (555\ldots54)^2 = 333\ldots33$$

so that if $(555 \ldots 57)$ and $(555 \ldots 54)$ each have a certain equal number of digits, the number of the digits in $(333 \ldots 33)$

is greater by just one than the number of digits either in (555 . . . 57) or in (555 . . . 54). The correctness of this can be observed from the following:

$$57 + 54 = 111 \quad \text{and} \quad 57 - 54 = 3$$
$$557 + 554 = 1111 \quad \text{and} \quad 557 - 554 = 3$$
$$5557 + 5554 = 11111 \quad \text{and} \quad 5557 - 5554 = 3$$
$$55557 + 55554 = 111111 \quad \text{and} \quad 55557 - 55554 = 3$$
$$. . . . .$$

In every case multiplication of the respective sum and difference produces a product that consists of a series of 1. The number of these 1's is always greater by one than the number of the digits in either of the figures to be squared.

Let us take two numbers, such that their sum is 11 and their difference is 5. Then

$$8^2 - 3^2 = 64 - 9 = 55$$

Here also we can obtain the following relations:

$$58^2 - 53^2 = 555$$
$$558^2 - 553^2 = 5555$$
$$5558^2 - 5553^2 = 55555$$
$$. . . . .$$

and it is possible to prove that $(555 \ldots 58)^2 - (555 \ldots 53)^2 = 555 \ldots 55$, so that if $(555 \ldots 58)$ and $(555 \ldots 53)$ each contain a certain equal number of digits, the number of the digits in $(555 \ldots 55)$ is greater by just one than the number of the digits either in $(555 \ldots 58)$ or in $(555 \ldots 53)$. This may be checked in the same manner as shown in the preceding example.

In a similar manner, if we start with a set of numbers whose sum is 11 and whose difference is 7 we can obtain the following set of relations:

$$9^2 - 2^2 = 77$$
$$59^2 - 52^2 = 777$$
$$559^2 - 552^2 = 7777$$
$$. . . . .$$

and proceed along the usual steps to show that $(555 \ldots 59)^2 - (555 \ldots 52)^2 = 777 \ldots 77$.

Again, if we take two numbers such that their sum is 11 and their difference is 9, we obtain relationships of the same type. For instance, such numbers are 10 and 1. Thus we have $10^2 - 1^2 = 99$ and we can obtain:

$$60^2 - 51^2 = 999$$
$$560^2 - 551^2 = 9999$$
$$5560^2 - 5551^2 = 99999$$
and so on

Here are two more cases similar in nature:

$$11^2 - 0^2 = 121$$
$$61^2 - 50^2 = 1221$$
$$561^2 - 550^2 = 12221$$
$$5561^2 - 5550^2 = 122221$$
and so on

$$12^2 - (-1)^2 = 143$$
$$62^2 - 49^2 = 1443$$
$$562^2 - 549^2 = 14443$$
$$5562^2 - 5549^2 = 144443$$
and so on

Note that in the first case of these two examples the sum and the difference of the numbers is 11. In the second case the sum of the numbers is 11, and the difference is 13. In the consecutive pairs of numbers the sum remains constant; that is, for each set of pairs it is 11, but for the last set of pairs of numbers we obtained a difference 13 (the situation was interchanged because we introduced a negative number). Every pair led to a factor all made up of the digit 1. We could likewise construct many more pairs such that the sum of the two numbers will be 11, 111, 1,111, etc., while the difference for each set will be 15, 17, 19, 21, etc. In every such set the difference will be expressed by some number whose digits denote some regularity.

The method of obtaining these numbers is as follows. One of the numbers is negative in the first pair of every set. Then each number is added to 50. This gives the second pair. The third pair is obtained by adding the original numbers to 550, the fourth pair by adding the original numbers to 5,550, and so on. Thus we have the following first pairs of numbers, each giving rise to a set of pairs:

12	and	−1	17	and	− 6
13	and	−2	18	and	− 7
14	and	−3	19	and	− 8
15	and	−4	20	and	− 9
16	and	−5	21	and	−10

and so on

Construction of some of these sets is left to the reader as an exercise.

11. Starting with two numbers whose sum is 22 and whose difference is 2 write the sequences of the differences of the squares of these numbers similar to those given on pages 167-169. [Answer:

$$12^2 - 10^2 = 44$$

$$112^2 - 110^2 = 444$$

$$1112^2 - 1110^2 = 4444$$

$$\cdots\cdots]$$

12. Starting with two numbers whose sum is 33 and whose difference is 3 write the sequences of the differences of the squares of these numbers similar to those given on pages 167-169. [Answer:

$$18^2 - 15^2 = 99$$

$$168^2 - 165^2 = 999$$

$$1668^2 - 1665^2 = 9999$$

$$\cdots\cdots]$$

- 13 -

The Algebra of Number Giants and Pygmies

The Fifth Operation: Making and Mastering Googols

Thus far we have been concerned with the four arithmetic operations, addition, subtraction, multiplication, and division. However, we have made some slight acquaintance with the repeated multiplication and we have learned also how to write in symbols numbers that were multiplied by themselves several times. Now, recalling some number giants and number pygmies, we shall restate in algebraic symbols some of their characteristics and, as well, discuss the operation known as "the raising to a power."

Is there any need for this fifth operation? Since the raising to a power is nothing but repeated multiplication (for the time being we shall accept this description literally), introduction of another operation with numbers might seem superfluous; after all, we might be content with writing the same number several times as a repeated factor. And, too, one might inquire whether there is any really urgent need for this fifth operation from the practical point of view. In this chapter the reader will find ample opportunity to decide the validity of these objections.

Algebra at times is characterized by the use of letters instead of numbers, but to insist that this is its main characteristic would be erroneous. The distinction of algebra lies not in the use of numbers but in the use of operations in addition to the four arithmetic operations. If we have made use of raising to a power in connection with number giants and number pygmies in arith-

171

metic, it is because we found it convenient to borrow algebra to simplify our development. Could the reader write a googol and, if he could, be certain that he has written the correct number of zeros? Or, if a googolplex were written, could he read it at a glance? Algebra enables us to write it at once; it is 10^{googol}.

Taxi to the Moon

Between wars, scientists like to speculate on the possibility of traveling to the moon and other planets by rocket. Volumes have been written on the subject. Governments have been issu-

ing patents to inventors of rocket ships, and magazines and special journals have devoted columns to the idea.

Suppose you could just step into any taxi on the street and tell the chauffeur: "To the moon, driver." (We may skip his probable reply.) What would be the fare? Generally, taxi fare is twenty cents for the first quarter of a mile and five cents for any additional quarter mile. Let us assume the flat rate is twenty cents a mile. Since the distance from the earth to the moon is 240,000 miles, the fare would be

$$240,000 \cdot 20 \text{ cents} = 4,800,000 \text{ cents}$$

or $48,000. Let us assume, too, that the national debt of the United States is $260,000,000,000. This sum could pay for the transportation of

$$\frac{260,000,000,000}{48,000} = 5,416,666 \text{ men}$$

to the moon, or 2,708,333 on round trips.

These computations are simple, but caution is essential where there are such large numbers; it is easy to write one zero more or less, and when many are written it is difficult to detect an error.

Previously we have used a simplified method for numbers with many zeros, writing them as products, thus:

$$260,000,000,000 = 260 \cdot 10^9$$

Observe how simple and foolproof becomes our computation when we write numbers in this simplified form. Let us repeat the computations; we have

$$24 \cdot 10^4 \cdot 20 = 48 \cdot 10^5$$

Since $48 \cdot 10^5$ is the number of cents and there are $100 = 10^2$ in a dollar, we may translate the cents into dollars as follows:

$$\frac{48 \cdot 10^5}{10^2} = 48 \cdot 10^3$$

As the debt is about $260 \cdot 10^9$ dollars, we divide this number by the cost of a trip to the moon and we have

$$\frac{260 \cdot 10^9}{48 \cdot 10^3} = 5,416,666.$$

Jujitsu for Number Giants

These computations are the same in nature as those we performed in dealing with number giants and number pygmies, and now we shall state and examine the rules for working with numbers written in compact form.

Since this compact method of writing number giants and pygmies is used in multiplication and division, let us examine in a general way what actually takes place, ignoring the numbers used as factors, and repeated several times. These factors may be 10 or be any other number. Let us denote the general number by a.

Then, if a is repeated as a factor, as $a \cdot a$, we write a^2. If a is repeated as a factor three times, we write

$$a \cdot a \cdot a = a^3$$

If a is repeated as factor any number of times, say n, we write

$$a \cdot a \cdot a \cdot \ldots \cdot a = a^n$$

Thus, the figure written on the right of the number, just above it, is the indicator, and tells how many times the number is a factor of itself. This indicator is called "the exponent of a," and the number a with its exponent is called "the power of a." To be consistent, when the number a is written without an exponent—that is, it is not even a second power of itself—its exponent is assumed to be 1. Thus,

$$a = a^1$$

Let us examine the rules that govern the operations with exponents of powers of numbers:

a) *Multiplication.* We multiply a^3 and a^5. This may be represented as $(a \cdot a \cdot a)(a \cdot a \cdot a \cdot a \cdot a)$. Removing the parentheses, we have

$$a^3 \cdot a^5 = a \cdot a \cdot a \cdot a \cdot a \cdot a \cdot a \cdot a = a^8$$

But $3 + 5 = 8$. Thus since the product may be represented as

$$\underbrace{(a \cdot a \cdot a \cdot \ldots \cdot a)}_{m \text{ factors}} \underbrace{(a \cdot a \cdot a \cdot \ldots \cdot a)}_{n \text{ factors}}$$

Generalizing, we have a^{m+n}.

Thus we have the rule:

The product of powers of the same quantity (or number) is also a power whose exponent is the sum of the exponents of the respective factors. For example

$$2^2 \cdot 2^3 \cdot 2^5 = 2^{10}, \quad \text{since} \quad (2 + 3 + 5 = 10)$$

b) *Division.* Derivation of the rule for division of powers of the same number or quantity is performed in the same manner. Let us divide a^7 by a^3. This may be represented as

$$\frac{\cancel{a} \cdot \cancel{a} \cdot \cancel{a} \cdot a \cdot a \cdot a \cdot a}{\cancel{a} \cdot \cancel{a} \cdot \cancel{a}} = a \cdot a \cdot a \cdot a$$

Note that in the above fraction we cancelled an equal number of factors in the numerator and denominator. The result, however, is a^4. But $4 = 7 - 3$. Now, we may generalize that the quotient of a^m and a^n, which may be represented as

$$\frac{\overset{\displaystyle m \text{ factors}}{\overbrace{a \cdot a \cdot a \cdot \,\cdots\, \cdot a}}}{\underset{\displaystyle n \text{ factors}}{\underbrace{a \cdot a \cdot a \cdot \,\cdots\, \cdot a}}}$$

This we may generalize as a^{m-n}.

Thus we have the rule:

The quotient of two powers of the same quantity or number is also a power whose exponent is the difference of the exponent of the dividend and the exponent of the divisor. For example

$$5^6 \div 5^2 = 5^4, \quad (6 - 2 = 4)$$

PROBLEMS

1. The wheat production of the world is about $4.5 \cdot 10^9$ bushels a year. A bushel of wheat weighs 60 pounds. One pound of wheat contains about 9,000 grains of wheat. How many grains are there in a yearly crop of wheat?

2. In 1920 railway passengers in the United States traveled about $47 \cdot 10^9$ miles. The average journey per passenger was about 37 miles. About how many passengers were carried by trains in 1920?

3. The total production of the fisheries in the United States and Alaska is about $4.8 \cdot 10^9$ pounds yearly, and the value of the products is estimated as about $9.3 \cdot 10^7$ dollars. What is the value per pound of fish?

4. The total crop land in the United States is estimated at approximately $1.2 \cdot 10^9$ acres. The farm population is estimated as about $3.2 \cdot 10^6$. How much land does this make per capita?

5. The value of the farm lands is estimated as about $3.3 \cdot 10^{10}$ dollars. What is the average price per acre?

Some Puzzling Results

The rules for operations with powers of numbers lead to some absorbing results. Let us examine them in detail.

a) How to Write 1. Here is a puzzler that may stump those not familiar with the rules: Write 1 with a figure of any number of places and a digit, but addition, subtraction, multiplication, and division must not be used.

Since we know the rule for the division of powers of the same number or quantity, we know that when a number is divided by itself the quotient is always 1. Then any power of a number when divided by itself must also yield 1 as a quotient. But, according to the rule for the division of powers, the exponents of the dividend and divisor of the powers are subtracted from one another. And here we arrive at a curious result. We know that when a number is subtracted from itself the difference is 0. For example, $5 - 5 = 0$. Thus

$$a^5 \div a^5 = a^0 = 1$$

Thus we know that any number that is raised to the zero power (that is, whose exponent is 0) is always equal to 1. Hence

$$123{,}456{,}789^0 = 1, \quad 6{,}450{,}348{,}697{,}502{,}357{,}813^0 = 1$$

b) Farewell to Fractions. Now we return to the rule for the division of two powers of the same quantity or number. According to this rule, the exponent of the quotient is obtained as the difference of the exponents of the dividend and the divisor. In other words, if the dividend is a^m and the divisor is a^n, then the exponent of the quotient is $(m - n)$. Now, if m is greater than n (in symbolic language this is expressed as $m > n$), then the difference is positive. But, if m is less than n (symbolically $m < n$), then the difference is negative. For example, if $m = 12$ and $n = 8$, then $m - n = 12 - 8 = 4$. But, if $m = 6$, and $n = 17$, then $m - n = 6 - 17 = -9$.

What meaning is attached to a quotient whose exponent is negative? It may happen that $(m - n)$ will at all times be negative. Let us examine this; suppose we divide 2^5 by 2^9. We perform this as follows:

$$\frac{2 \cdot 2 \cdot 2 \cdot 2 \cdot 2}{2 \cdot 2 \cdot 2 \cdot 2 \cdot 2 \cdot 2 \cdot 2 \cdot 2 \cdot 2} = \frac{1}{2 \cdot 2 \cdot 2 \cdot 2}$$

Thus

$$\frac{1}{2 \cdot 2 \cdot 2 \cdot 2} = 2^5 \div 2^9 = 2^{5-9} = 2^{-4}$$

Therefore,

$$\frac{1}{2^4} = 2^{-4}$$

In other words we now have a new method of writing fractions. We take the number that is in the denominator, change the sign of its exponent (if it is positive, we make it negative, and if negative, we make it positive) and write the number with the new exponent as a factor of the numerator. For example,

$$\frac{a^2}{b^3} = a^2b^{-3} \quad \text{and} \quad \frac{m^5}{n^{-4}} = m^5n^4$$

All these facts will materially simplify the calculations in the sections that follow.

PROBLEMS

6. Write the smallest integer (whole number) by using the ten digits, but each digit should be used once only.

7. What is the largest number that can be written with four 2's?

8. What is the largest number that can be written with three 5's?

9. Write the largest number by using 1, 2, 3, and 4, each digit to be used once only.

10. Write the largest number by using 6, 7, and 9, each digit to be used once only.

1,900,000,000,000,000,000,000,000,000,000,000

No, this isn't a bookkeeper's nightmare—it is the weight of the sun in grams.

But now we know how to write this number in compact form, $19 \cdot 10^{32}$. Numbers of this magnitude cannot be expressed in words, and the compact writing conveys some immediate picture of their magnitude.

Astronomers make constant use of this method of writing number giants. But if you think the weight of the sun is expressed by a big-brother number giant, compute the distance to the farthest known universe of stars. It takes light not less than $2 \cdot 10^8$ years to reach the earth, and light travels at the rate of about $3 \cdot 10^5$ kilometers a second. We have

$$2 \cdot 10^8 \cdot 3 \cdot 10^5 \cdot 365 \cdot 24 \cdot 60 \cdot 60 = 5 \cdot 10^{20} \text{ approximately}$$

and this is only the number of kilometers. Now, there are 1,000 meters in a kilometer and 1,000 millimeters in a meter. Thus the distance to the farthest known universe of stars in millimeters is

$$5 \cdot 10^{20} \cdot 10^3 \cdot 10^3 = 5 \cdot 10^{26}$$

which is still a small number giant. As a matter of fact, this number is about $4 \cdot 10^6$, or four million times smaller than the number of grams in the weight of the sun.

PROBLEMS

11. If the mass of the sun were distributed within a sphere having a radius of $2 \cdot 10^8$ kilometers, how many grams of the sun's mass would be allotted to 1 cubic kilometer? (In order to obtain the volume of a sphere, cube the radius and multiply the result by 4.18.)

12. The radius of the sun's sphere is about $5 \cdot 10^5$ kilometers. How much does a cubic centimeter of the sun weigh?

13. What is the weight of the sun in tons? (1 ton = 1,000 kilograms, and 1 kilogram = 1,000 grams.)

14. The weight of an electron is $9 \cdot 10^{-27}$ gram. How many times is the sun heavier than an electron?

15. If the radius of our universe is taken as one billion light-years, and if the number of electrons in the universe is 10^{83}, and if all these electrons were uniformly distributed in space, how many electrons would there be in 1 cubic centimeter?

Up for Air: $50,000,000,000 Worth

We often hear of barometric pressure, or the pressure of the air. Weather reports mention it regularly. How strong is this pressure?

Every square centimeter of the earth's surface is subject to a pressure of about 1 kilogram. This means that a column of air reaching out to the outer parts of the atmosphere, perhaps 100 miles or more, with a base of 1 square centimeter in area, weighs about a kilogram, or about 2.2 pounds. The total weight of the air is then easily computed. All that we must know is the area of the earth's surface in square centimeters. It is known that the area of the earth's surface is about 510,000,000 square kilometers, or

$$51 \cdot 10^7 \text{ square kilometers}$$

Let us translate this into square centimeters; 1 kilometer $= 10^5$ centimeters, and a square kilometer is equal to $10^5 \cdot 10^5$ square centimeters. Then the area of the surface of the earth is equal to

$$51 \cdot 10^7 \cdot 10^5 \cdot 10^5 = 51 \cdot 10^{17} \text{ square centimeters}$$

Then the weight of the air, since every column with a base with an area of a square centimeter weighs about 1 kilogram, is

$$51 \cdot 10^{17} \text{ kilograms}$$

Every 1,000 (or 10^3) kilograms are equal to 1 ton. Hence, in tons, the weight of the earth's atmosphere is

$$51 \cdot 10^{17} \div 10^3 = 51 \cdot 10^{14}, \quad \text{or about } 5 \cdot 10^{15} \text{ tons}$$

Let us examine how tremendous this weight is. Let us assume that the debt of the United States is roughly fifty billion dollars, or $5 \cdot 10^{10}$ dollars, or $5 \cdot 10^{12}$ cents, and that if the earth's atmosphere were purchased with this amount, for every cent we could buy $\quad 5 \cdot 10^{15} \div 5 \cdot 10^{12} = 10^3, \quad \text{or 1000 tons of air}$

or 1,000,000 kilograms of air. This air would cover 10^6 square centimeters of ground. One meter is equal to 100 centimeters, and a square meter is equal to 10,000 square centimeters. Thus the ground would be about $1,000,000 \div 10,000 = 100$ square meters, or about 1,008 square feet.

The total weight of the earth is about $6 \cdot 10^{21}$ tons. Thus the earth's atmosphere is a

$$\frac{5 \cdot 10^{15}}{6 \cdot 10^{21}} = \frac{5}{6} 10^{-6}$$

part of the total weight of the earth, about one-millionth part.

We have used one multiplication in this section which should be given special attention because it can be simplified. When we computed the number of the square inches in a square kilometer we multiplied 10^5 by itself. This may be represented symbolically as a power also; that is, $10^5 \cdot 10^5 = (10^5)^2$. But $10^5 \cdot 10^5 = 10^{5+5} = 10^{10}$. Moreover, $10 = 2 \cdot 5$. We can then write $10^{10} = 10^{2 \cdot 5}$. Thus, when we raise a power to some power, we multiply the exponents. For example

$$(a^3)^4 = a^{12}$$

PROBLEMS

16. If the weight of the earth's atmosphere is $5 \cdot 10^{15}$ tons, and if we consider that the air is made up of electrons, how many electrons would there be in the earth's atmosphere? (An electron weighs $9 \cdot 10^{-27}$ gram.)

17. What would be the price of 1 electron, if 1000 tons of air could be bought for 1 cent?

18. If the electrons in the earth's atmosphere were distributed uniformly throughout the known universe (see Problem 5), how many electrons would there be in a cubic centimeter?

19. A square centimeter = 0.155 square inch, and 1 kilogram = 2.2 pounds. Assuming that the volume of a column of air 100 miles high, and with a square centimeter as a base, weighs 1 kilogram, what is the weight of the air in a room that measures 14 by 20 by 10 feet?

20. If 1,000 tons of air cost 1 cent, what would be the cost of the air in a room of the size given in Problem 19?

Wood Is Always Burning

Wood, almost anyone will tell you, burns at a very high temperature. The burning of wood, however, really is a chemical process, the combining of oxygen and carbon, and can take place at any temperature. Most of us think a high temperature is required because our senses are so crude that we cannot observe a slow process. When we think of burning we have in mind a conflagration fully equipped with fire trucks.

The speed of a chemical reaction diminishes with the lowering of the temperature. For a drop of 10 degrees Centigrade the speed is approximately halved; in other words, if a substance burns completely in 1 second at 100 degrees Centigrade, then at 90 degrees it will burn completely in 2 seconds, at 80 degrees in $2^2 = 4$ seconds, and at 70 degrees in $2^3 = 8$ seconds. At 0° it will take $2^{10} = 1,024$ seconds, or 17 minutes and 4 seconds.

Now suppose a quantity of wood burns completely in 1 second at 600 degrees Centigrade. How long will it take at 0°? Under the general law, in 600 degrees there are $600 \div 10 = 60$ intervals of 10 degrees each, and thus it will take 2^{60} seconds. How large is this number? To compute it we shall resort to some simplifications (the number is so large that an approximate answer will be just as good). We observe that $2^{10} = 1,024$, then we may take

$$2^{10} = 1,000 = 10^3 \text{ approximately}$$

Then

$$2^{60} = (2^{10})^6$$

which is approximately equal to

$$(10^3)^6 = 10^{18}$$

Thus, the burning will be completed in 10^{18} seconds. To translate this into years, we may take $3 \cdot 10^7$ as the number of seconds in a year. Then the number of years will be

$$10^{18} \div (3 \cdot 10^7)$$

Which is approximately equal to

$$3 \cdot 10^{10} \text{ years, or about 30 billion years}$$

Wood, then, is constantly burning, no matter what its temperature, but we observe this burning only when heat speeds up the combustion.

PROBLEMS

21. If a quantity of wood burns completely in 1 second at 600 degrees Centigrade, how long would it take it to burn completely at the temperature of absolute zero, -274 degrees Centigrade?

22. How long would it take for wood to burn completely at 1,000 degrees Centigrade?

23. What temperature would be necessary to make the wood in Problem 21 burn completely in 4 minutes and 16 seconds?

24. What temperature would it take the same wood to burn completely in about 10^{-3} second?

25. The temperature of the surface of the sun is about 6,000 degrees Centigrade. If the wood in Problem 21 were placed on the surface of the sun, how long would it take to burn completely?

Double Strength

Suppose you are given a piece of thin paper that weighs 10 grams and are asked to fold it so you can cut it into equal halves, then take a half and fold it again and cut it into equal halves. How many times would you have to continue this process to get down to one theoretical electron ($9 \cdot 10^{-27}$ gram)?

Since 10^3 is approximately equal to 2^{10}, we can replace 10^{-27} by $(10^3)^{-9}$ or by $(2^{10})^{-9} = 2^{-90}$. Likewise 9 is approximately equal to 2^3. Thus $9 \cdot 10^{-27}$ can be replaced by $2^3 \cdot 2^{-90} = 2^{-87}$. Thus, we would have to perform this operation of folding and cutting into halves only eighty-seven times to get down to 1 electron, and an electron is a very small substance. However, should you ask this question you would invariably get the most absurd replies, some of them estimating millions of times.

PROBLEMS

26. How many times would it take to cut the sun in half, and then the half into halves, and so on, until we would get one electron? Take the radius of the sun's sphere as $5 \cdot 10^5$ kilometers.

27. How many times would it take to apply the process described in Problem 26 to the earth's sphere? Take the radius of the sphere as 6,400 kilometers. The radius of an electron is about $7.5 \cdot 10^{-12}$ centimeter.

28. If the radius of the universe is taken as one billion light-years, and if it takes light about eight minutes to reach from the sun to the earth, how many times would it take to apply the process described in Problem 26 to the radius of the universe in order to obtain the distance from the earth to the sun?

29. If the radius of the solar system, the distance from the sun to the farthest planet, Pluto, is about $5 \cdot 10^9$ miles, how many times would it take to apply the process described in Problem 28 to obtain this distance?

30. There is a legend that the inventor of chess requested as a prize for his invention a certain quantity of wheat. This was to be determined as follows. There are sixty-four squares on the chessboard. On the first square one grain was to be placed, on the second square two grains, on the third four grains, and so on; on every next square the number of grains to be twice the number on the preceding square. How many grains would have to be placed on the sixty-fourth square?

Number Giants with a Few Digits

By means of the fifth operation, or the raising to a power, it is possible to write very large numbers in a very compact form. Let us consider a few examples.

Write the largest possible number with four 1's, excluding arithmetic operations. The number 1,111 is not the largest number; the correct answer is 11^{11}. The reader, if he has sufficient patience, will obtain, by multiplying 11 eleven times by itself, 285,311,670,611.

In Chapter 4 a very large number was obtained by means of three 9's,

$$9^{9^9}$$

Now let us take up this problem from a more general point of view; let us examine whether the same principle of writing very large numbers holds, if any three (but the same) digits are taken and are again excluded. Let us start with three 2's. Will

$$2^{2^2}$$

be the solution? We can answer this question by performing the calculations. We have $2^4 = 16$. Apparently 222 is a larger number. But $2^{22} = 4,194,304$. Thus our resort to analogy failed.

How about three 3's? We have four choices:

$$333, \; 33^3, \; 3^{33}, \; \text{and} \; 3^{3^3}$$

Let us start with the last. It is equal to 3^{27}. Obviously, 3^{27} is smaller than 3^{33}.

How about three 4's? We have four choices:

$$444, \; 44^4, \; 4^{44}, \; \text{and} \; 4^{4^4}$$

Again let us start with the last. It is equal to 4^{256}, and this number is considerably larger than 4^{44}. In the case of three 4's the same arrangement as in the case of three 9's holds.

Let us write the largest possible number with four 2's. Here eight combinations are possible:

$$2,222, \; 222^2, \; 22^{22}, \; 2^{222}, \; 22^{2^2}, \; 2^{22^2}, \; 2^{2^{22}}, \; \text{and} \; 2^{2^{2^2}}$$

Obviously, 2,222 is the smallest of all the eight numbers. Let us compare 222^2 and 22^{22}. We can write $22^{22} = (22^2)^{11} = 484^{11}$. Obviously, 484^{11} is greater than 222^2 because 484 is greater than 222, and 11 is greater than 2. Now, let us compare 22^{22} with 2^{222}. If we write 32^{22} instead of 22^{22}, we take a larger number. But $32 = 2^5$, then $32^{22} = (2^5)^{22} = 2^{110}$, and this number is smaller than 2^{222}. Thus, when 22^{22} is replaced by a larger number we still obtain a number that is smaller than 2^{222}. Thus, we eliminated three numbers, and now we must compare

$$2^{222}, \quad 22^{2^2}, \quad 2^{22^2}, \quad 2^{2^{22}}, \quad \text{and} \quad 2^{2^{2^2}}$$

We can eliminate the last at once, because it is equal to 2^{16}. The fifth combination, 22^{2^2}, is equal to 22^4, and is smaller than 32^4 which may be written as 2^{20}. Thus, this is also eliminated. Now we are left with three only:

$$2^{222}, \quad 2^{22^2}, \quad \text{and} \quad 2^{2^{22}}.$$

We note that 2^{222} is smaller than the second of these, because $22^2 = 484$, and hence 2^{222} is smaller than 2^{484}. But 2^{22} is equal to 4,194,304. Thus

$$2^{2^{22}} = 2^{4,194,304}$$

is the largest possible number that can be written with four 2's.

Let us examine the same problem when four 3's are used. We have eight possible combinations, and these must be examined along the same lines as the combinations obtained in the case of four 2's. We thus have:

$$3{,}333, \quad 333^3, \quad 33^{33}, \quad 3^{333}, \quad 33^{3^3}, \quad 3^{33^3}, \quad 3^{3^{33}}, \quad \text{and} \quad 3^{3^{3^3}}$$

The first, $3{,}333$, is eliminated at once. We may write 333^3 as $(3 \cdot 3 \cdot 37)^3 = (3^2)^3 \cdot 37^3$. Now if we replace 37 by 81 we obtain a much larger number. But $81 = 3^4$. Then we have

$$(3^2)^3 \cdot (3^4)^3 = 3^6 \cdot 3^{12} = 3^{18}$$

We may write 33^{33} as

$$(3 \cdot 11)^{33} = 3^{33} \cdot 11^{33}$$

Now if we replace 11 by 9 we obtain a much smaller number. But $9 = 3^2$. Then we have

$$3^{33} \cdot (3^2)^{33} = 3^{33} \cdot 3^{66} = 3^{99}$$

This eliminates 333^3, as well as 33^{33}. Thus, we are left with five combinations:

$$3^{333}, \quad 33^{3^3}, \quad 3^{33^3}, \quad 3^{3^{33}}, \quad \text{and} \quad 3^{3^{3^3}}$$

We already have eliminated the last combination. The second one is equal to 33^{27}, and this may be written as $3^{27} \cdot 11^{27}$, and if 11 is replaced by $27 = 3^3$, we obtain a larger number. Then 33^{27} is smaller than $3^{27} \cdot (3^3)^{27} = 3^{27} \cdot 3^{81} = 3^{111}$. Thus 33^{3^3} is smaller than 3^{333}, and it is also eliminated. We are then left with three combinations:

$$3^{333}, \quad 3^{33^3}, \quad \text{and} \quad 3^{3^{33}}$$

We observe that 333 is less than 33^3, and 33^3 is less than 3^{33}. Thus, the largest possible number that can be written with four 3's is

$$3^{3^{33}}$$

The reader will find no difficulty in arriving at the conclusion that the largest possible number that can be written with four 4's is

$$4^{4^{4^4}}$$

PROBLEMS

Write the largest possible number with each of the following groups:

31. With 2, 4, and 6
32. With 3, 5, and 7
33. With 5, 7, and 9
34. With 5, 6, 7, 8, and 9.
35. Which is larger: googolplex or myriad^{myriad}? (See pp. 59 and 74.) [Answer: googolplex]
36. Which is larger: googolplex^{myriad} or myriad^{googolplex}? [Answer: myriad^{googolplex}]

The Grammar of Algebra

The Heirs' Problem

John Robertson's estate of $462,000 was left to his family under a peculiar will, designed to forestall any disagreement among his heirs:

"I leave my estate to my wife, my four daughters, and my six sons. Every son shall receive three times as much as every daughter. To my wife I leave one-half of what my children receive.

"Should any one of my children contest this division on the ground that it is unfair, then the share of my wife shall be equal to the difference between what my sons and my daughters receive.

"Should my wife contest this will then her share shall be twice the shares of one son and one daughter."

What were the shares of the widow, each son, and each daughter under the various provisions?

Under the first provision each daughter received one share and each son three shares. The four daughters and six sons thus received $4 + 18 = 22$ shares. The widow's part consisted of eleven shares. In other words, the entire estate was to be divided into thirty-three equal parts. Thus every daughter was to receive $14,000, every son $42,000, and the widow $154,000.

Under the second provision the children were still entitled to twenty-two shares. But the widow's part in the inheritance this time was to be equal to $18 - 4 = 14$ shares. Thus the entire estate would be divided into thirty-six equal parts. Each daughter would receive $12,833.33, each son $38,500, and the widow $179,666.62.

Under the third provision the children were still entitled to twenty-two shares, but the widow's part this time would be equal to $2(1 + 3) = 8$ shares. Thus the entire estate would be divided into $8 + 22 = 30$ equal parts. Each daughter would receive $15,400, each son $46,200, and the widow $123,200.

This problem is simply arithmetical in nature, and no special techniques are necessary for its solution. The reader will recall that in Chapter 10 it was pointed out that every problem must be treated according to a certain scheme and that the processes of treatment are very clear, the most important process being careful analysis of the conditions set forth.

However, algebra introduces a procedure that simplifies the attack upon any problem, whether or not the problem has a solution. The quantity sought, or the unknown quantity, is denoted by some letter (usually one of the last few of the alphabet). Then this letter is regarded as though it were a number and is subjected to the specified conditions of the particular problem. Let us illustrate:

The previous problem is proper distribution of the inheritance. Since the share of a daughter determines that of a son, and the inheritance of all the children determines the share of the widow, we may denote the inheritance of a daughter by x (dollars). Then the share of a son is $3x$. Since there were four daughters and six sons, their total share was

$$(4x + 18x) = 22x$$

Under the first stipulation the widow's share was $11x$ and thus the entire estate was equal to $33x$.

Under the second stipulation the widow's share was $14x$ and the estate was equal to $36x$.

Under the third stipulation the widow's share was $2(4x) = 8x$ and the estate was equal to $30x$.

Thus we may set up three equations:

a) For the first stipulation.................. $33x = \$462,000$
b) For the second stipulation............... $36x = 462,000$
c) For the third stipulation.................. $30x = 462,000$

To obtain the value of the respective x's the value of the problem was "solved," the solving of an equation being some process by means of which we obtain the value of the letter. For this purpose we must free this letter from numerical factors (they are called "coefficients") as in the preceding case, or we must perform some other operations which will be described presently. In equations of the type given we divide the left and the right member of the equations by the coefficient of the x or, generally, of the unknown quantity which is represented by some letter.

Thus for the first stipulation

$$x = \frac{\$462,000}{33} = \$14,000$$

For the second stipulation

$$x = \frac{\$462,000}{36} = \$12,833.33$$

For the third stipulation

$$x = \frac{\$462,000}{30} = \$15,400$$

Then the share of each son is obtained from the expression $3x$. The coefficient 3 denotes that the share of each daughter, which is x, is multiplied by 3. Finally the share of the widow is obtained from the expressions $11x$, $14x$, and $8x$ according to the value of x for the respective stipulations. It should be understood that x has three values that correspond to the conditions of the three stipulations of the will.

PROBLEMS

1. Elmer Brown, a garage owner, never bothered to keep any record of his tire sales but one August 1st he decided to take inventory. His stock included both automobile and motorcycle tires. Although he remembered that he sold a set of tires each day during the last two months and the total number of tires sold was 208, he could not determine the number of each type sold. Can you help Elmer to straighten out his records?

2. A postoffice clerk is instructed thus by a girl presenting a five-dollar bill:

"Give me some one-cent stamps, then give me twice as many two-cent stamps, and for the balance give me five times as many three-cent stamps as the one- and the two-cent stamps together."

"How many stamps would you like to have?" the clerk asked.

"Well, let me see," the girl replied, "you will have to tear some of them from whole sheets."

"Never mind," said the clerk, "here are your stamps."

How many stamps of each denomination did he give her?

3. Luigi Caprini and his wife are counting the receipts of their day's business. "Look here, Rosa," he said, "one-half of our customers ordered minestrone, one-third ordered fried chicken, and three-fourths of these two ordered macaroni."

"Yes," Rosa replied, "and we sold seventy orders of these."

How many orders of each have there been?

Beware the Math-Minded Mother-in-Law!

Young Mrs. Martin called her mother on the telephone to ask help in learning her husband's income:

"This morning he told me that since we were married (and that was three years ago) we spent four-tenths of his yearly income on rent and the upkeep of the house, one-fourth on clothes and food, and one-tenth on other incidentals. He never told me what his income was. But only a few days ago I found his bank book, and he had saved up $1,500. Don't you think that I ought to know what my own husband earns?"

The mother knew some mathematics and promptly told her daughter exactly what her son-in-law earned each year. Can you find out?

Suppose the husband earned x dollars a year. Then $0.4x$ was spent on rent, $0.25x$ on clothes and food, and $0.1x$ was spent on incidentals. The total amount spent each year was

$$(0.4x + 0.25x + 0.1x) = 0.75x$$

The amount the husband saved was $x - 0.75x = 0.25x$. In three years he saved $1,500. Thus in one year he saved $500. We then can write the equation $0.25x = 500$, and from this we obtain that $x = 2,000$. In other words, his yearly income was $2,000.

Note the catch in the wording of this problem: The amount

saved refers to a three-year period, while the statements concerning expenditures refer to one year.

4. Mr. Collins was approached by his club for a contribution and was told that ten members had subscribed $10 each. He wrote out a check for a sum such that his contribution exceeded the average contribution by $20. What was his contribution?

5. Asked for another contribution, Collins pulled out his wallet in which there was a certain number of five-dollar bills. "I have here an odd number of five-dollar bills," he said. "I will put aside one bill and give you one-half of the remaining bills. If ten of you will contribute $10 each, then my contribution will exceed the average of all contributions by $50." How much had Collins in his wallet?

6. Mr. Collins at another time was accosted by four friends for contributions. To the first he gave one-half the money he had in his wallet and a dollar more. To the next he gave half of what was left in the wallet and a dollar more. To the third he gave half of what was left in the wallet and a dollar more. To the fourth he gave all that was left in the wallet. When the money was distributed, the first and the third received together $10 more than the second and the fourth friends. How much did he distribute and how much did each of his friends receive?

One for the Relief Administrator

A relief administrator was allowed to distribute shoes and was asked to submit a requisition stating the number of shoes (not pairs) he would require. He checked the relief rolls and discovered that one-twentieth of those listed had had one foot amputated. One-half of the remaining needy refused the free shoes. How many shoes did the relief administrator order?

This is a problem in which no numbers are given, but it can be solved if we remember that we may use letters as numbers. Let us assume that there were x persons on the relief rolls. Then $\frac{1}{20}x$ of these required each one shoe and for them he ordered $\frac{1}{20}x$ shoes. The remaining group consisted of $\frac{19}{20}x$, and only half of them,

$$\frac{1}{2}\left(\frac{19}{20}x\right)$$

wanted shoes. Every one of these received a pair of shoes. Then this group received

$$2 \cdot \frac{1}{2} \left(\frac{19}{20} x \right) = \frac{19}{20} x$$

shoes. Thus the relief administrator ordered

$$\frac{1}{20} x + \frac{19}{20} x = \frac{20}{20} x = x \text{ shoes}$$

That is, he ordered as many shoes as there were relief recipients.

PROBLEMS

7. Mr. Collins never refused to help a worthy cause. When his childhood friend, Henry Johnson, was running for sheriff of Elmville, Collins undertook to get out the vote for him. The voting population was 1,349. He offered a prize of $15 to every woman and $7.50 to every man to come to the polls and vote. Every man accepted this offer, but half of the women did not vote. How much was spent by Collins?

8. The regular Club of Elmville decided to hold a contest. Mr. Collins offered four prizes:

    1st prize—one-third of the total prize money plus $5.00.
    2nd prize—one-fourth of the remaining money plus $5.00.
    3rd prize—one-fifth of what remains after the first two prizes
                are awarded plus $5.00.
    4th prize—the remainder of the money.

Collins declared that this would allot to the first three prizes twice as much as to the fourth prize. How much was offered in prizes and how was the money distributed?

9. The infirmary in Elmville needed a certain sum to build an additional garage for an automobile that Collins had donated. He offered to bear the expenses of construction, too, and offered a certain sum. When plans were prepared, it was found that Collins' contribution was not sufficient to cover the cost. If the garage would have cost one-eighth of the cost of the automobile, then $50 would have been needed to complete the garage. If the cost of the garage were three-fourths of the cost of the automobile, then the infirmary would have had $575 left (if Collins would have provided these three-fourths of the cost of the automobile). How much has Collins paid for the automobile, and what was the cost of the garage?

A Rolling Pin Is How Heavy?

Mr. Jones and his wife Mary were testifying in court. The judge asked her age, but she refused to tell. Jones then was called and the judge cautioned him that he must tell the whole truth, but when he was asked how old his wife was he hesitated. His wife looked warningly at him, but so did the judge. Then Jones said:

"Your Honor, we have a dog, Patsy. Four years ago Mary was eleven times as old as Patsy; now she is six times as old."

Mary beamed until the judge told her she was forty-eight years old. How did the judge arrive at her age?

Let us apply algebra to this problem: supposing the present age of Patsy is x, we have the following table:

	Patsy's Age	Mary's Age
At present........	x	$6x$
Four years ago....	$x - 4$	$6x - 4$

and four years ago Mary was eleven times as old as Patsy. Thus if the age of Patsy were multiplied by 11 we would get Mary's age. Then

$$11(x - 4) = 6x - 4$$

or

$$11x - 44 = 6x - 4$$

Subtract $6x$ from both sides of the equation and add 44 to both sides, then

$$11x - 6x - 44 + 44 = 6x - 6x + 44 - 4$$

or

$$5x = 40, \quad \text{and} \quad x = 8$$

Now, since Patsy is now eight years old and Mary is six times as old as Patsy, Mary is forty-eight years old.

In the transformation of the equation we have subtracted a certain quantity from both sides and added a certain quantity to both. The quantities added and subtracted were such that in the ultimate result the unknown quantity appeared on one side of the equation and the known quantity on the opposite side of the same equation. This procedure may be simplified. The reader will observe that actually the respective quantities were transposed to the opposite sides of the equation with their signs changed. Thus, in our equation

$$11x - 44 = 6x - 4$$

we finally obtained

$$11x - 6x = 44 - 4$$

We shall use this method of solution from now on.

PROBLEMS

10. Professor Bigelow was asked by a student, "How old are you?"
"Well," he replied, "how old are you?"
When the student gave his age, Bigelow said, "When I was as old
as you are now, I was nine times as old as you were. However, in
seven years our combined ages will be 92."
How old were the professor and his student?

11. "Daddy, how old are you?" asked Professor Bigelow's son.
"When I was as old as you are now, I had to wait," he replied,
"thirteen years until you were born. But when you are twice as old
as you are now, I will be twice as old as you will be."
How old were Bigelow and his son?

12. Professor Bigelow was six years older than his wife. One day
he told her, "You know, we are married twenty-two years. Since
we were married our combined ages have exactly doubled."
How old were Bigelow and his wife when they were married?

Million-Dollar Swap

Mr. Armstrong and Mr. Holding fell into a discussion of taxes.
Armstrong complained of his federal income tax as a very heavy
burden. Holding replied: "Why do you complain so much? If
you give me a million dollars of your income my tax will be
twice as large as yours."

"Well," Armstrong replied, "give me a million dollars of your
income, and our taxes will be the same."

How much have these two earned?

Let the income of Armstrong be x dollars and the income of
Holding be y dollars, then we can construct the following table
of relationships:

Armstrong takes away a million dollars....................	$x - 1,000,000$
Armstrong gives it to Holding...	$y + 1,000,000$
Holding has twice as much as Armstrong..................	$y + 1,000,000 = 2(x - 1,000,000)$
or	$2x - y = 3,000,000$
Holding takes away a million dollars....................	$y - 1,000,000$
Holding gives it to Armstrong...	$x + 1,000,000$
Then the two have equal amounts.	$x + 1,000,000 = y - 1,000,000$
or	$y - x = 2,000,000$

Thus we have two equations:

$$2x - y = 3,000,000$$
$$y - x = 2,000,000$$

Add the two equations; that is, add the members on the left of the equality signs separately, and add the members on the right of the equality signs, and then equate the sums

We have then $x = 5,000,000$, and from the equation $y - x = 2,000,000$ we have

$$y = x + 2,000,000, \quad \text{or} \quad y = 5,000,000 + 2,000,000 = 7,000,000$$

Armstrong's income thus was five million dollars and Holding's seven million.

In this problem we had two unknown quantities, and these were denoted by x and y respectively. To solve it, obtaining the unknown values, the two equations had to be considered simultaneously, and this is why such equations are known as "simultaneous." The process consisted of two fundamental steps. First, one of the unknown quantities was eliminated from the equations by means of the addition, subtraction, and at times multiplication or division of the two equations. Secondly, after one of the unknowns is eliminated, the value of the second is learned from the equation obtained in the process of eliminating one of the unknowns.

PROBLEMS

13. Professor Bigelow was asked how old his two sons were. He replied, "Their combined ages are four times the difference of their ages. Three years ago one was twice as old as the other." How old were the sons?

14. "How many birds and how many animals are there in your zoo?" a keeper was asked.

"We have fifteen more animals than birds; if we had as many birds as there are animals and as many animals as there are birds, then there would be only two-thirds as many legs as there are now," he replied.

How many birds and how many animals were there in the zoo?

15. In a club debate at Elmville neither faction would give in, and a number of members left. Collins remarked to his friend Johnson, "I am disgusted; I have a strong desire to leave also."

To this replied Johnson, "Well, if you and I go, two-fifths of the members will be absent."

"This is correct," replied Collins, "but if Jones, Smith, and Brown would have stayed, we would have had two-thirds of the membership present this would have given us a quorum."

How many members were there at the opening of the meeting, and how many have left?

Help Wanted: One Stag Line, Slightly Used

Lucy Phillips attended her first dance after she left school. The dance was given by Joan Metcalf. It was a huge success, and Lucy decided to give a dance of her own, with a larger attendance. While at Joan's dance she had counted the number of guests, sixty-three, but had forgotten to count the number of young men present. But Lucy made up her mind. At her dance, the number of those invited and those who attended must exceed the number of Joan's guests.

Lucy telephoned Jane in hope that Jane might supply the information needed, but Jane, too, had failed to count the number of men. She told Lucy, however, that she had danced with nine different ones. Lucy then called up all the girls who attended the dance, but none could help her. However, she did obtain this information:

> Gracie danced with 8 men
> Jane   danced with 9 men
> Pat   danced with 10 men

and so on, every other girl dancing with one more man until finally Joan, the most popular, danced with all the men. Joan, though, was no help when it came to the exact number of stags in her party line. Fortunately, Lucy was good at algebra and soon had the answer.

Lucy reasoned this way: suppose that the number of the girls was x. Then

> The 1st girl, Gracie, danced with $7 + 1$ men
> The 2nd girl, Jane,   danced with $7 + 2$ men
> The 3rd girl, Pat,   danced with $7 + 3$ men
> and so on
> The xth girl, Joan, danced with $7 + x$ men

Thus we have the equation

$$x + 7 + x = 63 \quad \text{and} \quad 2x = 63 - 7 \quad \text{or} \quad 2x = 56, \text{ that is } x = 28$$

Since among the sixty-three guests there were twenty-eight girls, there were $63 - 28 = 35$ men.

PROBLEMS

16. To raise funds for the orphanage in Elmville the Regular Club organized a raffle. The Ladies' Auxiliary of the Club offered to sell tickets for this raffle. Mr. Stone, an old bachelor, opposed the idea, but women were allowed to sell tickets. As it happened, every woman sold twice as many tickets as every man. The price of a ticket was 50 cents. When all the tickets were sold, Stone remarked to Collins that the men had done a wonderful job. "True," said Collins, "but if every man sold twice as many tickets as every woman sold, we would have had $150 more, and we would have sold twice as many tickets."

"How many tickets were sold by the women?" asked Stone.

"Figure it out for yourself," replied Collins. Can you?

17. The Regular Club was negotiating about a long-term lease on a building that Collins owned in which the clubhouse was located. The members wanted a forty-two-year lease, and this was satisfactory to Collins, but he wanted $500 a year rent and members thought this too high. "Gentlemen," he said, "I know that in the years to come our club will have many more members. Probably my price is too high for the club at present. Let us fix the rent at $400 a year for a certain number of years; to be exact, for so many years that one-third of them will be equal to one-fourth of the number of years that the lease will be in force afterward. After this number of years will elapse the rent will be $600 a year."

The members voted to accept. Who was the loser and what was the difference in the total rent under the two types of terms?

18. The picnic committee of the Regular Club could not agree on a price for the tickets. Finally, Collins suggested that the price for men be set at 50 cents and for women at 25 cents. However, if there should be more than a certain number of men this price should be 40 cents, and those who bought at 50 cents should get a refund of 10 cents. Some of the committee objected because free sandwiches were to be distributed, two sandwiches for every man and one for every woman. "You need not worry," replied Collins, "if you have a certain number of men and a certain number of women you will collect $95, and you will have enough money for the sandwiches. If you have twice as many men you will collect $45 more."

On how many tickets for men did he base his estimate and on how many for women has he based his estimate?

Men at Work: Fractions Ahead—Proceed at Own Risk

A group of public workers that consisted of Tom, the foreman, and Jack and Dick were sent to repair a road. An inspector figured that

> Jack and Dick could complete the work in 12 days
> Dick and Tom could complete the work in 15 days
> Jack and Tom could complete the work in 18 days

In how many days would the work be completed if the foreman were put to work also? In how many days could Tom, Jack, and Dick complete the work if each worked alone?

Let the number of days that Jack can complete the work alone be x; the number of days that Dick can complete the work alone be y; and the number of days that Tom can complete the work alone be z. Then in one day Jack can complete $\dfrac{1}{x}$th part of the job; Dick, $\dfrac{1}{y}$th part of the job; and Tom, $\dfrac{1}{z}$th part of the job. And thus we can construct the following equations:

If Jack and Dick work together they will complete in one day

$$\left(\frac{1}{x}+\frac{1}{y}\right)\text{th part of the entire job,}$$

which is equal to $\frac{1}{12}$ part, since they complete the work in 12 days, and

$$\frac{1}{x}+\frac{1}{y}=\frac{1}{12}$$

Similarly we have

$$\frac{1}{y}+\frac{1}{z}=\frac{1}{15}$$

and

$$\frac{1}{x}+\frac{1}{z}=\frac{1}{18}$$

If we add all the terms on the left sides of the equations separately and then add the fractions on the right sides separately, and finally equate the two sums, we have

$$\frac{1}{x}+\frac{1}{y}+\frac{1}{y}+\frac{1}{z}+\frac{1}{x}+\frac{1}{z}=\frac{1}{12}+\frac{1}{15}+\frac{1}{18}$$

or

$$2\left(\frac{1}{x}+\frac{1}{y}+\frac{1}{z}\right)=\frac{1}{3}\left(\frac{1}{4}+\frac{1}{5}+\frac{1}{6}\right)$$

or, dividing the both sides of the equation by 2, we have

$$\frac{1}{x}+\frac{1}{y}+\frac{1}{z}=\frac{1}{6}\left(\frac{1}{4}+\frac{1}{5}+\frac{1}{6}\right)$$

Let us compute $\frac{1}{6}(\frac{1}{4}+\frac{1}{5}+\frac{1}{6})$. This is equal to

$$\frac{1}{6}\left(\frac{1}{4}+\frac{1}{5}+\frac{1}{6}\right)=\frac{1}{6}\left(\frac{15+12+10}{60}\right)=\frac{37}{360}$$

Thus when two workers and their foreman work together they will complete in one day $\dfrac{37}{360}$ part of the job, and the entire work will be completed in $\dfrac{360}{37}$ days, or about $9\frac{3}{4}$ days.

Take the two equations:

$$\frac{1}{x} + \frac{1}{y} + \frac{1}{z} = \frac{37}{360} \quad \text{and} \quad \frac{1}{x} + \frac{1}{y} = \frac{1}{12}$$

and subtract the second from the first. We have

$$\frac{1}{z} = \frac{37}{360} - \frac{1}{12} = \frac{37 - 30}{360} = \frac{7}{360}$$

Thus Tom will complete in one day $\dfrac{7}{360}$ part of the entire job, and if he were working alone it would take him $\dfrac{360}{7}$ days or about $51\frac{1}{2}$ days to complete the job.

To obtain the answers concerning Jack and Dick we take the two pairs of equations

$$\frac{1}{x} + \frac{1}{y} + \frac{1}{z} = \frac{37}{360}$$

$$\frac{1}{y} + \frac{1}{z} = \frac{1}{15}$$

and

$$\frac{1}{x} + \frac{1}{y} + \frac{1}{z} = \frac{37}{360}$$

$$\frac{1}{x} + \frac{1}{z} = \frac{1}{18}$$

and follow the same procedure. We then obtain

$$\frac{1}{x} = \frac{37}{360} - \frac{1}{15} = \frac{37 - 24}{360} = \frac{13}{360}$$

and

$$\frac{1}{y} = \frac{37}{360} - \frac{1}{18} = \frac{37 - 20}{360} = \frac{17}{360}$$

Thus after the last fractions are inverted, we obtain the required results. This is left to the reader. Summing up, we find that Tom, the foreman, can complete the job alone in about $51\frac{1}{2}$ days; Jack, in about $27\frac{3}{4}$ days; and Dick, in about $21\frac{1}{8}$ days.

PROBLEMS

19. An office manager as a test of efficiency handed portions of a manuscript to two typists. The two began to type at the same time and completed the work simultaneously 1 hour and 12 minutes later. Then each typist was told to copy the entire manuscript alone. It took one one and a half times as long. How many pages were there in the manuscript if the slower typist copied ten pages in an hour?

20. The Regular Club's house needed repainting. John undertook to do the job in five days; Jim said that he could complete the work in six days, and Jack insisted that he would need seven days. Each painter quoted the same price. Mr. Collins was consulted and promised that he would complete the work in a trifle less than two days.

"You don't mean that you will do the painting yourself?" the building committee queried.

"Certainly not," replied Collins. "You just leave it to me. According to my scheme the job will cost $4 more, but I will pay the difference myself."

What was the scheme, to whom was the money paid, and how much? The job was estimated to cost $210.

21. Pierre Renan always grumbled at the air-raid alarm. He was not afraid of bombs but disliked dropping his work at night when the lights went out. He had some candles saved but was frugal. One raid night especially, he wanted to continue his work and reached for two candles. Here his troubles began. He lit two of equal length, but one was thinner than the other. He remembered that the storekeeper told him that the thick candle would last six hours and the thin one four hours. After some time the thick candle burned down to a length twice as long as that of the thin one. He put out the candles and went to sleep. Suddenly it dawned upon him that he failed to notice the time when he lit the candles or the time when he put them out. He had to find out how long he had worked by candlelight. Could you help him?

The Erring Speed Cop

Traffic Patrolman O'Hara, always insistent on strict observance of the law, sped on his motorcycle after an autoist.

"Pull over to the curb," he ordered a man in the car. "I have been trailing you for two miles. The speed limit on this highway is 45 miles an hour, and you were going 46 miles an hour on the average. You'd better have a good story for the judge."

In court O'Hara pronounced his usual charge, specifying on a slip he handed to the judge:

1 mile at 41 miles an hour........ 41 miles
1 mile at 51 miles an hour........ 51 miles
Total...................... 92 miles

$$\frac{92}{2} = 46$$

But the motorist wrote something on the slip and the judge promptly dismissed the case, explaining to O'Hara:

"You charged this man for driving at an average speed that exceeded the statutory limit, and your charge was not correct. Figure it out for yourself. You claim that the motorist travelled the first mile at the rate of 41 miles an hour and the second mile at the rate of 51 miles. Now, when he was making 51 miles an hour it took him less time to cover the distance of one mile than at the rate of 41 miles. If you add the time it took to cover the first mile and the time it took to cover the second mile, and then divide the total distance of two miles by this total time you should get the average speed. Or you may divide the distance of two miles by the average speed and you will get the time it took to cover these two miles. This is exactly what the motorist has done, and although the result he has obtained differs from the statutory limit by a very small fraction of a mile, I felt that I ought to give him the benefit of the doubt. Now here is what the motorist wrote . . ."

He showed O'Hara this calculation:

Suppose that the average speed is x miles per hour. Then

$$\frac{2}{x} = \frac{1}{41} + \frac{1}{51}$$

$$\frac{1}{x} = \frac{41 + 51}{2 \cdot 41 \cdot 51} = \frac{92}{4{,}182}$$

$$x = \frac{4{,}182}{92} = 45.4$$

"Now," the judge continued, "you charge him with driving at an average speed of 46 miles an hour. Had your charge been that he drove at the rate of 51 miles I would have imposed a fine, but you failed to charge correctly."

22. The distance from Elmville to Oak Bluffs is 180 miles. Johnson, the sheriff of Elmville, was called to Oak Bluffs in a hurry and made the trip in two and one-half hours. On the way back he made the trip in five hours. Later he boasted that he averaged such speed that he could make the trip in 3 hours and 20 minutes.

Said Collins: "If what you say is correct, then your round trip would last 6 hours and 40 minutes, but you just told us that it took seven and a half hours to do this."

What was wrong with Johnson's arithmetic?

23. Professor Bigelow offered his son Eddie the following problem: "We need a new car. Just the other day I took mother to Canarsie University for the President's reception. We traveled an hour with no mishap. Then we had a flat. It took me ten minutes to change the tire, and we proceeded at four-fifths of the original speed. But luck was against us, and we arrived a half hour late. Now, if we had traveled ten more miles after the first hour, and then had had a flat tire, and spent ten minutes on changing it, and proceeded at four-fifths the original rate, we would have been only twenty minutes late. All this proves that our car should be replaced. By the way, can you tell me how far is Canarsie University from here and at what speed we started out from here?"

Can you help Eddie?

24. Brown once went from Elmville to Bolton in his automobile. He agreed to meet Stone in Penville, which was 32 miles from Bolton. He was to take Stone to Bolton and bring him back to his farm, which was just as distant from Elmville as Penville was from Bolton. Stone agreed to share the gasoline expenses with Brown. How much of the gasoline cost of the total should be Stone's share? The distance from Elmville to Bolton is 96 miles.

An Accountant's Headache

Hastings and Harrison were partners in a wholesale grocery business for many years. Hastings' share in the business was three-fifths as large as that of Harrison's. As both were aging, they agreed to take in as a partner Harrison's son-in-law, Thompson. Thompson agreed to pay them $10,000 with the condition that after he became a partner everybody should own exactly one-third of the business. When distribution of the $10,000 was to take place, Hastings insisted that he be paid $3,750. He argued that his share was three-fifths as large as Harrison's share, and whatever capital was being distributed as well as profits, should be equitably divided; this was the practice for years, and he saw no reason why it should not be continued. Meek Harrison kept his peace, but Thompson, contrary to the wish of his father-in-law, insisted that Hastings was wrong; either the money would be distributed according to his plan or he would call off the deal. Thompson had studied algebra and put down his plan on paper and submitted it. This convinced Hastings that Thompson was right. What was Thompson's plan?

Thompson suggested they suppose that one share in the business, prior to the reorganization, was worth x dollars. Then Harrison's share was $5x$, and Hastings' was $3x$, and the total business was worth

$$5x + 3x = 8x$$

Now, Thompson is paying for one-third of the business $10,000, then the business must be worth $30,000. Then

$$8x = 30,000, \text{ and } x = 3,750$$

Then Harrison's share is worth

$$5 \cdot 3,750, \text{ or } \$18,750$$
and

Hastings' $3 \cdot 3,750,$ or $\$11,250$

Every original partner, Thompson argued, must be paid the difference between what his share was worth and the value of a third in the business, that is, $10,000. Then Harrison must receive $8,750, and Hastings $1,250.

Notice that in the solution of this problem we used a new technique. It was stated that Hastings' share was three-fifths of Harrison's. In other words, for every "5-worth" of property in the business owned by Harrison, Hastings owned "3-worth." We might then reason that if there were x such portions the value of Hastings' share would be worth $3x$ dollars, and Harrison would own $5x$ dollars' worth.

25. The Regular Club of Elmville for its annual outing appointed Brown to buy sandwiches, these to be sold at cost. Brown bought 300 sandwiches, but before the picnic 60 of these were eaten at a meeting of the organization committee. Now the club had only 240 sandwiches, and Brown insisted that the price remain unchanged.

"But who will pay for the 60 sandwiches?" he was asked.

"I don't know, but we must not sell them at any other price; we cannot change the rules," replied Brown. Then Collins intervened and suggested a scheme by which every member was to buy two sandwiches, the price of the second sandwich being half the price of the first. Thus one sandwich was sold below cost. Still the club had not incurred any loss on the sale. What was the scheme that Collins suggested? Incidentally, it was originally proposed that the price of a sandwich be raised 3 cents, and that would have covered the loss.

26. Professor Bigelow said to his wife, "Eddie has a keen sense for selling. Yesterday he sold his baseball bat and baseball for $1.55. He made a 25 per cent profit on the bat and took a 25 per cent loss on the ball. I just cannot figure it out how he does things like these."

"But how could this be?" she asked. "Quite simple," replied Bigelow, "the ball cost two-fifths as much as the bat."

How did the professor arrive at his answer?

27. Stone and Parker owned the bus company in Elmville. To enlarge their business they needed additional capital. Parker's original investment was $600, and Stone's was $400. They agreed to take in Brown as a partner. Brown agreed to pay into the business $2,500 with the provision that Stone own one-fifth of the business, and that Parker's share would be two-sevenths of the business. These conditions set off a barrage of claims by Stone. He argued that Parker's share was reduced to two-sevenths while his share was reduced to one-fifth; that is, in terms of shares Parker lost less than he. Therefore he claimed more because he lost half his share while Parker lost less than a third of his share. Could you straighten Stone out?

Algebra and Common Sense

The solution of problems such as illustrated in the preceding sections does not require special techniques. Generally, if a problem is approached with complete understanding of all the implications and with knowledge of what the objective is and of the respective relationships of the quantities involved, a solution becomes simple. There is one principal rule of procedure: *Express the given relationships in the form of equations in which the known and unknown quantities are involved.* The equations represent statements of these relationships—or, in other words, the equation is a statement in symbolic form. Thus the rules of written language are applicable to the rules of writing algebraic statements of the relations between known and unknown quantities. There are no other secrets, though common sense may often simplify the procedure. The following two problems will illustrate.

a) Three racing automobiles are tested on a proving ground. It is known that the speed of one car (car *A*) is 10 miles more per hour than the speed of car *B* and 10 miles less per hour than that of car *C*. The three cars cover the entire length of the proving ground. Car *A* arrives 10 minutes after *B*, and *C* arrives 8 minutes and 45 seconds before car *A*. What are the respective speeds of the cars, what is the length of the proving ground, and how long does it take each car to cover this length?

Apparently there are seven quantities to be found. If we start with seven unknown quantities (that is, with seven distinct letters), we shall complicate our procedure immensely. A little reflection will show that actually we have two unknown quantities, namely, a speed of one car (the other two are obtainable from it) and the length of the proving ground. Let us denote the speed of car *A* by *x*, and let the length of the proving ground be *y*. We then can represent the various relations in tabular form as follows:

	Speed	Time Required to Cover the Proving Ground
Car *A*	x	$\dfrac{y}{x}$
Car *B*	$x - 10$	$\dfrac{y}{x - 10}$
Car *C*	$x + 10$	$\dfrac{y}{x + 10}$

Before we proceed with construction of the equations let us translate the given intervals of time (10 minutes, and 8 minutes, 45 seconds) in fractions of an hour, because the respective speeds are also given in terms of hours. We then have 10 minutes = 1/6 of an hour, and 8 minutes and 45 seconds = 7/48 of an hour. Then, we have the equations

$$\frac{y}{x-10} - \frac{y}{x} = \frac{1}{6}$$

and

$$\frac{y}{x} - \frac{y}{x+10} = \frac{7}{48}$$

These may be transformed as follows:

$$6(yx - yx + 10y) = x(x - 10), \quad \text{or} \quad 60y = x(x - 10)$$
$$48(yx + 10y - yx) = 7x(x + 10), \quad \text{or} \quad 480y = 7x(x + 10)$$

Dividing one equation by the other, we have

$$\frac{60y}{480y} = \frac{x(x - 10)}{7x(x + 10)}$$

or

$$\frac{1}{8} = \frac{x - 10}{7(x + 10)}$$

Thus we have $7x + 70 = 8x - 80$, or $x = 150$

Then the respective speeds are:

Car A, 150 miles per hour
Car B, 140 miles per hour
Car C, 160 miles per hour

The length of the proving ground is obtained from the equation $60y = x(x - 10)$ in which the value of x (150) is substituted. We have $60y = 150 \cdot 140$, or $y = 350$. Thus, the length of the proving ground is 350 miles. The time required on the proving ground is then:

Car A: 350/150 = 7/3 hours, or 2 hours and 20 minutes
Car B: 350/140 = 5/2 hours, or 2 hours and 30 minutes
Car C: 350/160 = 35/16 hours, or 2 hours, 11 minutes
and 15 seconds

In solution of the foregoing problem we had two unknowns, x and y, but one, y, was eliminated by division, and after the value of x was determined the value of y was computed from one of the equations that were set up.

This problem, if paraphrased, may become an interesting puzzler. Suppose a proving ground is 350 miles long. On it three cars are tested, each car covering the entire length of the ground and all starting at the same time. Car *A* travels at the rate of 140 miles an hour, *B* at 150 miles an hour, and *C* at 160 miles an hour. At what intervals will these three cars cross the finish line?

The answer that suggests itself, that they will cross the finish line at equal intervals, is not correct. The earlier computations demonstrate this.

PROBLEMS

28. A fleet squadron consisted of several battleships, cruisers, and destroyers. The entire squadron proceeded at the speed of the battleships, 26 miles per hour. At a certain position one of the destroyers that could travel 33 miles per hour was instructed to scout the waters ahead for a distance of 40 miles. How long would it take the destroyer to complete the task and rejoin the squadron?

29. At a certain position the destroyer of Problem 28 was instructed to scout ahead and return in seven hours? When, after its departure, will the destroyer turn back, and how far ahead of the squadron will it have traveled?

30. Sheriff Johnson was asked to come to Bolton at 5 o'clock in the afternoon. He found that if he traveled at 45 miles per hour he would reach Bolton at five-thirty. But if he made 50 miles per hour he would arrive 20 minutes too early. At what speed would you advise him to travel? And what was the distance he had to travel?

b) Here is a problem that is patterned along the lines of a problem of Isaac Newton, which will be found among the exercises:

On a certain pasture the grass grows at an even rate. It is known that 70 cows can graze on it for 24 days before the grass is exhausted, but 30 cows can graze there only 60 days. For how many cows will this pasture last for 96 days?

If we attempt to solve this problem in the usual way, we shall obtain very curious results. If it takes 70 cows to consume the grass in 24 days, then in 96 days only one-fourth of this number of cows will be fed. One-fourth of 70 is 17 1/2. This is the first stumbling block. What is meant by half of a cow? But this is not all. If it takes 60 days to feed 30 cows, then it will take $30 \cdot 60 = 1,800$ cows to eat the grass in one day, and in 96 days $1,800/96 = 18\ 3/4$ cows will be fed. Now this is a contradiction; let us reason further. If for 70 cows the pasture suffices for 24 days, then for one cow the pasture will last $24 \cdot 70 = 1,680$ days, and for 30 cows only 56 days, and not the 60 days as stated in the problem. Finally you may give this problem up in disgust, thinking the numbers do not agree. Something is wrong, but not with the problem. Have we taken into consideration the growth of the grass? While some part of the grass is eaten, it continues to grow.

To solve this problem we must take into account the daily growth of the grass, which should be expressed as a fraction of the grass on the pasture. Let us denote the amount of the grass on the pasture by 1, and the growth in grass as x. Then in 24 days the amount of the grown grass will be $24x$, and in 24 days the supply of the grass eaten by the 70 cows is $1 + 24x$, and in one day the 70 cows will eat

$$\frac{1 + 24x}{24}$$

and one cow will eat

$$\frac{1 + 24x}{24 \cdot 70}$$

Following the same line of reasoning, we find that for the 30 cows there will be $1 + 60x$ of grass, and one cow will eat

$$\frac{1 + 60x}{30 \cdot 60}$$

of grass.

The assumption is that every cow eats the same amount. Then

$$\frac{1 + 24x}{24 \cdot 70} = \frac{1 + 60x}{30 \cdot 60}$$

and

$$30 \cdot 60(1 + 24x) = 24 \cdot 70(1 + 60x)$$

or

$$15(1 + 24x) = 14(1 + 60x)$$

or

$$15 + 360x = 14 + 840x$$

and

$$480x = 1, \quad \text{or} \quad x = \frac{1}{480}$$

Now, since we know the value of x, we can compute the amount of grass (in terms of the entire supply) that one cow will eat in one day. We have

$$\frac{1 + 24x}{24 \cdot 70} = \frac{1 + 24 \cdot \frac{1}{480}}{24 \cdot 70} = \frac{\frac{21}{20}}{24 \cdot 70} = \frac{1}{1,600}$$

Then we construct the equation for 96 days and an unknown number of cows,

$$\frac{1 + 96 \cdot \frac{1}{480}}{y \cdot 96} = \frac{1}{1,600}$$

This becomes

$$\frac{1 + \frac{1}{5}}{96y} = \frac{1}{1,600}$$

or $1,600 + 320 = 96y$, or $96y = 1,920$ and $y = 20$. Thus 20 cows will eat all the grass in 96 days.

PROBLEMS

31. This is the problem proposed by Isaac Newton:
Three pastures are covered with grass of equal density that grows at an even rate. The first pasture has an area of 33 acres, the second an area of 100 acres, and the third 240 acres. If the first pasture can feed twelve oxen for four weeks, and the second pasture can feed twenty-one oxen for nine weeks, how many oxen can be fed on the third pasture for eighteen weeks?

32. Said Farmer Jones, "The feed we bought will last our chickens for fifteen days. If we had twenty-one more chickens, and if we would give each chicken two-thirds of what we are giving daily now, the feed would last twelve days."
How many chickens were there on Jones' farm?

$$\cong 15 \cong$$

Algebra, Boss of Arithmetic

How the Stage Magician Does It

We examined, back in Chapters 9 and 12, some of the methods of rapid calculation, including one generally used by stage magicians; our studies now have advanced us to the point where we may attain a far better understanding of this spectacular, and useful, department of mathematics. It will be recalled that we then performed the multiplication of 94 by 88 as follows:

$$94 \cdot 88 = (82 + 12)88 \; = 82 \cdot 88 + 12 \cdot 88.$$

or

$$82 \cdot 88 = 82(100 - 12) = 8{,}200 - 12 \cdot 82$$
$$12 \cdot 88 = 12(82 + 6) \;\;= 12 \cdot 6 \; + 12 \cdot 82$$

$$\overline{94 \cdot 88 = 8{,}200 + 72 \;\;= 8{,}272}$$

Note that we took the larger number 94 and represented it as a sum of the complement of the smaller number 88 to 100 (that is, $100 - 88 = 12$) and the difference between the larger number and this complement. Thus $94 = 82 + 12$. Then the product $94 \cdot 88$ is written as $(82 + 12)88$, which occurs in the first line above. Then $82 \cdot 88$ is written $82(100 - 12)$, and this product is developed in the second line. Note, too, that in this development we obtain the expression $12 \cdot 82$, which is negative. Finally $12 \cdot 88$ (see the first line) is written as $12(82 + 6)$, a step prompted by the necessity of obtaining the expression $12 \cdot 82$ (this time positive). Thus when the negative $12 \cdot 82$ is added to the positive $12 \cdot 82$, the sum is 0.

209

The product of 94·88 was obtained as

$$8,200 + 72 = 8,272$$

and to get it without going through all these steps we proceeded in this way:

a) We obtained the complements of 94 and 88 to 100:

	Number	Complement
Multiplicand........	94	6
Multiplier..........	88	12

b) We obtained the difference between a factor and the complement of the other factor. Thus

$$94 - 12 = 82, \quad \text{and} \quad 88 - 6 = 82$$

This difference represented the first two digits of the product. Finally the product of the two complements represented the last two digits of the product.

All this may seem unduly complicated, so let us examine the method by means of algebra; instead of any particular numbers we shall use letters. Suppose we have two two-place numbers a and b; we obtain their complements to 100:

	Number	Complement
Multiplicand........	a	$100 - a$
Multiplier..........	b	$100 - b$

and obtain the difference between a factor and the complement of the other factor. Thus

$$a - (100 - b) = a + b - 100.$$

and

$$b - (100 - a) = b + a - 100$$

We note that we need not take two differences; they are equal and, therefore, one will suffice. The product of the complements is

$$(100 - a)(100 - b) = 100 \cdot 100 - 100a - 100b + ab$$

The difference between a factor and the complement of the other factor represents the first two digits of the product and when we have two two-place numbers, represents the number of the 100's in the product. We multiply this difference by 100 and we have

$$100(a + b - 100) = 100a + 100b - 100 \cdot 100$$

To this product we add the product of the complements. We have then

$$100a + 100b - 100 \cdot 100 + 100 \cdot 100 - 100a - 100b + ab = ab$$

This result shows that our procedure and our rule are correct. Let us consider an example:

The product of 87 and 76 is obtained as follows:

	Number	Complement
Multiplicand........	87	13
Multiplier..........	76	24

The difference between a factor and the complement of the other factor is $87 - 24 = 63$.

The product of the two complements is $13 \cdot 24 = 312$. Finally,

$$\text{the product } 87 \cdot 76 = 6,300 + 312 = 6,612$$

The reader may check the result by actual multiplication.

Performing with Three-Place Numbers

Now suppose we wish to obtain the product of 985 and 973. We obtain the complements to 1,000:

	Number	Complement
Multiplicand........	985	15
Multiplier..........	973	27

The difference between a factor and the complement of the other factor is $985 - 27 = 958$. The product of the complements is $15 \cdot 27 = 405$. The product of 985 and 973 is then written as 958,405.

Examining this procedure by means of algebra, suppose the two numbers are a and b. We have then

	Number	Complement
Multiplicand........	a	$1,000 - a$
Multiplier..........	b	$1,000 - b$

The difference between a factor and the complement of the other factor is

$$a - (1,000 - b) = a + b - 1,000$$
and
$$b - (1,000 - a) = b + a - 1,000$$

Here again we observe that there is no need to obtain two differences; they are equal and, therefore, one will suffice.

When the product of two three-place numbers is obtained, the difference between a factor and the complement of the other factor represents the number of the 1,000's in the product of the two numbers. If we multiply this difference by 1,000, we obtain one part of the product, as

$$1,000(a + b - 1,000) = 1,000a + 1,000b - 1,000 \cdot 1,000$$

When to this we add the product of the complements

$$(1,000 - a)(1,000 - b) = 1,000 \cdot 1,000 - 1,000a - 1,000b + ab$$

we obtain the product of the numbers as

$$1,000a + 1,000b - 1,000 \cdot 1,000 +$$
$$1,000 \cdot 1,000 - 1,000a - 1,000b + ab = ab.$$

This proves our rule for the multiplication of two three-place numbers, as an example will show:

The product of 951 and 982 is obtained:

	Number	Complement
Multiplicand........	951	49
Multiplier..........	982	18

The difference between a factor and the complement of the other factor is $951 - 18 = 933$. The product of the two complements is $49 \cdot 18 = 882$, which can be obtained as $49 = 50 - 1$, and $49 \cdot 18 = (50 - 1)18 = 50 \cdot 18 - 18 = 900 - 18 = 882$. Finally the product of 951 and 982 is

$$951 \cdot 982 = 933,882$$

Making It Easier

When we illustrated the method of rapid multiplication of two numbers, we introduced one limitation: When they are two-place numbers, that they be close to 100, and when three-place numbers that they be close to 1,000. We shall now, obtaining another rule, substitute a short-cut for this.

Suppose we have two two-place numbers a and b, both less than 50. We apply the same method used for the product of two-place numbers when they are close to 100 and obtain their complements to 50. Then we have

	Number	Complement
Multiplicand........	a	$50 - a$
Multiplier..........	b	$50 - b$

The difference between a factor and the complement of the other factor is

$$a - (50 - b) = a + b - 50, \quad \text{and} \quad b - (50 - a) = b + a - 50$$

Again we need not obtain both differences; one will suffice.

The difference between one factor and the complement of the other factor gives the number of 50's in the product of the two numbers. Thus if we multiply this difference by 50, as

$$50(a + b - 50) = 50a + 50b - 50 \cdot 50$$

and we add to this the product of the two complements

$$(50 - a)(50 - b) = 50 \cdot 50 - 50a - 50b + ab$$

we have

$$50a + 50b - 50 \cdot 50 + 50 \cdot 50 - 50a - 50b + ab = ab$$

This result points to the rule for multiplication of two numbers that are close to 50. We obtain their respective complements to 50, then obtain the difference between one factor and the complement of the other factor. This difference must be multiplied by 50 and, since $50 = 100/2$, we multiply by 100 and divide by 2. This product, when the product of the complements is added to it, gives the required result, the product of the two numbers. For example, the product of 48 and 38 is obtained as follows:

	Number	Complement
Multiplicand........	48	2
Multiplier..........	38	12

The difference between one factor and the complement of the other is $48 - 12 = 36$. The product of 36 and 50 is $36 \cdot 50 =$

1,800, and the product of the complement is $2 \cdot 12 = 24$. Finally the product of 48 and 38 is

$$48 \cdot 38 = 1,800 + 24 = 1,824$$

Another short-cut can be introduced here. Instead of multiplying the difference between one factor and the complement of the other by 50, we may divide this difference by 2 and consider the quotient as the number of the 100's in the product. Then on its left we write the product of the complements of the two factors. Thus $36/2 = 18$, and the product is 1,824.

If the difference between one factor and the complement of the other factor is odd as, for example, 41, we proceed in the same manner. We divide 41 by 2 and obtain 20.5. Then we write to the left of 20 the sum of the product of the complements and 50. Let us obtain the product of 47 and 44. We have

	Number	Complement
Multiplicand........	47	3
Multiplier..........	44	6

The difference between a factor and the complement of the other factor is $47 - 6 = 41$. The product of the complements is $3 \cdot 6 = 18$. We write $41/2 = 20.5$, $50 + 18 = 68$, and the product of 47 and 44 is $47 \cdot 44 = 2,068$.

If one number is less than 50 and the other greater than 50, the procedure is the same, but in this case the reader must note the signs of the complements of the two numbers. One complement (of the number that is greater than 50) will be negative. Let us multiply 62 and 48:

	Number	Complement
Multiplicand........	62	−12
Multiplier..........	48	2

The difference between a factor and the complement of the other is $62 - 2 = 60$ (or $48 - [-12] = 48 + 12 = 60$). The product of the two complements is $-12 \cdot 2 = -24$. This time the product of the complements is negative and, therefore, it will have to be subtracted from the product of 50 and the difference between a factor and the complement of the other factor. The result of our multiplication is then

$$62 \cdot 48 = 60 \cdot 50 - 24 = 3,000 - 24 = 2,976$$

If we have two three-place numbers, both of which are close to 500, their product may be obtained as in the case of two three-place numbers close to 1,000. Let us examine this procedure by means of algebra; suppose the two three-place numbers are a and b. Then

	Number	Complement
Multiplicand........	a	$500 - a$
Multiplier..........	b	$500 - b$

The difference between a factor and the complement of the other factor is

$$a - (500 - b) = a + b - 500$$

and

$$b - (500 - a) = b + a - 500$$

Here again we observe that these differences are equal, and one will suffice.

The difference between a factor and the complement of the other factor gives us the number of the 500's in the product of the two three-place numbers. Thus if we multiply this difference by 500, as

$$500 (a + b - 500) = 500a + 500b - 500 \cdot 500$$

and we add to this the product of the two complements

$$(500 - a)(500 - b) = 500 \cdot 500 - 500a - 500b + ab$$

we obtain the product of the two three-place numbers. We have then

$$500a + 500b - 500 \cdot 500 + 500 \cdot 500 - 500a - 500b + ab = ab$$

This result indicates the correctness of our methods, for example:
For the product of 463 and 497:

	Number	Complement
Multiplicand........	463	37
Multiplier..........	497	3

The difference between a factor and the complement of the other factor is $497 - 37 = 460$, and the product of the complements is $37 \cdot 3 = 111$. The product of 460 and 500 may be obtained by multiplying 460 by 1,000 and dividing it by 2 (because $1,000/2 = 500$). Then the product of 463 and 497 is

$$463 \cdot 497 = 460 \cdot 500 + 111 = 230,000 + 111 = 230,111$$

We may also proceed in this way. We divide 460 by 2, and to the left of it write the product of the two complements of the two factors. This may be done so because the quotient of 460 and 2 gives us the number of the 1,000's in the product of the two three-place numbers. Then $460/2 = 230$, and the product is 230,111.

Should the difference between one factor and the complement of the other be odd, the procedure remains unchanged. We may multiply the difference between a factor and the complement of the other by 1,000 and divide the result by 2, or we may divide this difference by 2. But if the difference between a factor and the complement of the other is divided by 2 we obtain a decimal, 0.5. This decimal is detached and 500 is added to the product of the two complements. Then the sum obtained is written to the left of the whole part of the previously obtained quotient. For example, for the product of 483 and 458:

	Number	Complement
Multiplicand........	483	17
Multiplier..........	458	42

The difference between one factor and the complement of the other is $458 - 17 = 441$. The product of the complements is $17 \cdot 42 = 714$. Also $441/2 = 220.5$. We have then

$$714 + 500 = 1,214$$

and the product is

$$221,214$$

Short-Order

By means of simple algebraic properties we may obtain, too, squares of large numbers. Suppose, for instance, we have a number that is close to 1,000, say 986. We compute 986^2 as

$$986^2 = 986 \cdot 986 = (986 + 14)(986 - 14) +$$
$$14^2 = 1.000 \cdot 972 + 196 = 972,196$$

Let us examine this by means of letters. Suppose our number is a; we obtain a number b such that $1{,}000 - a = b$. We write then

$$(a + b)(a - b) + b^2 = a^2 + ab - ab - b^2 + b^2 = a^2,$$

or

$$a^2 = (a + b)(a - b) + b^2$$

Thus $a = 986$, and $b = 1{,}000 - 986 = 14$.

The same method may be applied if the number is close to 500. In this case $b = 500 - a$.

For example, 483^2 is calculated as

$$483^2 = 483 \cdot 483 = (483 + 17)(483 - 17) + 17^2 = 500 \cdot 466 + 17^2$$

To obtain the product $500 \cdot 466$, we multiply 466 by $1{,}000$ and divide the result by 2, or $466{,}000/2 = 233{,}000$. Then

$$483^2 = 233{,}000 + 289 = 233{,}289$$

A simple method for squaring numbers that end in 5 is developed by means of algebra. Let the number of 10's in this number be a, and the number of units be b, then this number may be represented as $10a + b$. For example

$$35 = 10 \cdot 3 + 5, \qquad 175 = 10 \cdot 17 + 5$$

We recall that if we have two numbers c and d, the square of their sum is

$$(c + d)^2 = c^2 + 2cd + d^2$$

Now we may write that

$$(10a + b)^2 = (10a)^2 + 2 \cdot 10ab + b^2$$

or

$$(10a + b)^2 = 100a^2 + 20ab + b^2$$

But when the number ends in 5, $b = 5$. We then have that

$$(10a + 5)^2 = 100a^2 + 20a \cdot 5 + 5^2$$

or

$$(10a + 5)^2 = 100a^2 + 100a + 25$$

The expression $100a^2 + 100a$ may be rewritten as

$$100a^2 + 100a = 100 \cdot a(a + 1)$$

We then have

$$(10a + 5)^2 = 100 \cdot a(a + 1) + 25$$

a result giving us a hint concerning the squaring of numbers that end in 5: every such number has a square that ends in 25. The digits to the left of the 25 are the result of the multiplication of the number of the 10's by a number that is one greater. Thus in 35^2 the number of the 10's is 3. One greater than 3 is $(3 + 1) = 4$. Then $3 \cdot 4 = 12$. Write 25 to the right of the 12, and we have

$$35^2 = 1,225$$

In a similar manner 105^2 is calculated as

$$10 \cdot 11 = 110$$

and $105^2 = 11,025$, or 145^2 is calculated as $14 \cdot 15 = 210$, and $145^2 = 21,025$.

Rapid Extraction of Roots

Square roots of numbers are obtained either from tables (such a table is given in the Appendix of this book) or there are special methods for their extraction (calculation).

The usual method of extraction as found in algebra textbooks is lengthy and requires much numerical work. Now we may learn a method which is not cumbersome, yet yields satisfactory results.

This method utilizes one important idea employed in mathematics: If we have a fraction (or a number very small in comparison with some other number), the square of the fraction is so small that it may be discarded in computation. For example, suppose we have a fraction 0.01 which is a part of a number, say 4.21. This number may be written as $4.2 + 0.01$. Now if we square this number, we have

$$4.21^2 = (4.2 + 0.01)^2 = 4.2^2 + 2 \cdot 4.2 \cdot 0.01 + 0.01^2$$
or
$$4.21^2 = 17.64 + 0.084 + 0.0001$$

The square of 0.01, which is 0.0001, may be disregarded and discarded; if 4.21 is correct to three significant digits, its square will also be correct to three significant digits and 0.0001 is of no value to us.

With this in mind we may proceed with the extraction of square roots; suppose we wish to calculate $\sqrt{14}$. To check on our method we obtain its value as given in tables of square roots and have that $\sqrt{14} = 3.742$. We know that $\sqrt{14}$ is greater than 3 ($3^2 = 9$), and is less than 4 ($4^2 = 16$). Let

$$\sqrt{14} = 3 + x$$

where x is some fraction. Square both sides of the equation. We then have

$$14 = 3^2 + 2 \cdot 3x + x^2$$

or

$$14 = 9 + 6x + x^2$$

Now since x is a fraction, x^2 is also a fraction, but much smaller than x. We therefore discard x^2 and have

$$14 = 9 + 6x$$

Solving this equation for x we have that

$$14 - 9 = 6x, \quad \text{or} \quad 6x = 5$$

and

$$x = \tfrac{5}{6}$$

From this we have that

$$\sqrt{14} = 3\tfrac{5}{6}$$

which is only an approximate value. In decimals then

$$\sqrt{14} = 3.83$$

Since we have one approximation to the value of $\sqrt{14}$, we may use this as a basis and apply the same method once more. We may say then that $\sqrt{14} = 3\tfrac{5}{6} + y$ (y may be either positive or negative). Again squaring both sides of the equation we have

$$14 = (\tfrac{23}{6})^2 + 2(\tfrac{23}{6})y + y^2$$

Since y is a fraction we discard its square and have the equation

$$14 = \tfrac{529}{36} + \tfrac{23}{3}y$$

and from this, by solving for y, we have that

$$y = \frac{3}{23}\left(\frac{504 - 529}{36}\right)$$

or

$$y = -\tfrac{25}{276}, \quad \text{or} \quad y = -\tfrac{25}{275} = -\tfrac{1}{11}$$

Then

$$\sqrt{14} = 3\tfrac{5}{6} - \tfrac{1}{11} = 3.83 - 0.09 = 3.74$$

This is a second approximation, and we may proceed with another calculation to obtain a third approximation. We write $\sqrt{14} = 3.74 + z$ where z may be either positive or negative. Squaring both sides of the equation we have

$$14 = 3.74^2 + 7.58z + z^2$$

We again discard z and we have

$$14 = 13.9876 + 7.58z \quad \text{and} \quad 7.58z = 0.0124$$

From this we obtain that $z = 0.0016$ or, rounding, $z = 0.002$. Then

$$\sqrt{14} = 3.742$$

and this checks with the value of the square root as obtained from a table.

Less Work, Same Result

Often we must perform computations in which small fractions are involved, and these may require tedious work. Moreover, to be certain that our results are correct, we must perform the same work twice, in the process called "checking the computations."

If, however, we take into consideration the agreement that when small fractions are involved we may discard their squares and larger powers, we may reduce the load of work and at the same time perform computations that are considerably more simple and more easily checked.

Let us consider, for example, this customary calculation of the value of a fraction:

$$\frac{3}{1 + \dfrac{1}{10000000}} = \frac{3}{\dfrac{10000000 + 1}{10000000}} = \frac{3}{\dfrac{10000001}{10000000}} = \frac{30000000}{10000001}.$$

Now, after the fraction is simplified in form, comes the job of
long division:

```
30000000       | 10000001
20000002       | 2.9999997
 99999980
 90000009
  99999710
  90000009
   99997010
   90000009
    99970010
    90000009
     99700010
     90000009
      97000010
      90000009
       70000010
       70000007
              3
```

By this time the reader has no doubt ceased to wonder why it is
called "long" division. However, a little algebra and as much
reflection will enable anyone to dispense with so much work if
we remember what was said concerning fractions that are very
small. Let us examine the expression

$$\frac{1}{1 + a}$$

when a is a small fraction. Also let us consider the expression

$$(1 + a)(1 - a) = 1 - a^2$$

Now if a is a very small fraction, a^2 is still smaller. Then, as we
now know, a^2 may be discarded. We may then write

$$(1 + a)(1 - a) = 1, \text{ approximately}$$

Dividing both sides of this equation by $(1 + a)$ we have

$$\frac{1}{1 + a} = 1 - a, \text{ approximately}$$

If, as we have learned, we substitute subtraction for division
(and long division, too), we must take care of one fact: In the

numerator of the expression calculated above there is a number, 3, different from 1.   Let us suppose that we have the expression

$$\frac{A}{1 + a}$$

The value of A may be any number (in the above expression it is 3).   Here again we apply algebra before we proceed, and write

$$A(1 + a)(1 - a) = A$$

that is, both sides of the equation $(1 + a)(1 - a) = 1$ are multiplied by A.   Then we have

$$\frac{A}{1 + a} = A(1 - a)$$

approximately.   Now if $A = 3$ and $a = 0.0000001$, we perform the calculation of

$$\frac{3}{1 + \dfrac{1}{10,000,000}}$$

as

$$\frac{3}{1 + 0.0000001} = 3(1 - 0.0000001) = 3 - 0.0000003 = 2.9999997.$$

We arrive at the same result, but we eliminated a lot of work. Moreover, in the place of long division we applied subtraction. Division must be checked either by a repeated division or by multiplication, and there is no need to point out that checking the division of 30,000,000 by 10,000,001 by multiplication of 2.9999997 by 10,000,001 is tedious and lengthy.   On the other hand, checking the subtraction of 0.0000003 from 3 by means of the addition of 0.0000003 to 2.9999997 is very simple.

If in the equation

$$A(1 + a)(1 - a) = A$$

we divide both sides of the equation by $(1 - a)$ we obtain another formula that may be used in economizing our work in the process of calculation

$$\frac{A}{1 - a} = A(1 + a)$$

Thus the expression $\dfrac{2.75}{0.999975}$ may be calculated as

$$\frac{2.75}{0.999975} = \frac{2.75}{1 - 0.000025} = 2.75(1 + 0.000025)$$

and this is calculated as

$$2.75(1 + 0.000025) = 2.75 + 0.000025 \cdot 275$$

Finally we obtain the result $2.75 + 0.00006875 = 2.75006875$

In a similar manner we can obtain the following approximate formulas which may simplify computations.

$$(1 + a)^2 = 1 + 2a + a^2 \quad \text{and} \quad (1 - a)^2 = 1 - 2a + a^2$$

Since a is very small, a^2 is much smaller. We may discard a^2, and we have

$$(1 + a)^2 = 1 + 2a \quad \text{and} \quad (1 - a)^2 = 1 - 2a$$

Also, let

$$\sqrt{1 + a} = 1 + x \quad \text{and} \quad \sqrt{1 - a} = 1 - x$$

Squaring both sides of these expressions we have

$$1 + a = 1 + 2x + x^2 \quad \text{and} \quad 1 - a = 1 - 2x + x^2$$

Again, if a is very small, x is very small, and x^2 is much smaller. We may then discard x^2. We have then

$$1 + a = 1 + 2x \quad \text{and} \quad 1 - a = 1 - 2x$$

Solving these equations for x we find that in each case

$$x = \frac{a}{2}$$

We then have two more approximate formulas

$$\sqrt{1 + a} = 1 + \frac{a}{2}$$

and

$$\sqrt{1 - a} = 1 - \frac{a}{2}$$

The reader will find an application of the last formula in Chapter 31.

≠ 16 ≠

Algebra Looks at Instalment Buying

Debt on the Instalment Plan

In almost every publication there is at least one advertisement addressed to YOU. You are pressed to take some product TO-DAY, and pay the purchase price, "plus a small charge," in weekly or monthly instalments. This is known as instalment buying and, while generally quite fair as operated by reputable houses, often is abused, either by the seller or the buyer.

Fundamentally it is just as legitimate and reasonable as any other business dealing, except that in many cases the purchaser fails to understand the full import of the transaction. In instalment buying the buyer must consider, besides the usual aspects of a simple cash-down purchase, that he also borrows a sum of money from the seller. And when money is borrowed, it is common to pay for the use of it.

This price for the use of money is known as "interest." For every dollar borrowed, the borrower is expected to pay a certain amount (a certain fraction of the dollar) over the period the money is in his theoretical possession. It is a common practice to compute the interest on the basis of a year, a borrower paying four, five, or six cents a year for every dollar borrowed for a year.

Naturally this money is a form of commodity and the privilege of using it must have a price, such as any other product or service has. Generally this price, or interest, is fixed by state law, but these are not uniform throughout the country, varying from six cents on a dollar per year to three cents on a dollar per month.

An advertisement that appeared recently contained a description of a radio with the price, $49.95, in large type. And the purchaser was urged to have it delivered at once without paying a cent for it; the payment was to follow later. But a three-word sentence, revealing that there was a "small" credit charge, was almost hidden far below under an illustration of the radio.

What this "small" charge was, one can only imagine. It would have to take care of the interest for a year, of the credit investigation, of the insurance on the radio (when you buy on instalments you do not own the article purchased until your debt is all cleared up) and of many other incidentals. Or it may happen that the cash price of the radio is less than $49.95, and only on $49.95 will the interest be charged.

A prospective buyer should consider whether he is wise when he borrows money and pays too much for the use of it. We generally pay too little attention to the cost of using money, for a dollar bill does not bear a tag telling how much it will cost us to borrow and keep it for a year. This we must first know how to compute.

How to Learn the Price of Money

When money is borrowed, the borrower pays to the lender an agreed-upon price for the privilege of using it. Thus the lender is able to earn on his money, a legitimate procedure provided the charge is within the legal limits. If the interest is greater, the procedure is known as usury, and the interest is branded as usurious.

Interest is computed on the basis of the cost per dollar per year, and is a certain fraction of a dollar. Since there are 100 cents in a dollar, this fraction is stated in terms of a certain number of the hundredth parts of a dollar, and the amount of interest is called "per cent," which is derived from the Latin "centum" for hundred. Thus "per cent" actually means so much per hundred. Thus 1 per cent is synonymous with one per hundred, or one-one hundredth; 10 per cent means ten-one hundredths.

The symbol for percent is %. Thus when we say 5% we may interpret it as 0.05. To transform a statement of a certain number of per cents into a fraction, we simply divide the number by 100; thus 65 per cent is equivalent to $65/100 = 0.65$. On the other hand, to transform a fraction into per cents, we multiply it by 100; for example, 0.15 is equivalent to $0.15 \cdot 100 = 15$ per cent.

There are many problems besides those involving money that lean to the use of percentage and the methods we shall observe are applicable to all.

Suppose we have a quantity and want to find a certain per cent of it. For example, let us find 24 per cent of 500. We know that 24 is equivalent to 0.24 and the problem reduces to the finding of $24/100$ of 500. We multiply 500 by 0.24, and have $500 \cdot 0.24 = 120$.

Very often we are confronted with a per cent problem "in reverse." There are two distinct cases in this type of a problem. Note that in finding a per cent of a number we actually had three numbers:

a) The quantity a certain per cent of which was to be found, to be denoted by q.
b) The statement of the per cent, to be denoted by p.
c) The result, which is the part of the quantity q that is p per cent of it.

Note that whatever arithmetic operations are performed with per cents, the per cents are translated into fractions by multiplying the numerical statement of the percentage by 100; that is, we work with $100p$. We then have the relation

$$q \cdot \frac{p}{100} = r$$

This equation states the relation between the three quantities represented by the letters p, q, and r. Thus, if we know any two of these quantities, we may compute the third one. The equation

$$q \cdot \frac{p}{100} = r$$

represents the relation used when we computed $24/100$ of 500. If we know q and r, we can compute the value of p; that is, if we have the quantity and another quantity which is a certain per cent of it, we can compute the numerical value of this per cent. We thus have

$$p = \frac{100r}{q}$$

For example, the population of the United States in 1950 was about 150,000,000 and in 1940, about 130,000,000. The increase of population in the ten-year period was about twenty millions. In terms of per cent this increase is

$$20,000,000 \cdot \frac{100}{140,000,000} = \frac{2000}{140}$$

or about 14.3 per cent.

If we know p and r—that is, if we know a certain quantity—and we also know that this quantity is a certain percentage of some other quantity (the one denoted by q), we can compute the value of q by means of the equation

$$q = \frac{100r}{p}$$

For example, $34 is 8.5 per cent of

$$\frac{100 \cdot 34}{8.5} = \frac{3,400}{8.5} = \$400$$

With the process used in these three types of problems, all the per cent problems can be solved.

In computation of interest, the amount of interest is stated in terms of per cents which are computed on a yearly basis. Thus when we refer to a 6 per cent interest, we imply that this represents the price for the privilege of using borrowed money for one year. If, however, the interest is to be paid for a shorter period, say four months, then the amount of per cent is prorated; that is, the yearly interest is reduced to a four-month period. Thus the interest for four months on a 6 per cent yearly basis will be

$$\frac{6\%}{12} \cdot 4 = 2\%$$

Very often interest on borrowed money is regularly paid at intervals shorter than a year. On many occasions this interest is not actually paid but is added to the debt, and the enlarged debt is thus earning greater interest. The method of computation in this case is somewhat more complicated than direct computation of the earlier noted interest, which is known as "simple" interest. Addition of the interest to the debt so that it also may draw interest results in the accumulation of interest or, as we may say, the earnings on the money compounded. This kind of interest is known as "compound" interest.

Advertising Is an Art

Let us return now to the advertisement offering a radio for $49.95, plus the "small" credit charge. This credit charge depends on the cash price of the article. If the cash price is $49.95, then the instalment price will have to include the interest charges as well as other fixed charges to an extent depending on the practices of the particular store. This additional charge may run from 15 to 20 per cent and the interest rate on instalments is generally 6 per cent per year. We shall now consider the two in detail.

Let us assume that the price of the radio, $49.95, is the cash-down price. Then the additional charge, assuming that it is 20 per cent of the cash price, is $49.95 \cdot 0.20 = 9.99, and the total price of the radio is $49.95 + $9.99 = 59.94. To this a 6 per cent per year interest charge is added. This charge is $59.94 \cdot 0.06 = 3.5964, or $3.60. Thus the total indebtedness of the purchaser will be

$$\$59.94 + \$3.60 = \$63.54$$

This amount is divided into twelve equal parts, and each part must be paid as a monthly instalment. We have then

$$\frac{\$63.54}{12} = \$5.295$$

or $5.30.

Now let us assume that $49.95 is not the sale price and that it includes the 20 per cent mark-up of the additional charges. If the cash-sale price is $100, then the additional charge is $20, and the price to the purchaser, without the interest charge, is $120. If the sale price is taken as 100 per cent, then the additional charge is 20 per cent and the price to the purchaser, not including the interest charge, is 120 per cent of the cash-sale price. Thus $49.95 is 120 per cent of the cash price. Then, according to the method developed in the preceding section, we can compute the cash-sale price in the formula

$$q = \frac{100r}{p}$$

where $r = \$49.95$, and $p = 120$ per cent. We have then a cash-sale price of

$$\frac{100 \cdot 49.95}{120} = \$41.625$$

or $41.63.

The indebtedness of the purchaser will be $49.95 and the interest charge of 6 per cent per year interest on this amount will be $49.95 \cdot 0.06 = \$2.997$, or $3.00. Thus the total indebtedness of the radio purchaser will be $49.95 + \$3.00 = \$52.95$. This amount is divided into twelve equal parts, and each of these parts,

$$\frac{\$52.95}{12} = \$4.4125, \quad \text{or} \quad \$4.42$$

is the amount of the monthly instalment to be paid.

What Makes the Instalment Wheels Go 'Round and 'Round

If the purchaser had cash and could buy the radio for the cash-sale price, he could save all the additional charges as well as the interest charge. If the radio were selling for $49.95 cash, his saving would amount to

$$\$9.99 + \$3.60 = \$13.59$$

If the radio were selling for $41.63 cash, his savings would amount to

$$\$52.95 - \$41.63 = \$11.32$$

When an article is purchased by instalments, the purchaser's debt is getting smaller as he makes his regular payments. Let us analyze his debt in detail. When the cash price of the radio is $49.95, the purchaser owes:

$63.54 for 1 month.
After paying $5.30 he owes $58.24 for 1 month.
After paying $5.30 he owes $52.94 for 1 month.
After paying $5.30 he owes $47.64 for 1 month.
After paying $5.30 he owes $42.34 for 1 month.
After paying $5.30 he owes $37.04 for 1 month.
After paying $5.30 he owes $31.74 for 1 month.
After paying $5.30 he owes $26.44 for 1 month.
After paying $5.30 he owes $21.14 for 1 month.
After paying $5.30 he owes $15.84 for 1 month.
After paying $5.30 he owes $10.54 for 1 month.
After paying $5.30 he owes $ 5.24 for 1 month.
After paying $5.24 more his debt is finally paid.

These transactions may be interpreted as follows. The indebtedness of the purchaser is changing each month. In other words, since his debt is considered on the one-month basis, if we add his monthly indebtedness we may consider that he owed the total sum for one month only. Adding these monthly debts, we have

$63.54
58.24
52.94
47.64
42.34
37.04
31.74
26.44
21.14
15.84
10.54
5.24
————
$412.68

Thus the purchaser actually might have borrowed $412.68 for one month. This transaction cost him the amount that he could have saved had he paid cash for the radio; that is, it cost him $13.59, the interest that he paid for using $412.68 for one month. In terms of per cent, by the formula

$$p = \frac{100r}{q}$$

where $r = \$13.59$, $q = \$412.68$, and p is equal to one-twelfth of the yearly rate of interest, the yearly rate of interest is

$$\frac{12 \cdot 100r}{q}, \text{ or } \frac{12 \cdot 100 \cdot 13.59}{412.68} = \frac{16,308}{412.68} = 39.5 \text{ per cent, approximately}$$

So the purchaser borrowed $49.95 and paid about 39.5 per cent yearly interest on this loan.

If the cash price of the radio were $41.63, the buyer-borrower owes:

$52.95 for 1 month.
After paying $4.42 he owes $48.53 for 1 month.
After paying $4.42 he owes $44.11 for 1 month.
After paying $4.42 he owes $39.69 for 1 month.
After paying $4.42 he owes $35.27 for 1 month.
After paying $4.42 he owes $30.85 for 1 month.
After paying $4.42 he owes $26.43 for 1 month.
After paying $4.42 he owes $22.01 for 1 month.
After paying $4.42 he owes $17.59 for 1 month.
After paying $4.42 he owes $13.17 for 1 month.
After paying $4.42 he owes $ 8.75 for 1 month.
After paying $4.42 he owes $ 4.33 for 1 month.
After paying $4.33 more his debt is finally paid.

We may likewise interpret this transaction as if the purchaser borrowed a certain amount of money for one month only. His debt in the preceding transaction is changing every month on the monthly basis, and the total sum of the monthly debts is

$52.95
48.53
44.11
39.69
35.27
30.85
26.43
22.01
17.59
13.17
8.75
4.33
───────
$343.68

Thus the purchaser actually might have borrowed this sum for a month, and the transaction cost him the amount he could have saved had he paid cash for the radio, or $11.32, the interest he had to pay for using $343.68 for the month. Following the same procedure we find that the yearly interest he had to pay is

$$\frac{12 \cdot 100 \cdot 11.32}{343.68} = \frac{13,584}{343.68} = 39.5 \text{ per cent, approximately}$$

In other words, the purchaser borrowed $41.63 and paid about 39.5 per cent yearly interest on this loan, and the "small" credit charge mentioned turned out to be about six and one-half times as large as the average interest charge, 6 per cent per year, made by banks.

Before we proceed to examine some other types of purchases on instalments, such as mortgages and loans from finance companies, we shall develop some short-cuts in computation which will enable the reader to learn interest costs without much arithmetic work.

The How-Much Ladder

The reader may have noticed that in computing the rate of interest in the preceding section we added a column of twelve numbers. These, however, were not ordinary numbers; they were related to one another in that the difference between every two consecutive numbers was the same. For example, let us consider the following numbers

5.24	
	5.30
10.54	
	5.30
15.84	
	5.30
21.14	
	5.30
26.44	
	5.30
31.74	
	5.30
37.04	
	5.30
42.34	
	5.30
47.64	
	5.30
52.94	
	5.30
58.24	
	5.30
63.54	

Note that in the column to the right are shown the differences between any two of these consecutive numbers. These differences are all equal and represent the monthly instalments paid to reduce and finally eliminate the debt. Thus

$$10.54 - 5.24 = 5.30$$
$$15.84 - 10.54 = 5.30$$
$$21.14 - 15.84 = 5.30$$
and so on

So, if we know the first member of such a group of numbers and also know the magnitude of the difference, we are in a position to construct the group of numbers. For example, if the first member of such a group is 5.24, and the difference is 5.30, we have:

The second term is $5.24 + 5.30 = 10.54$.
The third term is $10.54 + 5.30 = 15.84$.
The fourth term is $15.84 + 5.30 = 21.14$.
The fifth term is $21.14 + 5.30 = 26.44$.

However, let us examine this same property without recourse to any specific numbers and study the properties of such a sequence from a general point of view.

Suppose the first member of a sequence of the type illustrated above is a, and the difference is d. Then our sequence is as follows:

The first term is a.
The second term is $a + d$.
The third term is $a + d + d = a + 2d$.
The fourth term is $a + 2d + d = a + 3d$.
The fifth term is $a + 3d + d = a + 4d$.

Note that in the terms of the sequence the coefficients (the numerical factors) of the d's are as follows:

In the first term the coefficient is 0 ($a + 0 \cdot d = a$).
In the second term the coefficient is 1 ($1 \cdot d = d$).
In the third term the coefficient is 2 ($2 \cdot d = 2d$).
In the fourth term the coefficient is 3 ($3 \cdot d = 3d$).

Also note that

$$0 = 1 - 1$$
$$1 = 2 - 1$$
$$2 = 3 - 1$$
$$3 = 4 - 1$$

In other words, the coefficients depend on the number of the term, and the value of the coefficient in each case is one less than the number of the term. The reader may convince himself by writing down a sequence of any number of terms. He will obtain the following results:

> The coefficient of the fifth   term is 4.
> The coefficient of the sixth   term is 5.
> The coefficient of the seventh term is 6.
> The coefficient of the tenth   term is 9.

Generally, then, if we have the kth term, its coefficient is $(k-1)$. Thus the coefficient of the 100th term is 99, the coefficient of the 500th term is 499.

This result enables us to write down, as well as any term of such a sequence, the sequence of numbers possessing the property described in this section. For example, if the first term is 15 and the difference is 2, the sequence is 15, 17, 19, 21, 23, . . . The 25th term is $15 + 24 \cdot 2 = 15 + 48 = 63$; the 70th term is $15 + 69 \cdot 2 = 15 + 138 = 153$.

An interesting property of such a sequence is that we can obtain the sum of its members without recourse to addition of all of them. Let us consider the following example. The sequence 1, 2, 3, 4, 5, . . . possesses the property of a sequence described in this chapter. Its first term is 1, and the difference is 1. Suppose we wish to add the first twenty-five numbers

1	2	3	4	5	6	7	8	9	10	11	12	13	14	15	16	17	18	19	20	21	22	23	24	25
25	24	23	22	21	20	19	18	17	16	15	14	13	12	11	10	9	8	7	6	5	4	3	2	1
26	26	26	26	26	26	26	26	26	26	26	26	26	26	26	26	26	26	26	26	26	26	26	26	26

Below the sequence of the first twenty-five numbers we write the same sequence, term by term, in the same sequence but in reversed order, then we add the terms vertically. Note that in each case the sum is 26. Now there are twenty-five such sums, hence the sum of the two sequences is $25 \cdot 26 = 650$. But we added two sequences of the first twenty-five numbers. Therefore, the sum of one such sequence is $\dfrac{650}{2} = 325$.

This procedure may be applied to the addition of any sequence. Note that the addition of the first twenty-five numbers was reduced to adding the first and the last term, and the sum thus obtained was multiplied by the number of terms in the sequence.   Finally the product was divided by 2.

Let us write two same general sequences, with one in reverse order.   If the number of the terms is n, and the last term therefore $a + (n - 1)d$, we have then:

$$a, \qquad\qquad a + d, \qquad\quad a + 2d, a + 3d, \cdots, \quad a + (n - 1)d$$
$$\underline{a + (n - 1)d, \quad a + (n - 2)d, \cdots\cdots\cdots\cdots\cdots\cdots a}$$
$$2a + (n - 1)d, 2a + (n - 1)d, \cdots\cdots\cdots\cdots\cdots, 2a + (n - 1)d$$

Note that in the case of the general sequence each vertical sum is $2a + (n - 1)d$, and there are altogether n terms in each of the two sequences.   Thus the sum of the two equal sequences is

$$n[2a + (n - 1)d]$$

and the sum of one sequence is

$$\frac{n[2a + (n - 1)d]}{2}$$

However, note that $2a + (n - 1)d$ is the sum of the first and the last terms of the sequence.   If we denote the last term by l, this sum can be written as $(a + l)$, and the sum of the sequence is

$$\frac{n(a + l)}{2}$$

If this expression is applied to the two sequences given in the preceding section, we have

$$a = 5.24, \quad l = 63.54, \quad \text{and} \quad n = 12$$

The sum of the sequence is then

$$\frac{12(5.24 + 63.54)}{2} = 6 \cdot 68.78 = 412.68$$

Also $a = 4.33$, $l = 52.95$, and $n = 12$.   The sum of the sequence is then

$$\frac{12(4.33 + 52.95)}{2} = 6 \cdot 57.28 = 343.68$$

How to Buy a House on Instalment

There are many instalment-payment plans for purchasing a house, but we shall examine here only two of the most practical examples and defer study of mortgage procedure to the next section. Frequently a house is bought by paying down a certain per cent of the cash price, the rest to be paid in equal instalments with the interest on the unpaid balance, or by paying down a certain per cent of the cash price with the rest to be paid, after the interest is added to it, in equal instalments.

Suppose a house sells for $6,000. Usually a 10 per cent down payment is made, and the balance paid in monthly instalments for 10 or 20 years. Let us suppose that the interest is 6 per cent per year. Thus the down payment is $600 and the balance $5,400. If the ten-year payment plan is adopted, the monthly instalments are $\frac{\$5,400}{10 \cdot 12} = \$45$. The payment plan is then as follows:

After expiration of the first month, the payment is $45 plus interest at 6 per cent per year for one month on $5,400. The balance of the debt is $5,400 − $45 = $5,355.

After expiration of the second month, the payment is $45 plus interest at 6 per cent per year for one month on $5,355. The balance of the debt is $5,355 − $45 = $5,310.

After expiration of the third month, the payment is $45 plus interest at 6 per cent per year for one month on $5,310. The balance of the debt is then $5,310 − $45 = $5,265.

Thus we note that every month the debt is decreased by $45, and the interest is correspondingly becoming smaller. The interest for one month at 6 per cent per year is $\frac{6\%}{12} = 0.5$ per cent. Thus the actual instalments, when paid up, will total $5,400. The total amount of interest paid can be computed as follows:

The monthly balances of the debt represent a sequence in which the first term is $45, and the last term is $5,400. The number of terms in this sequence is 120. Thus the sum of this sequence, according to the formula earlier obtained, is

$$\frac{120(45 + 5,400)}{2} = \frac{120 \cdot 5,445}{2} = \frac{653,400}{2} = 326,700$$

On each term of this sequence 0.5 interest is paid, and therefore the total interest on the total amount is $0.005 \cdot 326,700 =$ $1,633.50.

Suppose that the same $6,000 house is bought with a down payment of $600, the balance to be paid in monthly instalments of $60 each for 10 years. What is the rate of interest on this plan? We can reason as follows:

     The first   payment, $60, is unpaid for   1 month.
     The second payment, $60, is unpaid for   2 months.
     The third   payment, $60, is unpaid for   3 months.
     The last   payment, $60, is unpaid for 120 months.

Thus we may proceed as if $60 were unpaid $(1 + 2 + 3 + \ldots 119 + 120)$ months, or

$$\frac{120(1 + 120)}{2} = 60 \cdot 121 = 7,260 \text{ months}$$

Suppose the rate of interest is x per cent per year. Then per month this rate is $\frac{x}{12}$ per cent. The total amount paid will be $60 \cdot 120 = \$7,200$. But the unpaid balance is $5,400. Then the interest is $7,200 - \$5,400 = \$1,800$. This $1,800 is equal to the interest at $\frac{x}{12}$ per cent per month on $60 for 7,260 months. Then

$$7,260 \cdot \frac{1}{100} \cdot \frac{x}{12} \cdot 60 = 1,800$$

and after cancelling out and solving for x, find that the rate of interest is

$$x = \frac{1800 \cdot 100 \cdot 12}{7260 \cdot 60} = \frac{600}{121} = 4.96 \text{ per cent, approximately}$$

We can solve this problem in general, developing a formula by means of which we shall be able to determine the best method of payment, the type of payment, the most convenient (or desirable) interest rate.

Suppose the price of a house is P dollars, and the down payment is D. Then $P - D$ represents the debt incurred.

We shall denote the rate of interest by r per cent (in computation this will be changed into the fraction $r/100$) per year. We shall denote the number of payments in a year (generally 12) by k. Then the rate of interest for each portion of a year is r/k per cent (in computation this latter will be changed into the fraction $r/100k$).

Let the number of instalments be n, representing the number of times payments of the equal instalments are made.

The first instalment is owed 1 month, or one period if the arrangement is by some other intervals than months.
The second instalment is owed 2 months, or two periods.
The last payment is owed n months, or periods.

We then may consider as if a payment is owed

$$(1 + 2 + 3 + 4 + \cdots + n) = \frac{n(n+1)}{2}$$

months or periods. The amount paid in each instalment will be denoted by A. Then the total amount of interest paid is

$$\frac{r}{100k} \frac{n(n+1)}{2} A$$

On the other hand, after n instalments each equal to A dollars—that is, nA dollars—are paid, the debt is paid up completely But the amount the purchaser is expected to pay is the balance $(P - D)$ and the interest computed above. This sum must be equal to nA. We have then the following formula

$$nA = P - D + \frac{r}{100k} \frac{n(n+1)}{2} A$$

This formula enables us to compute the amount of each of the equal instalments when we know the rate of interest, or, if we know the amount of the instalment, to compute the interest.

For example, suppose that the price of the house $P = \$6,000$; the down payment $D = \$600$; the instalments are on a monthly basis, $k = 12$; the rate of interest is 5%; and the debt is to be paid up in 15 years, $n = 12 \cdot 15 = 180$. What should be the amount of each monthly instalment A?

Substitute these numbers in the above formula. We have then

$$180A = 6{,}000 - 600 + \frac{5}{100 \cdot 12} \frac{180 \cdot 181}{2} A$$

or

$$180A = 5{,}400 + \frac{5 \cdot 180 \cdot 181}{100 \cdot 12 \cdot 2} A$$

Now, $5{,}400 = 30 \cdot 180$. Therefore, both sides of the equation may be divided by 180. We have then

$$A = 30 + \frac{5 \cdot 181}{100 \cdot 12 \cdot 2} A$$

and

$$A = 30 + \frac{181}{20 \cdot 24} A$$

or

$$A = 30 + \frac{181}{480} A$$

Now we are ready to solve this equation for A. We have

$$A - \frac{181}{480} A = 30$$

or

$$\frac{480 - 181}{480} A = 30$$

finally

$$A = \frac{30 \cdot 480}{299} = \frac{14{,}400}{299} = \$48.16$$

Suppose that on the house, with the down payment still $600, the balance is to be paid in equal monthly payments of $45 for 20 years. At what rate of interest is this debt paid off? We make the substitution in the above formula and have

$$240 \cdot 45 = 6{,}000 - 600 + \frac{r}{100 \cdot 12} \frac{240 \cdot 241}{2} 45$$

or

$$240 \cdot 45 = 5{,}400 + \frac{2}{100 \cdot 12} \frac{240 \cdot 241}{2} 45$$

Dividing both sides of the equation by 120·45, we have

$$2 = 1 + \frac{r}{100 \cdot 12} \frac{2 \cdot 241}{2}$$

Then

$$1 = \frac{r \cdot 241}{1,200}$$

and

$$r = \frac{1,200}{241} = 4.98 \text{ per cent approximately}$$

The above formula is not exact, because the exact formula must consider that interest is compounded during a long period. However, this formula is sufficiently reliable for practical purposes.

The Rich Get Rich, and the Poor Try to Borrow

Highly useful if you are contemplating a loan from a finance company is the formula

$$nA = P - D + \frac{r}{100k} \frac{n(n + 1)}{2} A$$

where A is the amount of the monthly instalment,
n is the total number of the payments made,
P is the price,
D is the down payment,
r is the rate of interest per year,
k is the number of payments made each year.

First let us take a look at the table below which is similar to those published by many finance companies. Generally, many of us accept such figures as correct, but with the above formula it is easy to check them, especially as to the statement that the interest on payments is calculated at the rate of 2.5 per cent per month. This rate is not actually less than the lawful maximum on all loans. In the State of New York, for example, that rate is 3 per cent per month on loans to $150, and 2.5 per cent per month on the remainder. The same rate is legal for Illinois; in Alabama the rate is 8 per cent per year, and in Wisconsin, 2.5 per cent to $100, 2 per cent to $200, and 1 per cent on the remainder

Tables of maximum legal rates in other states are easily available. Here is a typical finance company chart:

BORROW $20 TO $300 WITH THESE SMALL MONTHLY PAYMENTS

Cash Loan You Get	Amount you repay each month (including all charges) for following periods								
	2 mos.	4 mos.	6 mos.	8 mos.	10 mos.	12 mos.	16 mos.	18 mos.	20 mos.
$20	$10.38	$ 5.32	$ 3.63	$ 2.79	$ 2.29	$ 1.95			
30	15.56	7.97	5.45	4.18	3.43	2.92			
40	20.75	10.63	7.26	5.58	4.57	3.90			
50	25.94	13.29	9.08	6.97	5.71	4.87			
60	31.13	15.95	10.89	8.37	6.86	5.85	$ 4.60	$ 4.18	$ 3.85
70	36.32	18.61	12.71	9.76	8.00	6.82	5.36	4.88	4.49
80	41.51	21.27	14.52	11.16	9.14	7.80	6.13	5.57	5.13
90	46.69	23.92	16.34	12.55	10.28	8.77	6.89	6.27	5.77
100	51.88	26.58	18.15	13.95	11.43	9.75	7.66	6.97	6.41
125	64.85	33.23	22.69	17.43	14.28	12.19	9.57	8.71	8.02
150	77.82	39.87	27.23	20.92	17.14	14.62	11.49	10.45	9.62
175	90.79	46.52	31.77	24.41	20.00	17.06	13.40	12.19	11.23
200	103.77	53.16	36.31	27.89	22.85	19.50	15.32	13.93	12.83
225	116.74	59.81	40.85	31.38	25.71	21.93	17.23	15.68	14.43
250	129.71	66.45	45.39	34.87	28.56	24.37	19.15	17.42	16.04
275	142.68	73.10	49.93	38.35	31.42	26.81	21.06	19.16	17.64
300	155.65	79.75	54.46	41.84	34.28	29.25	22.98	20.90	19.24

These figures are based on prompt repayment. Advance payment reduces the cost of your loan proportionally, since you pay only for the actual time you have the money. Payments are calculated at the rate of 2½% per month, which is less than the lawful maximum on all loans.

For convenience in the above formula we shall replace the expression $P - D$ with L, which represents the amount of the loan. We have then

$$nA = L + \frac{r}{100k} \frac{n(n + 1)}{2} A$$

Let us examine the rate of interest on a $200 loan which is to be repaid in twenty months in equal instalments of $12.83 a month. We have then

$$20 \cdot 12.83 = 200 + \frac{r}{100 \cdot 12}, \frac{20 \cdot 21}{2} 12.83$$

or, dividing both sides of the equation by 20, we have

$$12.83 = 10 + \frac{r}{100 \cdot 12} \cdot \frac{21}{2} \cdot 12.83$$

and

$$2.83 = \frac{r}{100 \cdot 12} \cdot \frac{21}{2} \cdot 12.83$$

Finally, we have then

$$r = \frac{2.83 \cdot 100 \cdot 12 \cdot 2}{21 \cdot 12.83}$$

and

$$r = \frac{6,792}{269.43} = 25.2 \text{ per cent, approximately}$$

Now this is only 4.8 per cent below the legal limit claimed in the table, but when pennies count, every extra cent is important, and other loan offers may not be so advantageous.

Consider the same $200 loan with the ten monthly instalments of $22.85. We then have

$$10 \cdot 22.85 = 200 + \frac{r}{100 \cdot 12} \cdot \frac{10 \cdot 11}{2} \cdot 22.85$$

Dividing both sides of the equation by 10 we have

$$22.85 = 20 + \frac{r \cdot 11 \cdot 22.85}{100 \cdot 12 \cdot 2}$$

and

$$2.85 = \frac{r \cdot 11 \cdot 22.85}{100 \cdot 12 \cdot 2}$$

Finally, we have

$$r = \frac{2.85 \cdot 100 \cdot 12 \cdot 2}{11 \cdot 22.85} = \frac{6,840}{251.35} = 27.2 \text{ per cent, approximately}$$

In this case the rate of interest is 2.8 per cent below the legal limit claimed in the table.

As an exercise, the reader may check some other statements in the table to determine the rate of interest charged on the various payment plans.

Some finance companies operate under a different plan. Suppose you wish to borrow $100 for a year, to be repaid in equal instalments. This loan is chargeable to you at 6 per cent per year, but the interest is paid in advance. In other words, before you get the loan you pay the company $6. Thus instead of $100 you receive only $94. But your instalments are computed so that you continue to pay additional 6 per cent on the $100. According to the above formula your monthly instalments will be computed as follows:

$$12A = 100 + \frac{6}{100 \cdot 12} \cdot \frac{12 \cdot 13}{2} A$$

or

$$12A - \frac{78A}{200} = 100$$

From this we have

$$2{,}400A - 78A = 20{,}000$$

or

$$A = \$8.62$$

The amount of interest that will thus be paid is

$$\$8.62 \cdot 12 - \$94 = \$103.44 - \$94 = \$9.44$$

Now, if we use the formula once more we can compute the actual interest charged on this loan. We then have

$$8.62 \cdot \frac{x}{100 \cdot 12} \cdot \frac{12 \cdot 13}{2} = 9.44$$

From this we obtain

$$x = \frac{9.44 \cdot 100 \cdot 2}{8.62 \cdot 13} = \frac{1{,}888}{112.06} = 16.85 \text{ per cent, approximately}$$

Thus, even if you thought that you were charged 12 per cent (6 per cent + 6 per cent) interest you would be about 4.85 per cent off. Here, as in any other instalment transactions, the rule should always be: *Stop, look, and compute.*

To conclude our examination of the rates of interest on loans, let us consider now the case of a mortgage. Generally, when there is a loan by mortgage the borrower gives to the creditor (that is, the one from whom he obtains the loan) a bonus, its magnitude depending on agreement. Let us consider an average case where a 10 per cent bonus is paid. Suppose that $1,000 is obtained on a mortgage. The usual plan is to repay in yearly instalments, with the interest on the unpaid balance. Thus, less the bonus, the borrower obtains $900, but his debt is $1,000. Suppose that the rate of interest is 5 per cent. His payments are then as follows:

At the end of the first year
he pays $200 and $50 interest. He still owes $800.
At the end of the second
year he pays $200 and $40 interest. He still owes $600.
At the end of the third
year he pays $200 and $30 interest. He still owes $400.
At the end of the fourth
year he pays $200 and $20 interest. He still owes $200.
At the end of the fifth year
he pays $200 and $10 interest.

His mortgage is thus paid off. He paid as interest.

$$\$100 + \$50 + \$40 + \$30 + \$20 + \$10 = \$250$$

It may seem that each year cost him $50, and this is exactly 5 per cent interest on a $1,000 loan. But is this so? Let us examine this case in detail.

He owed $200 once for 5 years, once for 4 years, once for 3 years, once for 2 years, and once for 1 year. Thus we may consider the following equation (denoting the interest rate by x per cent per year),

$$200 \cdot \frac{x}{100} \frac{5 \cdot 6}{2} = 250, \quad \text{or} \quad \frac{2x \cdot 5 \cdot 6}{2} = 250$$

Finally, we have

$$x = \frac{250}{30} = 8.33 \text{ per cent, approximately}$$

Even if the above formula is not exact, though for practical purposes sufficiently serviceable, the result shows that the interest rate is greater by 3.33 per cent than the 5 per cent per year interest rate. Thus, we see that the old-time mortgage melodrama where the villain was always foreclosing on Little Nell may not be full-throated farce after all. For, despite twentieth-century legislation in many states, borrowing is still the poor man's folly.   All too often, only the rich can afford it—and generally they know better.

1. How should a loan of $300 be paid off in 15 monthly instalments at the rate of 4% per annum?

2. A loan of $300 is made. A 6% service charge is made deductible in advance. The loan is paid off in 20 monthly instalments of $16.50 each. What is the yearly rate of interest charged?

3. An article selling for cash for $75 is bought on instalment basis. $10 is paid down, and 20 monthly payments of $4 are arranged. What is the yearly rate of interest charged? What would be the yearly interest rate if the $4 were paid weekly?

4. A loan of $100 may be paid off in monthly instalments of $9 or weekly instalments of $2.10. A service charge of $5 is deductible when the loan is advanced on the monthly plan, and a similar charge of $4.50 is made when the loan is advanced on the weekly plan. Which of the two plans carries a lower yearly interest rate?

5. A loan of $300 is made on an automobile. A service charge of 6% is deductible in advance. Also an insurance charge of 5% is deductible in advance. The loan is repaid in 20 monthly instalments with an interest of 2% on the unpaid balance (this is not a yearly interest rate, but 2% per month). What is the yearly interest rate charged on this loan?

Chain-Letter Algebra

The Silk-Stocking-Bargain Bubble

Several years ago the Government prosecuted some ingenious business houses for an odd swindle and, strangely enough, based its case on some sleuthing in mathematics that revealed many interesting facts. Not the least of these was the fact that whoever conceived the scheme was well acquainted with a certain branch of algebra which we shall examine in this chapter. For those who expected something for almost nothing and were victimized could have avoided reddened faces had they known the simple mathematical guards against such frauds.

The mail-order business in general is a great and convenient institution, with the buyer well protected by rigid postal regulations, but in this case a flood of alluring and plausible letters descended upon thousands all over the country. The gist of these letters was that the recipient could get three pairs of pure-silk stockings for only fifty cents and should write to the undersigned company for particulars. Advertisements inserted in the newspapers and magazines also broadcast the same bargain, "within the reach of everyone." The plan appeared so simple and so enticing that it soon swept the country and other businesses began to copy it. The plan was:

The prospective buyer was to send fifty cents to the company, but this alone did not bring her the three pairs of stockings. In reply she would receive four coupons, which she was to sell to her friends for fifty cents each. She was to remit the two dollars to the company, and then receive the stockings. True, these cost her also some selling, but it was worth while. What happened to the four coupons she sold?

Each purchaser of a coupon (her name and address was sent to the company) received five more coupons. When she sold these and sent the $2.50 to the company, she received her stockings, costing her only the fifty cents she paid for her own coupon. Thus the first four persons sold twenty coupons to twenty different individuals. These, in turn, sold five each, or one hundred coupons. We shall enumerate the sales of the coupons below:

The first purchaser bought 1 coupon and sold.	4 coupons
The 4 purchasers sold..............	20 coupons
The 20 purchasers sold..............	100 coupons
The 100 purchasers sold..............	500 coupons
The 500 purchasers sold..............	2,500 coupons
The 2,500 purchasers sold..............	12,500 coupons
The 12,500 purchasers sold..............	62,500 coupons
The 62,500 purchasers sold..............	312,500 coupons
The 312,500 purchasers sold..............	1,562,500 coupons
The 1,562,500 purchasers sold..............	7,812,500 coupons
The 7,812,500 purchasers sold..............	39,062,500 coupons

On the surface, this scheme appeared quite innocent, but let us suppose that the number pyramids to 1,562,500 purchasers and that these sell their 7,812,500 coupons. The 7,812,500 purchasers, in turn, sell their 39,062,500 coupons and get their three pairs of stockings. But the final 39,062,500 purchasers must sell 195,312,500 coupons to get theirs, and there aren't any more customers left. This was why the Government stepped in.

A scheme such as this (reminiscent of the frequent personal "send a dollar" letter fads) is known as the "chain-letter," but it serves many legal purposes, particularly in political campaigns. A campaigner writes a letter to a number of friends. These, in turn, send copies of it to the same number of friends, and so on. In a short time even millions of persons could be reached with the message, provided the chain were unbroken.

The reader may have observed that the series of numbers used above increased with a definite regularity. Beginning with the number 4, every succeeding number was five times as large as the preceding one.

This relation between numbers, such that every two neighboring numbers are in a certain ratio (for example, above we had a series such that every two numbers succeeding one another were in the ratio of one to five) is common in the practical experience of man as well as in nature, as we shall see.

Dream for an Opium Eater

The drug opium is obtained from the opium poppy plant. A single ripe poppy yields about 3,000 poppy seeds, and from each seed a new plant may be grown. Let us see how many poppy plants we could have at the end of ten years if no seeds were lost and all were planted and grew into plants. Starting with one plant, at the end of a year we have 3,000 seeds. Then:

At the end of the second year,

we have $3{,}000 \cdot 3{,}000 = 9{,}000{,}000 = 9 \cdot 10^6$ seeds.

At the end of the third year,

we have $3{,}000 \cdot 9 \cdot 10^6 = 27 \cdot 10^9 = 3^3 \cdot 10^9$ seeds.

At the end of the fourth year,

we have $3{,}000 \cdot 3^3 \cdot 10^9 = 3^4 \cdot 10^{12}$ seeds.

There is no need to write out all the numbers of seeds at the end of each year, which would represent the number of plants during the next year; let us examine the numbers obtained thus far.

Note that the number of seeds at the end of the third year is $3^3 10^9$, or $3^3 (10^3)^3$.

The number at the end of the fourth year is $3^4 10^{12}$, or $3^4 (10^3)^4$.

At the end of the fifth year we shall have $3{,}000 \cdot 3^4 (10^3)^4 = 3^5 (10^3)^5$ seeds.

Thus we observe that the exponents of the 3 and of the (10^3) are the same as the number of the year at the end of which the seeds are obtained. Then at the end of ten years we shall have $3^{10} (10^3)^{10}$ poppy seeds, which would give the same number of plants. This is one of our number giants. The reader will find that it is

$$59{,}049{,}000{,}000{,}000{,}000{,}000{,}000{,}000{,}000{,}000{,}000$$

Let us suppose that the entire surface of the earth were suitable for the cultivation of poppy plants. The radius of the earth is about 4,000 miles, or about $4,000 \cdot 5,280 = 21,120,000$ feet. The area of the surface of a sphere is obtained by the formula $A = 4\pi r^2$, where r is the radius of the sphere. Then the area of the surface of the earth is

$$4 \cdot 3.14 \cdot (21,120,000)^2$$

or

$$560,244,326,400,000,000$$

or

$$6 \cdot 10^{17} \text{ square feet}$$

The number of the poppy seeds at the end of ten years, or the number of the plants at the beginning of the eleventh year, is $6 \cdot 10^{34}$. Thus for every square foot of ground there will be

$$\frac{6 \cdot 10^{34}}{(6 \cdot 10^{17})} = 10^{17}$$

$$100,000,000,000,000,000 \text{ poppy plants}$$

which would be a problem of squeezing for even the stoutest subway guard.

The Family-Minded Fly

The common fly is not only annoying but appallingly prolific; what harm a single one may cause if it and its progeny are allowed to live and breed offers an interesting study.

Let us suppose that one female fly on April 1 (April Flies' Day) lays 200 eggs, all of which hatch, and that a fly reaches maturity within three weeks after the eggs have been laid. How many flies will there be on October 6, at the end of 189 days? Let us suppose, too, that out of these 200 eggs 100 female flies will hatch.

At the end of the first three weeks (April 21) the 100 females each will lay 200 eggs, from which 100^2 females will hatch at the end of the second period of three weeks.

At the end of the third period of three weeks there will hatch $100 \cdot 100^2 = 100^3$ female flies. Between April 1 and October 6 there are nine three-week periods; thus at the end of the ninth period there will hatch 100^9 female flies and as many males, or $200 \cdot 100^8$ flies. We assumed that none is to die, so if all nine generations survived, their population is the sum of all the generations. Calculating the last generation only, with the number of flies on October 6 at $2 \cdot 10^{18}$, let us suppose that each fly is 0.2 inch, or $2 \cdot 10^{-1}$ inch long. Then all these flies would form a line $2 \cdot 10^{18} \cdot 2 \cdot 10^{-1} = 4 \cdot 10^{17}$ inches long. Since there are 12 inches in a foot and 5,280 feet in a mile, the line would stretch

$$\frac{4 \cdot 10^{17}}{12 \cdot 5,280} = \frac{10^{17}}{15,840} = \frac{10^{16}}{1,584} \text{ miles}$$

Let us round 1,584 to 2,000. We have then

$$\frac{10^{16}}{2,000} = 5 \ 10^{12} = 5,000,000,000,000 \text{ miles}$$

The distance from the earth to the sun is about 92,000,000 miles. The line of flies would be about

$$\frac{5,000,000,000,000}{92,000,000} = 50,000 \text{ times}$$

longer than the distance from the earth to the sun. It is indeed just as well that nature provides that not all the eggs are hatched, and that there are bald men and other natural enemies to see that not all the flies survive.

The Arithmetical Plague of Australia

One of Australia's early colonists brought with him a few rabbits, which soon escaped into the open country. A few years later, hordes of rabbits were overrunning the farms and destroying crops. Not until almost the entire population of Australia was drafted into a war of extermination were they checked.

A female rabbit can bear seven litters a year, each litter consisting of about eight baby rabbits. These mature very quickly, and within a year can have litters of their own. Let us assume that one female has fifty rabbits a year, half of which are females, and that these, in turn, bear fifty rabbits a year, and so on. Thus the progeny of one female can be tabulated as follows:

At the end of 1 year,   50
At the end of 2 years, $50 + 50 \cdot 25$
At the end of 3 years, $50 + 50 \cdot 25 + 50 \cdot 25 \cdot 25$
At the end of 4 years, $50 + 50 \cdot 25 + 50 \cdot 25 \cdot 25 + 50 \cdot 25 \cdot 25 \cdot 25$

Note that the number of progeny of one female at the end of a certain year is a sum of several numbers.

The first   is   50
The second is $50 \cdot 25$
The third   is $50 \cdot 25 \cdot 25$
The fourth is $50 \cdot 25 \cdot 25 \cdot 25$

We note that each number is 25 times larger than the preceding one. Also, the second term contains 25 as a factor once, the third term contains 25 as a factor twice, the fourth term contains 25 as a factor three times. Thus, every term contains 25 as a factor one less times than the number of the term. The fifth term will be

$$50 \cdot 25 \cdot 25 \cdot 25 \cdot 25, \quad \text{or} \quad 50 \cdot 25^4$$

Thus at the end of ten years the progeny of one female rabbit will be

$$50 + 50 \cdot 25 + 50 \cdot 25^2 + 50 \cdot 25^3 + 50 \cdot 25^4 + 50 \cdot 25^5 +$$
$$50 \cdot 25^6 + 50 \cdot 25^7 + 50 \cdot 25^8 + 50 \cdot 25^9$$

We can obtain the sum of these numbers as follows:

50	$=$	50
$50 \cdot 25$	$=$	1,250
$50 \cdot 25^2 = 50 \cdot 625$	$=$	31,250
$50 \cdot 25^3 = 50 \cdot 15,625$	$=$	781,250
$50 \cdot 25^4 = 50 \cdot 390,625$	$=$	19,531,250
$50 \cdot 25^5 = 50 \cdot 9,765,625$	$=$	488,281,250
$50 \cdot 25^6 = 50 \cdot 244,140,625$	$=$	12,207,031,250
$50 \cdot 25^7 = 50 \cdot 6,103,515,625$	$=$	305,175,781,250
$50 \cdot 25^8 = 50 \cdot 152,587,890,625$	$=$	7,629,394,531,250
$50 \cdot 25^9 = 50 \cdot 3,814,697,265,625$	$=$	190,734,863,281,250

Total.................... 198,682,149,251,300

In approximately ten years the progeny of one female rabbit will then consist of

$$200,000,000,000,000 = 2 \cdot 10^{14} \text{ rabbits}$$

Above we found that the total area of the surface of the earth is about $6 \cdot 10^{17}$ square feet. About 0.3 of this, or about

$$0.3 \cdot 6 \cdot 10^{17} = 1.8 \cdot 10^{17} \text{ square feet}$$

is dry land. Then for every rabbit there will be about

$$\frac{1.8 \cdot 10^{17}}{2 \cdot 10^{14}} = 900 \text{ square feet of dry land}$$

Such computation of the sum of the number sequence used is a very long process; we shall see in the next section whether a short-cut is possible.

The How-Many-Times Ladder

Let us examine in general a sequence of numbers such that each succeeding one is a certain number of times larger (or smaller, as we shall see presently) than the one immediately preceding it. Let the first term of such a sequence be a, and the next term be r times greater; that is, the second term is ar. The third term is then $ar \cdot r = ar^2$. We then have the sequence:

$$\begin{array}{lll} \text{The first} & \text{term is} & a \\ \text{The second} & \text{term is} & ar \\ \text{The third} & \text{term is} & ar^2 \\ \text{The fourth} & \text{term is} & ar^3 \\ \text{The fifth} & \text{term is} & ar^4 \end{array}$$

Note that there is some relation between the exponent of the letter r (known as the "common ratio" of this sequence) and the number of the term. Thus, we have the following exponents of r:

$$\begin{array}{ll} \text{In the second term, 1} & (2-1=1) \\ \text{In the third \quad term, 2} & (3-1=2) \\ \text{In the fourth term, 3} & (4-1=3) \\ \text{In the fifth \quad term, 4} & (5-1=4) \end{array}$$

We see that the exponent of r is a number that is 1 less than the number of the term. Thus the exponent of r in the tenth term is 9 $(10 - 1 = 9)$, and in the twenty-fifth term, 24 $(25 - 1 = 24)$. Then:

The tenth term is ar^9
The twenty-fifth term is ar^{24}
Finally the kth term is ar^{k-1}

We may point out here that the above method of determining the exponent of r holds for the first term of the sequence also. The first term is a, and the exponent of r in this term is $1 - 1 = 0$. It is accepted that any number raised to the power zero is 1. Thus $r^0 = 1$, $ar^0 = a \cdot 1 = a$, $5^0 = 1$, $125^0 = 1$.

If we have a sequence in which the first term is a, the common ratio is r, and the number of terms is n, then it can be written as

$$a, ar, ar^2, ar^3, ar^4, ar^5, \ldots ar^{n-1}$$

Thus if $a = 2$, $r = 3$, and $n = 15$, the sequence is

$$2, 2 \cdot 3, 2 \cdot 3^2, 2 \cdot 3^3, 2 \cdot 3^4, 2 \cdot 3^5, 2 \cdot 3^6, 2 \cdot 3^7, 2 \cdot 3^8, 2 \cdot 3^9, 2 \cdot 3^{10}, 2 \cdot 3^{11},$$
$$2 \cdot 3^{12}, 2 \cdot 3^{13}, 2 \cdot 3^{14}$$

The writing of the sequence of the terms does not represent the important phase of the problem that arises in connection with such a sequence. Generally it is the sum of such a sequence that is of greater interest to us than the individual terms (members) of the sequence.

Suppose that we have the sequence

$$a, ar, ar^2, ar^3, ar^4, \ldots, ar^{n-1}$$

Multiply each term of this sequence by r. We have then another sequence

$$ar, ar^2, ar^3, ar^4, ar^5, \ldots, ar^n$$

Let us write these two sequences as follows (as sums of their terms):

$$S = \quad\quad ar + ar^2 + ar^3 + ar^4 + ar^5 + \ldots + ar^n$$
$$s = a + ar + ar^2 + ar^3 + ar^4 + \ldots + ar^{n-1}$$

If we obtain the difference $S - s$, we have (note that the terms $ar, ar^2, ar^3, \ldots, ar^{n-1}$ will all cancel out)

$$S - s = ar^n - a$$

But if we recall that the sequence S was obtained by multiplying the sequence s by r, that is, $S = sr$. We have then that

$$sr - s = ar^n - a, \quad \text{or} \quad s(r - 1) = ar^n - a$$

From this, by dividing both sides of the last expression by $(r - 1)$, we find that the sum of the sequence is

$$s = \frac{ar^n - a}{r - 1}$$

This is the formula for the sum of the n terms of the sequence and this sequence is known as the "geometric series."

Let us apply this formula to our computation of the number of progeny of the fly. The sequence is

$$200, \ 200 \cdot 100, \ 200 \cdot 100^2, \ 200 \cdot 100^3, \ 200 \cdot 100^4, \ 200 \cdot 100^5,$$
$$200 \cdot 100^6, \ 200 \cdot 100^7, \ 200 \cdot 100^8$$

and here $a = 200$, $r = 100$, and $n = 9$. The sum of this sequence is thus

$$\frac{200 \cdot 100^9 - 200}{100 - 1} = \frac{200(1{,}000{,}000{,}000{,}000{,}000{,}000 - 1)}{100 - 1}$$

Our computation is then

$$\frac{200 \cdot 999{,}999{,}999{,}999{,}999{,}999}{99} = 200 \cdot 10{,}101{,}010{,}101{,}010{,}101$$

or $\qquad 2{,}020{,}202{,}020{,}202{,}020{,}200$

A Sequence for the Rabbits

Now let us apply our ladder formula to the female-rabbit problem. To prevent too rapid increase, breeders of rabbits usually kill some and sell the meat and fur. Let us suppose that 80 per cent of each generation of rabbits is slaughtered. What will be the number of rabbits left alive after ten years?

After one year there will be left $50 - 0.8 \cdot 50 = 50 - 40 = 10$ rabbits ($10 = 0.2 \cdot 50$), half of them females; after two years,

$$5 \cdot 10 + (50 \cdot 0.2)5 = 10 + 10 \cdot 5$$

and after three years,

$$10 + 10 \cdot 5 + 10 \cdot 5^2$$

Thus we have a sequence of terms. The first is $a = 10$, the common ratio is $r = 5$, and the number of terms is $n = 10$. The sum of the terms of this sequence is

$$\frac{10 \cdot 5^{10} - 10}{5 - 1} = \frac{10(5^{10} - 1)}{4}$$

or

$$\frac{10 \cdot 9{,}765{,}625 - 1}{4} = \frac{10 \cdot 9{,}765{,}624}{4} = 24{,}414{,}060 \text{ rabbits}$$

A Clever Rat

Psychologists have a theory that much about human nature can be learned by observing the behavior of rats. Every psychological laboratory has a pampered collection of white rats, some of which are taught to perform various tricks. They learn quickly, but whether the things they do correspond to what we humans do is a debatable point. However, to avoid antagonizing the psychologists, we shall grant them their assumption, since it won't affect our discussion of this somewhat more fantastic problem:

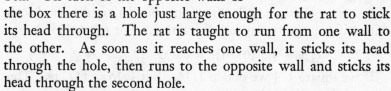

A psychologist places a white rat in a box. On each of the opposite walls of the box there is a hole just large enough for the rat to stick its head through. The rat is taught to run from one wall to the other. As soon as it reaches one wall, it sticks its head through the hole, then runs to the opposite wall and sticks its head through the second hole.

At the start, it takes the rat one minute to get from one wall to the opposite one. The return trip, however, consumes half a minute. The next trip requires only one-fourth of a minute, the next one-eighth of a minute, the next one-sixteenth, and so on. Every time the rat makes a trip, the following trip requires half the time consumed for the previous trip. This goes on indefinitely. How long will it take the rat to have its head sticking out of both holes at the same time?

Let us write the sequence of the numbers that represent the lengths of the trips:

The first   trip takes   1 minute.
The second trip takes   ½ minute.
The third   trip takes   ¼ minute.
The fourth trip takes   ⅛ minute.
The fifth   trip takes   ⅟₁₆ minute, etc.

Thus we have a sequence of numbers, the first term of which is *a*. The common ratio of this sequence is 1/2, because each succeeding term is half the preceding one. Let the number of terms be *n*. We do not know how many trips will be required to accomplish the feat of sticking one head out of the holes in the opposite walls at the same time, but we are safe in assuming the number will be large.

The sum of the terms of our sequence is then

$$\frac{1 \cdot (\frac{1}{2})^n - 1}{\frac{1}{2} - 1}$$

To be able to compute this expression let us examine what happens to a fraction that is less than 1, such as 1/2, 1/3, 1/5, when such a fraction is multiplied by itself, or when it is squared, as

$$\tfrac{1}{2} \cdot \tfrac{1}{2} = \tfrac{1}{4}$$

But 1/4 is less than 1/2. Thus when we square a fraction less than 1 we obtain a smaller fraction. Similar results will be obtained if we square any other fraction. For example,

$$(\tfrac{1}{3})^2 = \tfrac{1}{9}, \quad (0.001)^2 = 0.000001, \quad (\tfrac{3}{7})^2 = \tfrac{9}{49}$$

If we square 1/4 we obtain 1/16. But $1/16 = (1/2)^4$. Thus we see that when a fraction is raised to a power the result is smaller than the original fraction. And when the exponent of the power is great the fraction becomes very small. For example,

$$(\tfrac{1}{2})^{64} = \frac{1}{18,446,744,073,709,551,616}$$

This fraction is so small that it is almost negligible in magnitude.

Now, if we have $(1/2)^n$, and *n* is very large, say 10,000,000,-000,000, the value of $(1/2)^n$ is so small that we may disregard it.

Let us take, for example, $(1/2)^{64}$ and use it in the expression for the sum of our sequence. We have then

$$\frac{1 \cdot (\tfrac{1}{2})^{64} - 1}{\tfrac{1}{2} - 1} = \frac{\dfrac{1}{18{,}446{,}744{,}073{,}709{,}551{,}616} - 1}{\tfrac{1}{2} - 1}$$

Multiply both the numerator and the denominator of the fraction above by (-1), and this will not change the value of the fraction. We have then

$$\frac{1 - \dfrac{1}{18{,}446{,}744{,}073{,}709{,}551{,}616}}{1 - \tfrac{1}{2}} = \frac{\dfrac{18{,}446{,}744{,}073{,}709{,}551{,}616 - 1}{18{,}446{,}744{,}073{,}709{,}551{,}616}}{\tfrac{1}{2}}$$

$$= \frac{\dfrac{18{,}446{,}744{,}073{,}709{,}551{,}615}{18{,}446{,}744{,}073{,}709{,}551{,}616}}{\tfrac{1}{2}} = \frac{2 \cdot 18{,}446{,}744{,}073{,}709{,}551{,}615}{18{,}446{,}744{,}073{,}709{,}551{,}616}$$

$$= \frac{36{,}893{,}488{,}147{,}419{,}103{,}230}{18{,}446{,}744{,}073{,}709{,}551{,}616} = 1.9999999999999999999$$

approximately.

Now, if we disregard in our expression for the sum of the sequence (after we multiply its numerator and denominator by -1)

$$\frac{1 - (\tfrac{1}{2})^n}{1 - \tfrac{1}{2}}$$

the fraction $(1/2)^n$, provided we know that n is very large, we obtain

$$\frac{1}{1 - \tfrac{1}{2}} = \frac{1}{\tfrac{1}{2}} = 2$$

and this result differs only by 0.0000000000000000001 from the result obtained by us above.

Thus, theoretically (and "theoretically" is emphasized) the answer to our question is that it will take the rat exactly two minutes to stick its head out of both holes at the same time. Of course, the rat will never accomplish this feat, but mathematically the answer is entirely correct. Here, however, the reader should take note that we made use of a new friend, "infinity." We assumed that the number of terms (the number of trips that the rat will have to make from one wall to the other) is $n = \infty$.

There are many curious problems based on the assumption that a diminishing sequence, similar to the one used above, having an infinite number of terms, itself is infinite. For example, the Greek mathematician Zeno, who lived about 400 B.C., contended that Achilles (who was also a famous runner) could not win a race with a turtle. Zeno reasoned as follows:

Suppose that Achilles is 1,000 feet behind the turtle at the start of the race and that Achilles can run ten times as fast as the turtle. Thus, when Achilles covers 1,000 feet, the turtle will have covered 100 feet; when he covers 100 feet the turtle will have covered 10 feet, when Achilles covers 10 feet, the turtle will have covered 1 foot. Consequently, regardless of the distance covered by Achilles, the turtle will always be one-tenth of that distance ahead of him. We may tabulate the race in this fashion:

| Stage of Race | Distance Covered by | | Distance between Them in Feet |
	Achilles	The Turtle	
Start			1,000
First lap......	1,000	100	100
Second lap....	100	10	10
Third lap......	10	1	1
Fourth lap....	1	0.1	0.1
Fifth lap......	0.1	0.01	0.01
Sixth lap......	0.01	0.001	0.001
Seventh lap....	0.001	0.0001	0.0001

If we sum these three sequences separately, we shall find that Achilles will have covered, if we assume that the number of the laps is infinite,

$$\frac{1,000}{1 - 0.1} = \frac{10,000}{9} \text{ feet}$$

The turtle then will have covered

$$\frac{100}{1 - 0.1} = \frac{1,000}{9} \text{ feet}$$

The difference between these two distances is

$$\frac{10,000}{9} - \frac{1,000}{9} = \frac{10,000 - 1,000}{9} = \frac{9,000}{9} = 1,000 \text{ feet}$$

Since this is exactly the original distance between Achilles and the turtle, Achilles will therefore overtake the turtle under the conditions set by Zeno, but it will take him an infinite number of laps.

We will learn in Chapter 31 that when we join the midpoints of the sides of a triangle with a straight line this straight line is equal to one-half the third side. Now, suppose that we obtain three such lines in a triangle. Each of them will be equal to one-half the third side. Thus

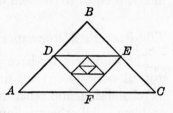

$$DE = 0.5\,AC$$
$$EF = 0.5\,AB$$

and

$$DF = 0.5\,BC$$

Then

$$DE + EF + DF = 0.5\,(AB + AC + BC)$$

that is, the sum of the sides of the inner triangle is equal to one-half the sum of the sides of the outer triangle.

If we repeat this process and obtain an inner triangle inside the inner triangle by joining the midpoints of the sides of the first inner triangle, we shall find that the sum of the sides of the second inner triangle is $0.5\,(DE + EF + DF)$.

Thus, if the sum of the sides of the first triangle is s, then the sum of the sides of the first inner triangle is $0.5s$, the sum of the sides of the second inner triangle is $0.5^2 s$, the sum of the sides of the third inner triangle is $0.5^3 s$, and so on. We thus have a sequence whose first term is s, and whose common ratio is 0.5, and whose number of terms may be n. If n is infinitely large, the sum of our sequence of the sums of the sides of the triangles is

$$\frac{s - 0.5^n s}{1 - 0.5}$$

But, if n is infinitely large, 0.5^n becomes very small (because 0.5 is a fraction less than 1), and the sum of the sequence may be written as

$$\frac{s}{1 - 0.5}$$

and this is equal to $2s$. Thus the sum of the sides of all the triangles obtained by consecutively joining the midpoints of the sides of the inner triangles, if this process is continued indefinitely, is equal to the sum of the sides of the first triangle.

The Banker's Mathematics

The sequences we have just discussed are not merely mathematical curiosities; they find universal application in banking, merchandising, and other industry. Let us consider the simplest problem. All others follow from it.

Suppose that you have a savings account of $100, and the bank pays 2 per cent interest per year. At the end of the year the interest is $0.02 \cdot 100 = \$2$. Thus at the end of the year the savings account will be

$$100 + 0.02 \cdot 100 = 100(1 + 0.02) = \$102$$

If the $102 is kept in the bank for another year, the interest on it will be $0.02 \cdot 102$, and the savings account at the end of the second year will be

$$102 + 0.02 \cdot 102 = 102(1 + 0.02)$$

But, since

$$102 = 100(1 + 0.02)$$

therefore

$$102(1 + 0.02) = 100(1 + 0.02)(1 + 0.02) = 100(1 + 0.02)^2$$

At the end of the third year the interest on the $100(1 + 0.02)^2$ is

$$0.02[100(1 + 0.02)^2]$$

and the savings account at the end of the third year is

$$100(1 + 0.02)^2 + 0.02[100(1 + 0.02)^2] = 100(1 + 0.02)^2(1 + 0.02)$$

or

$$100(1 + 0.02)^3$$

Thus we see that when the money is left untouched, the original amount at the end of the first year is multiplied by $(1 + 0.02)$, and the product so obtained is the new amount on the savings account. The same process is repeated at the end of every year, the amount left on the savings account at the beginning of the year being multiplied by $(1 + 0.02)$, and the product so obtained representing the money on the account at the end of the year. Thus at the end of the second year the savings account will be

$$102 \cdot 1.02 = \$104.04$$

and at the end of the third year

$$104.04 \cdot 1.02 = \$106.1208. \quad \text{or} \quad \$106.12$$

Now we can develop a general formula for this method of computing interest, which is known as "compound interest" because the interest is added to the original amount, or compounded, and interest is earned on the new amount.

Suppose that the original amount is A, and the interest rate in decimal fractions is r. Then at the end of the first year the new amount will be $A(1 + r)$. During the second year $A(1 + r)$ will earn $r \cdot A(1 + r)$, and the new amount will be

$$A(1 + r) + r \cdot A(1 + r) = A(1 + r)^2$$

At the end of the third year the new amount will be $A(1 + r)^3$. Generally, if the original amount is left untouched for n years, and the interest rate is r, the final amount will be

$$A(1 + r)^n$$

Now suppose that A dollars is deposited at the beginning of every year, and the interest rate is r. Then at the end of the first year the amount will be

$$A(1 + r)$$

and at the beginning of the second year,

$$A + A(1 + r)$$

At the end of the second year the amount will be

$$[A + A(1 + r)](1 + r) = A(1 + r) + A(1 + r)^2$$

and at the beginning of the third year,

$$A + A(1 + r) + A(1 + r)^2$$

At the end of the third year the amount will be

$$[A + A(1 + r) + A(1 + r)^2](1 + r)$$

or

$$A(1 + r) + A(1 + r)^2 + A(1 + r)^3$$

Generally, then, at the end of the *n*th year the amount will be, if yearly deposits of A dollars are made regularly,

$$A(1+r)+A(1+r)^2+A(1+r)^3+A(1+r)^4+ \ldots +A(1+r)^n$$

This is our sequence: its first term is $A(1 + r)$, and its common ratio is $(1 + r)$, and the number of terms is n. The sum of this sequence is

$$\frac{A(1 + r)(1 + r)^n - A(1 + r)}{(1 + r) - 1} = \frac{A(1 + r)^{n+1} - A(1 + r)}{r}$$

Thus, for example, if someone deposits $100 at the beginning of every year for five years, and the interest rate is 2 per cent, then at the end of five years he will have

$$\frac{100(1.02)^6 - 100 \cdot 1.02}{0.02}$$

We compute by multiplication $(1.02)^6 = 1.1262$, approximately. Then $100 \cdot 1.1262 - 100 \cdot 1.02 = 112.62 - 102 = 10.62$. Finally

$$\frac{10.62}{0.02} = \$531$$

approximately. A result correct to cents would be obtained if we used seven decimals in $(1.02)^6$.

Before going ahead with compound interest and its applications to various banking and business transactions, we shall need a new tool to facilitate computations with such expressions as the sum of a sequence. In the next chapter we shall forge the tool and put it into production.

PROBLEMS

1. The inventor of chess asked that on the first square of the chessboard one grain of wheat be placed, on the second square two grains, and so on until the sixty-fourth square was reached, each time the number of grains being doubled.

a) How many grains of wheat was he to receive?

b) If a cubic meter contains 15,000,000 grains of wheat, how many cubic meters of wheat would be his reward?

c) If the grains that he was to receive were counted one each second, how long would it take to count them all?

2. The progeny of a rat is about 800 a year. Assuming that half are females and that all the rats survive, what will be the progeny of one female rat at the end of five years?

3. If someone deposits $500 at the beginning of every year for three years, and the rate of interest is 4 per cent, what will be the amount at the beginning of the fourth year?

4. Someone learns a news item at 9 A.M. and tells it to three of his friends. Every one of these, in turn, tells it within half an hour to three of his friends. This process continues until 2 P.M. How many persons will learn the news by that time?

5. What is the value of the unending decimal fraction 0.444444 . . .?

6. What is the value of the unending fraction 3.36363636 . . .? [Answer: $3\frac{4}{11}$]

7. Refer to the problem of the triangle on page 259. The area of every triangle obtained by joining the midpoints of the sides of the first triangle is equal to one fourth of the area of the first triangle. Suppose that we obtain *all* the consecutive triangles by joining the midpoints of the sides of the inner triangles. What will be the sum of the areas of all such triangles? Let the area of the first triangle be A. [Answer: $\frac{1}{3}A$]

△ 18 △

Streamlining Everyday Computation

Napier's Escape from Drudgery

The golden age of mankind—in science if not in morality—may appear to have been already attained by recent technological progress. We can speed through space at more than 400 miles an hour. We can tune in any part of our earth world by the flip of a dial or take a peek through telescopic eyes at worlds millions of light-years away. We can choose our own atmosphere and breathe air fresher than the great outdoors. We have learned how to split atoms and to harness unseen rays that can pass through ten feet of lead; we have amazing new weapons by which we can blitzkrieg disease, capture bodily energy, and prolong life. And, not to forget our mathematics, we have machines that can solve problems beyond the human brain.

But, strangely enough, in computations we still depend upon a very simple device invented some three centuries ago, a device that over these years has represented the most striking example of simplification in man's work with numbers.

Even in this book whenever we had to perform computations such as $(1.02)^6$ we had to resort to multiplying 1.02 by itself six times. The calculation of

$$\frac{(\frac{1}{2})^{64} - 1}{(\frac{1}{2} - 1)}$$

involved numbers that would have taxed the energy and patience of anyone. But problems of this kind, as we shall see presently, are not uncommon in the everyday life of the average citizen.

Consider a simple multiplication such as 6,378·7,931. So far we know of only one method by which the product can be obtained; we must multiply in this fashion:

$$
\begin{array}{r}
6378 \\
7931 \\
\hline
6378 \\
19134 \\
57402 \\
44646 \\
\hline
50583918
\end{array}
$$

Multiplication of three numbers becomes even more complicated; for example the product of 476, 5,834, and 3,897:

$$
\begin{array}{r}
5834 \\
3897 \\
\hline
40838 \\
52506 \\
46672 \\
17502 \\
\hline
22735098 \\
476 \\
\hline
136410588 \\
159145686 \\
90940392 \\
\hline
10821906648
\end{array}
$$

We need not dwell on division, the raising to a power. Nor need we consider the extraction of square roots, as for square roots we may use tables such as those in the Appendix. But square roots are not the only roots in common use, as we shall discover when we examine the method of computation that took the drudgery out of numerical work. This method was invented by the Scottish nobleman Lord John Napier, who made it public in 1614. Almost immediately it revolutionized every branch of mathematics and science pure or applied, and its application simplified and speeded up computation to such an extent that not one of the modern machine inventions that can solve "unsolvable" problems can be compared with it. The invention of Napier truly marked a great advance in the progress of man. To be able to grasp fully the import of Napier's invention we shall first recall certain facts from our earlier algebra.

Napier's Clue: Addition Is Easier

When we multiply a number by itself this can be recorded symbolically, supposing the number is a, as $a \cdot a$. When we multiply the same number three, four, five, or n times, for example, we can record these multiplications as, respectively,

$$a \cdot a \cdot a$$
$$a \cdot a \cdot a \cdot a$$
$$a \cdot a \cdot a \cdot a \cdot a$$

and

$$a \cdot a \cdot a \cdot a \cdot \ldots \cdot a \text{ (the letter } a \text{ is repeated } n \text{ times)}$$

However, instead of writing all the factors which are the same, a simplification is introduced by means of which the number of factors in each product is recorded by a special number written as an exponent on the right of a factor just above it. Thus $a \cdot a \cdot a$ is written as a^3, and, generally, $a \cdot a \cdot a \cdot \ldots \cdot a$ (n repeated factors) is written as a^n. Thus 100 can be written as 10^2, or 16 as 2^4, or 125 as 5^3.

We have a special name for numbers that the products of several repeated, or identical, factors; we call them "the powers" of that number. A number when multiplied by itself several times is called the power of that number, and the repeated multiplication of a number by itself a certain number of times is called "the raising to a power" of that number.

The product of two or more powers of the same number is recorded as follows, assuming that we multiply a^3 by a^5. Now

$$a^3 = a \cdot a \cdot a$$

and

$$a^5 = a \cdot a \cdot a \cdot a \cdot a$$

Then

$$a^3 \cdot a^5 = a \cdot a \cdot a \cdot a \cdot a \cdot a \cdot a \cdot a = a^8$$

But

$$8 = 3 + 5$$

Thus the process of multiplication was turned into the addition of exponents.

Generally the product of a^m and a^n is recorded as

$$a^m = a \cdot a \cdot a \cdot \ \ldots \ \cdot a \ (m \text{ repeated factors})$$

and

$$a^n = a \cdot a \cdot a \cdot \ \ldots \ \cdot a \ (n \text{ repeated factors})$$

Then

$$a^m \cdot a^n = \underbrace{a \cdot a \cdot a \cdot \ \ldots \ \cdot a}_{(m \text{ factors})} \cdot \underbrace{a \cdot a \cdot a \cdot \ \ldots \ \cdot a}_{(n \text{ factors})} = a^{m+n}$$

If we have three powers, a^m, a^n, and a^r, their product is

$$a^m \cdot a^n \cdot a^r = \underbrace{a \cdot a \cdot a \cdot \ \ldots \ \cdot a}_{(m \text{ factors})} \cdot \underbrace{a \cdot a \cdot a \cdot \ \ldots \ \cdot a}_{(n \text{ factors})} \cdot \underbrace{a \cdot a \cdot a \cdot \ \ldots \ a}_{(r \text{ factors})} = a^{m+n+r}$$

We have then the rule for the multiplication of powers of the same number: The product of several powers of the same number is a power of this number, and the exponent of this power is obtained as the sum of the individual exponents of the respective powers. For example:

$$16 \cdot 64 \cdot 256 \cdot 32 = 2^4 \cdot 2^6 \cdot 2^8 \cdot 2^5 = 2^{4+6+8+5} = 2^{23}$$

The division of a power of some number by another power of this number is recorded according to a similar method. Suppose we are to divide a^6 by a^3. Now

$$a^6 = a \cdot a \cdot a \cdot a \cdot a \cdot a, \quad \text{and} \quad a^3 = a \cdot a \cdot a$$

Then

$$\frac{a^6}{a^3} = \frac{a \cdot a \cdot a \cdot a \cdot a \cdot a}{a \cdot a \cdot a} = a \cdot a \cdot a = a^3$$

But

$$3 = 6 - 3$$

Therefore the process of division was turned into the subtraction of the exponents.

Generally the quotient of a^m and a^n is recorded as

$$a^m = a \cdot a \cdot a \cdot \ \ldots \ \cdot a \ (m \text{ repeated factors})$$

and

$$a^n = a \cdot a \cdot a \cdot \ \ldots \ \cdot a \ (n \text{ repeated factors})$$

Then

$$\frac{a^m}{a^n} = \frac{\overbrace{a \cdot a \cdot a \cdot \ \ldots \ \cdot a}^{(m \text{ factors})}}{\underbrace{a \cdot a \cdot a \cdot \ \ldots \ \cdot a}_{(n \text{ factors})}} = a^{m-n}$$

The correctness of this result can be checked by multiplying the quotient by a^n. We have then

$$a^{m-n} \cdot a^n = a^m$$

The rule for the division of powers of the same number is then: The quotient of powers of the same number is a power of this number, and the exponent is obtained as the difference between the exponent of the dividend (the numerator of the fraction) and the divisor (the denominator of the fraction). For example

$$243 \div 9 = 3^5 \div 3^2 = 3^{5-2} = 3^3 = 27$$

Thus when we multiply or divide powers of the same number multiplication is replaced by addition of exponents, and division is replaced by subtraction of exponents.

The division of powers of the same numbers leads to some other interesting results. Suppose we divide a power of some number by itself. According to the rule for the division of powers of numbers, the exponents must be subtracted (the exponent of the divisor subtracted from the exponent of the dividend). Then

$$a^n \div a^n = a^{n-n} = a^0 = 1$$

Since a may be any number, we have that any number raised to the zero power is 1, an agreement we make to be consistent, as it will be seen presently.

Suppose the exponent of the dividend is less than the exponent of the divisor and, for example, we divide a^3 by a^5. We have then

$$\frac{a^3}{a^5} = \frac{a \cdot a \cdot a}{a \cdot a \cdot a \cdot a \cdot a} = \frac{1}{a \cdot a} = \frac{1}{a^2}$$

But according to the rule for the division of powers of the same number, the exponents are subtracted from one another. Then $a^3 \div a^5 = a^{3-5} = a^{-2}$. In other words,

$$a^{-2} = \frac{1}{a^2}$$

In general,

$$a^{-m} = \frac{1}{a^m}$$

Thus we have that a number that is raised to a negative power is a fraction whose numerator is 1 and whose denominator is this same number raised to the same, but positive power. For example, $1/25$ is 5^{-2}.

These are not the only arithmetic operations where one type of process (say multiplication) is replaced by another (addition). We shall examine other operations presently. It was this search for an easier way to multiply, however, that enabled Napier to formulate the methods of computation embodied in his invention.

Number's Common Denominator: The Lowly Logarithm

Now we are ready to examine the Napier invention more fully. To simplify our discussion, we shall present a description of it in modern dress, as Napier's development is somewhat more involved.

Let us write the powers of the number 2, considering, to present a complete picture, both the positive and negative powers. We have then

$$\ldots 2^{-5},\ 2^{-4},\ 2^{-3},\ 2^{-2},\ 2^{-1},\ 2^{0}, 2^{1},\ 2^{2},\ 2^{3},\ 2^{4},\ 2^{5}, \ldots$$

Now let us enlarge the description of this sequence of powers. We write above it a line consisting of the exponents only and below it a line containing the values of these powers after they have been calculated. We have then

...	-5	-4	-3	-2	-1	0	1	2	3	4	5	...
...	2^{-5}	2^{-4}	2^{-3}	2^{-2}	2^{-1}	2^{0}	2^{1}	2^{2}	2^{3}	2^{4}	2^{5}	...
...	$\frac{1}{32}$	$\frac{1}{16}$	$\frac{1}{8}$	$\frac{1}{4}$	$\frac{1}{2}$	1	2	4	8	16	32	...

Thus we note that for every number in the third line there corresponds a number (which is the exponent of 2) in the first line. Moreover, note that the first line is a sequence of numbers known to us. It is an arithmetic progression—a "how-much" ladder. The third line is also a sequence of numbers known to us, a geometric progression—a "how-many-times" ladder. In the first line every two neighboring numbers (terms) differ from one another by a fixed quantity (it happens to be 1), while in the third line every two neighboring numbers are in definite ratio to one another (it is called the "common ratio," and it happens to be 2).

Thus we may call the first line the line of exponents, and the third line contains the numbers that correspond to these. We may also say that the exponents correspond to the numbers. However, these two sets are related to one another under one condition, that the link between them be the number 2 that constantly appears in the second line. The number 2, when raised to the power indicated by the exponent in the first line, will give rise to a corresponding number in the third line. We call such a link between the two sets the "base."

By means of the exponents given in the first line we can perform multiplication and division according to the rules obtained in the preceding section, and to simplify the work may well prepare a table of numbers and exponents that correspond to them. Moreover, since the negative exponents correspond to fractions whose numerators are all 1, we shall not record the negative exponents but shall remember that they correspond to fractions of the type just mentioned. Here is such a table:

Number	Exponent	Number	Exponent
1	0	1,024	10
2	1	2,048	11
4	2	4,096	12
8	3	8,192	13
16	4	16,384	14
32	5	32,768	15
64	6	65,536	16
128	7	131,072	17
256	8	262,144	18
512	9	524,288	19

The product of 512 and 1,024 is then obtained as follows: the exponent of 512 is 9; the exponent of 1,024 is 10; the exponent of the product is 19. From the table we find that the number whose corresponding exponent is 19 is 524,288, and the required product is then 524,288.

The product of 262,144 and $\frac{1}{8,192}$ (or the quotient $\frac{262,144}{8,192}$) is obtained as follows: The exponent of 262,144 is 18; the exponent of $\frac{1}{8,192}$ is -13; the exponent of the quotient is 5. From the table we find that the number whose corresponding exponent is 5 is 32, and the required quotient is then 32.

The quotient $\frac{4,096}{131,072}$ is obtained is follows: The exponent of 4,096 is 12; the exponent of $\frac{1}{131,072}$ is -17; the exponent of the quotient is -5. The table shows that the number whose corresponding exponent is 5 is 32, but our exponent is negative. Then the required quotient is $\frac{1}{32}$.

The number 2 need not necessarily be the base for which the exponents and the numbers to which they correspond may be calculated; we may have any other, but for whatever base we construct a table in which the exponents are expressed in whole numbers, we shall not have calculated all the numbers to which these exponents correspond. The problem before us reduces to this: What is the most convenient base, and how can we satisfy the requirement that we can perform the multiplications and divisions of all numbers and not only a few?

Let us write the powers of 10. We have then

$$10^0 = 1$$
$$10^1 = 10$$
$$10^2 = 100$$
$$10^3 = 1,000$$
$$10^4 = 10,000$$
$$10^5 = 100,000$$
$$10^6 = 1,000,000$$

Note that fractions can also be written in terms of powers of 10, as

$$10^{-1} = 0.1, \quad 10^{-2} = 0.01, \quad 10^{-3} = 0.001, \quad 10^{-4} = 0.0001$$

A table of exponents and the numbers to which they correspond, if our base were 10, would be of little practical use to us.

How, for example, could we multiply 347 by 658 with the help of such a table?

The difficulty is not as formidable as it seems at first. Let us write the table of exponents and the numbers to which they correspond when they are calculated for the base 10:

Number	Exponent
1	0
10	1
100	2
1,000	3
10,000	4
100,000	5

Suppose we consider 37, a number between 10 and 100. It is quite reasonable to expect that the exponent corresponding to it must be greater than 1 but less than 2. In other words there must be some exponent, say x, such that when 10 is raised to the power x we obtain 37. We may record this as $10^x = 37$.

This is an equation which we do not know how to solve at this moment. However, we can obtain the value of x. We may write our solution as: $x =$ the exponent corresponding to 37 when 10 is the base. This is a long statement. Napier invented a special name for the exponent at any base—"logarithm," in short "log." The number used for a base (Napier's base was a number different from 10) is written to the left, just below the word "log," thus $\log_{10}$. Since we shall make use of no base other than 10, we shall not repeat the number 10 when we write "log." Thus the solution of the equation $10^x = 37$ is $x = \log 37$.

Now if we know that the exponents of all the numbers are calculated for the base 10, the numbers may be thought of as powers of 10. We already know how to multiply and divide powers of the same number. Thus, if we have a table of logarithms (exponents) of all numbers, the work involved in multiplication and division (later we shall extend the use of logarithms to other operations) may be simplified and speeded up. This, then, was Napier's invention: *He reduced every number to a common denominator and made the corresponding exponent the number's identifying numerator.*

A Mathematical Rogue's Gallery: Every Number Has Its Fingerprint

When we determine a base and calculate the logarithms of all the numbers, we obtain complete identification of these numbers; for every number there is only one logarithm. On the other hand, should we have a logarithm (and know the base for which it was calculated) we can identify the number to which it corresponds. Thus the logarithm at a given base is a compact, identifying instrument which is as effective as fingerprints.

Naturally for every base we may have a complete set of the logarithms of all the numbers. Moreover, if a certain number is taken, its logarithms calculated for different bases will all be different, except the logarithms of 1. We know that any number raised to the power zero is 1 and, therefore, the logarithm of 1 at any base is 0. But the logarithm of 2 at the base 3 is not equal to the logarithm of 2 at the base 4 or at the base 5 or at any other base, and the same is true for any other number.

One more important fact must be kept in mind, since we decided to have logarithms calculated for the base 10; only the logarithms of the numbers that are whole powers of 10 (positive or negative) are whole numbers; all other logarithms are fractions. The nature of logarithms is such that none of these fractions can be calculated exactly. Thus,

$$
\begin{aligned}
\log 0.001 &= -3, & \log 1 &= 0, \\
\log 0.01 &= -2, & \log 10 &= 1, \\
\log 0.1 &= -1, & \log 100 &= 2, \\
\log 1000 &= 3 &&
\end{aligned}
$$

But the logarithms of all other numbers can be calculated only approximately. So far there has been little uncertainty about even the biggest numbers we have met. Now, however, we have an infinity of numbers that cannot be expressed exactly. These are the logarithms of numbers.

Tables of logarithms of numbers calculated for the base 10 are now available with almost any number of decimal places in the fractional values of the exponents of 10. The calculation of logarithms when many decimal places are required is a long and tedious process; for practical purposes, however, logarithms with three places are often sufficient, since the calculation of these logarithms is comparatively easy and since no special knowledge of intricate procedures is necessary. Thus if you do not have a table of logarithms handy when you need one you can, in a very short time, construct your own.

Two facts, however, must be kept in mind when logarithms are calculated: Some numbers can be represented as products of several factors, but others cannot be split into factors other than 1 and themselves. For example, $12 = 2 \cdot 2 \cdot 3$, and $13 = 13 \cdot 1$. Those numbers that cannot be split into factors other than 1 and themselves are called "prime numbers." This fact enables us to reduce the work in calculating logarithms. Thus, if we know the logarithms of 2 and 3, we can calculate the logarithm of, say, 12. Before we proceed with actual calculation of the logarithms, however, we must know something more of their properties.

We now know that the product of two (or more) powers of the same number is a power of this number whose exponent is the sum of the individual exponents. Thus if we have $A = 10^a$, $B = 10^b$, and $C = 10^c$, then

$$A \cdot B \cdot C = 10^{a+b+c}$$

But from the definition of a logarithm we have $a = \log A$, $b = \log B$, and $c = \log C$, and from this we also have

$$\log (A \cdot B \cdot C) = a + b + c = \log A + \log B + \log C$$

This signifies that the logarithms of the product of several numbers is equal to the sum of the logarithms of the individual numbers.

Now suppose that $A = B = C$. Then our product may be written as A^3, and if the numbers are equal, their logarithms are all the same. Therefore

$$\log A^3 = a + a + a = 3a = 3 \log A$$

Generally,

$$\log A^n = a + a + a + \dots + a = na = n \log A$$
$$(n \text{ addends})$$

Thus we have another property: The logarithm of a power of a number is equal to the product of the exponent of that power by the logarithm of the number.

The reader will now conclude that the logarithm of a quotient of two numbers is obtained as the difference between the logarithm of the dividend and the logarithm of the divisor. This can be verified as follows.

Suppose that $A = 10^a$ and $B = 10^b$, then

$$\frac{A}{B} = \frac{10^a}{10^b} = 10^{a-b}$$

But

$$a = \log A, \quad \text{and} \quad b = \log B,$$

and

$$\log (A/B) = a - b = \log A - \log B$$

Thus the logarithm of a quotient is equal to the difference between the logarithms of the dividend and the divisor. The reader can then readily see that if we know the logarithms of 2 and 3 we can calculate the logarithms of $12 = 2^2 \cdot 3$, and of $18 = 2 \cdot 3^2$, $24 = 2^3 \cdot 3$.

The process of calculation of logarithms then reduces to calculation of the logarithms of the prime numbers. The logarithms of these numbers enable us afterwards to calculate the logarithms of those numbers in which these prime numbers are factors. Thus to construct a table of logarithms of numbers from 1 to 100 we must calculate the logarithms of the numbers:

2, 3, 5, 7, 11, 13, 17, 19, 23, 29, 31, 37, 41, 43, 47, 53, 59, 61, 67, 71, 73, 79, 83, 87, 89, 91, and 97

Calculation of the logarithms of these numbers is based on the use of logarithms known to us. At present we know that $\log 10 = 1$, $\log 100 = 2$, and $\log 1000 = 3$. We shall obtain some power of 2 (this is the first number whose logarithm will be calculated) that differs little from some whole power of 10.

When we dealt with number giants, we found that $2^{10} = 1024$. Then $10 \log 2 = \log 1024$, and

$$\log 2 = \frac{\log 1024}{10}$$

Now we do not know $\log 1024$, but we know that $\log 1000 = 3$. If we take $\log 1000$ instead of $\log 1024$, we introduce a certain amount of error which we shall correct presently. We have then

$$\log 2 = \frac{\log 1000}{10} = \frac{3}{10} = 0.30, \quad \text{approximately}$$

The error introduced in the above substitution is 24 in 1,000, or 0.024, and this must be divided by 10 (the numerator of the fraction). Thus the error is about 0.0024, which for 0.30 is equal to

$$0.30 \cdot 0.0024 = 0.000720$$

or, rounding, to 0.001, approximately. Adding this error to the calculated approximate value $\log 2 = 0.30$, we have

$$\log 2 = 0.30 + 0.001 = 0.301$$

This is still an approximate value, correct to three decimal places.

The calculation of $\log 3$ is performed (the reader should bear in mind that now we know the value of $\log 2$ also) as $3^4 = 81$, and $80 = 2^3 \cdot 10$. Then we have $4 \log 3 = \log 81$, and

$$\log 3 = \frac{\log 81}{4}$$

But we may also write that

$$\log 3 = \frac{\log 80}{4} = \frac{3 \log 2 + \log 10}{4} = \frac{3 \cdot 0.301 + 1}{4} = \frac{1.903}{4}$$

$$= 0.476, \quad \text{approximately}$$

The error that must be corrected here is 1 in 80; that is, 1/80, which must be divided by 4, or 1/320, and for 0.476 this correction is

$$\frac{0.476}{320} = 0.001, \quad \text{approximately}$$

Then

$$\log 3 = 0.476 + 0.001 = 0.477, \quad \text{approximately}$$

correct to three decimal places.

The succeeding calculations are self-explanatory:

$$\log 4 = \log 2^2 \qquad = 2 \log 2 \qquad = 2 \cdot \ 0.301 \qquad = 0.602$$
$$\log 5 = (10/2) \qquad = \log 10 - \log 2 = 1 - 0.301 \qquad = 0.699$$
$$\log 6 = \log (2 \cdot 3) \ = \log 2 + \log 3 \ = 0.301 + 0.477 = 0.778$$

The calculation of log 7 is performed as follows. We select a power of 7 in the same manner as a power of 2 (or a power of 3) was selected; $7^2 = 49$ gives a number close to 50, but this number is not sufficiently large; $7^3 = 343$, and the nearest number is 340, which is of no value to us because $340 = 2 \cdot 17 \cdot 10$, and we do not know the logarithm of 17. But $7^4 = 2,401$, which is close to 2,400, and $2,400 = 2^3 \cdot 3 \cdot 100$. Thus 2,400 can be used for the calculation of log 7. We have then $7^4 = 2,401$, and $4 \log 7 = \log 2,401$. Then.

$$\log 7 = \frac{\log 2,400}{4} = \frac{3 \log 2 + \log 3 + \log 100}{4}, \quad \text{approximately}$$

Finally we obtain the approximate value of log 7:

$$\log 7 = \frac{0.903 + 0.477 + 2}{4} = \frac{3.380}{4} = 0.845$$

The correction is

$$\frac{1}{2,400} \cdot \frac{1}{4} \cdot 0.845 = \frac{0.845}{9,600} = 0.00008, \quad \text{approximately}$$

This correction is so small that it will not affect the third decimal place (that of the thousandths) in the value of $\log 7 = 0.845$. Thus we find that the approximate value of log 7 is 0.845, correct to three decimal places.

The calculation of log 11 is performed by means of the relation

$$99^2 = 3^4 \cdot 11^2 = 9,801$$

and we take the approximate relation

$$3^4 \cdot 11^2 = 9,800 = 2 \cdot 7^2 \cdot 100$$

Then

$$11^2 = \frac{2 \cdot 7^2 \cdot 100}{3^4}$$

and

$$2 \log 11 \ = \log 2 + \log 7^2 + \log 100 - \log 3^4$$

and

$$\log 11 = \frac{\log 2 + 2 \log 7 + \log 100 - 4 \log 3}{2} , \text{ approximately}$$

Finally we have

$$\log 11 = \frac{0.301 + 1,690 + 2 - 1.908}{2} = \frac{2.083}{2}$$

$$= 1.041, \text{ approximately}$$

The correction may be discarded because it is too small.

The calculation of log 13 is performed as follows: $13^3 = 2,197$, and this is close to 2,200. We have then the approximate relation $13^3 = 2,200 = 2 \cdot 11 \cdot 100$, and $3 \log 13 = \log 2 + \log 11 + \log 100$. Then

$$\log 13 = \frac{\log 2 + \log 11 + \log 100}{3} = \frac{0.301 + 1.041 + 2}{3}$$

$$= \frac{3.342}{3} = 1.114$$

Here also the correction is too small and may be discarded.

Below are listed the hints for the calculation of the logarithms of other prime numbers up to 100:

Prime Number		Calculation			
$17^3 =$	4,913	$4,900 =$	$7^2 \cdot$		100
$19^4 =$	130,321	$130,000 =$	$13 \cdot$		10,000
$23^3 =$	12,167	$12,000 =$	$2^2 \cdot$	3	$\cdot 1,000$
$29^2 =$	841	$840 =$	$2^2 \cdot$	3 $\cdot$	$7 \cdot 10$
$31^2 =$	961	$960 =$	$2^5 \cdot$	3 $\cdot$	10
$37^2 =$	1,369	$1,360 =$	$2^3 \cdot$	17	$\cdot 10$
$41^2 =$	1,681	$1,680 =$	$2^3 \cdot$	3 $\cdot$	$7 \cdot 10$
$43^2 =$	1,849	$1,850 =$	$5 \cdot$	37 $\cdot$	10
$47^2 =$	2,209	$2,200 =$	$2 \cdot$	11 $\cdot$	100
$53^2 =$	2,809	$2,800 =$	$2^2 \cdot$	7 $\cdot$	100
$59^2 =$	3,481	$3,480 =$	$2^2 \cdot$	3 $\cdot$	$29 \cdot 10$
$61^2 =$	3,721	$3,720 =$	$2^2 \cdot$	3 $\cdot$	$31 \cdot 10$
$67^3 =$	300,763	$300,000 =$	$3 \cdot$	$100,000$	
$71^2 =$	5,041	$5,040 =$	$2^3 \cdot$	$3^2 \cdot$	$7 \cdot 10$
$73^2 =$	5,329	$5,310 =$	$3^2 \cdot$	59	$\cdot 10$
$79^2 =$	6,241	$6,240 =$	$2^4 \cdot$	3 $\cdot$	$13 \cdot 10$
$83^2 =$	6,889	$6,880 =$	$2^4 \cdot$	43 $\cdot$	10
$89^2 =$	7,921	$7,920 =$	$2^3 \cdot$	$3^2 \cdot$	$11 \cdot 10$
$97^2 =$	9,409	$9,400 =$	$2 \cdot$	47 $\cdot$	100

After all the logarithms of the prime numbers have been calculated, the remaining logarithms necessary to complete the table
of logarithms of numbers from 1 to 100 can be calculated by
means of those already on hand.

The use of 10 as the base has one great advantage. We noted
that the logarithms of whole powers (positive and negative) of
10 are whole numbers, while all other logarithms are fractions.
However, this is only one part of the entire story: If we write
the logarithms of the whole powers of 10 as shown below, we
may note another property that is very important:

$$
\begin{aligned}
\log 0.0001 &= -4 \\
\log 0.001 &= -3 \\
\log 0.01 &= -2 \\
\log 0.1 &= -1 \\
\log 1 &= 0 \\
\log 10 &= 1 \\
\log 100 &= 2 \\
\log 1{,}000 &= 3 \\
\log 10{,}000 &= 4
\end{aligned}
$$

Since all other numbers have logarithms that are fractional,
this arrangement of the whole numbers enables us to determine
the whole part of the fractional number that is the logarithm of
some number other than a power of 10. Let us take, for example, the logarithm of 57. Now 57 is greater than 10 but less
than 100. Its logarithm must be somewhere between 1 and 2.
It will be greater than 1 but less than 2. Thus the logarithm will
be a fractional number whose whole part will be 1. The logarithm of 672 will have a whole part that is 2. We note that 672
is greater than 100 but less than 1,000, and the logarithm of 672
is greater than 2 and less than 3. So we have a clue for determination of the whole part of the logarithm of a number. Note
that 57 has two digits and the whole part of its logarithm is 1.
Also 672 has three digits, and the whole part of its logarithm is 2.
Again, a number of four digits (when there is no decimal part) is
greater than 1,000 but less than 10,000. Thus its logarithm is
greater than 3 and less than 4. We conclude that the number of
the digits in the whole part of a number diminished by 1 will
give the whole part of the logarithm. Thus the whole part of

the logarithm of 45.783 is 1, and the whole part of the logarithm of 8.125 is 0. Therefore, if a number has a whole part and also has a fractional part, such as 183.24, we pay no attention to the fractional part when the whole part of the logarithm is determined.

The whole part of a logarithm is known as the "characteristic," and the fractional part as the "mantissa." The characteristic relates to the number of places to the left of the decimal point (the whole part) of a number, and the mantissa may be viewed as the fingerprint of the number for which the logarithm is given. Thus the numbers 6.72, 67.2, 672, and 67,200 will all have the same mantissa, but their characteristics will be different—0, 1, 2, and 4, respectively.

If the number whose logarithm is to be obtained is a decimal fraction only, and has no whole part, its logarithm is negative, as it can be observed above. However, to simplify the computational work with a logarithm it is customary to preserve the mantissa as if the number were not a fraction at all; the characteristics of decimal fractions are kept negative. For example, to obtain the logarithm of 0.2. We can write $\log 0.2 = \log(2/10) = \log 2 - \log 10 = 0.301 - 1$. To simplify this, we write the 1 with a bar over it. The logarithm is therefore written as $\log 0.2 = \bar{1}.301$. Similarly, we find that

$$\log 0.02 \ = \log (2/100) \ \ = \log 2 - \log \ \ 100 = 0.301 - 2 = \bar{2}.301$$
$$\log 0.002 = \log (2/1,000) = \log 2 - \log 1,000 = 0.301 - 3 = \bar{3}.301$$

The reader can observe a regularity in determination of the characteristic of the logarithm of a decimal fraction. The negative characteristic is greater by 1 than the number of zeros in the decimal fraction between the decimal point and the first digit on the left of the fraction other than zero. Thus in 0.2 there are no zeros and the characteristic is $\bar{1}$; in 0.02 there is one zero and the characteristic is $\bar{2}$; in 0.002 there are two zeros and the characteristic is $\bar{3}$.

What You Pay the Middle-Men

The consumer is generally far removed from the producer of the goods that he may require and the modern delivery, or distribution, of these goods is an industry that employs millions of people. A service of this kind, however, must be paid for, and the cost of distribution is added to the price paid for the goods by the consumer. The initial collection of all these goods, their sorting, examination and inspection, and their shipping must all be provided for in the retail price.

Let us assume that a product must pass through four different organizations, including the manufacturer, before it reaches the ultimate consumer; that the consumer pays two and a half times as much as this costs the manufacturer; and the manufacturer and the three agencies that serve the consumer mark up the price the same per cent. What is the mark-up in per cents?

Suppose the cost of a product is a and the mark-up is r per cent (in the process of computation this is transformed into a decimal fraction). Then the price to the first agent is

$$a + ar = a(1 + r)$$

To the second agent,

$$a(1 + r) + r \cdot a(1 + r) = a(1 + r)(1 + r) = a(1 + r)^2$$

To the third agent,

$$a(1 + r)^2 + r \cdot a(1 + r)^2 = a(1 + r)^2(1 + r) = a(1 + r)^3$$

And finally, to the consumer,

$$a(1 + r)^3 + r \cdot a(1 + r)^3 = a(1 + r)^3(1 + r) = a(1 + r)^4$$

This price is equal to $2.5a$. We have then the equation $a(1 + r)^4 = 2.5a$, or $(1 + r)^4 = 2.5$. To solve this we must extract the fourth root from both sides of this equation. We have then $1 + r = \sqrt[4]{2.5}$, and from this, $r = \sqrt[4]{2.5} - 1$.

Extraction of the fourth root by direct means is not an easy process. However, if we make use of logarithms we shall find it simple, although we shall need some additional information concerning the properties of roots and logarithms when so applied. The root implies an operation that undoes the raising to a power; the number from which a root is to be extracted is considered as the result of the operation of raising to a power. The problem then resolves into finding the number which, if raised to the power indicated by the exponent of the root, will give a numerical result indicated by the number under the radical sign. For example, when we refer to the fourth root of 2.5, or $\sqrt[4]{2.5}$, we assume that there must be a number, say a, such that $a^4 = 2.5$.

Let us approach our problem of the extraction of roots from the point of view of the rule for the multiplication of powers of the same number. When we are considering the fourth root of 2.5 we think of a number such that if it were multiplied by itself four times it would be 2.5. However, this number must be some power of 2.5, because the result is a power of 2.5. Thus, if we denote the exponent of the factor by x, we have

$$2.5^x \cdot 2.5^x \cdot 2.5^x \cdot 2.5^x = 2.5, \quad \text{or} \quad 2.5^{4x} = 2.5^1$$

Then $4x = 1$, and $x = 1/4$.

This result introduces a new method for writing roots of numbers. The number under the radical sign may be written with an exponent, but this exponent is a fraction whose numerator is 1 and the denominator is the indicator (the exponent) of the root. Thus

$$\sqrt[4]{2.5} = 2.5^{\frac{1}{4}}$$

If the number under the radical sign has an exponent of its own, then this exponent is written as the numerator of the fractional exponent. For example,

$$\sqrt[7]{a^3} = a^{\frac{3}{7}}$$

This method of writing roots allows us the application of logarithms to the extraction of roots. If we have a number from which a root is to be extracted, we transform it so that it is written with a fractional exponent, and then we treat the problem in the same manner as in the case of any other exponent. Then the extraction of the fourth root of 2.5 is performed as follows:

$$\log \sqrt[4]{2.5} = \frac{1}{4} \log 2.5 = \frac{0.3979}{4} = 0.0995$$

Then from a table of logarithms in the Appendix we find the number that corresponds to a logarithm that is 0.0995; this is 1.258 or, when rounded, 1.26, approximately.

Our equation

$$r = \sqrt[4]{2.5} - 1$$

becomes

$$r = 1.26 - 1 = 0.26$$

and in terms of per cent the mark-up is 26 per cent at every one of the four instances.

Logarithm Declares a Dividend

When we examined the method for the computation of interest on savings where the original amount as well as the interest is left in the bank so that interest can be earned on interest, we assumed that the original amount was A and the yearly interest rate was r, in decimal fractions. Then at the end of the first year the savings and the interest on them would be equal to

$$A + r \cdot A = A(1 + r)$$

At the end of the second year,

$$A(1 + r) + r \cdot A(1 + r) = A(1 + r)(1 + r) = A(1 + r)^2$$

And at the end of the third year,

$$A(1 + r)^2 + r \cdot A(1 + r)^2 = A(1 + r)^2(1 + r) = A(1 + r)^3$$

Generally, if this is allowed to continue for n years and if the interest is computed on the yearly basis, the amount at the end of the nth year would be equal to $A(1 + r)^n$.

Some banks, however, compute and pay interest biennially (twice a year), other banks quarterly. But when the interest is computed twice a year, and the yearly rate is r, then the half-yearly rate is $r/2$, but the number of periods for which the interest is computed, if the savings are kept in the bank n years, is doubled, or the number of periods is $2n$. Then the formula for the amount at the end of n years is $A(1 + r/2)^{2n}$.

When the interest is computed and paid four times a year, and the yearly rate of interest is r, then the quarterly rate is $r/4$. If the savings are kept in the bank for n years, the number of periods for which the interest is computed is then quadrupled, the number of periods is $4n$. Then the formula for the amount at the end of n years is $A(1 + r/4)^{4n}$.

Generally if the yearly interest is r and the interest is computed and paid m times a year while the savings are kept in the bank for n years, the total amount at the end of the n years is computed by the formula $A(1 + r/m)^{mn}$. Thus by means of logarithms the computation of the growth of capital when interest is compounded is simplified and speeded up. Let us consider a few typical problems.

At what yearly rate of interest will capital be doubled in 15 years if the interest is paid semiannually? Let the amount placed in the bank be A, the yearly rate of interest, r, and the number of years, $n = 15$. Then we have

$$A \left(1 + \frac{r}{2}\right)^{30} = 2A, \quad \text{or} \quad \left(1 + \frac{r}{2}\right)^{30} = 2$$

Taking the logarithms of both sides of the equation, we have

$$30 \log \left(1 + \frac{r}{2}\right) = \log 2, \quad \text{and} \quad 30 \log \left(1 + \frac{r}{2}\right) = 0.3010$$

Finally we have

$$\log \left(1 + \frac{r}{2}\right) = \frac{0.3010}{30} = 0.0100, \quad \text{approximately}$$

From the table of logarithms we find that 0.0100 corresponds to the logarithm of 1.023. Then

$$\log \left(1 + \frac{r}{2}\right) = \log 1.023$$

and

$$1 + \frac{r}{2} = 1.023$$

From this we find that $r/2 = 0.023$, and $r = 0.046$; that is, the yearly rate of interest is about 4.6 per cent.

What would be the yearly rate of interest in this problem if the interest were paid monthly? Our formula for this problem is

$$A\left(1 + \frac{r}{12}\right)^{180} = 2A$$

and

$$\left(1 + \frac{r}{12}\right)^{180} = 2$$

Note that here we face the problem of extracting the 180th root from 2. Logarithms make this simple. We have then

$$180 \log \left(1 + \frac{r}{12}\right) = \log 2$$

and

$$180 \log \left(1 + \frac{r}{12}\right) = 0.3010$$

Finally

$$\log \left(1 + \frac{r}{12}\right) = \frac{0.3010}{180} = 0.00167$$

Rounding the quotient, we find that the number that corresponds to the logarithm that is 0.0017 is approximately 1.004. Then

$$1 + \frac{r}{12} = 1.004$$

and

$$\frac{r}{12} = 0.004$$

This leads to $r = 0.048$, and therefore the yearly rate of interest is about 4.8 per cent.

Sing a Song of Sixpence

When you have saved money, you can well afford to whistle in the rain, for there is a closer relationship between your bankbook and your tune than a mere feeling of security.

Let us consider that you have deposited a dollar and that the bank pays 6 per cent yearly. How long must you keep this dollar in the bank to have two dollars on your account?

According to the formula for compound interest we have

$$(1 + 0.06)^x = 2$$

or

$$1.06^x = 2$$

Then

$$x \log 1.06 = \log 2$$

or

$$x = \frac{\log 2}{\log 1.06} = \frac{0.3010}{0.0253} = 12, \quad \text{approximately}$$

Thus your dollar will be doubled in about twelve years.

Now let us turn from money to the somewhat loftier realm of music. The reader will recall that on the piano scale the keyboard is arranged in octaves of seven white and five black keys. Sound is transmitted through the air by vibrations produced when the keys strike the strings. The number of the vibrations of each note is fixed, a note that is an octave higher has twice as many vibrations. Thus, if the middle C has 264 vibrations, the C an octave higher (to the right on the piano keyboard) will have 528 vibrations while the C an octave lower, to the left, has 132.

The twelve notes that correspond to the twelve keys within one octave are so arranged that the numbers of their respective vibrations form a sequence such that every two neighboring numbers are in the same ratio to one another. Such an arrangement is known as the tempered scale, and reduces to a simple problem. We have a sequence of thirteen terms (remember that we must include the middle C and the C one octave higher). The thirteenth term is twice as large as the first term, and every two neighboring terms are in the same ratio, known as the common ratio. What is this ratio?

We find then that the first term is 264 and, as the common ratio is unknown, let it be r. The number of terms is n, and we have a how-many-times sequence. The thirteenth term of this sequence (the C whose vibration is 528) is

$$264 \cdot r^{12} = 528$$

or

$$r^{12} = 2$$

We know now how to solve such equations. Take the logarithms of both sides and we have

$$12 \log r = \log 2$$

or

$$\log r = \frac{0.3010}{12} = 0.0251, \quad \text{approximately}$$

and

$$r = 1.06, \quad \text{approximately}$$

The sequence is then

$$264, \quad 264 \cdot 1.06, \quad 264 \cdot 1.06^2, \quad 264 \cdot 1.06^3, \dots, \quad 264 \cdot 1.06^{12}$$

Thus the number of vibrations of the successive notes on the keyboard grows at the rate of 6 per cent, the same as the usual yearly rate of interest.

The Roar of a Lion and the Twinkle of a Star

Noise as well as music can be measured by mathematics. Scientists have another name for music, or noise. They call it "the loudness of sounds" and the unit of measure is called the "bel" in honor of the inventor of the telephone, Alexander Graham Bell. The rustle of the leaves of a tree represents the noise of 1 bel. A noise whose measure is 2 bels is 10 times stronger than 1 bel; one whose measure is 3 bels is 10 times stronger than 2 bels, and 100 times stronger than 1 bel. In practical work, however, the bel is considered to be a large unit, and a smaller unit, the "decibel," equal to one-tenth of a bel, is used.

The strength of noise is its measure in bels, but the magnitude, when expressed in whole bels, form a sequence in which neighboring members are in the same ratio, the common ratio in this sequence being 10. We can represent the relation in the form of a table

Strength of noise (in bels)	1	2	3	4	5	6 ...
Magnitude of noise	10	10^2	10^3	10^4	10^5	10^6 ...

Thus the number of bels is the exponent of 10 when the magnitude of the noises is expressed in powers of ten. The relation between the strength of noise and the magnitude of noise is a logarithmic one; when we have measured the strengths of two different noises in bels, we have the logarithms of the numbers that measure the respective magnitudes.

For example, the average conversation is about 6.5 bels strong, 5.5 bels louder than the rustle of leaves. How many times, in a simple number, is conversation louder than the rustle of leaves? We have then

$$\frac{10^{6.5}}{10} = 10^{6.5-1} = 10^{5.5}$$

If we apply logarithms, we have

$$6.5 \log 10 - \log 10 = 6.5 - 1 = 5.5$$

(log 10 at the base 10 is equal to 1)

The number whose logarithm is 5.5 is therefore 316,000, approximately. Note that the characteristic of the logarithm is 5 and therefore the whole part of the number must have six places.

The roar of a lion is about 8.7 bels strong. The difference between the noise produced by an average conversation and that produced by a lion is

$$8.7 \text{ bels} - 6.5 \text{ bels} = 2.2 \text{ bels}$$

The number whose logarithm is 2.2 is approximately 158. Thus the roar of a lion is 158 times louder than the average conversation. If you have an audience of about 2,000 people in a theater and all of them talk at the same time, the noise of their conversations is about equal to the noise that would be produced by

$$\frac{2,000}{158} = 13 \text{ lions}$$

The noise of Niagara Falls is about 9 bels strong. The difference between this and an average conversation is

$$9 \text{ bels} - 6.5 \text{ bels} = 2.5 \text{ bels}$$

The number whose logarithm is 2.5 is approximately 316. So the noise produced by Niagara is about 316 times louder than that of an average conversation. If we have 316 men in a room, all of them talking at the same time, their noise is equal to that of Niagara. Our theater audience of 2,000 thus is equal to

$$\frac{2,000}{316} = 6.5 \text{ Niagaras, approximately}$$

Our modern world, parenthetically, is full of noises from all sides—a passing train, a fire engine, the horn of an automobile, the slam of a door. It has been found that a man can withstand a noise about 13 bels strong; any stronger noise is harmful.

Now let us turn to silence and the brightness of the stars. In the country on a moonless night these appear as tiny flickers of fire (there are now instruments that can measure their heat). Some of these stars are very bright, many others not so bright. There are literally billions that are so faint that very powerful telescopes are necessary to observe them, and most of them cannot even be observed in telescopes. We learn of their existence from photographs that often require several nights for million-dollar instruments to register their light.

Astronomers have catalogued most of the stars that we can see without a telescope and have measured their size, their temperatures, their distance from us, their make-up, and their apparent brightness, this latter being termed "magnitude." One class is known as "stars of the first magnitude," and so on down to the dimmest star that can be seen with the naked eye, which is classed as a star of the sixth magnitude.

It was agreed that a star of the first magnitude is about a hundred times as bright as one of the sixth magnitude, an artificial but very useful arrangement. Moreover, the scale by means of which the brightness of the stars is judged is so arranged that the ratio of the brightness of those of two consecutive magnitudes as expressed in whole numbers is always the same number. In other words, a star of the first magnitude is a certain number of times brighter than one of the second magnitude, and so on.

Suppose that the number of times a star of one magnitude is brighter than a star of the next is n. With this assumption and the fact that a star of the first magnitude is one hundred times brighter than one of the sixth magnitude, we shall attempt to determine the value of n. If we compare the brightness of the stars with the brightness of a star of the sixth magnitude we have the following table:

A star of the fifth   magnitude is n times brighter.
A star of the fourth magnitude is n^2 times brighter.
A star of the third   magnitude is n^3 times brighter.
A star of the second magnitude is n^4 times brighter.
A star of the first   magnitude is n^5 times brighter.

But we know that a star of the first magnitude is about 100 times brighter than a star of the sixth magnitude. Thus we have the equation $n^5 = 100$.

Taking the logarithms of both sides of this equation, we have

$$5 \log n = \log 100, \quad \text{or} \quad \log n = \tfrac{2}{5} = 0.4$$

and, by means of the table of logarithms, we find that $n = 2.5$, approximately. Thus as the number of the magnitude of the star increases, the brightness of the star of that magnitude is 2.5 times dimmer than the brightness of the star of the preceding magnitude, or a star of the second magnitude is 2.5 times dimmer than one of the first magnitude.

Now we can have a table where instead of the brightness of the stars we shall take their dimness:

The magnitude	1	2	3	4	5	6	7	8	9	...
The dimness	1	2.5	2.5^2	2.5^3	2.5^4	2.5^5	2.5^6	2.5^7	2.5^8	...

(number of times)

Here 2.5 may be considered as the base of the logarithms, and the magnitudes may be considered as the logarithms of the number of times the stars are dimmer than a star of the first magnitude.

The Algebra of Starlight: 437,000 Full Moons = 1 Bright Day

If all the stars were such that their magnitudes could be expressed in whole numbers, astronomers could get along without recourse to algebra, but the magnitudes run the whole gamut of numbers. Moreover, there are stars that are brighter than those of the first magnitude. Some of these are brighter than the star of the zero magnitude, which is 2.5 times brighter than a star of the first magnitude. Thus to keep the system of measuring consistent, astronomers had to take refuge in negative numbers, and they talk of the -1 and -2 magnitudes. Thus a star of the -1 magnitude is $2.5^2 = 6.25$ times brighter than one of the first magnitude, and so on.

It was found also that the brightness of our sun on a cloudless day is about -26.8, and the brightness of the full moon on a cloudless night about -12.7. The brightest star is Sirius (the Dog Star) which is visible on winter nights in the southeastern sky, just below the constellation Orion. Its magnitude is about -1.6. A candle at a distance of 1 meter, or about 1.1 yards, has a brightness of -14.2.

With these facts stored in our brainpan, we may solve some interesting problems of celestial light. For instance, how much more light do we receive from the sun than from the full moon? Since our table refers to the order of the dimness of the stars, for convenience we shall restate our problem: How much dimmer is the full moon than the sun? We have then

$$x = \frac{2.5^{-12.7}}{2.5^{-26.8}} = 2.5^{14.1}$$

By means of the table of logarithms we find that

$$\log x = 14.1 \log 2.5 = 14.1 \cdot 0.4 = 5.64$$

and

$$x = 437,000, \quad \text{approximately}$$

Thus we get about 437,000 times as much light from the sun; it would take 437,000 full moons to make a bright day.

The brightest star in the sky, Sirius, whose magnitude is -1.6, is

$$\frac{2.5^{-1.6}}{2.5^{-26.8}} = 2.5^{26.8-1.6} = 2.5^{25.2}$$

times dimmer than the sun. By means of logarithms we can compute the value of $2.5^{25.2}$. We have

$$25.2 \log 2.5 = 25.2 \cdot 0.4 = 10.08$$

and then from the table of logarithms we find that

$$2.5^{25.2} = 12000000000, \quad \text{approximately}$$

that is, Sirius is twelve billion times dimmer than the sun. It will take about twelve billion stars, all of them as bright as Sirius, to turn the darkest of nights into a bright sunlit day.

Very often we hear of lamps that produce light similar to sunlight. How many candles would it be required to place at a distance of about 1 yard in order to produce the same illumination as that produced by the sun? If we reword our problem, we may state it as follows: How many times is a candle, at a distance of about 1 yard, dimmer than the sun? We have then that this is

$$\frac{2.5^{-14.2}}{2.5^{-26.8}} = 2.5^{26.8-14.2} = 2.5^{12.6}$$

times. By means of logarithms we can compute the value of $2.5^{12.6}$, and we have that

$$12.6 \log 2.5 = 12.6 \cdot 0.4 = 5.04$$

and then from the table of logarithms we find

$$2.5^{12.6} = 110000 \quad \text{approximately}$$

that is, it would require about 110,000 candles all placed at a distance of about 1 yard from you in order to produce the effect of sunlight.

The Trade-in Value of Your Car: $a = A(1 - r)^n$

Let us examine the mathematics of a product which was distributed brand new but has outlived its usefulness to you. Suppose you have a car costing $800 delivered at your door. Let us assume that 25 per cent of this represents the cost of delivery and the cost of selling it to you. Thus the actual value of the car is $600. Suppose now that you keep the car a few months and desire to sell it.

You will not receive the entire amount you have paid, since as soon as it is delivered to you its resale value is always less than the original cost. Let us assume that in the case of your $800 car the loss is about 10 per cent, and its delivered value is $720.

Let us suppose, too, that after ten years of service the trade-in value is $50, the car losing $670 in value, to be determined by a certain per cent of loss equal throughout the ten years. Thus if this per cent is r (expressed in decimal fractions), the value of the car at the end of the first year will be

$$720 - 720r = 720(1 - r)$$

At the end of the second year,

$$720(1 - r) - 720(1 - r)r = 720(1 - r)(1 - r) = 720(1 - r)^2$$

At the end of the third year,

$$720(1 - r)^2 - 720(1 - r)^2r = 720(1 - r)^2(1 - r) = 720(1 - r)^3$$

Thus we note that the exponent of the expression $(1 - r)$ is equal to the number of years the car was in use. Then at the end of ten years the value will be

$$720(1 - r)^{10} = 50$$

To determine the value of r we must solve the equation obtained above. We can do this by means of logarithms. We have then

$$\log 720 + 10 \log(1 - r) = \log 50$$

or

$$10 \log (1 - r) = \log 50 - \log 720$$

and, finally,

$$\log (1 - r) = \frac{\log 50 - \log 720}{10}$$

From the table of logarithms we obtain

$$\log (1 - r) = \frac{1.6990 - 2.8573}{10} = \frac{-1.1583}{10}$$

$$= -0.1158, \quad \text{approximately}$$

Keeping the mantissa of the logarithm positive, we add and subtract 1 from -0.1158. We have then $-1 + 1 - 0.1158 = -1 + 0.8842 = \bar{1}.8842$, and then we have $\log(1 - r) = \bar{1}.8842$, or $1 - r = 0.766$. Then $r = 0.234$, or the yearly loss in value is 23.4 per cent.

By means of the above expression

$$720(1 - r)^n$$

where n is not greater than 10 and corresponds to the number of years that the car was in use, we can determine the trade-in value at the end of any year up to ten years under the stated conditions. Thus at the end of the fifth year the value of the car is

$$720(1 - r)^5$$

We find that the logarithm of the value is

$$\log 720 + 5 \log (1 - r)$$

and then, substituting the values of $\log 720$ and $\log(1 - r)$, we have

$$2.8573 + 5(-0.1158) = 2.8573 - 0.5790 = 2.2763$$

and the value of the car is \$189.

A general formula for the problem of the trade-in value of your car then would be: the delivery value is A, the number of years that the car is in service is n, the rate of loss in value (known as "the rate of depreciation" and stated in per cents) is r, and the trade-in value at the end of n years is a. Then

$$A(1 - r)^n = a$$

÷ 19 ÷

The Bankers' Number—Jack of All Trades

Simple Life

Now is a good time to meet a meek little letter that nevertheless provides a safety valve for the vast world of finance, and enters with the effectiveness of a numerical giant in the complex computations of submarine building, of long-distance telephoning, and similar familiar activities

First, however, we may well learn more about banker's procedure. We know that when he pays simple interest we may collect it at the end of the year, and there the transaction ends; he does not pay interest on the interest as well as the principal if we leave it another year. This is also true of a bond when the interest is paid by coupons.

Even if the bank should pay simple interest twice a year, or quarterly, or monthly, or n times a year, our total interest would not be increased since the bank still pays no interest on simple interest, and the rate of payment would be unchanged. For semiannual payment, for instance, it would be only 2 per cent instead of 4 per cent and so on.

How to Make Money Breed

The more advantageous method (from your point of view, provided you are not a banker) of computing interest earned allows the addition to your capital of the interest already earned, and the subsequent computing of interest on the entire amount. This is the compound interest that we noted earlier.

295

Suppose that a certain amount, A dollars, is on deposit and the compound interest is paid at the rate of r per cent a year. At the end of the first year the amount on deposit will be

$$A + Ar = A(1 + r)$$

In all the formulas that follow, the value of r is expressed in decimal fractions. At the end of the second year the amount will be

$$A(1 + r) + A(1 + r)r = A(1 + r)(1 + r) = A(1 + r)^2$$

at the end of the third year,

$$A(1 + r)^2 + A(1 + r)^2r = A(1 + r)^2(1 + r) = A(1 + r)^3$$

and, generally, at the end of the nth year, will be

$$A(1 + r)^n$$

Suppose the interest is paid twice a year. If the yearly rate is r, the interest for both periods will be $\frac{r}{2}$. At the end of the first six months the amount on deposit is

$$A + A \cdot \frac{r}{2} = A\left(1 + \frac{r}{2}\right)$$

and at the end of the second period

$$A\left(1 + \frac{r}{2}\right) + A\left(1 + \frac{r}{2}\right) \cdot \frac{r}{2} =$$

$$A\left(1 + \frac{r}{2}\right)\left(1 + \frac{r}{2}\right) = A\left(1 + \frac{r}{2}\right)^2$$

Let us compare the amount on deposit at the end of the first year, when compound interest is paid once a year, and when compound interest is paid twice a year. We have then

$$A(1 + r) \ ? \ A\left(1 + \frac{r}{2}\right)^2$$

The question mark is inserted because we do not at present know whether they are equal. If equal we will replace the question mark by the equality sign; if unequal, one of the two expressions must be greater in magnitude, and we shall then insert the sign $<$ if $A(1 + r)$ is less than $A\left(1 + \frac{r}{2}\right)^2$, or the sign $>$ if $A(1 + r)$ is greater than $A\left(1 + \frac{r}{2}\right)^2$.

We know that

$$A\left(1 + \frac{r}{2}\right)^2 = A\left(1 + \frac{2 \cdot r}{2} + \frac{r^2}{4}\right) = A + Ar + \frac{Ar^2}{4}$$

Then

$$A + Ar \ ? \ A + Ar + \frac{Ar^2}{4}$$

Since A and r are positive, we conclude that

$$A + Ar + \frac{Ar^2}{4}$$

is greater than $A + Ar$. Then we have that

$$A(1 + r) < A\left(1 + \frac{r}{2}\right)^2$$

So if interest is compounded semiannually the amount on deposit will earn more interest than when interest is paid only once a year. This advantage, of course, persists in the years that follow if all the money is left in the bank.

At the end of a year and a half the amount on deposit at semi-annual compound interest will be equal to

$$A\left(1 + \frac{r}{2}\right)^2 + A\left(1 + \frac{r}{2}\right)^2 \cdot \frac{r}{2} =$$
$$A\left(1 + \frac{r}{2}\right)^2\left(1 + \frac{r}{2}\right) = A\left(1 + \frac{r}{2}\right)^3$$

At the end of two years, four periods, the amount will be equal to

$$A\left(1 + \frac{r}{2}\right)^3 + A\left(1 + \frac{r}{2}\right)^3 \cdot \frac{r}{2} =$$
$$A\left(1 + \frac{r}{2}\right)^3\left(1 + \frac{r}{2}\right) = A\left(1 + \frac{r}{2}\right)^4$$

Thus we see that the exponent of the expression $\left(1 + \frac{r}{2}\right)$ is always equal to the number of the periods for which the interest was computed. Then, generally, if the money is kept n years, the number of intervals is $2n$, and the amount of money on deposit at the end of n years is equal to

$$A\left(1 + \frac{r}{2}\right)^{2n}$$

Here is another example. Two men deposited $100 each in two banks, one of which pays 3 per cent compound interest annually, and the other bank pays 3 per cent compound yearly interest semiannually; the two deposits are kept untouched for ten years. How will the two deposits compare at the end of the ten years?

The deposits then will be

$$100(1 + 0.03)^{10} \quad \text{and} \quad 100(1 + 0.015)^{20}$$

respectively, or

$$100(1.03)^{10} \quad \text{and} \quad 100(1.015)^{20}$$

By means of logarithms we obtain the following results:

$$\log 100 + 10 \log 1.03 = 2 + 10 \cdot 0.0128 = 2 + 0.1280 = 2.1280$$

and the number whose logarithm is 2.1280 is 134.3; that is, the amount will be $134.30. Also

$$\log 100 + 20 \log 1.015 = 2 + 20 \cdot 0.0065 = 2 + 0.1300 = 2.1300$$

and, since the number whose logarithm is 2.1300 is 134.9, the amount will be $134.90 by the semiannual payment.

Suppose the interest is compounded quarterly. If the yearly interest rate is r per cent, then the quarterly interest is $r/4$, and at the end of the first year the amount on deposit is equal to

$$A\left(1 + \frac{r}{4}\right)^{4}$$

At the end of the second year it is equal to

$$A\left(1 + \frac{r}{4}\right)^{2 \cdot 4} = A\left(1 + \frac{r}{4}\right)^{8}$$

at the end of the third year

$$A\left(1 + \frac{r}{4}\right)^{3 \cdot 4} = A\left(1 + \frac{r}{4}\right)^{12}$$

and, generally, if the money is kept on deposit for n years, to

$$A\left(1 + \frac{r}{4}\right)^{4n}$$

The formula for the amount compounded for n years at the yearly rate of r per cent, if the interest is compounded monthly, thus is equal to

$$A\left(1 + \frac{r}{12}\right)^{12n}$$

If the interest is compounded daily (bankers consider the year equal to 360 days), the amount on deposit at the end of n years is equal to

$$A\left(1 + \frac{r}{360}\right)^{360n}$$

Apparently when interest is added every day, the money on deposit may grow at a tremendous rate, but would compounding interest at such short periods break a bank?

The Shortest Insurance Policy Ever Written: 'e'

Suppose A dollars is deposited in a bank that pays yearly interest of r per cent, and the interest is compounded n times a year. At the end of the first year the amount will be equal to

$$A\left(1 + \frac{r}{n}\right)^{n}$$

at the end of the second year,

$$A\left(1 + \frac{r}{n}\right)^{2n}$$

at the end of the third year,

$$A\left(1 + \frac{r}{n}\right)^{3n}$$

and, generally, if left in the bank untouched for t years will be equal to

$$A\left(1 + \frac{r}{n}\right)^{tn}$$

We may reason that the smaller we make the 1/nth part of a year, the more periods for which interest will be computed and added to the original capital. In such a situation we might expect the original capital would grow so fast that the depositor would become tremendously wealthy. But suppose a bank should pay interest every hour, or every tenth of a second, or, since we allow our imagination full play, every millionth of a second; suppose we even allow n to become so large that it will be almost infinite in size.

To simplify this we can advantageously modify our problem. Suppose that only 1 dollar is deposited; that is, $A = 1$. Also let us suppose that the bank pays only a yearly interest rate of 1 per cent. And, finally, that this dollar is kept in the bank for one year only. Thus in the above formula $A = 1, r = 1$ per cent (or 0.01), and $t = 1$. Our formula then becomes

$$\left(1 + \frac{0.01}{n}\right)^n$$

We shall make one more modification. Suppose the banker is so goodhearted that he pays 100 per cent yearly interest, or $r = 100$ per cent (or 1.00). If the interest were paid once a year, the dollar would be doubled at the end of the year. If the interest is paid n times a year, then the amount on deposit is obtained by the formula $\left(1 + \dfrac{1}{n}\right)^n$. And n in this formula is allowed to become extremely large. Let us compute the values of the above expression for some values of n:

For $n = 1$ we have $(1 + \frac{1}{1})^1 = 2$
For $n = 2$ we have $(1 + \frac{1}{2})^2 = 2.25$
For $n = 3$ we have $(1 + \frac{1}{3})^3 = 2.37$, approximately

For other values of n we shall make use of logarithms. For $n = 10$, we have $(1 + 0.1)^{10} = (1.1)^{10}$, or

$$10 \log 1.1 = 10 \cdot 0.0414 = 0.4140$$

and the value is 2.594, approximately.

For $n = 100$ we have $(1 + 0.01)^{100} = (1.01)^{100}$, or

$$100 \log 1.01 = 100 \cdot 0.0043 = 0.4300$$

and the value is 2.691, approximately.

For $n = 1,000$ we have $(1 + 0.001)^{1,000} = (1.001)^{1,000}$, or

$$1,000 \log 1.001 = 1,000 \cdot 0.00043 = 0.43000$$

(for this and other computations we must use tables of logarithms with more than four places in their mantissas), and the value is 2.70.

For $n = 5,000$ we have

$$\left(1 + \frac{1}{5,000}\right)^{5,000} = (1 + 0.0002)^{5,000} = (1.0002)^{5,000}$$

or

$$5,000 \log 1.0002 = 5,000 \cdot 0.0000869 = 0.4345000$$

and the value is 2.72, approximately. We cannot rely on any more places in our answer because all the numbers used in the computation are approximate, and more than three digits would therefore introduce error.

More refined computations (not by means of logarithms, but by special expressions whose nature is beyond the scope of this book) calculate $\left(1 + \frac{1}{n}\right)^n$ as

$$1 + 1 + \frac{1}{1 \cdot 2} + \frac{1}{1 \cdot 2 \cdot 3} + \frac{1}{1 \cdot 2 \cdot 3 \cdot 4} + \frac{1}{1 \cdot 2 \cdot 3 \cdot 4 \cdot 5} + \cdots$$

and show that its value is 2.71828, correct to six places. It can be computed to any number of places, but at no time is the value of $\left(1 + \frac{1}{n}\right)^n$ greater than 2.72. The calculation of this value may be performed as follows:

Take 1	1.000000
Divide 1 by 1	1.000000
Divide by 2	0.500000
Divide 0.500000 by 3	0.166667
Divide 0.166667 by 4	0.041667
Divide 0.041667 by 5	0.008333
Divide 0.008333 by 6	0.001389
Divide 0.001389 by 7	0.000198
Divide 0.000198 by 8	0.000025
Divide 0.000025 by 9	0.000002
Total	2.718281

Thus, if the banker were paying 100 per cent interest, and the number of periods during a year were infinite, he would not have to pay out more than $1.72 interest, and your hopes of becoming infinitely rich would be blasted.

The value of $\left(1 + \dfrac{1}{n}\right)^n$ when n is infinitely large is so important in mathematics and science that it has a special symbol, e. The banker is thus insured against his bank being broken, and his insurance policy is the simple e; no wonder then that we call this "the bankers' number."

Now let us consider the general formula obtained,

$$A\left(1 + \frac{r}{n}\right)^{tn}$$

Let $\dfrac{r}{n} = \dfrac{1}{x}$.   Then $n = rx$. We can rewrite our formula as

$$A\left(1 + \frac{1}{x}\right)^{trx}, \quad \text{or} \quad A\left(1 + \frac{1}{x}\right)^{xtr}$$

If n becomes very large, then rx (which is equal to n) also becomes very large.   But r is fixed in value; it is the yearly rate of interest.   The only possibility is that x must also become very large, and then $\left(1 + \dfrac{1}{x}\right)^x$ must have the value e.   Substitute this in the expression

$$A\left(1 + \frac{1}{x}\right)^{xtr}$$

and we have

$$Ae^{tr}$$

This formula gives the amount that will be on deposit when A dollars is placed in a bank that pays interest continuously (the intervals being so small that we may think of them as being almost at zero), and the yearly rate of interest is r per cent, while the capital is kept in the bank for t years.   The bankers' number, we see, is a part of this formula.

If $100 is deposited in a bank paying a yearly rate of 6 per cent interest compounded continuously, then at the end of the first year the amount on deposit will be

$$100 \cdot (2.718)^{0.06}$$

We have then

log 100+0.06 log 2.718 = 2+0.06·0.4343 = 2+0.0261 = 2.0261

and the number whose logarithm is 2.0261 is 106.2. Thus the amount at the end of the year will be equal to $106.20. If interest were paid only once a year, the amount would be $106.

If $100 is deposited at a yearly rate of interest of 4 per cent compounded continuously, at the end of ten years the amount will be

$$100 \cdot (2.718)^{10 \cdot 0.04} = 100 \cdot (2.718)^{0.4}$$

We have then

log 100 + 0.4 log 2.718 = 2 + 0.4·0.4343 = 2 + 0.1737 = 2.1737

and the number whose logarithm is 2.1737 is 149.17. Thus the amount at the end of ten years will be equal to $149.17. If interest were paid only once a year, the amount would be equal to

$$100(1 + 0.04)^{10} = 100(1.04)^{10}$$

We have then

log 100 + 10 log 1.04 = 2 + 10·0.0170 = 2 + 0.1700 = 2.1700

and the number whose logarithm is 2.1700 is 147.9. Thus the sum would be equal to $147.90. The difference in the interest earned under the two plans would be equal to

$$\$149.17 - \$147.90 = \$1.27$$

How Fast Your Money Can Grow

When we deposit our savings in a bank, most of us do not concern ourselves with any question other than the rate of interest, but there is another side to the problem. Suppose we make one deposit only, and the money is left to earn compound interest. We have computed that if the yearly rate of interest were 6 per cent compounded yearly it would take about twelve years to double the original deposit. But what happens during the intervening twelve years? How does our money change in size? Does the bank add a twelfth of our deposit every year? No, because 12·0.06 = 0.72, or twelve equal increments would not add even three-quarters of the original deposit. Besides, such equal additions would represent the payment of simple interest.

In simple interest the rate at which the money will grow is determined by the interest rate paid. If the yearly rate is r per cent, and the interest is paid once a year, then if the original amount deposited is A dollars the interest earned is Ar (r is expressed in decimal fractions). And this amount will be earned year in and year out. When the interest is compounded the problem of the rate of the growth of your money is not so simple, but it is not too difficult for us to solve.

We shall call the rate of growth of the money the "increase" in a year. When simple interest is paid, we say that the rate of growth is "constant," but when simple interest is compounded the money on deposit does not increase every year by the same sum, as we shall now see.

Let the amount deposited be A dollars and the yearly interest rate be r. At the end of the first year, the interest earned is

$$Ar$$

and the amount on deposit is

$$A(1 + r)$$

At the end of the second year, the interest is $A(1 + r)r$, and the amount on deposit is

$$A(1 + r)^2$$

At the end of the third year, the interest is $A(1 + r)^2r$, and the amount on deposit is

$$A(1 + r)^3$$

We note that the interest paid at the end of a certain year is computed on the basis of the money on deposit at the beginning of that year. Then at the end of the nth year, the interest earned will be

$$A(1 + r)^{n-1}r$$

and, generally, at the end of any year, whose number may be denoted by k, the interest earned will be

$$A(1 + r)^{k-1}r$$

Since the amount at the beginning of any year depends on how long this money was kept on deposit (that is, on the number of years or, as we may say, on the "time"), and since the amount on deposit changes from year to year because it grows, the rate of growth of the money when compound interest is paid varies.

If we denote the amount on deposit at the beginning of any year by A_k, then the interest earned during that year is $A_k r$. Thus we see that the amount of compound interest earned during any year depends on the amount on deposit at the beginning of that year. If the interest is paid at regular intervals several times a year, the same result is obtained. In this case, however, the amount on deposit will increase several times a year, and the speed with which it will grow will depend on the amount on deposit at the beginning of each period.

If the interest is compounded at intervals that during each year become infinite in number, the speed with which the amount grows also changes continuously, but even in this case the speed depends on the amount on deposit and is proportional to the amount at the beginning of each interval.

On the other hand, if there should be a change so that its growth is proportional to the amount recorded at the beginning of a period, the law of compound interest operates. And, since we now know that for very small intervals, or continuous growth, the relationship is based on the bankers' number e, we establish that e is most important in the nature of growth and the study of its laws.

However, growth may not be considered only from the point of view of increase, since we make use here of the principle that allows generalization. If growth by increase is a growth in one sense, and let us consider it as positive, we may think also of a growth that has an opposite sense, in which decrease is involved. This reasoning reminds us of the negative number which enabled us to extend the notion of numbers.

How Fast Your Money Can Go

We examined a problem of disappearing money when we computed the trade-in value of a car. Basically, we start out with a sum of money, and at the end of a definite period a certain portion of this is lost. In business practice this is called "depreciation." The longer machines, furniture, buildings, or similar properties are in use the more they depreciate in value.

Suppose that a certain article costs A dollars, and at the end of each year loses r per cent of its value. At the end of the first year its value will be equal to

$$A - Ar = A(1 - r)$$

at the end of the second year,

$$A(1 - r) - A(1 - r)r = A(1 - r)(1 - r) = A(1 - r)^2$$

and at the end of the third year,

$$A(1 - r)^2 - A(1 - r)^2 r = A(1 - r)^2(1 - r) = A(1 - r)^3$$

Thus we note that the method applied in computation of compound interest is applicable in the case of depreciation, but in computation of the latter the value of r is negative, and we have the general formula for the value of the object at the end of n years as $A(1 - r)^n$.

For example, suppose that a new truck costs $1,000; upon delivery its value is reduced to $700, and it depreciates at the rate of 15 per cent yearly. The value of the truck at the end of five years will be

$$700(1 - 0.15)^5 = 700(0.85)^5$$

By logarithms we obtain

$$\log 700 + 5 \log 0.85 = 2.8451 + 5 \cdot \bar{1}.9294 = 2.8451 - 5 \cdot 0.0706$$

or $2.8451 - 0.3530 = 2.4921$, and the number whose logarithm is 2.4921 is 310.5. Thus the value of the truck at the end of five years will be $310.50.

Depreciation need not be effected only at the end of the year; it may be effected at the end of every six months, or every three months, in the same manner as compound interest may be paid at shorter intervals. Thus if the truck is depreciated semiannually at the yearly rate of 15 per cent, it will have at the end of five years the value

$$700(1 - 0.075)^{10} = 700(0.925)^{10}$$

If the yearly interest rate is 15 per cent, then the interest rate is 7.5 per cent, and instead of "interest" we use "depreciation." We have then

$$\log 700 + 10 \log 0.925 = 2.8451 + 10 \cdot \overline{1}.9661 =$$
$$2.8451 - 10 \cdot 0.0339$$

or $2.8451 - 0.3390 = 2,5061$, and the number whose logarithm is 2.5061 is 320.64. Thus the truck at the end of five years will be worth \$320.64.

We found that when the depreciation is effected once a year, the value will be \$310.50, and when twice a year, \$320.64. Had we proceeded, the value under depreciation effected three times a year would be \$325.92, and, if every month, would be \$328.92.

In other words, if we make shorter the period at the end of which the depreciation is effected, we obtain a larger value. Now, if the periods are continuously made shorter, would we reach a stage when there will be no loss in value at all? Or if this does not take place, what does happen?

The Mathematics of Slow Death

Suppose an article that costs A dollars is depreciated at the yearly rate of r per cent and the depreciation is effected n times a year. At the end of the year its value will be equal to

$$A\left(1 - \frac{r}{n}\right)^n$$

at the end of the second year,

$$A\left(1 - \frac{r}{n}\right)^{2n}$$

at the end of the third year,

$$A \left(1 - \frac{r}{n}\right)^{3n}$$

and, generally, if the depreciation is continued for t years, the value at the end of t years will be equal to

$$A \left(1 - \frac{r}{n}\right)^{tn}$$

The value of n in the above formula may be made as large as we please. Naturally, the larger this value of n the shorter all these periods will be. We are thus confronted with a situation similar to the one discussed previously; the reader will recall that in compound interest the formula is

$$A \left(1 + \frac{r}{n}\right)^{tn}$$

We shall simplify our discussion by modifying this to

$$A \left(1 - \frac{r}{n}\right)^{tn}$$

and shall assume for the time being that the value of A is 1. We shall suppose further that the article becomes entirely valueless in one year when the depreciation is effected once, or $r = 100$. Our formula then becomes

$$\left(1 - \frac{r}{n}\right)^{tn}$$

and, since we are considering only one year, $t = 1$, and we have

$$\left(1 - \frac{1}{n}\right)^{n}$$

Let us compute the values of the above expression for some values of n:

For $n = 1$ we have $(1 - \frac{1}{1})^1 = 0$.
For $n = 2$ we have $(1 - \frac{1}{2})^2 = 0.25$.
For $n = 3$ we have $(1 - \frac{1}{3})^3 = (\frac{2}{3})^3 = \frac{8}{27} = 0.296$.
For $n = 4$ we have $(1 - \frac{1}{4})^4 = (\frac{3}{4})^4 = \frac{81}{256} = 0.316$.
For $n = 5$ we have $(1 - \frac{1}{5})^5 = (\frac{4}{5})^5 = \frac{1024}{3125} = 0.328$.

For other values of n we shall make use of logarithms. For $n = 1,000$ we have

$$(1 - 0.001)^{1,000} = (0.999)^{1,000}$$

or

$$1,000 \log 0.999 = 1,000 \cdot \overline{1}.9996 = -1,000 + 999.6 = \overline{1}.6000$$

and the value is 0.398, approximately. For $n = 100,000$ we have

$$(1 - 0.00,001)^{100,000} = (0.99999)^{100,000}$$

or

$$100,000 \log 99,999 = 100,000 \cdot \overline{1}.9999957 =$$
$$-100,000 + 99999.5700000 = \overline{1}.5700000$$

and the value is 0.3716, approximately, or correct to two places, 0.37.

Thus we see that with the increase in the value of n we obtain a decimal fraction which is greater than 0.3, and at the same time is less than 0.4. Let us examine the expression

$$\left(1 - \frac{1}{n}\right)^n$$

more closely. Let us replace $1 - \frac{1}{n}$ by $\frac{x}{1 + x}$. We have then

$$1 - \frac{1}{n} = \frac{x}{1 + x}$$

and

$$\frac{1}{n} = 1 - \frac{x}{1 + x}$$

which, when simplified, gives

$$\frac{1}{n} = \frac{1}{1 + x}$$

and

$$n = 1 + x$$

From this we conclude that when n becomes very large x must become very large also. We then have

$$\left(1 - \frac{1}{n}\right)^n = \left(\frac{x}{1 + x}\right)^{1 + x}$$

Now recalling the rules concerning exponents, we have

$$\frac{x}{1+x} = \frac{1}{\frac{1+x}{x}} = \left(\frac{1+x}{x}\right)^{-1}$$

Then

$$\left(\frac{x}{1+x}\right)^{1+x} = \left(\frac{1+x}{x}\right)^{-(1+x)} = \left(\frac{1+x}{x}\right)^{-x}\left(\frac{1+x}{x}\right)^{-1}$$

Now

$$\frac{1+x}{x} = 1 + \frac{1}{x}$$

and

$$\left(1 + \frac{1}{x}\right)^{-x} = \left[\left(1 + \frac{1}{x}\right)^{x}\right]^{-1}$$

But, since x becomes very large, $\left(1 + \frac{1}{x}\right)^{x} = e$. Moreover $\left(1 + \frac{1}{x}\right)^{-1}$, when x becomes very large, becomes equal to 1, because $\frac{1}{x}$ is then very small. Then we have the following result:

$$\left(1 - \frac{1}{n}\right)^{n} = e^{-1} = \frac{1}{e}$$

The numerical value of $\frac{1}{e}$ is approximately 0.36787.

If we consider the formula

$$\left(1 - \frac{r}{n}\right)^{tn}$$

let us make

$$\frac{r}{n} = \frac{1}{y}$$

Then $n = ry$. If we substitute these values in the formula above, we have

$$A\left(1 - \frac{1}{y}\right)^{try}, \quad \text{or} \quad A\left(1 - \frac{1}{y}\right)^{ytr}$$

If $\dfrac{r}{n} = \dfrac{1}{y}$, and if n becomes very large, while r is fixed in value, then y must become very large also. Then

$$\left(1 - \frac{1}{y}\right)^y = e^{-1}$$

and our formula becomes

$$Ae^{-tr}$$

By means of this we can compute the value of a depreciated article when the yearly rate of depreciation, the number of years are given, and the depreciation is assumed to be continuous; that is, the intervals at which the depreciation takes effect are so small that they may be considered imperceptible.

For example, if $100 is depreciated at the yearly rate of 10 per cent at the end of ten years, the amount left will be equal to

$$100 \cdot (2.718)^{-10 \cdot 0.1}$$

or to

$$100 \cdot 2.718^{-1} = 36.79$$

that is, to $36.79.

How Fast Is Slow Death?

The case of living beings, who gradually lose their energy and die, is similar to the problem of depreciation of a machine, and of the same formula, Ae^{-tr}, is applicable. The values of A, t, and r may differ, however.

If the value of A were divided into n equal portions, and at the end of a definite period one such portion were simply discarded, then the rate with which the value of A would be depreciated would be the same for all the periods. This reminds us of simple interest, when at the end of every year the same amount of money is to be added to the original sum, or of depreciation when the value of the article may decrease at the end of each period by the same amount. In business this latter may take place at times, but in nature it never occurs.

We shall call the speed with which an object depreciates (or deteriorates) the amount it loses during one year. Thus, if the rate of yearly depreciation is r per cent and the initial value of an object is A dollars, then if the depreciation is effected at the end of one year the value will be equal to $A - Ar$. During the first year the loss is therefore

$$Ar$$

At the end of the second year the value is

$$A(1 - r) - A(1 - r)r$$

and the loss is

$$A(1 - r)r$$

At the end of the third year the value is

$$A(1 - r)^2 - A(1 - r)^2r$$

and the loss,

$$A(1 - r)^2r$$

We note that the amount of the loss during any year is computed on the basis of the value of the object at the beginning of that year. Then at the end of the nth year the amount lost will be equal to

$$A(1 - r)^{n-1}r$$

Since the amount that represents the value of the object at the beginning of any year depends on how long the depreciation was taking effect—in brief, on time—the rate of depreciation does not remain constant, but changes. If we denote the value of an object at the beginning of any year (say, the kth) by A_k, then the amount lost during that year is A_kr. Thus we see that the amount of loss during any year (when the loss is compounded) depends on the value of the object at the beginning of that year. The rate of the yearly per cent of loss is constant, but the rate of the loss is not. Moreover, as the number of years that the depreciation is effected progresses, the actual amount of loss becomes smaller because the value of the object becomes smaller. Thus we may say that the speed of the depreciation is proportional to the value of the object. Since, with the progress of the years, this value becomes smaller, the speed of losing slows down, and depreciation may then be compared with the process of "slow death."

If the depreciation is effected at regular intervals several times a year, the same result is obtained. In this case, however, the loss will be effected several times a year, and the speed with which it will take place will depend on the value of the object at the beginning of each period. If the loss is effected at intervals so small that their number each year becomes infinite, the speed with which the loss will be effected also changes continuously. But even in this case the speed depends on the value of the object at each moment and is proportional to the value at the beginning of each interval.

Since the formula for the value of an object when the loss is effected continuously is Ae^{-tr}, then its value at the beginning of a certain interval is (let this interval be the kth)

$$A_k = Ae^{-kr}$$

where A is the original value and when $k = 0$. Note that $e^0 = 1$, and $A_0 = A$.

The Curves of Growth and Death

The formula for continuous growth,

$$Ae^{tr}$$

and the one for continuous depreciation,

$$Ae^{-tr}$$

are closely related to one another. This becomes obvious if we glance at their mathematical pictures, or "graphs" (see Chapter 24 for an explanation of this mathematical phenomenon and the mechanics of its "plotting"). To simplify our discussion we shall recall that the value of r is constant, and only the value of t changes. We shall, therefore, consider the two equations

$$y = e^x \quad \text{and} \quad y = e^{-x}$$

The values of these expressions for e^x and e^{-x} are so important in many branches of science, business, and industry that they have been calculated and tabulated for constant use.

The values of x and y are given in the following table:

x	e^x	e^{-x}
0.00	1.0000	1.0000
0.10	1.1052	0.9048
0.20	1.2214	0.8187
0.30	1.3499	0.7408
0.40	1.4918	0.6703
0.50	1.6487	0.6065
0.60	1.8221	0.5488
0.70	2.0138	0.4966
0.80	2.2255	0.4493
0.90	2.4596	0.4066
1.00	2.7183	0.3679
1.10	3.0042	0.3329
1.20	3.3201	0.3012
1.30	3.6693	0.2725
1.40	4.0552	0.2466
1.50	4.4817	0.2231
1.60	4.9530	0.2019
1.70	5.4739	0.1827
1.80	6.0496	0.1653
1.90	6.6859	0.1496
2.00	7.3891	0.1353
2.50	12.182	0.0821
3.00	20.086	0.0498
3.50	33.115	0.0302
4.00	54.598	0.0183
4.50	90.017	0.0111
5.00	148.41	0.0067
5.50	244.69	0.0041
6.00	403.43	0.0025
6.50	665.14	9.0015
7.00	1,096.6	0.0009
7.50	1,808.0	0.0006
8.00	2,981.0	0.0003
8.50	4,914.8	0.0002
9.00	8,103.1	0.0001
10.00	22,026.5	0.00005

"Pictures" of the two equations are shown below. Note that the graph of $y = e^{-x}$ is a mirror image of the graph of the equation $y = e^x$. If the graph of one curve is turned over (in the same manner as a page is turned over), it will fall on the graph of the other curve and will coincide with it. This is only a close graphical relationship, but the relationship as obtained directly from the equation shows that the values of e^{-x} are the reciprocals of e^x. because

$$e^{-x} = \frac{1}{e^x}$$

The values of e^x and e^{-x} will be useful in the discussions of certain properties and facts to which the following sections are devoted.

$$y = e^x$$

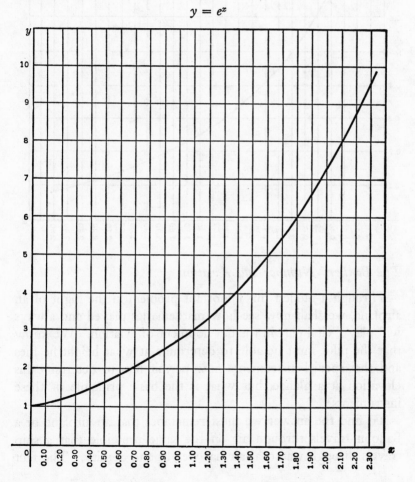

$$y = e^{-x}$$

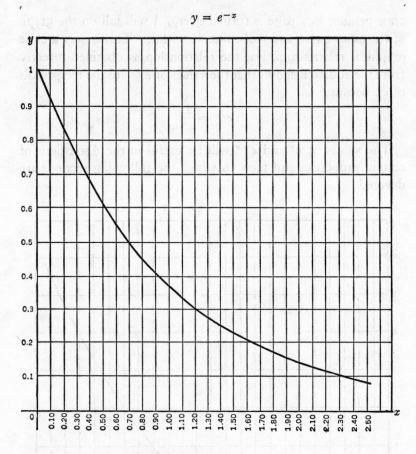

The Bankers' Number and Aviation

Through a modest but important problem in the flight of an airplane, we shall now see how mathematics played and always will play a vital part in the development of aviation. We know that the pilot must be able to determine at what height he flies and that special instruments now permit him to determine his elevation at a glance, but what is the basic principle of these instruments?

To find the answer we must remember that an airplane or a balloon travels through air on the same principle that a ship travels through water, as air has weight and density. The fact that air has weight was discovered by the Italian scientist Torricelli in 1643, and on the basis of his finding he invented the barometer by means of which we measure air pressure, known as barometric pressure.

That air exerts pressure can be easily demonstrated at home without special instruments. Fill a glass with water and put a card over it, then turn the glass over while holding the card tight over the top of the glass. When the glass is overturned, remove your hand. The card will stick to the glass, as illustrated, and the water will not be spilled.

It was found that the air pressure becomes lower with the rise above ground; at sea level at 0 degree Centigrade, when the air is dry, the air pressure on every square centimeter of the earth's surface with the weight of about 1 kilogram. This weight is usually represented by a mercury column whose base has an area of 1 square centimeter and whose  height is 76 centimeters, or 760 millimeters. It should be observed that it is not only elevation that causes a reduction in the pressure; temperature, wind, humidity, the pressure of dust, and many other factors influence its magnitude, but to learn the essentials of the law governing changes we must ignore all these and consider only the effect of elevation.

Let us assume that the air pressure at sea level is P. Then at some height, say h, it will be p. We know that p is less than P because at the height h the column of air with a base of 1 square centimeter is shorter than the column with the same base at sea level. Thus the difference in P and p is equal to the weight of a column of air whose base is 1 square centimeter and whose height is h. If we can compute the weight of this column and subtract this from P we shall obtain p.

Here, however, we are confronted with some difficulty. Air is lighter than water, and the ratio of the weight of a volume of air to the weight of the same volume of water is known as the density of the air. But the air density changes with pressure; thus it is not a constant magnitude but is proportional to air pressure. At great heights the air is very rarefied, and this is why we find it difficult to breathe on high mountain tops. To resolve this difficulty we shall divide the length h into a great number (say n) of equal parts. Each of these parts will then be h/n, and, since all are very small, we may assume that the density within each is constant. But the densities in every one of them are not the same; they change and become smaller.

Let us assume that the density of the air at sea level is d_1. Then, since the area of the base is 1 square centimeter and the height of the column is $\frac{h}{n}$, the volume is $\frac{h}{n}$ cubic centimeters, and the weight of the air, which exerts pressure, is $d_1\left(\frac{h}{n}\right)$. Also, since the density is proportional to the pressure, we may write

$$d_1 = kP$$

where k is known as the coefficient of proportionality whose value will be stated presently. Then instead of $d_1\left(\frac{h}{n}\right)$ we may write

$$\frac{kh}{n}P$$

Then the air pressure at the height $\frac{h}{n}$ above the sea level will be equal to

$$P - \frac{kh}{n}P = P\left(1 - \frac{kh}{n}\right)$$

Let us denote this air pressure by p_2.

Now let us consider the second strip of air, whose thickness also is $\frac{h}{n}$. Let the density of the air in it be d_2. Then the weight of the air in the strip will be $d_2\frac{h}{n}$. Also, since the density of the air is proportional to the air pressure, we have that $d_2 = kp_2$. Then the weight of the air in the second strip may be written as

$$\frac{kh}{n}p_2$$

and the air pressure at the height of $\dfrac{2h}{n}$ above sea level will be equal to

$$p_2 - \frac{kh}{n}\,p_2 = p_2\left(1 - \frac{kh}{n}\right)$$

But $p_2 = P\left(1 - \dfrac{kh}{n}\right)$. Then the air pressure at the height $\dfrac{2h}{n}$ above the sea level is equal to

$$P\left(1 - \frac{kh}{n}\right)^2$$

At the height of $\dfrac{3h}{n}$ the air pressure will be equal to

$$P\left(1 - \frac{kh}{n}\right)^3$$

This may be obtained if we denote the air pressure at the height of $\dfrac{3h}{n}$ by p_3 and the corresponding density of the air by d_3 and go through the same process as above.

Finally, at the height $\dfrac{hn}{n}$, that is, h, the air pressure will be equal to

$$P\left(1 - \frac{kh}{n}\right)^n$$

Naturally, the smaller the width of the strip $\dfrac{h}{n}$, the more refined will be the value of the air pressure. But, to make the width of the strip very small, we must make n, the number of these strips, very large. Thus here again we are confronted with a situation that is similar to the case of depreciation. If we make $kh = a$, we have $\left(1 - \dfrac{a}{n}\right)^n$, and this, we know, is equal to e^{-a}, or $\left(1 - \dfrac{kh}{n}\right)^n = e^{-kh}$. Thus the pressure of the air (barometric pressure) p at the height h above the sea level is equal to

$$p = Pe^{-kh}$$

By means of this formula it is possible to compute the elevation above sea level when the air pressure at the elevation is known. We proceed as follows:

$$\log p = \log P - kh \log e, \quad \text{or,} \quad kh \log e = \log P - \log p$$

$$h = \frac{1}{k \log e} (\log P - \log p)$$

The value of

$$\frac{1}{k \log e}$$

when the barometric pressure is given in millimeters is approximately 18,400, and this value enables us to compute the value of *h* in meters.

For example, the elevation of a point above sea level where the barometric pressure is 700 millimeters, while the barometric pressure at sea level is 760 millimeters, is

$$h = 18,400 (\log 760 - \log 700)$$

or

$$h = 18,400(2.8808 - 2.8451) = 18,400 \cdot 0.0357 = 656.88$$

or approximately 657 meters, or about 2,160 feet.

The same formula holds for the difference in the elevation of two points when the respective barometric pressures at these two points are given. In this case *P* is the barometric pressure at the lower point, and *p* the barometric pressure at the point above it. By means of this formula heights of mountains and the rise of balloons and airplanes may be computed. In such computations, however, the necessary corrections are introduced for temperature, humidity, wind velocity.

How Hot Is Your Coffee?

The homely process of cooling hot objects, when described mathematically, is very similar to the process of depreciation.

Suppose an object whose temperature is *T* is brought into a room in which the temperature is *t* (*T* is greater than *t*). If this hot object is left to itself, it will begin to cool off immediately, and as the process continues, the difference between the temperature of the room and that of the object will become smaller and smaller until there will be no difference. It was found that the rate of the decrease of this difference is proportional to the difference of the temperatures at that moment; thus when the difference is large the cooling is faster than when the difference is small.

In the expressions Ae^{rt} and Ae^{-rt}, which represent the two types of change, the first corresponds to growth and the second to depreciation, the values of r representing the percentage rate of change (or, as it is usually called, the "coefficient of proportionality"), and t representing the number of periods (or time). Since these types exhaust the various possibilities of change under the conditions described in this chapter, we shall avoid the lengthy derivation of the expressions in the analysis in this and the following sections.

Let us denote the difference between the two temperatures for a certain moment (say the nth) by A_n, and the original difference between the temperatures by A_0. Then, since the rate with which the differences decrease is proportional to the respective differences at the beginning of each period, we may write the relationship

$$A_n = A_0 e^{-kn}$$

where k is the coefficient of proportionality which is determined by experiment. In other words, k represents in per cent the loss in the difference between the two temperatures during any period.

We now may introduce some changes in the above relationship which will enable us to compute the temperature of the object for any moment after it begins to cool off. Since the temperature of the room is t, and the temperature of the object is T, we have

$$A_0 = T - t$$

Also, if the temperature of the object at the nth moment is T_n, and since the temperature of the room may be assumed to be constant, we have

$$A_n = T_n - t$$

Then, instead of

$$A_n = A_0 e^{-kn}$$

we may write
$$T_n - t = (T - t)e^{-kn}$$

From this we obtain the expression for the temperature of the object at the end of the nth moment,
$$T_n = t + (T - t)e^{-kn}$$

The value of k is not the same for all substances, and it must be determined by experiment as follows. The temperature of the object is measured for some definite moment, say the wth, and it was found to be T_w. Then, according to the relation obtained by us above, we have that
$$T_w - t = (T - t)e^{-kw}$$

and from this we obtain
$$e^{-kw} = \frac{T_w - t}{T - t}$$

Then, extracting the wth root from both sides of the equation, we find that
$$e^{-k} = \left(\frac{T_w - t}{T - t}\right)^{\frac{1}{w}}$$

However, this may eliminate the need to compute the coefficient of proportionality k. We may substitute the expression for e^{-k} in the expression $T_n - t = (T - t)e^{-kn}$. We have then
$$T_n = t + (T - t)\left(\frac{T_w - t}{T - t}\right)^{\frac{n}{w}}$$

Note that if $e^{-k} = S^{\frac{1}{w}}$, then $e^{-kn} = S^{\frac{n}{w}}$.

By means of the last formula we can compute the temperature of a cooling object. For example, suppose an object heated to 200 degrees Fahrenheit is brought into a room in which the temperature is 65 degrees Fahrenheit. After twenty-five minutes the temperature of the object drops to 130 degrees. What will its temperature be after another twenty-five minutes?

Translating the statement into algebra, we have

$$n = 50, \quad w = 25$$
$$t = 65, \quad T = 200, \quad \text{and} \quad T_w = 130$$

Then

$$T_n = 65 + (200 - 65) \left[\frac{(130 - 65)}{(200 - 65)} \right]^2$$

$$(50 \div 25 = 2)$$

and

$$T_n = 65 + \frac{(65)^2}{135}$$

By means of logarithms we compute $\frac{(65)^2}{135}$. We have

$$2 \log 65 = 2 \cdot 1.8129 = 3.6258$$

and

$$\log 135 = 2.1303$$
$$\overline{}$$
$$2 \log 65 - \log 135 = 1.4955$$

Since the number whose logarithm is 1.4955 is 31.3, then

$$T_n = 65 + 31.3 = 96.3$$

Thus the temperature after another twenty-five minutes will be 96.3 degrees. Suppose you are served, in some wonderful restaurant, a cup of coffee that is actually boiling hot (that is, its temperature is 212 degrees Fahrenheit). The room temperature is 75 degrees, and in about five minutes the temperature of the coffee drops to 172 degrees. How long will it take until its temperature will be 132 degrees?

We have here $t = 75°$, $T_w = 172°$, $T_n = 132°$, and $T = 212°$, and $w = 5$. Then

$$132 = 75 + (212 - 75) \left[\frac{(172 - 75)}{(212 - 75)} \right]^{\frac{n}{5}}$$

or

$$57 = 137 \left[\frac{97}{137} \right]^{\frac{n}{5}}$$

By means of logarithms we have

$$\log 57 = \log 137 + \frac{n}{5} (\log 97 - \log 137)$$

and

$$n = \frac{5(\log 57 - \log 137)}{\log 97 - \log 137}$$

or

$$n = \frac{5(1.7559 - 2.1367)}{1.9868 - 2.1367} = \frac{5(-0.3808)}{-0.1499} = 12.7, \text{ approximately}$$

Thus it would take about thirteen minutes for your coffee to cool to a pleasant sipping temperature.

The Bankers' Number Gets Around

These illustrations of the relations in which e plays an important part represent only a small fraction of its many applications in different fields. A few more may be of interest here.

However, the reader is warned that neither the applications already discussed nor those about to be considered represent the exact formulation of a relationship, since for practical brevity we must often disregard certain facts that produce comparatively little effect, or which may be corrected for error by means of special formulas. For example, when we considered the problem of the cooling coffee we paid no attention to the fact that the process of its cooling would slightly raise the temperature of the surroundings.

Nevertheless, we have obtained a formula that closely approximates the need and, in general, gives satisfactory results. The formulas and expressions that are given below will convince the reader that whenever there is a relationship in which one quantity varies (in respect to time, distance, or any other medium) so that its value is always proportional to the value of another quantity that also changes in a similar fashion, this relationship is of the form $A = A_0 e^{rt}$ or $A = A_0 e^{-rt}$, depending on the type of relationship. This may be a relationship of continued growth or a relationship of gradual death.

a) Motoring or Boating.

A motor boat moves at a speed of ten miles an hour. Suddenly its motor is stopped and after twenty seconds the speed is reduced to six miles per hour. Assuming that the resistance of the water to the motion of the boat is proportional to the speed of the boat, what will be the speed two minutes after the motor was stopped?

The relationship in this case is

$$v = v_0 e^{-\frac{k}{m}t}$$

Where v is the speed of the boat at t seconds after the motor was stopped,

v_0, the speed before the motor was stopped,

t, the number of seconds that elapse after the motor was stopped,

k, a proportionality coefficient that must be determined,

m, the weight of the motor boat.

Since k and m are not given, we shall attempt to eliminate these two as follows. The conditions state that after twenty seconds the speed of the boat was six miles an hour, then (changing seconds and minutes into fractions of an hour) we have two equations

$$6 = 10e^{-\left(\frac{k}{m}\right)\cdot\left(\frac{1}{180}\right)}$$

and

$$v = 10e^{-\left(\frac{k}{m}\right)\cdot\left(\frac{1}{30}\right)}$$

By means of logarithms we have

$$\log 6 = \log 10 - \left(\frac{k}{m}\right)\cdot\left(\frac{1}{180}\right)\log e$$

$$\log v = \log 10 - \left(\frac{k}{m}\right)\cdot\left(\frac{1}{30}\right)\log e$$

Then

$$\log 6 - 1 = -\left(\frac{k}{m}\right)\cdot\left(\frac{1}{180}\right)\log e$$

and

$$\log v - 1 = -\left(\frac{k}{m}\right)\cdot\left(\frac{1}{30}\right)\log e$$

Divide the second equation by the first, and we have

$$\frac{\log v - 1}{\log 6 - 1} = \frac{(1/30)}{(1/180)} = \frac{180}{30} = 6$$

Then $\log v - 1 = 6(\log 6 - 1)$, or $\log v = 6(\log 6 - 1) + 1$.
Then $\log v = 6(0.7782 - 1) + 1 = -6 \cdot 0.2218 + 1 = -1.3308 + 1 = -0.3308$; or

$$\log v = \overline{1}.6692$$

and

$$v = 0.467 \text{ mile per hour}$$

The same relationship holds for automobile driving provided the brakes are not applied and the road is level.

b) Parachute Jumping.

A parachutist jumps from an airplane; what will be the speed of his descent after t seconds? The formula is

$$v = \frac{\sqrt{g}}{\sqrt{k}} \frac{e^{2\sqrt{kg}\,t} - 1}{e^{2\sqrt{kg}\,t} + 1}$$

Where g is the gravitational constant, about 32.2 feet per second per second (or 980 centimeters per second per second),

k is a constant that depends on the weight of the parachutist and the size of the parachute, but on the average about 0.0050.

c) Long-Distance 'Phoning.

Conversations in long-distance telephoning usually "fade out" because of the damping effect on the lines. To counteract this damping the telephone company places at definite intervals stations which step up the intensity of the voice.

The damping effect on the wires can be determined from the equation

$$I = I_0 e^{-kd}$$

where I_0 is the initial strength of the electric current,

I, the strength of the current at d,

d, the distance,

k, a proportionality coefficient that is determined by experiment. When I is not less than 8 per cent of the initial strength of the current, the voice is still carried audibly.

d) *Loss of Light through a Transparent Medium.*

In its passage through a transparent medium, some of the intensity of light is lost, and the relationship is

$$I = I_0 e^{-kd}$$

where I_0 is the initial intensity,

I, the intensity of the beam after it has passed through a thickness d,

d, the thickness of the medium,

k, the "absorption constant" of the medium, to be determined by experiment.

e) *Submarine Warfare.*

When a submarine dives, the water outside produces pressure on its surface. At a depth of about 200 feet, this pressure is about 900 pounds a square inch. There is a depth below which the submarine cannot dive because the pressure will crush it. The relationship for the pressure and the depth is given by the equation

$$P = P_0 e^{kd}$$

where P_0 is a known pressure at some definite depth,

P, the pressure at the depth d below the surface of the sea,

d, the depth of the submarine's dive,

k, the coefficient of proportionality determined by experiment.

When a torpedo is fired from a submarine at a ship it usually travels under its own speed, being propelled by a special mechanism. However, the torpedo can travel only a certain distance because its propelling force is being gradually expended. Here again we have the relationship

$$v = v_0 e^{-\frac{k}{m}t}$$

where v_0 is the speed of the torpedo after the propelling mechanism stopped working,

v is the speed of the torpedo t seconds after the propelling mechanism stopped working, *t* is the number of seconds that elapse after the propelling mechanism stopped working,

k is a proportionality factor that is to be determined by experiment,

m is the weight of the torpedo.

In the application of this formula it is necessary to take into account the condition of the sea. This is introduced in the computations as a correction.

f) *Suspension Bridges.*

All suspension bridges have their middle spans (those supported by the cables) in the shape of a curve known as the catenary. This is a curve that is obtained when a chain is suspended from its ends and it attains a shape due to its own weight. The equation of this curve is

$$y = \frac{e^x + e^{-x}}{2}$$

Thus from these examples we may see that the bankers' number *e* is a mathematical jack of all trades who has turned his hand at almost every workshop of modern life.

△ 20 △

How to Have Fun with Lady Luck

Fickle as the Flip of a Coin

When you toss a coin, it lands with either "head" or "tail" up. (It could, conceivably, land on edge, but this would be a bad bet and we can safely leave this possibility out.) A flip of a coin thus illustrates one of the two basic eventualities, that of a situation where you cannot be certain of the outcome—either of two events is equally likely to happen.

On the other hand, there are situations where the outcome can be predicted with absolute certainty. If someone jumps without a parachute from an airplane 10,000 feet up, you may be sure he will land soon.

Thus all events may be divided into two categories—those events of which we are certain, and those that may or may not take place. The latter present some of the most important and interesting of all mathematical results.

When you flip the coin, two events are possible: either it will fall head-up or it will fall tail-up (provided the coin is honest). Any notion concerning the exact way it will fall is just a "hunch," which may or may not be good and which generally is merely an admission of ignorance. A surprisingly large number of people make a fetish of "fate" and often base their judgment and stake their money, and sometimes their lives, on hunches: this is the essence of gambling.

If you want to have fun, help yourself; but remember that luck is not a lady and, despite your most devoted attention, will turn on you if you give her half a chance. However, this chapter is not intended as moralizing; it will simply let mathematics measure the actual worth of these hunches.

How Good Is a Hunch?

Suppose someone tells you that a flipped coin will surely land head-up. There is no point in questioning him on the process of his reasoning; there is none—he "just has a hunch." However, there is a way we can actually measure the certainty of hunches.

This is an artificial measure devised on the assumption that in the occurrence of a certain event the several possibilities are equally possible, that is, no one of them is given any preference. When this democratic principle governs, we have the assurance that the mathematical investigation has no favorites and that the results are equally applicable to one event as well as to any other event in the same category.

When there are two events equally possible, and only one of them can take place, the measure of the certainty of the occurrence of one event is defined as a fraction. The numerator of this fraction is the number of the ways in which this event can take place. The denominator is the number of all possible events.

Thus in the case of a coin we have the three following facts: (1) A head can appear in one way only; (2) a tail can appear in one way only; and (3) the number of possible events is two. Then the certainty of the hunch that a tossed coin will fall head-up is $\frac{1}{2}$, and the certainty that it will fall tail-up is $\frac{1}{2}$. In other words, you cannot have any advance knowledge as to which of the two events is more likely to take place.

Before we proceed to measure hunches, let us answer the question: What is the measure of the certainty that some event will definitely occur? For example, we know that the sun rises every day; what is the measure of the certainty that it will rise tomorrow? We know that only one event can take place, and this event is the rising of the sun. Thus our fraction is

$$\frac{1}{1} = 1$$

A similar result may be obtained for any other event that must occur.

We can also answer the question: If we know that an event is to take place, what is the measure of the uncertainty that it will occur? We know that nonrising of the sun is an impossibility (in polar nights the sun also "rises" but does not come over the horizon); such an event does not exist, and its absence may be denoted by 0. Then our fraction is

$$\frac{0}{1} = 0$$

Here we may well introduce the name that is given to all such measures; they are known as the "measures of the probability" of the occurrence of an event.

Thus the probability that a tossed coin will fall head-up is $\frac{1}{2}$, as is the probability that it will fall tail-up.

We may also approach the problem of the probability of a certain event not from the viewpoint of its successful occurrence but from that of its failure to take place. Thus, for example, we may talk of the probability of a coin not falling head-up. This probability is $\frac{1}{2}$.

Note that the probability of the coin's falling head-up is $\frac{1}{2}$, that the probability of a coin's not falling head-up is also $\frac{1}{2}$, but that the sum of the probabilities is

$$\frac{1}{2} + \frac{1}{2} = 1$$

So the probability of the occurrence of an event and the probability of the nonoccurrence of the same event, if added, represent the probability that some event will take place under the defined conditions (in our case, the toss of a coin), but the nature of the event is not specified. The sum of the two probabilities is always 1; it is the probability of certainty.

Generally, if we have a certain number of events of one nature that we shall call "successes," and a certain number of events of opposite nature that we shall call "failures," then the total number of all the possible events is equal to the number of successes plus the number of failures.

Let us denote the number of the successes by s and the number of failures by f. We then find that the probability of a success is

$$\frac{s}{f+s}$$

and the probability of a failure is

$$\frac{f}{f+s}$$

We usually denote the probability of a success by p and the probability of failure by q. The reader can observe that $p + q = 1$. The sum of the two probabilities is also

$$\frac{s}{s+f} + \frac{f}{s+f} = \frac{s+f}{s+f} = 1$$

For example, if there are seven books on a shelf, of which three have red covers and four have blue covers, then the probability that, when blindfolded, we shall grasp a red book is $\frac{3}{7}$, and the probability that we shall take a blue one is $\frac{4}{7}$.

In a deck of 52 cards there are 13 spades and 39 other cards. The probability that we shall pull out a spade is

$$\tfrac{13}{52} = \tfrac{1}{4}$$

The probability that the card will not be a spade is

$$\tfrac{39}{52} = \tfrac{3}{4}$$

Note that in these two examples

$$\tfrac{3}{7} + \tfrac{4}{7} = 1 \quad \text{and} \quad \tfrac{1}{4} + \tfrac{3}{4} = 1$$

These examples show that we can calculate the probabilities in advance. Actual experience, provided we repeat the trials a great number of times, may show that in the long run these probabilities are fairly correct. Thus if a coin is thrown 200 times, the record may show that head came up 98 times and tail came up 102 times. Now

$$\tfrac{98}{200} = 0.49$$

and

$$\tfrac{102}{200} = 0.51$$

These results are close enough to the respective probabilities 0.5 and 0.5. If a coin is thrown 3,000 times, it may come up head 1,507 times and tail 1,493 times. We then have

$$\frac{1,507}{3,000} = 0.50233$$

and

$$\frac{1,493}{3,000} = 0.49767$$

Probabilities obtained after observation and experimentation are very important in many branches of business, as we shall see presently. The two cases above, however, should serve to emphasize that probabilities computed in advance are no definite insurance that an event will immediately take place according to the computed number. Nor are those probabilities computed after a great many observations and experiments any better insurance.

Mathematicians cannot be prophets where chance plays an important part. When a mathematician is able to predict the rise or fall of stocks, the hand you may hold in a game of bridge or poker, or the number of years you will survive, he will be a far more popular teacher. Meanwhile, we may as well be content that in gambling ignorance is still bliss.

The 'What' in 'What a Coincidence!'

We are often amazed at the accidental occurrence of two or more related events at the same time; we call such a phenomenon "coincidence." Now we shall determine the probability of a coincidence.

Recalling that the probability of the occurrence of an event is a fraction whose numerator represents the number of the possible favorable occurrences, or events, and whose denominator is the number of all the possible events, favorable and unfavorable, where the events are all independent and the possibility of their occurrence is equal, let us consider that two men toss two coins. We know the probability of a head-up turn when one coin is tossed, but when we have two coins tossed at the same time we may obtain several combinations:

First Coin	Second Coin
Head	Head
Head	Tail
Tail	Head
Tail	Tail

Thus in the case of two tossed coins there are four possible ways in which the two coins may fall. The probability of two heads is $\frac{1}{4}$; the probability of one head and one tail is $\frac{1}{2}$, and the probability of two tails is $\frac{1}{4}$.

Note that there are two ways in which we may obtain one head and one tail. Head may come up on the first coin, and tail on the second coin. On the other hand, tail may come up on the first coin, and head on the second. However, we may disregard the order of the appearance. Should the order of appearance be taken into consideration, the probability that the head will come up on the first coin and tail on the second is $\frac{1}{4}$, and the probability that tail will come up on the first coin and head on the second is $\frac{1}{4}$.

We observe that the sum of the probabilities obtained is $\frac{1}{4} + \frac{1}{2} + \frac{1}{4} = 1$. Here again we have the fact that the sum of the probabilities of the individual events is 1. We shall soon see that there isn't anything strange in this.

Let us denote the turning up of a head by H and the turning of a tail by T. The probability of H is $\frac{1}{2}$, and of T is $\frac{1}{2}$. Now, in the case of two coins, we have the combinations

HH, representing two heads
HT, representing head-up on the first coin and tail-up on the second
TH, representing tail-up on the first coin and head-up on the second
TT, representing two tails

If we disregard the order of the coins, we can represent our combinations as *HH*, 2*HT* (or 2*TH*), and *TT*.

Let us recall some simple facts from the algebraic method of writing products of several and the same factors. When a number is multiplied by itself, this product may be represented by writing this number with an exponent. This exponent is written to the right just above the factor that is repeated several times. Thus, if *n* is multiplied by itself four times, $n \cdot n \cdot n \cdot n$, it is written as n^4. We shall apply this notation to our symbolic representation of the combinations of the ways two tossed coins may fall.

We may consider *HH* as the product of *H*'s. The *HH* may be written as H^2. In a similar manner we may write T^2 for *TT*. Thus, our combinations may be written as H^2, 2*HT* (or 2*TH*), and T^2.

Let us denote the probability of *H* (a head-up) by *h*, and the probability of *T* (a tail-up) by *t*. Then in the case of one coin we have that

$$h + t = 1$$

Now in the case of two coins for every *H* we shall take the probability for every *H* and for every *T*. Then with *HH*, or H^2, the probability is *hh*, or h^2; with *HT*, or *TH*, the probability is *ht*, and with *TT*, or T^2, the probability is *tt*, or t^2. Then for two coins we have

$$h^2 + 2ht + t^2 = 1$$

But, if we remember the relation obtained in an earlier chapter,

$$(a + b)(a + b) = (a + b)^2 = a^2 + 2ab + b^2$$

we obtain the relation

$$h^2 + 2ht + t^2 = (h + t)^2 = 1$$

Note that this is also true because

$$h + t = 1$$

and the square of 1 is 1.

This result may be interpreted as follows. The relation of the probabilities of the head-up and tail-up in the case of one coin is

$$h + t = 1$$

In the case of two coins we obtain the relations of the respective probabilities as

$$h^2 + 2ht + t^2 = 1$$

The result is interesting also because it enables us to compute the probabilities of two coincident events when the probabilities of the individual events are known to us. The probability of two heads (or two tails) is the product of their respective probabilities; that is,

$$\tfrac{1}{2} \cdot \tfrac{1}{2} = \tfrac{1}{4}$$

Generally, if we have two events whose probabilities are known, then the probability of these two events being coincident is equal to the product of these two individual probabilities. For example, from the opposite sides of the same railroad platform trains depart in the opposite direction at equal intervals every ten minutes, but they leave the station at the same time. The probability that you and your friend will depart in the opposite directions within a ten-minute interval is computed as follows. The probability that you will catch your train as soon as you reach the station is 0.1. The probability that your friend will catch his train as soon as he reaches the station is also 0.1. The probability that the two of you will leave as soon as you reach the station is then

$$0.1 \cdot 0.1 = 0.01$$

This means that this may happen once every one hundred times.

We may also describe a coincidence as the occurrence of one event as well as the occurrence of another event. When we consider the occurrence of two heads-up and the probability of this event, we think of the two coins falling so that one coin turns head-up as well as the other coin turning head-up. Thus the probability of the coincidence of two events, also known as the "as-well-as probability," is obtained as the product of the two individual probabilities of the coincident events.

How about three or more coincident events? How are their probabilities computed?

Ten in a Row: Algebra Hits the Jackpot

Let us examine what may happen if three coins are tossed at the same time. We shall simplify our discussion by use of the symbols introduced in the preceding section; we shall denote a head-up of one coin by H (and its probability by h, which is $\frac{1}{2}$), and a tail-up of one coin by T (and its probability by t, which is $\frac{1}{2}$). When three coins are tossed at the same time, one of the following combinations may take place:

First Coin	Second Coin	Third Coin	The Probability
H	H	H	hhh, or h^3
H	H	T	hht, or h^2t
H	T	H	hth, or h^2t
T	H	H	thh, or h^2t
H	T	T	htt, or ht^2
T	H	T	tht, or ht^2
T	T	H	tth, or ht^2
T	T	T	ttt, or t^3

If we disregard the order in which the coins are considered we have only four distinct combinations, namely, three heads, two heads and one tail, two tails and one head, and three tails.

Among these there is one combination of three heads, one combination of three tails, and three combinations of two heads and one tail, and three combinations of one head and two tails. Thus the sum total of all the possible falls may be represented as H^3, $3H^2T$, $3HT^2$, and T^3. For the three coins the sum of the probabilities is then

$$h^3 + 3h^2t + 3ht^2 + t^3 = 1$$

The value of h and also of t is also $\frac{1}{2}$. Substituting these values in the expression above we have

$$\frac{1}{8} + \frac{3}{8} + \frac{3}{8} + \frac{1}{8} = 1$$

The probability that three coins will all fall head-up or tail-up is $\frac{1}{8}$, and the probability that two heads and one tail, or one head and two tails, will fall is $\frac{3}{8}$.

The reader will have noticed now that the probability is expressed by a number that is a fraction always less than 1. The smaller the fraction the less likely is the occurrence of the events that corresponds to it. Thus an event whose probability is $\frac{1}{8}$ is less likely to take place than the event whose probability is $\frac{3}{8}$. But this is no guarantee that three heads (or three tails) will not appear on the first toss of three coins. Presently we shall see that there is some usefulness in the value of the magnitude of a probability.

The reader will have observed also that the probabilities when several coins are tossed are obtained by means of the expression

$$h + t = 1$$

when the two sides of this expression are raised to the power whose exponent is equal to the number of the coins tossed. Thus when four coins are tossed we have

$$(h + t)^4 = 1$$

or

$$h^4 + 4h^3t + 6h^2t^2 + 4ht^3 + t^4 = 1$$

and the respective probabilities are:

For four   heads...................... $\frac{1}{16}$
For three heads and one   tail.......... $\frac{4}{16} = \frac{1}{4}$
For two   heads and two   tails......... $\frac{6}{16} = \frac{3}{8}$
For one   head and three tails......... $\frac{4}{16} = \frac{1}{4}$
For four   tails...................... $\frac{1}{16}$

Generally, then, if we have n coins, the respective probabilities are obtained by means of the expression

$$(h + t)^n = 1$$

To be able to obtain the individual terms of this expression when it is expanded, we shall make use of a table of the coefficients of the terms that are arranged in the decreasing order of the magnitude of exponents of one letter (say h) and the increasing order of the magnitude of the exponents of the other letter (say t). Note that in the expansions above the terms were arranged as follows:

$$h^2, \quad ht, \quad t^2$$
$$h^3, \quad h^2t, \quad ht^2, \quad t^3$$
$$h^4, \quad h^3t, \quad h^2t^2, \quad ht^3, \quad t^4$$

Generally, the terms of the expression of $(h + t)^n$ should be arranged as

$$h^n, \ h^{n-1}t, \ h^{n-2}t^2, \ h^{n-3}t^3, \ h^{n-4}t^4, \ \ldots, \ h^3t^{n-3}, \ h^2t^{n-2}, \ ht^{n-1}, \ t^n$$

Note that the sum of the exponents of each term is n. Thus

$$n - 1 + 1 = n, \quad n - 2 + 2 = n$$

The table that gives the coefficients of the respective terms when they are arranged as shown above is:

Exponent of $(h + t)$	Coefficients									
1	1	1								
2	1	2	1							
3	1	3	3	1						
4	1	4	6	4	1					
5	1	5	10	10	5	1				
6	1	6	15	20	15	6	1			
7	1	7	21	35	35	21	7	1		
8	1	8	28	56	70	56	28	8	1	
9	1	9	36	84	126	126	84	36	9	1
10	1	10	45	120	210	252	210	120	45	10	1

This table may be extended as follows: The first number (coefficient) on the left is always 1. The second (and every succeeding) number is obtained as the sum of the number just above it and the number on the left of that number. Thus for the exponent 10, we have:

The first	number is	1		
The second	number is	1 +	9 =	10
The third	number is	9 +	36 =	45
The fourth	number is	36 +	84 =	120
The fifth	number is	84 +	126 =	210
The sixth	number is	126 +	126 =	252
The seventh	number is	126 +	84 =	210
The eighth	number is	84 +	36 =	120
The ninth	number is	36 +	9 =	45
The tenth	number is	9 +	1 =	10
The eleventh	number is	1 +	0 =	1

Thus the expansion of $(h + t)^{10}$ is

$$h^{10} + 10h^9t + 45h^8t^2 + 120h^7t^3 + 210h^6t^4 + 252h^5t^5 + $$
$$210h^4t^6 + 120h^3t^7 + 45h^2t^8 + 10ht^9 + t^{10}$$

This enables us to compute the probabilities of the various combinations of heads and tails when ten coins are all tossed at the same time. We substitute the values of $h = \frac{1}{2}$ and $t = \frac{1}{2}$ and perform the indicated computations.

It should be pointed out, however, that tossing six coins at the same time is simply equivalent to tossing one coin six times in succession. Only once can there be six heads in succession, and only once can there be six tails in succession. The reader may work out other combinations as an exercise.

Mugwump Math: Head or Tail?

When two coins are tossed they may turn up two heads once; one head and one tail twice; and two tails, once. Thus a head, or a tail, may turn up in three combinations. Computing the probability of the occurrence of an event in such situations we take into account all possible events, either unfavorable or favorable. In other words, in the case of two coins there are four possible events. Of these, however, only three would result with at least one head. Then the probability that at least one head will turn up is $\frac{3}{4}$; the same probability holds for tails.

We may also obtain the above result if we add the respective probabilities of all those events in which at least one head (or one tail) turns up. Thus if asked the probability that at least one head will turn up after two coins are tossed, we may answer it from these probabilities of the individual events:

For two heads. . . . . $\frac{1}{4}$
For a head on the first coin and a tail on the second. . $\frac{1}{4}$
For a tail on the first coin and a head on the second. . $\frac{1}{4}$

Total. . . . . $\frac{3}{4}$

The occurrence of an event under such circumstances is not specified by any other conditions except that this event is expected to occur in some manner, either in one combination or in another. Generally the probability of an event under such conditions is larger than the probability of a coincidence, and the reason is simple. In the case of a coincidence the probability is computed as the product of the respective probabilities. Since a probability is measured in terms of a fraction that is less than one (1), the product of two or more such fractions will always be smaller than any of them. For example, we have three fractions, $\frac{1}{4}$, $\frac{1}{8}$, and $\frac{3}{16}$. The product of the three is $\frac{3}{512}$, and $\frac{3}{512}$ is smaller than $\frac{1}{4}$, $\frac{1}{8}$, or $\frac{3}{16}$. Thus occurrence of a coincidence may be considered rather rare. On the other hand, the sum of the three fractions is $\frac{9}{16}$, and it is larger than $\frac{1}{4}$, or $\frac{1}{8}$, or $\frac{3}{16}$. In other words, the "either-or" event is more common than a single event, and considerably more common than a coincidence.

In the case of an either-or event we cease to be choosers. We select no special event, because we refuse to make a definite choice, and our selection is much broader than in an individual occurrence. Thus the probability that at least one tail will appear when three coins are tossed is

$$\frac{3}{8} + \frac{3}{8} + \frac{1}{8} = \frac{7}{8}$$

The probability that at least one head will appear when four coins are tossed is

$$\frac{1}{16} + \frac{4}{16} + \frac{6}{16} + \frac{4}{16} = \frac{15}{16}$$

The probability that at least two heads will appear when four coins are tossed is

$$\frac{1}{16} + \frac{4}{16} + \frac{6}{16} = \frac{11}{16}$$

An Ancient Lullaby: Baby Needs Shoes

The game of dice, also known as shooting craps, was played in ancient times in Egypt and Persia, but the first "loaded," or dishonest, dice seem to have appeared in early Rome. We shall ex-amine some of the probabilities in the game assuming, of course, that the dice are tolerably honest. All dice, incidentally, are loaded whether intentionally or not; there are no perfect dice. A die, cubical in shape, has six faces, and on these faces there are dots numbering from 1 to 6.

The probability that one of the six numbers will turn up is ⅙. However, in the game of dice two cubes are used. Thus the probability that two identical faces will turn up is

$$\frac{1}{6} \cdot \frac{1}{6} = \frac{1}{36}$$

However, it is the sum of the dots that is decisive. Below are listed all the possible combinations of the numbers from one to six, according to the possible sums. It should be remembered that it is immaterial whether a number appears on one die or another, and thus the order in which the dice turn up on one throw is disregarded.

2	3	4	5	6	7	8	9	10	11	12
1 1	1 2	1 3	1 4	1 5	1 6	2 6	3 6	4 6	5 6	6 6
	2 1	2 2	2 3	2 4	2 5	3 5	4 5	5 5	6 5	
		3 1	3 2	3 3	3 4	4 4	5 4	6 4		
			4 1	4 2	4 3	5 3	6 3			
				5 1	5 2	6 2				
					6 1					

Thus, altogether, we have thirty-six possible combinations. The numbers appear as follows:

$$2—1 \text{ time}$$
$$3—2 \text{ times}$$
$$4—3 \text{ times}$$
$$5—4 \text{ times}$$
$$6—5 \text{ times}$$
$$7—6 \text{ times}$$
$$8—5 \text{ times}$$
$$9—4 \text{ times}$$
$$10—3 \text{ times}$$
$$11—2 \text{ times}$$
$$12—1 \text{ time}$$

Their respective probabilities are:

For 2, $\frac{1}{36}$

For 3, $\frac{2}{36} = \frac{1}{18}$

For 4, $\frac{3}{36} = \frac{1}{12}$

For 5, $\frac{4}{36} = \frac{1}{9}$

For 6, $\frac{5}{36}$

For 7, $\frac{6}{36} = \frac{1}{6}$

For 8, $\frac{5}{36}$

For 9, $\frac{4}{36} = \frac{1}{9}$

For 10, $\frac{3}{36} = \frac{1}{12}$

For 11, $\frac{2}{36} = \frac{1}{18}$

For 12, $\frac{1}{36}$

If we apply the method of computing the probabilities of a coincidence we may answer now a question that has long been a subject of debate among the poolroom professors. What is the probability that a 7 and an 11 will come up in succession? The probability of a 7, we find, is $\frac{1}{6}$, and of an 11, $\frac{1}{18}$. Then the probability that a 7 and an 11 will come up in succession is

$$\frac{1}{6} \cdot \frac{1}{18} = \frac{1}{108}$$

The reader may compute any other probability by the methods developed in the preceding sections.

What the 'Odds' Are

Very often we are prone to back with money our hunch or conviction that a certain event will take place. This may take the form of a straight bet, purchase of a lottery ticket, or investment in an insurance policy. In some cases we place a bet as protection, usually against some hazard such as death, fire, accident, or burglary. In such situations the bet takes the form of an agreement with a business concern which undertakes to recompense us in case we suffer a loss in one form or another. This type of a bet is legitimate and is generally recognized as a very reasonable procedure. Other forms of betting are usually labeled gambling.

We pointed out that a computed probability of some event does not necessarily represent a definite guarantee that this event will take place in strict accordance with this computed probability. In other words, if the computed probability is $\frac{2}{5}$, it does not necessarily follow that out of every five events two will be represented by the event under consideration. The computed probability refers to a considerable number of repeated trials, so that in the long run the ratio of the favorable events to the total number of events will be $\frac{2}{5}$. However, when a bet is placed on such an event, the bettor disregards this fact and takes a chance, a chance that may operate against him. This is straight gambling. There is even some element of gambling in insurance, but it is reduced to a minimum. Insurance probabilities are always computed on the basis of long experience and on recorded cases that run into hundreds of thousands, so that the general trend of the observed events may be discovered.

The common method of betting is usually based on the computed probability of an event. This is known as following the "odds." The computation of the odds is performed as follows. If we know the probability in favor of some event (let it be denoted by p), we can compute the probability against its occurrence. Their sum is 1. Then the probability against the occurrence of this event (let us denote it by q) is

$$q = 1 - p$$

The ratio of the probability in favor to the probability against an event is the odds in favor of the event. Thus if the probability in favor of an event is $\frac{2}{5}$, then the probability against this event is

$$1 - \frac{2}{5} = \frac{3}{5}$$

Then the odds in favor of this event are

$$\frac{2}{5} \div \frac{3}{5} = \frac{2}{3}$$

that is, two to three.

Betting is based on the odds. Thus, if the odds are two to three in favor of an event, then a person who wishes to back the possibility of its occurrence and base his backing on the computed probability, the computed odds, will bet in the ratio of two to three. So the betting arrangement in favor of this event should be $2 to the $3 offered by another person.

If the odds are given it is easy to compute the probability of the particular event. For example, if the odds against are 7 to 3, then the probability against the occurrence of this event is a fraction whose numerator is 7, and whose denominator is the sum of the two numbers in terms of which the odds are stated. Thus the probability against the occurrence of the event is

$$\frac{7}{7 + 3} = \frac{7}{10}$$

From this we find that the probability in favor of the occurrence of this event is $1 - \frac{7}{10} = \frac{3}{10}$. If the odds are stated as even, that is, one to one, the probability in favor of the occurrence of the event is

$$\frac{1}{1 + 1} = \frac{1}{2}$$

How Long Will You Live?

Insurance companies, to determine the cost of life policies, make use of a regularly revised table known as the American Experience Mortality Table. In it they have a record of some 100,000 persons from the ages of 10 to 95, with the number of living at the beginning of every year, the number of those who die each year, and the life expectation of those who survive. All additional information is computed from the data of this table, an example of which we see on page 347.

This table does not offer any definite information concerning any individual person, but in considering the whole population of the country through study of representative elements, gives a fairly good description of what happens to the average individual. Thus, if 100,000 children, all 10 years old, are taken at random, it is expected that 749 of them will die within a year, and only 99,251 will reach their eleventh birthdays.

The mortality table enables us further to compute the probability of survival. For example, what is the probability that a man thirty years old will survive one year? The number living at the age of thirty is 85,441, and the number of living at the age of thirty-one is 84,721. Then the probability of survival one year is

$$\frac{84,721}{85,441} = 0.992$$

and the probability of dying during the year is

$$1 - 0.992 = 0.008$$

What is the probability that a man twenty-five years old will reach the age of sixty? The number of those alive at twenty-five is 89,032. The number of those still alive at sixty is 57,917. The probability that a man twenty-five years old will live thirty-five years is

$$\frac{57,917}{89,032} = 0.65$$

and the probability that a man twenty-five years old will not reach his sixtieth birthday is

$$1 - 0.65 = 0.35$$

Let us examine a few more problems. A man of thirty marries a woman of twenty-five. What is the probability that he will become a widower fifteen years after their wedding? What is

Age	Number of Living	Number of Dying	Number of Years Expected to Live	Age	Number of Living	Number of Dying	Number of Years Expected to Live
10	100,000	749	48.72	53	66,797	1,091	18.79
11	99,251	746	48.08	54	65,706	1,143	18.09
12	98,505	743	47.45				
13	97,762	740	46.80	55	64,563	1,199	17.40
14	97,022	737	46.16	56	63,364	1,260	16.72
				57	62,104	1,325	16.05
15	96,285	735	45.50	58	60,779	1,394	15.39
16	95,550	732	44.85	59	59,385	1,468	14.74
17	94,818	729	44.19				
18	94,089	727	43.53	60	57,917	1,546	14.10
19	93,362	725	42.87	61	56,371	1,628	13.47
				62	54,743	1,713	12.86
20	92,637	723	42.20	63	53,030	1,800	12.26
21	91,914	722	41.53	64	51,230	1,889	11.67
22	91,192	721	40.85				
23	90,471	720	40.17	65	49,341	1,980	11.10
24	89,751	719	39.49	66	47,361	2,070	10.54
				67	45,291	2,158	10.00
25	89,032	718	38.81	68	43,133	2,243	9.47
26	88,314	718	38.12	69	40,890	2,321	8.97
27	87,596	718	37.43				
28	86,878	718	36.73	70	38,569	2,391	8.48
29	86,160	719	36.03	71	36,178	2,448	8.00
				72	33,730	2,487	7.55
30	85,441	720	35.33	73	31,243	2,505	7.11
31	84,721	721	34.63	74	28,738	2,501	6.68
32	84,000	723	33.92				
33	83,277	726	33.21	75	26,237	2,476	6.27
34	82,551	729	32.50	76	23,761	2,431	5.88
				77	21,330	2,369	5.49
35	81,822	732	31.78	78	18,961	2,291	5.11
36	81,090	737	31.07	79	16,670	2,196	4.74
37	80,353	742	30.35				
38	79,611	749	29.62	80	14,474	2,091	4.39
39	78,862	756	28.90	81	12,383	1,964	4.05
				82	10,419	1,816	3.71
40	78,106	765	28.18	83	8,603	1,648	3.39
41	77,341	774	27.45	84	6,955	1,470	3.08
42	76,567	785	26.72				
43	75,782	797	26.00	85	5,485	1,292	2.77
44	74,985	812	25.27	86	4,193	1,114	2.47
				87	3,079	933	2.18
45	74,173	828	24.54	88	2,146	744	1.91
46	73,345	848	23.81	89	1,402	555	1.66
47	72,497	870	23.08				
48	71,627	896	22.36	90	847	385	1.42
49	70,731	927	21.63	91	462	246	1.19
				92	216	137	0.98
50	69,804	962	20.91	93	79	58	0.80
51	68,842	1,001	20.20	94	21	18	0.64
52	67,841	1,044	19.49	95	3	3	0.50

the probability that she will become a widow fifteen years after? And what is the probability that they will be both alive fifteen years after? There is also another possibility, that both will be dead fifteen years after their wedding.

Let the probability that the man will be alive be denoted as M_a; the probability that he will be dead, M_d; the probability that the woman will be alive, W_a; and the probability that she will be dead, W_d. We have then the following combinations: (1) man alive and woman alive; (2) man alive and woman dead; (3) man dead and woman alive; and (4) man dead and woman dead. In symbols we have then, remembering that the probabilities of these four situations are the probabilities of coincidences, M_aW_a, M_aW_d, M_dW_a, and M_dW_d. We shall now compute the various probabilities.

The probability that a man thirty years old will survive fifteen years is

$$M_a = \frac{\text{Number alive at 45}}{\text{Number alive at 30}} = \frac{74,173}{85,441} = 0.868$$

The probability that a man thirty years old will not survive fifteen years is

$$M_d = 1 - 0.868 = 0.132$$

The probability that a woman twenty-five years old will survive fifteen years is

$$W_a = \frac{\text{Number alive at 40}}{\text{Number alive at 25}} = \frac{78,106}{89,032} = 0.881$$

The probability that a woman twenty-five years old will not survive fifteen years is

$$W_d = 1 - 0.881 = 0.119$$

Then M_aW_a, the probability that both husband and wife will be alive at the end of fifteen years of married life, is

$$0.868 \cdot 0.881 = 0.765$$

M_aW_d, the probability that the husband will become a widower at the end of fifteen years of married life, is

$$0.868 \cdot 0.119 = 0.103$$

M_aW_a, the probability that the wife will become a widow at the end of fifteen years of married life, is

$$0.132 \cdot 0.881 = 0.116$$

Finally, M_aW_a, the probability that both husband and wife will be dead at the end of fifteen years, is

$$0.132 \cdot 0.119 = 0.016$$

Note that the four probabilities computed exhaust all possible combinations. It should then be expected that their sum should be equal to 1. We have

$$0.765 + 0.103 + 0.116 + 0.016 = 1$$

Also note that there is some chance that the woman will become a widow rather than the man a widower. The probability that she will become a widow is 0.116, and the probability that he will become a widower is 0.103.

What Price Life?

When you buy a lottery ticket, say for \$2.50 with a chance of winning \$150,000 as the first prize, you may ask: What is this ticket really worth?

Let us suppose that 500,000 tickets are sold, and that there are three principal prizes, each of \$150,000, to be won. Thus only 3 of the 500,000 ticket holders are expected to win the big money. The probability of winning \$150,000 is then $\frac{3}{500,000}$. The value of the ticket is then

$$250 \cdot \frac{3}{500,000} = 0.0015 \text{ cent}$$

Let us suppose that altogether there are 1,000 possible prizes in this lottery. Then the probability of winning one is $\frac{1,000}{500,000} = \frac{1}{500}$, and the worth of the ticket is then $\frac{250}{500} = 0.5$ cent.

Now let us consider another example. A man is thirty years old and according to the mortality table may expect to live about thirty-five years. The average income in this country may be taken as about $800 a year. Then the average man of thirty years who looks forward to another thirty-five years may be expected to earn $800·35 = $28,000.

The World War cost the belligerents at least 250 billion dollars. About 8,500,000 men were killed. It has cost about

$$\frac{\$250,000,000,000}{8,500,000} = \$29,400$$

to kill one man. So it cost more to kill one man in World War I than the average man would have earned if he were left alive.

The product of the numerical value of the probability of some event under consideration by the magnitude of the monetary risk (or by any other magnitude that is associated with this event) is known as the "mathematical expectation" of the event. It should be understood that the numerical value of the probability of the event gives us a fairly satisfactory means for judging the risk that we undertake when we decide to back that event with money. If the probability in favor of the event is very small, the risk is considerable, and the value of the money wager is correspondingly low. On the other hand, if the probability is close to one—that is, the expectation is in favor of the event—we may consider the risk is comparatively smaller. However, it should be understood that the probability as expressed by some fraction is at no time a definite guarantee that the event will take place: any gamble is necessarily uncertain if honest.

Drop a Needle, Pick Up a Probability

An interesting number much used as a multiplier in computation of the circumference of a circle is the number known as π. It is approximately equal to 3.14159. We know that it is impossible to determine π exactly, but we shall see now that it is possible to approximate its value during the process of a very simple experiment in probability.

Take a needle and break off its sharp point so that it is of more uniform thickness. On a piece of paper draw a series of parallel lines so that the distance between them is twice as large as the length of the needle. Place this paper on a blotter and then drop the needle on the paper (the blotter will prevent the needle from bouncing off the paper). Continue dropping the needle on the paper 100 or 1,000 times; the greater the number the closer will be the result obtained. Each time you drop the needle note whether it crosses some line, considering it a crossing when even the end of the needle touches a line. Now, if the total number of times the needle was dropped is divided by the number of times it crossed a line, the result of the division will be the approximate value of π.

Suppose that the number of the crossings is A, and assume that any part of the needle has the same chance of falling across any of the lines. If the needle is two inches long, then, since every part of the needle has the same chance of falling across a line, the number of crossings for 1 inch is $A/2$. If the needle is divided into n equal parts, the number of crossings for each part is A/n. The number of crossings for two such parts is $2A/n$, and the number of crossings for ten such parts is $10A/n$. Thus we arrive at the conclusion that the number of the crossings is proportional to the length of the needle.

The needle need not be straight; suppose that it is bent as shown below. Suppose that BC contains m parts of the needle

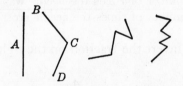

(after it is divided into n equal parts). Then the remaining portion of the needle (CD) will contain $n - m$ parts. Their respective number of crossings will be

$$\frac{mA}{n} \quad \text{and} \quad \frac{(n - m)A}{n}$$

and the total sum of the crossings is still equal to A. However, it should be noted that a bent needle may fall so that it will cross the same line several times. If this happens, all the crossings must be counted.

Suppose we have a needle that is bent into a circle and the radius of the circle is equal in length to our original needle. When such a circle is dropped onto the paper (the distance between the lines is thus equal to the diameter of the circle), it will either cross one line twice (a straight line intersects the circumference of a circle twice) or will touch two lines. Let us suppose that the number of times that the circular needle was dropped is B, then the number of crossings is $2B$, because every time that this circular needle is dropped it must either come in contact with one line twice or touch two lines. The length of the circular needle (if its radius is r, which is the length of our original needle) is $2\pi r$. Thus the circular needle is 2π times as large as the original needle. We also have established that the number of the crossings is proportional to the length of the needle. Thus the number of the possible crossings of the original needle, A, is 2π times smaller than $2B$. In other words,

$$A \cdot 2\pi = 2B$$

and from this we obtain

$$\pi = \frac{B}{A}$$

that is,

$$\pi = \frac{\text{Number of times the needle was dropped}}{\text{Number of times the needle crossed a line}}$$

Moreover, if we invert the fraction on the right of this equality we have

$$\frac{1}{\pi} = \frac{A}{B}$$

or

$$\frac{1}{\pi} = \frac{\text{Number of times the needle crossed a line}}{\text{Number of times the needle was dropped}}$$

This last result is the probability of the needle crossing a line, thus

$$\frac{1}{\pi} = 0.31831, \quad \text{approximately}$$

If the reader wishes to check the results obtained in this section and has sufficient patience, let him extend the experiment by dropping the needle ten thousand times. He may get quite tired, but he will undoubtedly be astounded by the results.

PROBLEMS

1. What is the probability that in two consecutive throws of two dice the same numbers will appear? [Answer:

$$\text{For 2, } \frac{1}{1296} \qquad\qquad \text{For 8, } \frac{25}{1296}$$

$$\text{For 3, } \frac{1}{324} \qquad\qquad \text{For 9, } \frac{1}{81}$$

$$\text{For 4, } \frac{1}{144} \qquad\qquad \text{For 10, } \frac{1}{144}$$

$$\text{For 5, } \frac{1}{81} \qquad\qquad \text{For 11, } \frac{1}{324}$$

$$\text{For 6, } \frac{25}{1296} \qquad\qquad \text{For 12, } \frac{1}{1296}]$$

$$\text{For 7, } \frac{1}{36}$$

2. What is the probability that a 19-year old bride marrying a 21-year old groom will not be a widow at the age of 45? [Answer: 0.62]

3. What is the probability that a 19-year old bride marrying a 25-year old groom will be a widow at the age of 50? [Answer: 0.21]

□ 21 □

The Thinking Machines

Hollywood Goes Mathematical

Once upon a time, and not so very long ago, a motion picture producer had a bright idea. For some time, according to the legend, his pictures invariably were termed dreary by the critics and, worse, had not clicked with the public. He changed the writers of his scripts and tried about every other possible remedy, but, strangely enough, all his efforts failed. Then, one day, came the bright idea; this is how he reasoned:

All successful motion pictures have some general idea. Let us list these ideas. Then every story, whether dramatic, comic, or melodramatic, has a central character, played by the leading man or woman. Next there are the various supporting casts. Let us list all these, and the various plots and the different localities where the actions take place. Thus he went through all the other phases usually considered important in the making of a profitable picture and carefully tabulated them.

Then he ordered the lists put on recording rolls, one roll for characters, another for the parts of the supporting casts, another for various plots, and so on. Finally, when all this was done, he ordered that the rolls be played off, but in a definite order. Each item on each roll was numbered from 1 up. Before playing the rolls, all were set on No. 1. Then the first roll was played off, and the combinations of items of the first roll were recorded with the other items that were numbered 1. After this was done, the second roll was set on item No. 2 and the first roll was played again. When it had been played once, and all the combinations were recorded, the second roll was set on item No. 3, and this procedure was repeated until all the items of the second roll were played off. Then the third roll was set on item No. 2, the first roll was played again, and after each complete playing of the first roll an item on the second roll was pushed forward. When the second roll was completely played off, item No. 3 on the third roll was set, and so on, until the third roll was completed, and the same procedure was started all over again, as the fourth roll came into the picture. At every setting a complete record of the combination obtained was recorded. Thus a number of combinations was obtained and the producer gave it to the script department for analysis and consideration. Whether this idea gave the producer a better box office is a matter of surmise. However, what should interest us is the question whether this story is just the spoofing of some publicity agent or whether such an experiment is physically possible. We shall have our answer in a moment.

That Good-Movie Formula

Let us now cast a mathematical eye upon the bright idea of the motion picture producer. The supercolossal is, of course, the minimum in the screen industry, but this experiment, if it were actually tried, must have set some sort of modest record.

Let us suppose that, after careful classification, the producer obtained ten (and that would be a very small number) classifications. Thus he had ten rolls. Let us suppose each roll contained only ten items, and that would be cutting to the bone some of the items. The total number of possible combinations is then $10^{10} = 10,000,000,000$.

Suppose the recording of each combination took 30 seconds. Thus the entire recording would take $3 \cdot 10^{11}$ seconds, or

$$3 \cdot 10^{11} \div 60 = 5 \cdot 10^9 \text{ minutes}$$

If a clerk worked about 400 minutes a day, the work would take about $125 \cdot 10^5$ days. If ten thousand clerks were employed it would take 1,250 working days, or about 4 years, Sundays and holidays excluded. And it must be understood that a great many combinations would be workable. So it may safely be assumed that by this time the producer, unless his luck had a sudden resurrection, is marching as a foot soldier in Hollywood's great army of has-beens.

PROBLEMS

1. Suppose that the physique of a human being is determined by 20 distinct characteristics, and each characteristic may have 10 variations. How many individuals, none of them alike, may there be?

2. A patent lock usually has five small bars in it. Each bar is generally cut in two parts, and for every lock the combination of the cut bars is different. If each bar may be cut in 100 different ways, how many possible combinations are there in a patent lock?

3. On a cosmetics counter there are lipsticks in 5 different shades, rouge in 5, nail enamels in 15, and face powders in 10. In how many ways can a girl make herself beautiful if she buys one item of each?

Memo for Burglars

A would-be burglar often faces the same type of problem as the producer (on a somewhat less colossal scale, of course): He knows he has all the answers, but he still can't pick the right one.

There are many types of combination locks; some are of dial arrangement, others have cylinder setting, and so on, but the principle of all is the same, and this discussion of a dial therefore can be applied to any type.

Suppose a combination lock has two dials with six letters on each:

| First dial | .... *A* | *B* | *C* | *D* | *E* | *F* |
| Second dial | .... *A* | *B* | *C* | *D* | *E* | *F* |

Usually only one setting of the two dials (that is, a definite combination) will unlock the lock. To obtain the possible combinations the first dial is turned. Thus, the letter *A* of the second dial is combined with the six letters of the first dial. Then the second dial is set on *B*, and the first dial is turned again. Thus we obtain all the possible combinations of *B* of the second dial with the letters of the first dial. Each time we thus get six combinations of the two letters. Altogether, we have six settings of the second dial, and each setting yields six combinations. All the possible combinations are

$$
\begin{array}{cccccc}
AA & AB & AC & AD & AE & AF \\
BA & BB & BC & BD & BE & BF \\
CA & CB & CC & CD & CE & CF \\
DA & DB & DC & DD & DE & DF \\
EA & EB & EC & ED & EE & EF \\
FA & FB & FC & FD & FE & FF
\end{array}
$$

Thus the total number of combinations of the two letters on the two dials is

$$6 \cdot 6 = 36$$

If there were eight letters on each dial, and we had two dials, the total number of the combinations would be

$$8 \cdot 8 = 64$$

Generally, if there were a letters on one dial and b letters on the other dial, then the total combinations of two letters (one from each dial) would be

$$a \cdot b$$

Now suppose that there are three dials on a lock. For simplicity we shall assume that there are only four letters on each dial:

First dial .... $A \quad B \quad C \quad D$
Second dial .... $A \quad B \quad C \quad D$
Third dial........... $A \quad B \quad C \quad D$

We then have the following combinations:

$$
\begin{array}{cccccccc}
AAA & ABA & ACA & ADA & AAB & ABB & ACB & ADB \\
AAC & ABC & ACC & ADC & AAD & ABD & ACD & ADD \\
BAA & BBA & BCA & BDA & BAB & BBB & BCB & BDB \\
BAC & BBC & BCC & BDC & BAD & BBD & BCD & BDD \\
CAA & CBA & CCA & CDA & CAB & CBB & CCB & CDB \\
CAC & CBC & CCC & CDC & CAD & CBD & CCD & CDD \\
DAA & DBA & DCA & DDA & DAB & DBB & DCB & DDB \\
DAC & DBC & DCC & DDC & DAD & DBD & DCD & DDD
\end{array}
$$

In this case we have $4 \cdot 4 \cdot 4 = 64$ combinations of three letters.

Generally, if there are three dials and one dial has a letters, the second dial b letters, and the third dial c letters, the total number of combinations of three letters is $a \cdot b \cdot c$.

Finally, here is the general rule: *The number of combinations for dials is equal to the total product of the number of letters of each dial.*

PROBLEMS

4. What is the possible number of combinations of a lock that has three dials with 10, 11, and 12 letters, respectively?

5. Four dials have the ten digits (0, 1, 2, 3, 4, 5, 6, 7, 8, 9) on each. How many numbers may be obtained by placing these dials in all possible combinations of positions?

6. Three parties are competing so that one number of each is assured of election. Each party has a ticket of several candidates. These three tickets have 25, 30, and 40 candidates. How many possible combinations of three candidates are there?

7. If you can travel to Albany by boat, train, automobile, or bicycle, and can then return to Manhattan by plane, bus, horseback, walking, or motorcycle, how many possible combinations are there?

8. On a restaurant menu there are listed 10 appetizers, 5 soups, 35 entrees, 4 salads, 20 desserts, and 7 beverages. How many different dinners can be ordered from this menu? (One item of each is ordered.)

Why Robbers Blow Up Safes

Bank safes have combination locks that are especially complicated. They are mechanical marvels, however, and their unlocking is quite simple, provided you know the combination. Usually a bank safe has a lock with five dials, and on each dial there are ten digits from 0 to 9 (other dials may have letters, and the number of letters may vary). On such a safe the total number of combinations is $10^5 = 100,000$, and only one of these will open it.

Suppose you decide to rob a bank's safe but haven't been able to meet any of the vice-presidents socially and can't even get the guard to talk about the weather. You are in a spot for the combination and have to try your luck on the dials. Let us assume that it takes about 30 seconds to try one setting. Then all the possible settings (and seeing whether the setting works) will take 3,000,000 seconds, or $3,000,000 \div 60 = 50,000$ minutes, or $50,000 \div 60 = 833$ hours and 20 minutes. Since robbing is usually done at night and you can spend at most only 8 hours an evening on this type of job, it would take about 104 nights of 8 hours each to finish your work. So, as a professional man with a reputation at stake, you must take the ultimate in mathematical short-cuts—nitroglycerin.

Wisdom by the Turn of a Crank

In *Gulliver's Travels* Lemuel Gulliver tells of a visit to the Grand Academy in Lagado in the Land of Laputa. Among the curious inventions demonstrated to him was a machine by means of which its inventor hoped to obtain and record everything that was published and could be published in all of science, art, philosophy, theology, literature, and so on. Gulliver's description of this remarkable machine said in part:

"The first professor I saw was in a very large room, with forty pupils about him. After salutation, observing me to look earnestly upon a frame, which took up the greatest part of both the length and breadth of the room, he said perhaps I might wonder to see him employed in a project for improving speculative knowledge by practical and mechanical operations. But the world would soon be sensible of its usefulness, and he flattered himself that a more noble exalted thought never sprang in any other man's head. Every one knew how laborious the usual method is of attaining to arts and sciences; whereas by his contrivance the most ignorant person at a reasonable charge, and with a little body labour, may write books in philosophy, poetry, politics, law, mathematics, and theology, without the least assistance from genius or study. He then led me to the frame, about the sides whereof all his pupils stood in ranks. It was twenty foot square, placed in the middle of the room. The superficies was composed of several bits of wood, about the bigness of a die, but some larger than others. They were all linked together by slender wires. These bits of wood were covered on every square with paper pasted on them, and on these papers were written all the words of their language, in their several moods, but without any order. The professor then desired me to observe, for he was going to set his engine at work. The pupils at his command took each of them hold of an iron handle, whereof there were forty fixed round the edges of the frame, and giving them a sudden turn, the whole disposition of the words was entirely changed. He then commanded six and thirty of the lads to read the several lines softly as they appeared upon the frame; and where they found three or four words that might make part of a sentence, they dictated to the four remaining boys who were scribes. This work was repeated three or four times, and at every turn the engine was so contrived that the words shifted into new places, as the square bits of wood moved upside down.

"Six hours a day the young students were employed in this labour, and the professor showed me several volumes in large folio already

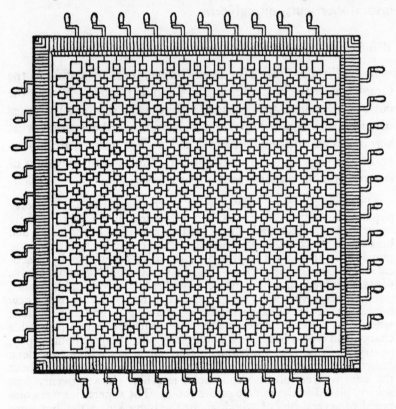

collected, of broken sentences, which he intended to piece together, and out of those rich materials to give the world a complete body of all arts and sciences; which however might be still improved, and

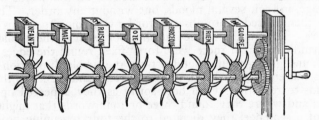

much expedited, if the public would raise a fund for making and employing five hundred such frames in Lagado, and oblige the managers to contribute in common their several collections.

"He assured me, that this invention had employed all his thoughts from his youth, that he had employed the whole vocabulary into his frame, and made the strictest computation of the general proportion there is in books between the number of particles, nouns, and verbs, and other parts of speech."

Gulliver's account is a satire on the British Royal Society, but the machine he described is not wholly fictitious. For centuries many men have believed it possible to accomplish what the Lagadan professor thought he had invented. The originator of this idea was a Spanish philosopher and alchemist, Raymond Lully, who lived in the thirteenth century. After him many attempted to revive the project, and at least one practical result has been obtained from this "thinking machine": the German mathematician Leibnitz, who lived in the end of the seventeenth century, developed a calculating machine in which he utilized some of the principles that Gulliver described. Thus a preposterous idea may at times lead to an important invention.

An Infinity of Nonsense

Just as a bit of fancy, let us imagine that we have a machine that does the work described by Gulliver, but on an extended scale. Instead of ready-made words, this machine will print words from single letters. To simplify the description we shall use multiples of 10.

Suppose this machine has 1,000 wheels, and on every wheel there are 100 inked letter and punctuation symbols. All the wheels are set on one axle. The mechanism is similar in principle to the dialing system described by us above. Thus after the first wheel makes one revolution the first symbol on the second wheel makes an impression on paper. After the second revolution of the first wheel, the second letter on the second wheel makes an impression. Thus after the first wheel makes 100 revolutions the second wheel will have completed a complete revolution, and this will bring in the third wheel with its first symbol. For every symbol of the third wheel the first wheel must make 100 revolutions. The third wheel will make a complete revolution after the first wheel has made 100^2 revolutions, and this will bring in

the fourth wheel with its first letter. We thus may construct
the following table of the number of revolutions:

REVOLUTIONS COMPLETED					WHEEL COMING IN
1st	*2nd*				
100	1				*3rd*
1st	*2nd*	*3rd*			
100^2	100	1			*4th*
1st	*2nd*	*3rd*	*4th*		
100^3	100^2	100	1		*5th*
1st	*2nd*	*3rd*	*4th*	*5th*	
100^4	100^3	100^2	100	1	*6th*

By analogy we may infer that when the first wheel will have
completed 100^{n-2} revolutions, the nth wheel will be coming in
with its first symbol. Thus for the 1,000th wheel to come in,
the first wheel will have to complete $100^{998} = (10^2)^{998} =
10^{1996}$ revolutions, and the 1,000th wheel will complete one
revolution after the first wheel will have completed $100^{999} =
10^{1998}$.

Let us assume that these wheels revolve with a tremendous
speed, say 25,000 revolutions a minute. In one year a wheel will
make

$$25,000 \cdot 60 \cdot 24 \cdot 365 = 1314 \cdot 10^7 \text{ revolutions}$$

or, for simplicity of computation, 10^{10}.

Then the sixth wheel will come in after the first wheel will
have completed $100^4 = 10^8$ revolutions, or after

$$\frac{10^8}{10^{10}} = 0.01 \text{ year, or about 4 days}$$

The seventh wheel will come in after the first wheel will have
completed $100^5 = 10^{10}$ revolutions, or after

$$\frac{10^{10}}{10^{10}} = 1 \text{ year}$$

The eighth wheel will come in after the first wheel will have
completed $100^6 = 10^{12}$ revolutions, or after

$$\frac{10^{12}}{10^{10}} = 100 \text{ years}$$

The ninth wheel will come in after the first wheel will have completed $100^7 = 10^{14}$ revolutions, or after

$$\frac{10^{14}}{10^{10}} = 10,000 \text{ years}$$

The tenth wheel will come in after 1,000,000 years, and the twelfth wheel after 10,000,000,000 years.

The 1,000th wheel will come in after

$$\frac{1,000^{1996}}{10^{10}} = 10^{1986} \text{ years}$$

and will complete its revolution after 10^{1988} years.

This is a number in comparison with which the total number of electrons in the whole universe (10^{83}) is the tiniest pygmy. How much sense and how much nonsense will then have been printed by this machine no one can know. The entire printing process would be purely mechanical. However, the work that would be required for the sorting and discarding of the nonessential material—the worthless accumulation of symbols—would be such a task that in the long run a machine of this type would be, to say the very least, wasteful.

A Tip for Radio Baritones

For some more fantasy in mathematics let us now turn from the Land of Laputa to Tin Pan Alley, and suppose that every man, woman, and child on earth should suddenly be endowed with the gift of composing music. Some will compose highbrow music, others popular songs, dance music, marches, or just simple tunes.

Let us assume that only four octaves of a piano keyboard are used. Within this limit there are forty-eight distinct keys, each for a particular note. Every melody is written in the pattern of eight bars. Also let us assume that for every bar we allow only four notes. Thus we have forty-eight notes and thirty-two notes. The forty-eight notes are the tunes. We may arrive at the number of the possible combinations if we assign to the forty-eight keys the property of the revolving wheels. Then we obtain

$$48^{32}$$

as the number of possible combinations.

Let us perform some transformations with this number: $48 = 2^4 \cdot 3$. Then

$$48^{32} = (2^4 \cdot 3)^{32} = 2^{128} \cdot 3^{32}$$

Now $3^4 = 81$. Then $3^{32} = (3^4)^8 = 81^8$. Instead of 81 we shall use 80. Then $80^8 = 8^8 \cdot 10^8$. But $8 = 2^3$. Then $8^8 = (2^3)^8 = 2^{24}$. Thus

$$48^{32} = 2^{128} \cdot 2^{24} \cdot 10^8 = 2^{152} \cdot 10^8$$

Now $2^{10} = 1,024$. Let us take 1,000, then 2^{10} may be replaced by 10^3. We have then, finally, that

$$48^{32} = 4 \cdot (10^3)^{15} \cdot 10^8 = 4 \cdot 10^{53}$$

There are about $2 \cdot 10^9$ inhabitants on earth. Suppose every inhabitant composes a combination every second. There are $(60 \cdot 60 \cdot 24 \cdot 365) = 3 \cdot 10^7$ (approximately) seconds in a year. Thus in one year

$$2 \cdot 10^9 \cdot 3 \cdot 10^7 = 6 \cdot 10^{16}$$

or, in round numbers, about 10^{17} different compositions will be made. This activity may then go on for $4 \cdot 10^{53} \div 10^{17} = 4 \cdot 10^{36}$ years.

Then the supply of original tunes is virtually inexhaustible; the sun will be extinguished and the earth crumbled before the last original composition may be written. Even radio singers could well afford to toss out some of their time-tattered tunes and launch into a brave new note now and then without fear of melodic exhaustion.

⌐ 22 ⌐

Postoffice Mathematics

How to Keep out of the Dead-Letter Department: An Introduction to Relativity

It may seem strange to associate the writing of a letter with mathematics, but we find an amazing number of mathematical relations and activities in situations least suspected in our daily experiences. Let us examine a common example, the addressing of a letter:

Suppose we address a letter to Mr. James Smith, who lives at 341 Main Street, Boise, Idaho, 83702. If we address it "Mr. James Smith, Boise," the letter probably will find a resting place in the dead-letter department of the postoffice, unless there is a return address on the envelope. Even if we write the name of the state, Mr. Smith may not be known to the postoffice in Boise, and the letter will not be delivered; furthermore, the addition of "341 Main Street" to the address may not be enough. Smith lives on Main Street at a definite place identified by a street number and also by a Zip Code number. Thus, we observe that the more completely his address is stated the better the chance that the letter will be delivered.

From a mathematical point of view, the problem of writing an address is very important, because it is related to a process of locating objects in relation to other objects whose location is known in advance; we may call this process the first step in com-

365

prehending the notion of relativity. An object in space with no other objects around it is not capable of being located, nor can a person in such a situation describe his own location and, in a sense, experiences. Knowledge is relative, and knowledge of the external world can be gained, described, and related to others only in terms of other objects—that is, relatively to other objects. As we develop understanding of mathematics and its application to the external world, we shall be confronted with numerous examples that will illustrate this fully, but at present we shall concern ourselves with the immediate processes that arise in the location of objects in the world that surrounds us.

Let us return to the problem of addressing a letter to Mr. James Smith at 341 Main Street, Boise, Idaho, 83702. There are many persons whose last name is Smith and who live in the United States. However, once we give the state, the number of Smiths is narrowed somewhat. The number of those whose full name is James Smith among the residents of Idaho is still smaller. When we specify Boise, we narrow the number further, but on Main Street in Boise there may be several James Smiths. The last step is the number 341 on Main Street, Zip Code 83702, and this important last fact clinches the address and places the addressee in a definite place. The consecutive delimitation in stating of the full name, the state, city, street, and number eliminates all other possible persons.

In mathematics, especially in geometry, this procedure is common. The following section will provide us with another example, not in mathematics but in a situation that may be viewed as mathematical.

'Somewhere' in Math: A Game of Chess

We are not concerned here with the techniques of playing checkers or chess, but the games are mathematical in nature and we shall find the boards exactly alike in both games, highly interesting.

The chessboard consists of sixty-four squares, with eight on each side, all so shaded that a square of one color is surrounded by squares of the second color. This is generally known as the chessboard arrangement.

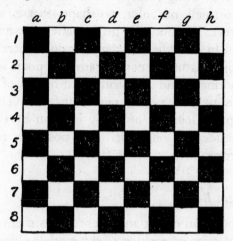

A very simple scheme illustrated above enables chess and checkers players to record the locations and movements of the figures on the board. The horizontal rows are numbered from 1 to 8, and the vertical columns are lettered a, b, c, d, e, f, g, h. The location of a particular square, or of a figure on the board, is determined by the intersection of a horizontal row and a vertical column. The reader will recall that we made use of this scheme in Chapter 2 when the sums or products of numbers written in the various systems of numeration were obtained; the scheme is in universal use in mathematics whenever values are presented in tabular form. Recording of the location of a definite figure in its square is thus done by writing a number and a letter, for example $4e$. The $4e$ square is definitely located at the intersection of the fourth row and the fifth column.

The location of a figure in a definite square is thus determined by two (and no more) facts. This process is similar to the statement that Mr. James Smith lives at 341 Main Street. A person who lives in the same town needs no additional information about Mr. Smith's address.

In mathematics this method of locating objects is primarily utilized in geometry, except that here the objects under consideration are mere points. And these points have only one property, that of being located "somewhere." They have no magnitude, no smell, no color, no shape—that is, they are just points. However it is not only mathematicians who make much use of points. In other fields, whenever and wherever the location of an object is under consideration, a point is usually the means of denoting it and the written expression of the location of this point is given by certain pertinent facts. Thus on a geographical map the location of a city is given by two numbers, signifying latitude and longitude. The postoffice requires more detailed information.

Where Einstein Began

The location of an object anywhere in space can be described only when we refer its position to some other object or objects. If we say that a man stopped at "a" corner, we convey no information. We probably refer then to a street corner, but we mention no street, and a street generally has more than one corner. When we say that a picture hangs on a wall, the statement is meaningless. We need to know on what wall, and where. A description of the location of an object is complete only when it is given in terms of some other objects whose locations are known, not only to the person who describes it but to the person to whom it is conveyed: that is, the description itself must be relative to facts already known to others. Thus we may say that with this simple procedure of describing the location of objects in space (wherever this may be) we are on the threshold of Dr. Albert Einstein's famous theory of relativity. In other words, any statement of the position of an object must be given in terms of other positions, that is, relatively to these. When we say that we walked two miles, unless we specify that we walked two miles north, or south, or two miles in the direction of some definite place, our statement will of necessity have no locational meaning.

In mathematics the location of points (and these may represent pictures of any object or objects) is done on paper. But whenever we make a picture in the mathematical sense we enter the house that geometry built. The procedure of locating points is no more difficult than the location of the chess or checkers figure on a board; the idea is exactly the same, and involves a procedure common not only with the mathematician but with men in almost all walks of life.

In order to use a common language, we agree to introduce a commonly accepted object of reference. Mathematicians have agreed to use two lines that are at right angles with each other, and we call this arrangement of the two lines "axes." These axes are not new to us; on the contrary, they are so common that we pay no attention to them. Any floor in any room is an example of such axes. Suppose that a hole must be drilled through this floor. The location of this hole can be described in one and only one way. Suppose that it is to be in the southwest corner, three feet from each wall. We then measure off three feet from the western wall and three feet from the southern wall, then the place to be drilled is definitely determined. Any other description will not enable us to drill the hole in the proper place. Suppose that we decide to drill the hole about 4 1/4 feet from the southwest corner. In the accompanying drawing such a situation is illustrated. Instead of a hole, a portion of the floor including the corner would then be cut. In the same drawing the correct method for locating the place for the hole is shown.

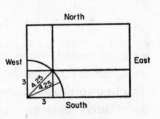

The general method for locating points is as follows: The two lines XX and YY that intersect in O make right angles at O. Mathematicians have a special name for lines that make right angles with one another: such lines are "perpendicular" to one another. When two such lines are used for locating points in the manner to be described, they are known as "coordinate axes." The position at any point is determined by its distance from the line XOX and from the line YOY. One of these distances will not give the exact location of a given point. Suppose we say that a point is five units away from the axis XOX. The reader will see from the following illustration that there are two lines, each five units from the axis *XOX*, one above and one below the axis *XOX*. To avoid confusion we should recall that we have agreed to represent numbers on a straight line by attention to the direction, and if we agree that one direction is considered as positive then the opposite direction is to be considered negative. Thus, if positive values are to be represented above the axis *XOX*, then below the axis *XOX* we shall have negative values. This agreement eliminates the line below the axis *XOX*, because it represents the distance of five negative units. Still we are un-

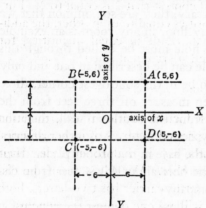

able to locate our point, but if we specify that the point must be six units away from the axis *YOY* we may perhaps be closer to a satisfactory solution of our problem.

Here again, however, we hit a snag. Instead of one line we again obtain two lines, each of them six units from the axis *YOY*. But now we know that we must impose one more restriction; we must consider whether the distance is positive or negative. If we agree to consider the direction to the right as positive and the direction to the left as negative, then the position of the point *A* is definitely determined. This point is located where the two lines, the +5 units away from the axis *XOX* and the +6 units away from the axis *YOY*, intersect. The illustration shows three more points, *B*, *C*, and *D*, obtained in the process of solving our problem.

The correct labeling (that is, the one generally accepted) of the points so located is as follows: Every point is denoted by a letter, and to the right of this letter two numbers are written in parentheses. The first number represents the distance from the axis *YOY* (which is measured along the axis *XOX*), and the second number represents the distance from the axis *XOX* (which is measured along the axis YOY). Generally the distances along the axis YOY (or the axis of the y's) are denoted by the letter y. Thus, generally any point is denoted by (x,y). The values of x and y for any definite point are known as its "coordinates."

Don't Let Relativity Disturb You: 2 Is Still 2

Here we shall relate some facts that are obvious but vitally important in mathematics and also in "logical thinking."

We usually agree that a thing is always equal to itself; no one but a dialectical diehard would contest that 2 is equal to 2. Furthermore, if we have two quantities equal to each other, the addition of a definite quantity will result in equal quantities; for example, if two quantities a and b are equal, then

$$a + c = b + c \quad \text{and} \quad a - c = b - c$$

We shall now make use of these facts in relation to determination of the location of a point as expressed in terms of its coordinates.

Suppose we have two points, say A and B, such that their coordinates are equal to one another. Will these points be distinct or the same? Suppose a letter carrier has two letters, both addressed to 341 Main Street; will anyone contest the conclusion that these two letters will be delivered to the same house? The reader may at this stage draw his own conclusions concerning the points A and B whose coordinates are the same. It is obvious that when two points have identical coordinates these two points are identical also. On the other hand, whenever two points have coordinates that are not identical, the two points are distinct, that is, different.

If All the World Were a Pancake

By means of the two coordinate axes it is possible to describe the positions and locations of all the points that are found in the plane, or the world of two coordinates. At present, however, the reader should accept the meaning of the word "all" with a grain of salt, because later we shall learn of some other numbers that are neither whole numbers nor fractions as these are known to us at present.

The plane, however, is a peculiar pancaked world. Flatface Phil, a two-coordinate individual who lives in a plane and whose

existence may be described in terms of two numbers (coordinates) may move freely within the plane. On the other hand, he will have no idea of height; as a matter of fact, he himself will be so flat that he will have no thickness at all. Moreover, he will be able to see only in the plane. If anyone looks at him from above, Flatface Phil will not see him. We might compare such a person with a bug that can crawl on the surface of the earth, but only horizontally.

In this world of two coordinates Flatface Phil will, from necessity, develop uncommon (from our point of view; we must not forget that we live in a world that is more varied than the world of two coordinates) notions of objects. The nature of Flatface Phil's world is such that he will never have any idea of the shape of things. Everything in the plane will appear to him as a point (when he will be looking at a straight line sidewise) or as a straight line. A circle as we know it will appear as a straight line. A square will appear to him as a straight line, and as he moves around such a square the length of the line will change; it will vary from the size of a side to the size of the diagonal of the square when he faces one of the corners, although he will never be able to point out this corner unless the sides of the square are shaded in various colors. A world of two coordinates is described in the small but fascinating book *Flatland* by A. Square (E. Abbott), Little, Brown & Co., Boston, 1929.

This Expanding Universe: Three-Dimensional Worlds

In this section we are not discussing modern theories in astronomy but shall demonstrate how by means of a very simple process the world of the plane may be changed so that our friend Flatface will be endowed with powers to learn much about objects and their properties that are unknown to him because of his two coordinate character. The world of the plane is not an artificial universe, although it may seem unnatural to us because we live in a world where we can transport ourselves not only in a plane but also in space. We are free to move in three directions: right (or left), forward (or backward), and up (or down), a compact but very graphical description of life in our world. The world of two coordinates is known also as the world of two degrees of freedom, and the world in which we live as the world of three degrees of freedom. To describe the position of an object in our world we need three coordinates, as we shall now see.

To locate an object—for example, in a room—we must know how far it is from one wall, another wall, and the floor, or ceiling. Two distances will not suffice because, as we have observed, two distances (or two coordinates) will locate an object or a point only in the plane, or the world of two coordinates. The accompanying drawing illustrates the process of locating a point in space in the world of three degrees of freedom.

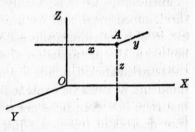

The point A is located by the distances:

x, which is measured along the axis OX and gives the distance from the plane YOZ;

y, which is measured along the axis OY and gives the distance from the plane XOZ;

z, which is measured along the axis OZ and gives the distance from the plane XOY.

It will be observed that the planes XOY, XOZ, and YOZ represent the walls of a room in the example.

The reader will ask, "Suppose you have only two coordinates, say, x and z; what will these two coordinates represent in the world of three coordinates?" At present we shall proceed best with the answer, to be amplified later, that two coordinates in this world determine a line that runs parallel to the plane YOZ

at the distance x from it, and parallel to the plane XOY at the distance z from it. If only one coordinate were given, say y, then this coordinate will represent a plane that runs parallel to the plane XOZ at the distance y from it.

We need not stop with the world of three coordinates, or three degrees of freedom. We can imagine a world of four degress of freedom in which four coordinates are necessary. As a matter of fact, we human beings live in such a world, because in addition to the three directions of space of which we are conscious also of time, and a correct description of the location of an object requires the statement of time. Just observe: If we say that we saw Mr. James Smith at some specified place our statement is actually incomplete, but if we add the information about the time we are definite. Unfortunately it is impossible to give a full picture of a world of four degrees of freedom (or of four "dimensions," as it is usually known); our physical world is three-dimensional, and we are just limited in respect to picturization of a four-dimensional object as our friend Flatface Phil is limited in the picturization of a three-dimensional object. Here the mathematician builds a world that is just a product of his mind and he must be content with a mind-picture. The mathematician, however, need not stop when he reaches a world with four degrees of freedom. Just by adding one more coordinate, he may jump into the world of five degrees, and go on adding coordinates indefinitely. With little strain on his imagination he may conceive a world of a million, or of googol, degrees of freedom.

The world of four dimensions is of great importance in physics. Whether worlds with many more degrees have any value we do not know; probably science may find some application for such worlds, as very often the mathematician's fancy finds application in the most unexpected situations.

Geometric Comet: $Y = 6$

We have mentioned that when the two-coordinate world is under consideration and only one coordinate is given, the location of an object or a point is impossible; the situation is similar to stating only that Mr. James Smith lives on Main Street. In other words, giving one coordinate only (or stating that Mr. Smith lives on Main Street) leads to the conclusion that the point may be anywhere on a line a certain number of units distant from a coordinate axis. The letter carrier might locate the addressee by walking all the length of Main Street and inquiring at every house until Mr. Smith's residence was located, but location of the residence would inevitably lead to introduction of the second coordinate, the number 341.

Thus, when one coordinate is given, we may assume that the point runs through the entire length of the line (and how long that line is no one knows). This leads to the supposition that the line may be thought of as traced out by the point. The point runs through a given distance from the coordinate axis, and as it does this it traces a line. This allows us to think of a line as the comet's tail traced by a moving point. Such an assumption is convenient, especially when the application of mathematics to practical problems is considered.

In the illustration following we see the trail of a point whose coordinate is $y = 6$. This means that this point generated a line that is 6 units above the X-axis and is parallel to this axis, always

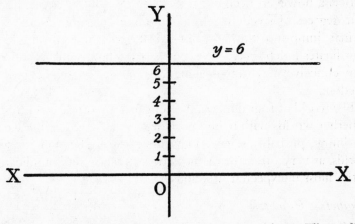

at the same distance. But $y = 6$ is also an equation. Thus a line may be represented by an algebraic equation, and conversely, once we have an equation, we may obtain the picture or "graph" of that equation. It should be remembered, however, that an equation never represents something static, immobile, but always is a statement of the trail of a point (generally a curved line), a line, a plane, or some other geometric object that is created as the result of motion.

PROBLEMS

1. Using graph paper, locate the points $(0, 0)$, $(0, 3)$, $(0, -4)$, $(2, -2)$, $(-7, -7)$.

2. Using graph paper, draw the graphs of the equations $x = 3$ $x = -5$, $y = 7$, $y = -10$.

≈ 23 ≈

New Worlds for Old

Totalitarian Utopia: World without Freedom

We have examined the worlds of two and three degrees of freedom (dimensions); we have glimpsed the world of four degrees, and found there is no reason why we cannot fancy worlds of any number of degrees. Now let us examine the world of zero degrees of freedom. "Zero" in this case means "no." Can there be a nonpolitical world of no degree of freedom?

Reflection will convince the reader that such a world, in which a person would be so limited that he would always be fixed in one definite place, does exist in mathematics. Once in this world, there's no moving out of it; for this tight little world has no dimension—no length, no width, no height. There could be only one inhabitant in such a world, and, though he would occupy it wholly, he would nevertheless show a strong family resemblance to the Little Man Who Wasn't There. In terms of mathematics such a world is known as a point. Now the reader should not think, for the time being, of this point as located somewhere else; there is just one, and a very lonely, point. The point that we may make on paper or on a blackboard is actually not such a world, because a point made by us has width, breadth, and thickness. We must imagine a point as an invisible world of zero degree of freedom.

This world without freedom may be called "the point world." It is a prison without bars where the prisoner occupies the entire cell and leaves not even breathing space.

377

The Inhibited Insect

No degree of freedom means that a being or an object is powerless to move; it is like a nail driven into a wall, staying there until it is extracted. Now, let us examine a world in which the beings are allowed only one degree of freedom. Such a world will have one dimension only. This may be length, or width, or height, but once length, or width, or height is selected, the remaining two dimensions are barred.

In such a world the point-world inhabitant is allowed to leave his prison but only on a very strict parole. He may not do everything he would like to do, for the world of one degree of freedom is limited to a line. Like the point, this line has no thickness—neither width nor height—but unlike the point, the line does have length. We may call such a world "the line world."

We may use as a crude example of the line world the inside tube of a thermometer. Let us suppose that a bug is placed in this inside tube, but this is a special bug, fitting snugly in the tube.

 Such a bug can move forward and backward but in no other manner. In the line world, the point will behave exactly as does our special bug. If two bugs could be placed in the same tube they would have serious traffic difficulties; they would inevitably collide. In the line world two points would have the same difficulties, but mathematicians, for reasons which will be explained, allow two or more points to meet. But when such points occupy the same position, they become one point, or two "coincidents," that is, two, or more, points that occupy the same place.

In the line world we may measure distances without difficulty. We recall how in Chapter 12 we described two kinds (in quality) of numbers, and devised a method of representing these two kinds on a straight line. At some place along the line we designated a starting point (the zero point), from which (if the line were horizontal) positive numbers were marked off to the right, and negative numbers to the left. Generally, if in some direction from the zero point positive numbers were marked off, then from the same zero point the negative numbers were marked off in the opposite direction. If we bear in mind this method of locating numbers on the line, the finding of a distance between two points is simple. Let us consider a few examples.

The distance between the point marked 8 and the point marked 2 shown in the following drawing is $8 - 2 = 6$. The distance between the point marked 6 and the point marked -3 is $6 - (-3) = 6 + 3 = 9$. The distance between the point marked -1 and the point marked -7 is $-1 - (-7) = -1 + 7 = 6$.

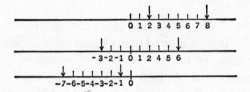

Now we shall consider the problem of finding the distance between two points on a straight line (or in the line world) in general. We shall apply the term "coordinate" to the markings on the straight line in the same manner as we applied it in the process of locating points in the preceding chapter. Let us determine the distance between point A, whose coordinate is x_1, and the point B, whose coordinate is x_2. We apply to these coordinates the same method as in the case of the foregoing numbers. This method, although mathematical in nature, is just a case of common sense. The point A is x_1 units away from the zero point (it should be noted that in the drawing there are sev-

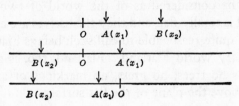

eral cases showing various locations of the point A), and the point B is x_2 units away from the zero point. The distance between these two points is the difference between their respective coordinates. It should be remembered, however, that we are concerned only with distance and have no regard for direction. This indicates that the distance between the two points must always be positive. For this purpose we may use the notation for absolute values of numbers as shown originally in Chapter 12. Thus we may write generally that the distance along a straight line between any two points, A (whose coordinate is x_1) and B (whose coordinate is x_2) is

$$|x_1 - x_2|$$

The Perils of Flatland

The world of one dimension is a very dull world, as we have now learned. It is so limited that a linear inhabitant may be compared to a prisoner under a very stiff sentence. However, in nature we rarely, if ever, find examples of such a world. On the

other hand, should we allow our prisoner some freedom of exercise, we may think of a world with one more degree of freedom, or two degrees. And conditions similar to the world of two degrees of freedom (two dimensions) are plentiful in nature.

Imagine the surface of a table, with a wingless bug or a worm placed on it and allowed to move freely in any direction. But once placed on the table, they cannot leave it ever. Moreover, let us imagine that they have no thickness. If such conditions prevail, these beings may be considered as of the world of two dimensions. Their world is totally flat, and they themselves are as flat as their world. It is quite reasonable to call such beings Flatlanders, and their imaginary world Flatland. Flatland, too, is a very bleak world; it has no trees, no grass, no markings of any sort that would rise above the plane of the flat surface.

A Flatlander may be endowed with all the senses of a human being, but he can see only those things which lie within the surface of his world. He may judge the shape of the objects in his world, but not as we do. His method may be compared to that of a blind person who, to determine whether an object is round, touches it with his hands; for a Flatlander must move around an

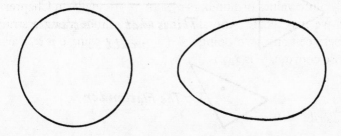

object to determine its shape. And it is doubtful that a Flatlander can really determine whether an object is circular or of some other shape unless he is able to measure distances and to keep some record of his traveling around a figure. The drawing illustrates how a Flatlander, if very intelligent, may determine whether an object is circular or egg-shape, for example. In the case of a perfectly circular object, a Flatlander may see this circular object as a straight line of the same length. On the other hand, in the case of any other round object, these lengths are not the same.

Life in our Flatland is extremely dangerous, since any object that has sharp corners may inflict injury. Suppose a Flatlander encounters some triangular object; if this object faces him with one of its corners, he has no means of determining whether it is triangular or is a straight line. The accompanying illustration shows such a situation. Suppose a Flatlander is also triangular in shape. On the left we have the situation as we would observe it if we could peek into Flatland from above. On the right we see a straight line only;

this is all a Flatlander would be able to observe. If there were some illumination, a Flatlander could see some shades on the outlines of the triangle. Now if a Flatlander would move toward the triangle, he would not only collide with it but at the moment

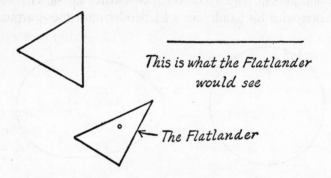

This is what the Flatlander would see

The Flatlander

he reached the corner its sharp point would pierce him. But suppose that instead of a triangle the Flatlander encounters a straight line. If he faces the straight line from the side, he sees it full length. But if he faces it straight ahead, he observes a point only, if a point could be seen. The meeting with a straight line would pierce the Flatlander as with a spear. Since points cannot be seen, a Flatlander may be in danger at every turn.

Life in Flatland would otherwise accord to him the same measure of privacy as that of our own world, except that a Flatlander's home cannot have a roof. If we human beings wanted to look into the home of a Flatlander, we could do it from above, and he would never know it. If a Flatlander were lifted from his plane, his friends and neighbors would never know what happened to him.

A light that would shine on Flatland from outside would mystify a Flatlander; it would appear to him to come from nowhere. We humans, living in three dimensions, would experience a similar sensation if out of thin air a miraculous light should suddenly burst upon us.

To be able to measure distances in the world of two dimensions a Flatlander must take into consideration the fact that the position of a point in a plane is determined by two numbers (coordinates). The method of locating points in a plane was described in Chapter 22, but, unlike the method of measuring distances in the line world, in Flatland the calculation of the distance between two points whose coordinates are given involves some additional (to subtraction) arithmetic operations. In the following sections this method will be fully described, and in such a way that it applies not only to Flatland but to a world of any number of dimensions.

An Arithmetic Oddity in a Geometric Dress

We have on several occasions met numbers that were results of a multiplication of a number by itself. Such numbers are called squares: for example, $5 \cdot 5 = 25$, or $5^2 = 25$, $16^2 = 256$, and, generally, any number n, when squared, is n^2.

Some pairs of numbers possess a remarkable property: If we take such two numbers, square them, and add them, the sum may be a perfect square. The reader should note that we used "may," and not "is." Thus for some numbers there may exist the relationship

$$a^2 + b^2 = c^2$$

but this does not mean that if we take two numbers a and b, square them and add them, we shall obtain a c^2. For example, $3^2 + 7^2 = 9 + 49 = 58$, and 58 is not a perfect square. On the other hand, $5^2 + 12^2 = 25 + 144 = 169$, and $169 = 13^2$. Thus,

$$5^2 + 12^2 = 13^2$$

This remarkable property of certain numbers was discovered about 2,500 years ago by the Greek philosopher and mathematician Pythagoras. But, and this is no disparagement of his fame, other ancient peoples knew of this property. The Egyptians knew that $3^2 + 4^2 = 25 = 5^2$, but since Pythagoras was the first to state this property in a general form, the sets of three numbers possessing this property are known as the Pythagorean numbers. However, the discovery of Pythagoras was not in arithmetic but in geometry. Here is how he came across the geometric property of such numbers:

A square is a special kind of a geometric figure such that

(1) It has four sides.
(2) All the four sides are equal.
(3) Every two neighboring sides make right angles with one another—that is, they are perpendicular to one another.

A mathematician would say that a square is a four-sided plane figure with equal sides and all angles right angles.

A plane figure (for example, a triangle, a square, a circle) encloses a portion of the plane. In the case of the square it is easy to compute the size of the portion of the plane that is enclosed by the figure, or the "area" of the square. The rule for computation of the area of the square is: *Measure the length of the side of the square and multiply the number by itself.* Thus, if the side of a square is three inches long, then the area of the square is nine square inches. Generally, if the length of the side of a square is a, then the area of the square is a^2.

Pythagoras observed that in every right triangle, that is, a triangle one of whose angles is a right angle, as in the accompanying illustration, where the angle C is a right angle, the sum of the areas of the squares on the sides making a right angle is equal to the area of

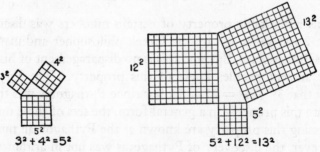

$$3^2 + 4^2 = 5^2 \qquad 5^2 + 12^2 = 13^2$$

the square on the side that is opposite the right angle, the largest side. Above are two examples illustrating Pythagoras' discovery.

These examples show the relations

$$3^2 + 4^2 = 25 = 5^2 \quad \text{and} \quad 5^2 + 12^2 = 169 = 13^2$$

Some of the many other known sets of three numbers that possess the Pythagorean property include

$$8^2 + 15^2 = 17^2, \quad 20^2 + 21^2 = 29^2, \quad 12^2 + 35^2 = 37^2,$$
$$9^2 + 40^2 = 41^2, \quad 28^2 + 45^2 = 53^2, \quad 11^2 + 60^2 = 61^2,$$
and $\qquad\qquad\quad 48^2 + 55^2 = 73^2.$

By means of the property of the Pythagorean numbers or, as it is generally known, the Theorem of Pythagoras, we may measure distances in the worlds of two or more degrees of freedom, provided the coordinates of the respective two positions (or points) are given.

Unsquaring the Square

We shall turn now to an arithmetic operation that we have mentioned in Chapter 18. In mathematics generally all operations are divided into two groups; in one group we have one kind of operations, and in the other we have operations that undo what was done originally. For example, if we add two numbers, we can undo the addition by taking the sum and subtracting one of the original numbers. If no mistakes are made, we obtain the other number that was originally added to the first. Thus if we add 12 and 34, we obtain 46; if we subtract 12 from 46, we obtain 34. The operation that undoes addition is known as subtraction. Also, if we multiply 5 and 7, we obtain the product 35. Now, if we take the product 35 and divide it by 5, we obtain the quotient 7. Thus the operation that undoes multiplication is known as division. We may list these arithmetic operations according to the two categories as follows:

The Original Operation	The Operation That Undoes It
Addition	Subtraction
Subtraction	Addition
Multiplication	Division
Division	Multiplication

However, we have learned about one more arithmetic operation, the raising to a power, and in particular we shall now be concerned with the squaring of numbers which is the multiplying of a number by itself. What is the operation that undoes the squaring? We have a number, say 225, and are told that it is the result of the multiplication of a number by itself. With this and no more information on hand, we are presented with the problem of finding that number which, when multiplied by itself, will give the product 225.

Now this is not a difficult operation, and there are methods that enable one easily to obtain the result whether the given number is a perfect square or not (in the latter case no exact result is possible). However, tables of the results of the operation that undoes the raising of a power, in particular those of squaring, have been calculated and simplify the work considerably. Such a table is found in the Appendix.

Now, we may name this operation: It is known as "the extraction of square roots." The mathematical symbol for this operation is $\sqrt{}$, called "the radical." The squared number is written under this sign, as $\sqrt{225}$, and to indicate the operation of the extraction of the square root was performed we write $\sqrt{225} = 15$, because $15^2 = 225$. Thus we may write

$$\sqrt{225} = \sqrt{15^2} = 15$$

Surveying in Flatland

Now we are ready to develop a method for the computation of distances in the world of two degrees of freedom, or Flatland.

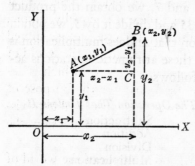

We have found that the distance in the line world is obtained for two points whose coordinates are x_1 and x_2 as $|x_1 - x_2|$.

In Flatland the position of a point is determined by two coordinates, x and y. In the drawing above we have two points A, whose coordinates are (x_1, y_1), and B, whose coordinates are (x_2, y_2). Now, if we draw through A a line parallel to the coordinate axis OX and if we draw at the same time through B

a line parallel to the coordinate axis OY (remembering, of course, that OX and OY are at right angles to one another), we obtain a right triangle ABC.

Now if we apply the Theorem of Pythagoras we have

$$AC^2 + BC^2 = AB^2$$

But from the drawing we have that

$$AC = x_2 - x_1 \quad \text{and} \quad BC = y_2 - y_1$$

Then

$$AB^2 = (x_2 - x_1)^2 + (y_2 - y_1)^2$$

or

$$AB = \sqrt{(x_2 - x_1)^2 + (y_2 - y_1)^2}$$

For example, if we have two points $(5, 8)$ and $(8, 12)$ the distance between these two points is

$$\sqrt{(8 - 5)^2 + (12 - 8)^2} = \sqrt{3^2 + 4^2}$$

or

$$\sqrt{25} = 5$$

PROBLEMS

Compute the distance between the two points (1) $(11, 14)$ and $(-4, -6)$; (2) $(0, -20)$ and $(9, 20)$; (3) $(-5, 0)$ and $(0, -12)$; (4) $(-7, 18)$ and $(5, -17)$; and (5) $(-9, 12)$ and $(11, -9)$.

"Seeing" Three-Dimensional Pictures

In the world of three degrees of freedom distances are computed in a manner similar to that just described. At the start it may seem more complicated, but in reality it is equally simple; many of us may fail to see its simplicity because we are limited in the method of picturization of the coordinates in the world of three degrees of freedom. We must use a plane (which is actually a world of two degrees of freedom) for the purpose of presenting a three-dimensional picture. We must be able to visualize the spatial picture; once we "see" the three dimensions the rest is simple.

In the drawing below, we left the coordinates of the world of two degrees of freedom, that is, the plane with the coordinate axes OX and OY horizontal. Since we agreed that all the coordinate axes must be perpendicular to one another, the axis OZ (of the third dimension) is perpendicular to the plane of OX and OY. Thus OZ should be considered vertical. To understand the picture better, the reader may think of a corner of a room.

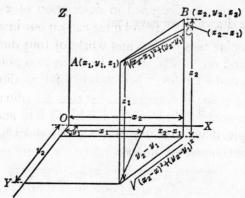

Now we have obtained the distance in the world of two degrees of freedom. When we introduced another dimension, it actually lifted this two-dimensional distance out of the horizontal plane. In our drawing, this distance is the line AC. Then the triangle ABC is a right one, and we thus can apply the Theorem of Pythagoras to it. Finally we have

$$AC^2 + BC^2 = AB^2$$

or

$$AB^2 = (x_2 - x_1)^2 + (y_2 - y_1)^2 + (z_2 - z_1)^2$$

and

$$AB = \sqrt{(x_2 - x_1)^2 + (y_2 - y_1)^2 + (z_2 - z_1)^2}$$

In other words, when we tacked on another dimension, we have introduced into the distance formula of the world of two degrees of freedom another addend $(z_2 - z_1)^2$, and we have immediately obtained the distance formula for the world of three degrees.

Formula for Creating a World: Algebra + Imagination

Since we live in a world in which there are only three physical degrees of freedom (dimensions), it is quite easy for us to visualize this world and to form distinct notions of the conditions that govern descriptions of objects located in it. Moreover, since the worlds of zero, one, and two degrees of freedom may be thought of as parts of the world of three degrees, we have no difficulty in understanding the natures of these worlds. When we begin to talk of worlds of four, five, or one hundred degrees of freedom, we are extremely handicapped in description of even the simplest objects in such worlds and must call on our imaginations.

Let us imagine that we live in a world of four dimensions and attempt to find out how distances between two points are measured or computed there. In a world of two dimensions the position of a point is determined by two coordinates, and the coordinate axes are taken perpendicular to one another. In a world of three dimensions the position of a point is determined by three coordinates, and the coordinate axes are again perpendicular to one another, as the lines in a corner of a room where the three walls meet. We also know now that whenever an additional degree of freedom, or dimension, is added we introduce an additional coordinate. Thus to determine the position of a point in our world of four dimensions, we shall need four coordinates and, naturally, four coordinate axes. And since we must follow the same pattern, these four coordinate axes must be perpendicular to one another. To draw a picture of four coordinate axes, all perpendicular to one another—that is, to draw a picture of such a four-dimensional object on paper—is impossible here.

Let the reader imagine that he is a Flatlander, living in a two-dimensional world. As we found out when we examined this type of world, he will be able to move around only in a plane, as in the space between two plates of glass. Moreover, he cannot see what is above him or below him and could only imagine a world of three dimensions.

A Flatlander may know everything about flat figures such as lines, triangles, squares, and circles, but he will have to use his imagination to picture a cube or a sphere. Suppose a sphere has suddenly descended upon Flatland. The Flatlander will have no idea of this object. All that he will be able to observe is a point appearing on his land when the sphere touches Flatland, and then a tiny circle. For some reason unknown to him this circle will continue to expand until it reaches a certain size, then will begin to contract until it turns into a point and finally vanishes as suddenly as it appeared. A mathematician will describe this phenomenon as the cutting of the sphere through Flatland. The reader may take an orange or an apple and cut it into slices. The rims of the slices will give a picture of what may happen in Flatland. But, the reader should understand, a Flatlander cannot see the rims; he can only move around them to gain some idea of the shape of the rim or circle. If we ask the Flatlander to make a drawing of a three-dimensional object, he will say that he has an idea of the three-dimensional object, but he cannot make a drawing of it.

Now let us return to the four-dimensional coordinate axes. We know that they must be perpendicular to one another. And here, instead of trying to do mathematical figuring, we shall ask the reader to do some reasoning. When we obtained the distance expression in the world of two coordinates, we had a right triangle, and from it we obtained the required expression, $\sqrt{(x_2 - x_1)^2 + (y_2 - y_1)^2}$. When we worked with the coordinates in the world of three degrees, we made use of the flat triangle and added to it another coordinate (and it was perpendicular to the distance line in the plane OXY). By this means we obtained another right triangle, and the expression

$$\sqrt{(x_2 - x_1)^2 + (y_2 - y_1)^2 + (z_2 - z_1)^2}$$

Now it is quite reasonable to proceed further. We shall take the distance line in the world of three degrees, add to it the fourth coordinate (which will be perpendicular to it), and this coordinate, together with the three-dimensional distance and the four-dimensional distance, will form a right triangle. If we have a right triangle, however, we know how to obtain the length of the longest side (and our four-dimensional distance must be the longest side, because it is not perpendicular to the other two lines). Thus, our distance in the world of four degrees of freedom (if we denote the fourth coordinates of the two points by w_1 and w_2 respectively) is

$$\sqrt{(x_1 - x_2)^2 + (y_1 - y_2)^2 + (z_1 - z_2)^2 + (w_1 - w_2)^2}$$

If we want to obtain the expression for the distance in the world of a hundred degrees of freedom, we must think of points that are each determined by one hundred coordinates. The coordinate axes must be all perpendicular to one another. The distance expression (or, as we usually say, distance formula) is a square root. Under the radical there will be a hundred squared differences between the respective coordinates of the points. In mathematics it is not always necessary to draw a picture; on the contrary, where a picture is either useless or impossible, an algebraic formula, plus the imagination of the reader, is sufficient.

PROBLEMS

6. Compute the distances between the points: (a) $(0, 1)$ and $(1, 0)$, (b) $(1, 1)$ and $(7, 9)$. [Answers: (a) $\sqrt{2} = 1.414$, (b) 10]

7. Compute the distances between the points: (a) $(0, 0, 1)$ and $(2, 2, 0)$, (b) $(5, 3, 1)$ and $(2, 4, 6)$. [Answers: (a) 3, (b) $\sqrt{35} = 5.916$]

8. Compute the distance between the points $(2, 3, 4, 5)$ and $(3, 4, 5, 6)$. [Answer: 2]

Passport for Geometric Figures

Moving Day: It's All Done by Math

If we move, we usually put on record at the postoffice our old and new addresses. This is actually a mathematical procedure and involves simple arithmetic only.

An inhabitant of a world of zero degrees of freedom (one of no dimensions) is unable to change his address; as we know, he occupies his world's entire space and cannot move.

In the line world of one degree of freedom motion is allowed, but only along a straight line. The inhabitant of this world is a point, and a traveling point may bump into another point and pass it, as there are no traffic accidents in the worlds built by mathematicians. The position of a point in the line world is determined by its distance from a designated starting point known as the "origin." Suppose that the coordinate of a point is $+5$ units as shown below and that at some other instant the position of the point is given by the coordinate $+3$. Thus the point has

moved two units toward the origin. Mathematicians, however, find it more convenient to look at the procedure differently; instead of viewing it as the record of a moving point, they endow the origin with the ability to change its address. Thus a mathematician says that the origin was moved two units toward the point, and the coordinate of the point in the second position is $+(5-2)=3$. This approach to a problem may seem topsy-turvy, but mathematicians find this interpretation more convenient in the general attack, as will be shown presently. Consequently, in mathematics when a point changes its address, the change is recorded as a change of the reference point, the origin.

Now we may state the procedure of changing the address in general form. If the coordinate of a point is x, and the origin is moved k units, then the new address of the point, that is, its new coordinate, is $(x - k)$. The k may be either positive or negative, and this does not affect the expression $(x - k)$. For example, if the coordinate of a point is -8 and the origin is moved -3, that is, three units to the left, then the new coordinate of the point is $[-8 - (-3)] = -8 + 3 = -5$. In other words the point was moved three units to the right. If the original coordinate of a point is $+10$, and the origin is moved $+7$, then the new coordinate of the point is $+(10 - 7) = +3$. In other words the point is moved seven units to the left.

This principle is applied to coordinates of points located in worlds of any number of degrees of freedom, or dimensions. For example, if the coordinates of a point in the plane world (Flatland) are $(6, -7)$, and the origin is moved to $(1, 3)$, then the coordinates of the point after the change of the origin are $(6 - 1, -7 - 3) = (5, -10)$. In other words, the point was moved one unit to the left and three units down.

Note that when the point is moved to the right its X coordinate is increased, and when it is moved to the left its X coordinate is decreased. If a point is moved upward, its Y coordinate is increased, and when it is moved downward its Y coordinate is decreased. In the illustration below the point A was moved to

the left and upward, and point B was moved to the right and downward.

Life on a Merry-Go-Round

In the preceding chapter we learned of the limitations imposed on a being confined to a line world, comparing him to a prisoner allowed to leave his cell-like point world on a very limited parole. But a release to the line-world degree of freedom is not the only means of letting a point-world being out on parole; there are innumerable ways and we shall examine a few of them, at the same time developing a method of describing these limitations in the grammar of algebra. The reader then will be able by himself to write a "passport" for any geometric figure.

Suppose that a point-world being is allowed to leave his cell under the following conditions: He is allowed to move freely

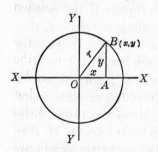

but always at a certain distance from the cell, and both his cell and his new quarters are to be in the same plane (imagine this to be the plane of this paper, or the plane of a table). This is something akin to a merry-go-round; mathematicians call such a figure a circle. Now let us describe a circle in mathematical terms.

The drawing above shows a special kind of circle. We placed the cell (the point world) of the paroled point-world being at the origin of our coordinates. We have a special name for the point around which the point-world being moves; it is called "the center of the circle." We shall make use of another special name: the distance from the center at which the paroled point-world being is moving (or, as we say, revolving) is known as "the radius of the circle." There was no special need to place the center of the circle at the origin; it can be anywhere in the plane.

The coordinates of the origin of the axes of coordinates (and of the center of the circle) are $(0, 0)$. Let us take any point of the circle. Now we know that the distance formula as developed in the preceding chapter enables us to compute the distance between any two points (in this case, in the plane). Thus, we have that the distance OB between the points O (the center of the circle, or the origin) and B on the circle is

$$OB^2 = OA^2 + AB^2 = (x - 0)^2 + (y - 0)^2 = x^2 + y^2$$

But the distance OB is, as we now know, the radius of the circle. Let us denote it by the letter r. Moreover, we must remember that the length of the radius r of the circle is the same for any point on the circle, the condition of the parole of the point-world being. Then we can rewrite our expression as

$$r^2 = x^2 + y^2, \quad \text{or} \quad x^2 + y^2 = r^2$$

This expression is known as the equation of a circle whose radius is r and whose center is at the origin, and describes the condition of the parole of the point-world being.

Now, if the center of the circle is placed anywhere in the plane, we can view the situation as though we had moved the origin. Suppose the center of the circle is at the point (a, b). We know from the preceding chapter that this is nothing but the procedure of changing the address. Then, according to this method, instead of x we shall write $(x - a)$ and instead of y we shall write $(y - b)$. The length of the radius of the circle, however, remains the same. Then the equation of the circle becomes

$$(x - a)^2 + (y - b)^2 = r^2$$

This is the equation of the circle for any location of its center. The values of a and b depend on the coordinates of the circle's center.

This general equation enables us to write the equation of any circle, but we must always know two facts:

(1) The length of the radius of the circle, and
(2) The position of the center of the circle.

Once we know these, our equation is easily obtained.

For example, if the radius of the circle is 5 and the center of the circle is at the origin, the equation of the circle is

$$x^2 + y^2 = 5^2, \quad \text{or} \quad x^2 + y^2 = 25$$

If the radius is 6 and the center of the circle is at the point $(1, 3)$, the equation of the circle is

$$(x - 1)^2 + (y - 3)^2 = 6^2, \quad \text{or} \quad (x - 1)^2 + (y - 3)^2 = 36$$

If the radius is 2 and the center of the circle is at the point $(-6, -8)$, the equation of the circle is

$$(x + 6)^2 + (y + 8)^2 = 2^2, \quad \text{or} \quad (x + 6)^2 + (y + 8)^2 = 4$$

However, it is not essential that the length of the radius be stated definitely. Since this length may be obtained if the position of the center of the circle and position of some point on the circle are both given, it follows that the equation of the circle may be obtained if we know:

(1) The location (coordinates) of the center of the circle, and

(2) The location (coordinates) of some point on the circle.

For example if some point is at the origin [that is, its coordinates are $(0, 0)$], and coordinates of the center of the circle are $(1, 2)$, then the length of the radius is

$$r = \sqrt{(1 - 0)^2 + (2 - 0)^2} = \sqrt{1^2 + 2^2} = \sqrt{1 + 4} = \sqrt{5}$$

and the equation of the circle is

$$(x - 1)^2 + (y - 2) = (\sqrt{5})^2, \quad \text{or} \quad (x - 1)^2 + (y - 2)^2 = 5$$

Note that the radius of the circle is $\sqrt{5}$. Now if we take a square root and square it, we actually undo the process of extraction of the square root. In other words, we thus obtain the expression (or the number) under the radical sign. Moreover, note that 5 is not a perfect square. Thus the extraction of a square root of a number that is not a perfect square cannot be performed exactly. This is why we left the expression $\sqrt{5}$ unchanged. We needed for the equation of the circle not the value of the radius but the square of its value, r^2.

1. Write the equation of the circle whose radius is 1, and whose center is at the origin.

2. Write the equation of the circle whose radius is $\sqrt{6}$, and whose center is the point $(0, -3)$.

3. Write the equation of the circle whose radius is 7, and whose center is the point $(-2, 0)$.

4. Write the equation of the circle whose center is the origin, and one point on the circle has the coordinates $(0, 1)$.

5. Write the equation of the circle whose center is at the point $(-5, 0)$, and one point on the circle has the coordinates $(0, -5)$.

6. Write the equation of the circle whose radius is $\sqrt{8}$, and whose center is the point $(-3, -5)$.

7. Write the equation of the circle whose center is at the point $(2, -3)$, and one point on the circle has the coordinates $(7, -8)$.

Some Points on the Way to Infinity

A point-world being confined to motion along a circle may not be as fortunate as one confined to motion along a straight line. The circle is a line (mathematicians call it a "curve") that is limited in length. A being that moves along a circle must sooner or later come back to the point from which it started. If it continues then to move along the circle, it must cover the same ground, but this may not be as monotonous as one might suspect.

Here we shall drop the viewpoint of the Flatlander. We are three-dimensional beings, and when we study the properties of geometric figures we shall make use of our ability to observe objects in three dimensions; we can look down on a plane, as though we were above and outside it. Now we shall see what a three-dimensional being can learn by observing what takes place in two dimensions.

We shall now make use of a geometric figure mentioned only casually thus far. We noted the right angle—that is, an angle formed by two perpendicular lines, such as the coordinate axes. Let us consider a circle whose center, to simplify the study, we shall place at the origin of the coordinate axes. Suppose that a point A moves along the circle, starting where the circle crosses the axis OX and moves in the direction indicated by the arrow in the drawing.

For every position of the point on the circle there corresponds a pair of numbers which are the coordinates of the point at that position. How many such pairs are there? The reader will re-

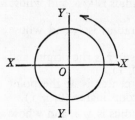

call that a point has no dimensions, and this means that it has no magnitude. Moreover, the motion along the circumference of the circle may be thought of as going around from point to point along points packed so close that they cannot be counted even in an eternity.

Every pair of these numbers, or coordinates, obeys the relation $x^2 + y^2 = r^2$ because the points that we discuss are on the circumference of the circle. However, we may obtain another interesting relation that is very important in mathematics and its practical application. Let us suppose that the point moving along the circumference is attached to the end of a straight line which is pivoted on the center of the circle. As the point moves the line sweeps around the circle with this point. We shall assume that the initial position of the point is on the axis OX where the circle cuts this axis as illustrated. Then, as the point departs from this initial position, the line to which it is attached (and this line is the radius of the circle) begins to make with the axis OX an angle (in the figure this angle for a certain position is AOB). The size of this angle increases with the distance traveled by the point.

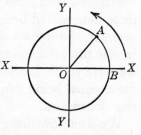

As the point reaches the axis OY above the axis OX (it is customary to allow the point to go around the circle in the counterclockwise direction as indicated by the arrow in the figure), we say that it covered one-quarter of the circumference of the circle. Moreover, we already know that the coordinate axes are perpendicular one to another. Thus, since perpendicular lines make right angles with one another, a quarter of the circle represents, in terms of the angle made by the sweeping radius of the circle, a right angle. As the point continues to move along the circumference of the circle

and reaches the axis *OX* on the left of the axis *OY*, the radius
will have swept through another quarter of the circle—that is,
another right angle. All in all, the radius will have swept then
through two right angles, or as it is generally denoted, through
a "straight angle." If the point continues to move along the circumference until it reaches the axis *OY* below the axis *OX*, the
radius will have swept through three right angles, as shown in
the figures below.

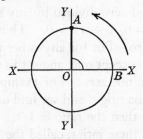 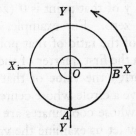

As the point continues to move along the circumference, it
will finally reach the position from which it originally started.
The radius of the circle then will have
swept the fourth and last quarter of the
circle. Thus, when the radius will have
completed one complete revolution an
angle equal to four right angles is obtained, as shown in the next figure. The
reader will observe that an angle of four
right angles is equal to two straight angles.
The point may continue to move around

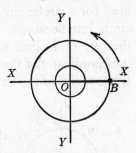

the circumference of the circle, for every complete revolution
making four right angles. This process may
be continued indefinitely.

As the point moves around the circle (and
for simplicity we shall consider the first
quarter of the circle only) it occupies various positions. If we consider some one position of the point on the circumference in
the first quarter, and we denote the coordinates of that position
of the point by (x, y) we may observe that the two numbers if

divided by one another give rise to another number, generally a fraction or, as we shall learn, a fraction known as "the ratio" of the two numbers. In other words, we now have the number y/x. For another position of the point on the circumference whose coordinates may be x_1 and y_1 there will be another ratio, y_1/x_1. Generally, for every position of the point along the circumference there is a corresponding ratio. When the point is on the circle at the place where the circle cuts the axis OX, the coordinate y of that point is 0 (zero), and zero divided by any number is zero. For example, $0 \div 5 = 0$, $0 \div 12 = 0$. Thus the value of the ratio of that point is zero. But for any other point within the first quarter of the circle (except one; about this more presently) the value of that ratio is not zero. For example, if we have a circle whose center is at the origin and we find on it a point whose coordinates are $(2, 3)$, then the ratio is $3/2$.

Now let us examine the values of these ratios, called the "tangents" of the angles that are formed by the radius of the circle in its various positions with the axis OX. Generally there is no need for a circle; any angle has a tangent, and we made use of a circle just because it was helpful in explaining the tangent. In the case of a circle whose center is at the origin, the values of the coordinates of the points in their various positions are limited. If the radius of the circle is r, the coordinates of the points where

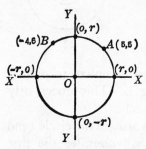

the circle cuts the axes OX and OY are indicated in the figure at left. They are $(r, 0)$, $(0, r)$, $(-r, 0)$, and $(0, -r)$. Any other point on the circumference has coordinates whose values are (in absolute value, that is, without consideration of the sign, whether positive or negative) less than the value of the radius r. The value of the tangent of the angle that the radius of the circle makes with the axis OX is, as the reader no doubt has observed, obtained by dividing the value of the ordinate, another name for the y, by the value of the abscissa, another name for the x, that is, by dividing y by x. For any point on the circumference of the circle, except two, we

have no trouble in obtaining the value of the tangent of the angle
that the radius of the circle drawn from that point makes with
the axis OX. But when we consider the points where the circle
cuts the axis OY we run into a grave difficulty; we get two ratios,
$r/0$ and $-r/0$. The second ratio is of little interest to us at the
moment, however, because we agreed to examine the angle in
the first quarter of the circle only.

Let us attempt to make some sense out of the ratio $r/0$; let us
take some points on the circumference that are very close to the
axis OY, to the right of it. Suppose that the values of the abscissas of these points are 0.01, 0.0001, 0.0000000000001. We
know that these numbers may be written as 10^{-2}, 10^{-4}, 10^{-13}.
The respective values of the ordinates of these points will be so
close to the value of the radius r of the circle that we may use
this value for computation of the tangents of the angles. We
have the three values of the tangents:

$$r/10^{-2} = r \cdot 10^{2} = 100r$$
$$r/10^{-4} = r \cdot 10^{4} = 10,000r$$
$$r/10^{-13} = r \cdot 10^{13} = 10,000,000,000,000r$$

If the radius of the circle is, say, 10, the values of the tangents
are 1,000, 100,000, and 100,000,000,000,000. In other words, the
closer the points on the circumference are to the axis OY (that
is, the nearer the angle is to a right angle) the greater is the
value of the tangent of the angle that the radius of the circle
makes with the axis OX. How great can the value of the tangent become? Suppose that the value of the abscissa of a point
is 1/googol, that is, $1/10^{100}$, or 10^{-100}. Then the value of the
tangent of the angle for that point is $r \cdot$ googol, or a googol times
the radius. Suppose that the value of the abscissa of a point on
the circumference of the circle is $1/\text{googol}^{\text{googol}}$. Then the value
of the tangent of the angle for that point is $\text{googol}^{\text{googol}}$ times the
radius and so on. But whatever the given value of the abscissas
of the points on the circle, the points are not on the axis OY;
they are very close to it, but not there. However, we note that
the value of the tangent becomes so great that we may go on
inventing names for new and larger numbers but still we cannot

reach the value of the tangent of the right angle. In order to stop somewhere, mathematicians have agreed that a right angle has no tangent; that is, when an angle gets near a right angle its tangent becomes so large that there is no value, no number, that can express its magnitude. The reader will recall that something of the same type of situation arose when the problem of the number of points on the circumference of the circle was considered; now we shall clarify it. Mathematicians have a special name for this goal that cannot be reached; they call it "infinity." Infinity is not a number because it is greater than any number; no matter how great a number we may write, speak, or think of, infinity is greater. If infinity were a number, it would cease to be infinity.

Babylonian Heritage: 360 Pieces of Circle

So far we have been talking about angles in general, but nothing has been said about their measure. We now know that one-quarter of a circle corresponds to a right angle, but this does not state the value of the magnitude of the angle—it is just a name for some kind of an angle, in fact an angle formed by two perpendicular lines. Angles have measures of their own, however. A unit of the measure of an angle is a certain portion of the revolution of the radius of a circle. It is 1/360th part of a complete revolution and is known as a "degree." Thus, when the radius of a circle completes one revolution it sweeps through an angle of 360 degrees, a small circle is written on the right, just above, the number of the degrees. Thus 360 degrees is written 360°.

Division of a circle into 360 parts has no valid reason. We inherited this from the Babylonians, whose priests studied the stars and the motion of the sun among them. They observed that it takes the sun $364\frac{1}{4}$ days to complete one trip around the heavens, and established this as the period of the year. For every day but four, or five every fourth or "leap" year, they had a particular god or goddess. The four "godless" days became special holidays. Possibly this breakdown of the year into 360 "regular" days accounts for our present use of the number.

Now we may have the measure of a right angle. It is 90 degrees, and a straight angle is 180 degrees. Every degree is divided into 60 parts, each known as a minute, and a minute is divided into 60 parts, known as seconds—our system of measuring time. This method of division also was inherited from the Babylonians, who used a method of numeration whose base was 60. The symbol for a minute is ′, and that for a second is ″. Thus an angle 42° 16′ 37″ designates 42 degrees, 16 minutes, and 37 seconds.

In the preceding section we allowed the point to travel along the circumference of the circle in the counterclockwise direction. When an angle is formed by a sweeping radius moving in such direction, the angle is considered positive; if the sweeping radius rotates in the opposite direction, clockwise, the angle formed by this radius and the axis OX is considered negative. This agreement, of course, is entirely arbitrary, but has been elevated to the status of a rule, just as we agreed to consider as positive the numbers to the right or above the origin, and as negative numbers to the left or below the origin.

Now let us return to the first quarter of the circle. We know that the ratio of the ordinate to the abscissa, y/x, gives us the tangent of the angle formed by the radius drawn from the point on the circumference of the circle (whose coordinates are given) and by the axis OX. However, there are two more ratios that are very important in mathematics. We may take the ratios x/r and y/r, which have a definite fixed value for every position of the point that moves around on the circumference. They are known as follows: x/r is the "cosine" of the angle, and y/r is the "sine" of the angle.

Thus we have three ratios, the sine, the cosine, and the tangent of the angle. This then raises the question whether these ratios are respectively the same for a given angle. Suppose we have two circles such that the radius of one is twice the radius of the other, but we have the positions of the points such that the angles corresponding to them are of equal size; would the respective ratios be the same? This examination is not a proof, but we hope we shall obtain evidence sufficient to convince us. In the

following drawing we have two such circles. Their equations
are

$$x^2 + y^2 = r^2 \quad \text{and} \quad x^2 + y^2 = 4r^2$$

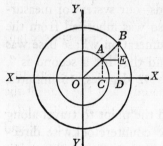

respectively.

Let the line OB form the angle BOD.
We then have two points, $A(x_1, y_1)$
and $B(x_2, y_2)$. Since these two points
are on their respective circles, they
must satisfy their respective equations.
We then have

$$x_1^2 + y_1^2 = r^2 \quad \text{and} \quad x_2^2 + y_2^2 = 4r^2$$

Divide the first equation by x_1^2 and the second equation by x_2^2.
We have then

$$1 + \frac{y_1^2}{x_1^2} = \frac{r^2}{x_1^2}$$

and

$$1 + \frac{y_2^2}{x_2^2} = \frac{4r^2}{x_2^2}$$

and

$$\frac{y_1^2}{x_1^2} = \frac{r^2}{x_1^2} - 1$$

$$\frac{y_2^2}{x_2^2} = \frac{4r^2}{x_2^2} - 1$$

In order that the ratios y_1/x_1 and y_2/x_2 be equal (and this is the
same as the equality of their squares) we must have

$$\frac{r^2}{x_1^2} - 1 = \frac{4r^2}{x_2^2} - 1$$

or

$$\frac{r^2}{x_1^2} = \frac{4r^2}{x_2^2}$$

Dividing both sides of the last equation by r^2 we have

$$\frac{1}{x_1^2} = \frac{4}{x_2^2}$$

or

$$4x_1^2 = x_2^2$$

From this we have

$$2x_1 = x_2$$

In other words, in a situation such as the one specified in our problem, when the radius of one circle is twice as large as the radius of the other circle, when we have the same angle (and the centers of the circle are both at the origin) the x coordinate of one point is twice as large as the x coordinate of the other point. If this condition is fulfilled, then the ratios that represent the tangents of the angles (which are the same) are equal.

Draw a line AE parallel to the axis OX; we also note that $OA = AB$ (remember what was stipulated about the radii of the circles, that one was twice as large as the other), and $OC = AE$. If we use the original equations and instead of dividing by x_1^2 and x_2^2 respectively we divide by y_1^2 and y_2^2, we may obtain, if we followed the method above, the condition that $y_2 = 2y_1$ also. Then we have that $BE = AC$. Now, reversing the process and if conditions obtained by us really exist, the tangents are equal. To obtain valid proof of what we have convinced ourselves by circuitous methods, we would have to use much geometry, and we do not think it necessary here to burden the reader. Complete proof may be found in any geometry textbook, especially in those parts dealing with similar triangles.

If we denote the angle that corresponds to a certain position of a point on the circumference of a circle by A, then we may write (abbreviating sine to "sin," cosine to "cos," and tangent to "tan")

$$\frac{y}{r} = \sin A, \quad \text{or} \quad y = r \sin A$$

and

$$\frac{x}{r} = \cos A \quad \text{or} \quad x = r \cos A$$

Finally if we divide

$$\frac{\frac{y}{r}}{\frac{x}{r}} = \frac{\sin A}{\cos A}$$

we have $y/x = \sin A/\cos A = \tan A$.

Moreover, if we take the equation $x^2 + y^2 = r^2$ and divide it by r^2 we have

$$\frac{y^2}{r^2} + \frac{x^2}{r^2} = 1$$

or

$$\sin^2 A + \cos^2 A = 1$$

which is the Pythagorean relation for the ratios connected with an angle.

The reader has no doubt observed that here we have obtained two relations,

$$y = r \sin A$$

and

$$x = r \cos A$$

These connect the coordinates of a point on the circumference of a circle of a given radius with the angle that corresponds to the position of that point. This is another form of the equation of a circle whose radius is r and whose center is at the origin. The reader will find no difficulty in "changing the address" of this circle if the origin is placed at the point (a, b). In the next chapter we shall make use of the ratios associated with an angle and learn of their application to practical problems.

How to Run Around in Distorted Circles

Thus far we allowed our prisoner in the point-world cell to leave it on parole, provided that he move always at a certain distance from his cell. We found that the parolee was to move along the circumference of a circle whose radius was equal to the stipulated distance. Thus our point-world prisoner would be under a constant surveillance.

Now let us suppose that our prisoner is a dangerous fifth columnist who might at any moment either disappear or commit another sabotage. In order to keep him under close surveillance, one guard (as in the case of the circle) is naturally insufficient. When the parole is granted to our prisoner it is decided that he should be watched always by two guards so located that the sum of the distances from him to his watchers will always be the same.

Suppose that the assigned sum of the distances is $2a$ (an expression selected merely to simplify our work). In the illustration below one of the positions of the paroled prisoner is shown.

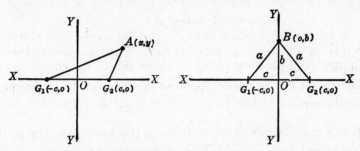

The two fixed points, or guards, are located at the points G_1 and G_2 at equal distances on the axis OX from the axis OY. The coordinates of the guards are then $G_1(-c, 0)$ and $G_2(c, 0)$. Moreover, in two cases our paroled prisoner will be at equal distances from his guards, that is, when he crosses the axis OY. Let his coordinates be $(0, b)$ and $(0, -b)$. For this reason we selected $2a$ as the sum of the distances, because when he crosses the axis OY he will be a distance away from each guard. Let us assume that coordinates of our paroled prisoner are (x, y); we shall now proceed to the situation by simple algebra:

According to the distance formula for two points (x_1, y_1) and (x_2, y_2),

$$d^2 = (x_2 - x_1)^2 + (y_2 - y_1)^2$$

we can write the expressions for the following distances:

$$AG_1^2 = (x + c)^2 + y^2 \quad \text{and} \quad AG_2^2 = (x - c)^2 + y^2$$

or

$$AG_1 = \sqrt{(x + c)^2 + y^2} \quad \text{and} \quad AG_2 = \sqrt{(x - c)^2 + y^2}$$

But according to the stipulation of the parole, $AG_1 + AG_2 = 2a$, or

$$\sqrt{(x + c)^2 + y^2} + \sqrt{(x - c)^2 + y^2} = 2a$$

This expression can be rewritten as

$$\sqrt{(x + c)^2 + y^2} - 2a = -\sqrt{(x - c)^2 + y^2}$$

Now square both sides of the equation, remembering that

$$(a + b)^2 = a^2 + 2ab + b^2$$

and we have

$$(x + c)^2 + y^2 - 4a\sqrt{(x + c)^2 + y^2} + 4a^2 = (x - c)^2 + y^2$$

or

$$x^2 + 2cx + c^2 + y^2 - 4a\sqrt{(x+c)^2+y^2} + 4a^2 = x^2 - 2cx + c^2 + y^2$$

We may drop the same terms on either side of the equation, and we have

$$2cx - 4a\sqrt{(x + c)^2 + y^2} + 4a^2 = -2cx$$

and this may be rewritten as follows (by moving $-2cx$ to the left side and $4a\sqrt{(x + c)^2 + y^2}$ to the right side of the equation and not forgetting to change their respective signs).

$$4cx + 4a^2 = 4a\sqrt{(x + c)^2 + y^2}$$

We can divide both sides of the equation by 4, and we have

$$cx + a^2 = a\sqrt{(x + c)^2 + y^2}$$

Again we have a complicated expression, although we got rid of one square root. Now if we square both sides of the equation, we shall eliminate the square root on the right of the equation. After squaring we have

$$(cx + a^2)^2 = a^2[(x + c)^2 + y^2]$$
$$c^2x^2 + 2a^2cx + a^4 = a^2x^2 + 2a^2cx + a^2c^2 + a^2y^2$$

On either side of the equation we have $2a^2cx$, and this may be dropped. We then have

$$c^2x^2 + a^4 = a^2x^2 + a^2c^2 + a^2y^2$$

We now can rewrite the equation as

$$a^2x^2 - c^2x^2 + a^2y^2 = a^4 - a^2c^2$$

and this may be rewritten as

$$(a^2 - c^2)x^2 + a^2y^2 = a^2(a^2 - c^2)$$

Now if we recall what was said about the two positions of the paroled prisoner when he crosses the axis OY, when its coordinates are $(0, b)$ and $(0, -b)$, we observe from the drawing that

$$b^2 + c^2 = a^2, \quad \text{or} \quad a^2 - c^2 = b^2$$

and the reader will recall that this is obtained from the Pythagorean relationship for right triangles. If we replace in our last equation $(a^2 - c^2)$ by b^2, we have

$$b^2x^2 + a^2y^2 = a^2b^2$$

Now, divide both sides of the equation by a^2b^2, and we obtain

$$\frac{x^2}{a^2} + \frac{y^2}{b^2} = 1$$

which is the equation of the curve along which our paroled prisoner must travel to comply with the conditions of the parole. Notice that if a and b were equal we would have

$$\frac{x^2}{a^2} + \frac{y^2}{a^2} = 1$$

or

$$x^2 + y^2 = a^2 \quad \left(\text{or} \ \frac{x^2}{b^2} + \frac{y^2}{b^2} = 1, \quad \text{and} \quad x^2 + y^2 = b^2\right)$$

In other words, this curve is a distorted circle, not a true circle: it is known as an "ellipse." The preceding equation is for a particular kind of an ellipse, with the points G_1 and G_2 on the axis OX equally distant from the origin of the coordinate axes.

If the address of the prison (in the foregoing case it is at the origin of the coordinate axes) is changed to some other point whose coordinates are (h, k), and the guards are located on a line parallel to the axis OX at equal distances from the prison on that line, then the equation of the curve along which the paroled prisoner must travel becomes

$$\frac{(x - h)^2}{a^2} + \frac{(y - k)^2}{b^2} = 1$$

Nature's Favorite: The Ellipse

There is a popular notion that the circle is the most common and "most perfect" (whatever this may mean) curve in nature and that there is abundant evidence that the circle is present in numerous natural phenomena and in many forms of life and vegetation. Nothing could be further from the truth; it is not the circle that is most common in nature, it is the ellipse.

It is often said, too, that the earth, the sun, the moon, the planets, and stars are large spheres, and that their images appear as circles (a sphere, as it will become evident in a later section of this chapter, is closely related to a circle). Not one of these heavenly bodies, however, is spherical in shape. It suffices to say that the earth and the sun as well is flattened out at the poles and bulges at the equator because of the centrifugal force generated by its revolution on the axis, the shape of the body resembling a rotated ellipse. But what is the appearance of an ellipse?

It is quite simple to draw an ellipse, but we must remember the conditions imposed on the paroled point-world prisoner. He was allowed to move in such a manner that the sum of his distances from two fixed points was the same for every point on the curve. We select two fixed points and a length that is equal to the sum of the two distances. We then measure off this sum of the distances on a piece of string. Drive pins into two selected points. Attach the string to the pins (this makes it obvious that the distance between the two selected points must be always less than the sum of the two distances represented on the string) and

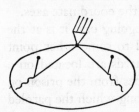

place a pencil point so that the string is drawn taut, but not very tight. Then let the pencil slide, and it will trace an ellipse as shown on the left.

Thus there is considerable difference between an ellipse and a circle. A circle has one center; an ellipse has two points, which are known as "focuses" or "foci." A circle has a radius which is the same for a given circle; the ellipse does not have a radius. A circle has a diameter which is twice the length of the radius, and the diameter is the same for a given circle; this is not so in the case of an ellipse. An ellipse has a smallest and a largest diameter (they are known as the "minor" and "major" axes). Only one diameter of an ellipse passes through the foci of the ellipse, and the diameters of an ellipse vary in size.

The foci of an ellipse possess an unusual property. In a room with a floor in the shape of an ellipse, the slightest whisper of a person standing where one focus is can easily be heard in the place where the other focus is. For any other place in the room this is impossible. This is known as the "whispering gallery effect." You may see such a whispering gallery in the Capitol at Washington.

The earth and other planets move around the sun not in circles but in ellipses, and the sun is located in the place which is the focus of every respective ellipse. This is also true of other stars. The moon moves around the earth along an ellipse, and in this case, too, the earth is in the place which is the focus of this ellipse.

All circles are of the same shape, but ellipses vary. The shape of an ellipse depends on the distance between its two foci and on the sum of the distances of a point on the ellipse from the two foci. If this sum does not differ much from

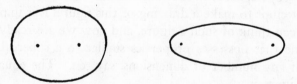

the distance between the two foci, the ellipse is elongated, and it seems to be flattened out, as in the drawing above. If, however, the sum of the distances of a point on the ellipse from the two foci is many times greater than the distance between the foci, the ellipse tends to assume the shape of a circle, as in the above drawing. Finally, when the distance between the foci is zero, and the two foci become one point, the ellipse actually becomes a circle.

Meet the Circle's Fat Friends: Sphere, Hypersphere, and Ellipsoid

We have learned how easy it is to extend the distance formula for two points to any number of dimensions; now we shall apply the same method to figures related to the circle and to the ellipse when these figures possess the properties of many dimensional objects. We shall first consider the extension of the circle.

The circle is a figure such that all its points are at exactly the same distance from a point in its plane, and this point is known as the center of the circle. In three dimensions (we should remember that the circle is in two dimensions) we have a figure such that all its points are at exactly the same distance from one point inside that figure. Applying the method of extension used in the preceding chapter, we write the equation of this figure:

$$x^2 + y^2 + z^2 = r^2$$

This figure is known as the "sphere."

It is quite simple to write the equation of a figure in four dimensions that will have properties similar to the sphere. This equation will be

$$x^2 + y^2 + z^2 + w^2 = r^2$$

Now this figure is not a sphere; mathematicians call it a "hypersphere" (supersphere) in four dimensions. The reader is advised not to attempt to make a drawing of this figure; it is impossible. But we can think of such a figure, and now we are ready to imagine one that possesses properties similar to a sphere but is a figure of any number of dimensions, say ten. The equation of such a figure is

$$x^2 + y^2 + z^2 + w^2 + t^2 + s^2 + u^2 + v^2 + o^2 + q^2 = r^2$$

To draw a picture of such a figure is impossible, but the equation tells us all its properties. We know that it is in ten dimensions and that all its points are exactly equally distant from a point within it known as the center. And the center is at the origin.

How about the ellipse?

The equation of an ellipse is

$$\frac{x^2}{a^2} + \frac{y^2}{b^2} = 1$$

where, as we now know, $2a$ is the major axis and $2b$ is the minor axis, and the origin of the coordinate axes is at the point where the major and minor axes of the ellipse intersect (they are also perpendicular to one another).

For three dimensions we obtain by the same method the equation

$$\frac{x^2}{a^2} + \frac{y^2}{b^2} + \frac{z^2}{c^2} = 1$$

which represents a figure similar to an ellipse. It has three axes, $2a$, $2b$, and $2c$. They are all perpendicular to one another, and the origin of the coordinates is at the point of their intersection. This figure is known as an "ellipsoid."

For four dimensions we obtain by means of the same method the equation

$$\frac{x^2}{a^2} + \frac{y^2}{b^2} + \frac{z^2}{c^2} + \frac{w^2}{d^2} = 1$$

which represents a figure similar to an ellipsoid in three dimensions. It has four axes, $2a$, $2b$, $2c$, and $2d$. They are all perpendicular to one another, and the origin of the coordinates is at the point of their intersection. The reader may give this figure any name he pleases, and now he may write the equation of a figure similar (in properties) to an ellipsoid of any number of dimensions.

This Curve May Kill You: The Parabola

Let us suppose that in the world of mathematics both capital punishment and life imprisonment are abolished and that even the meanest prisoner must be let out on parole some day. Let us suppose, then, that our prisoner is an extremely dangerous killer, and that in his parole he is allowed to move only in such a manner that he must always be at the same distance from one guard and from an infinite number of guards all posted along a straight line.

Let one guard be posted along the axis OX at the distance a to the right of the origin, and the infinite number of guards along a line parallel to the axis OY at a distance a to the left of the origin. Suppose that at some instant the prisoner is at the point A whose coordinates are (x, y). This situation is shown in the diagram below. Then $AG = AB$. But $AB = a + x$; moreover, the triangle AFG is a right triangle. According to the Pythagorean relationship then

$$AF^2 + FG^2 = AG^2 = AB^2$$

Or, since $AF = y$, $FG = a - x$, and $AG = AB = a + x$, we have

$$y^2 + (a - x)^2 = (a + x)^2$$

or

$$y^2 + a^2 - 2ax + x^2 = a^2 + 2ax + x^2$$

This equation may be simplified by dropping $a^2 + x^2$ from both sides of the equation, and we have after we transfer $-2ax$ to the right side of the equation (not forgetting to change its sign)

$$y^2 = 4ax$$

This curve, shown in the accompanying diagram, is known as

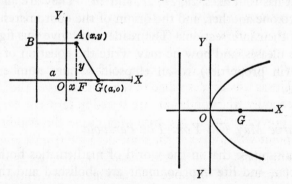

the "parabola" and is important in nature as well as in the arts of war and industry. Bombs, bullets, baseballs, automobile headlights, concert stages, fountains—all these are subject to a certain physical law that is expressed in some form of the foregoing equation. We shall examine the parabola's properties in more detail later.

Now we can dispose of the question that may have arisen earlier: What would happen to the ellipse if the distance between the foci became infinite? Although a mathematical answer would require much algebraic work, we can arrive at a satisfactory conclusion if we just reflect a little. As the distance between the foci of the ellipse becomes larger and larger, the ellipse becomes more elongated. But as the distance between the foci becomes infinite, we lose sight of one end of the ellipse; as far as we are concerned, it disappears because we never can reach infinity. The other end of the ellipse will thus have moved away from us, and the curve becomes a parabola.

How to Get Your Geometric Passport

At the start a promise was made to the reader that if he followed closely the development of the material in this chapter he would be able to write a "passport" for any geometric figure. To be able to write this passport (that is, the equation which describes the nature as well as the position of the curve) it is necessary to have definite information and to know how to translate it into mathematical language. The steps are usually as follows:

a) Select a suitable system of coordinate axes. If the figure is in the world of two dimensions then two coordinate axes *OX* and *OY* are chosen.

b) Take note of the description of the behavior of a moving point. This is usually described in the conditions of the problem.

c) Generally, the conditions are stated in terms of certain distances. For example, in the case of a circle the condition was that the point was always at the same distance from a given point in the same plane. The magnitude of the distance is then also given. Express this distance by taking some arbitrary point (x, y) and the given point (or points). The fundamental assumption in taking an arbitrary point is that this point is on the geometric figure whose passport is to be written. The expression for the distance thus obtained is the required passport.

d) Perform whatever operations are indicated in the expression that was obtained in (*c*) and try to simplify its appearance.

To illustrate the procedure outlined above we shall consider the following example. A point moves so that its distance from the point (2, 0) is always twice as large as its distance from the point (−1, 0). Along what kind of a curve does this point move?

a) We draw two coordinate axes *OX* and *OY* (shown below) and mark off the two points (1, 0) and (−2, 0).

b) We take some point in the plane and assume that its coordinates are (*x*, *y*). Let that point be marked *A*, while the point (2, 0) is marked *B* and point (−1, 0) is marked *C*. Join point *A* with points *B* and *C*. Then, according to the conditions of our problem,

$$AC = 2AB$$

c) By means of the distance formula that expresses the distance between two points (x_1, y_1) and (x_2, y_2),

$$d = \sqrt{(x_1 - x_2)^2 + (y_1 - y_2)^2}$$

we write

$$AB = \sqrt{(x - 2)^2 + y^2}$$

and

$$AC = \sqrt{(x + 1)^2 + y^2}$$

Since $AB = 2AC$, we write

$$\sqrt{(x - 2)^2 + y^2} = 2\sqrt{(x + 1)^2 + y^2}$$

d) The expression that was obtained in (*c*) contains square roots. However we may eliminate them by squaring both sides of the equation. We then have

$$(x - 2)^2 + y^2 = 4[(x + 1)^2 + y^2]$$

Now we proceed with simplification of this expression. First we perform the squaring of the expressions (*x* − 2) and (*x* + 1). We have

$$x^2 - 4x + 4 + y^2 = 4(x^2 + 2x + 1 + y^2)$$

Then, multiplying the right side of the equation as indicated by 4, we have

$$x^2 - 4x + 4 + y^2 = 4x^2 + 8x + 4 + 4y^2$$

Now if we collect the similar terms on the same side of the equation, we have

$$4x^2 - x^2 + 8x + 4x + 4y^2 - y^2 + 4 - 4 = 0$$

or

$$3x^3 + 12x + 3y^2 = 0$$

Divide the equation by 3 and we have

$$x^2 + 4x + y^2 = 0$$

Now observe that if we add 4 to the expression $x^2 + 4x$ we obtain $x^2 + 4x + 4$, which is of the form $x^2 + 2 \cdot 2 \cdot x + (2)^2$, and this is the square of $(x + 2)$. But if we add 4 to one side of the equation we must balance this with a similar addition to the other side of the equation. We then have

$$x^2 + 4x + 4 + y^2 = 4$$

or

$$(x + 2)^2 + y^2 = 4$$

By this time we know that this equation is of the form

$$(x - a)^2 + (y - b)^2 = r^2$$

which is the equation of a circle whose center is at the point (a, b) and whose radius is r. Thus our curve is a circle whose center is at the point $(-2, 0)$ and whose radius is 2. Note that y^2 is the same as $(y - 0)^2$ and that $(y - 0)$ is generally considered superfluous and is written as y. The diagram below illustrates the solution of our problem.

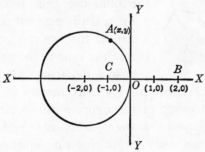

PROBLEMS

8. A point moves so that its distance from the point $(2, -4)$ is always the same. What is the passport of the geometric figure along which this point moves?

9. A point moves so that the sum of its distances from the points (1, 0) and (0, 1) is always the same. Obtain the expression for the passport of the geometric figure along which this point travels.

10. A point moves so that the difference of its distances from the given points $(c, 0)$ and $(-c, 0)$ is always the same, say $2a$. Write the passport of the geometric figure along which this point travels. (The reader is advised to refer to the equation of the ellipse and follow its development closely.)

11. A point moves so that its distance from a given point (1, 0) is half the distance from a line that is parallel to the axis OY and passes the axis OX at the point $(-2, 0)$. Find the expression for the passport of the geometric figure along which this point travels.

12. Obtain the expression for the passport of the geometric figure along which a point moves in such a manner that its distance from the point (3, 0) is three times as large as its distance from the point (0, 3).

13. Obtain the expression for the passport of the geometric figure along which a point moves in such a manner that its distance from the point (1, 1) is equal to its distance from the point (2, 2).

Every Passport Has Its Picture

So far we were concerned with writing the passport of a geometric figure when definite information was given concerning the behavior of a point that was moving along it. Now we shall

concern ourselves with the problem of the passport of a geometric figure in reverse order. In other words, if we have the passport of a geometric figure, what does it look like? Two methods lead to the solution of this problem:

First, if the passport is stated in such a manner that we can immediately recognize the type of the geometric figure, we can derive from the equation (which is another name for the passport) information which will enable us to make a drawing of the figure with almost no difficulty. For example, suppose that the equation is $(x - 4)^2 + (y - 2)^2 = 25$. We immediately know that this equation represents a circle, illustrated below, whose radius is 5 (because $5^2 = 25$) and whose center is at the point whose coordinates are (4, 2):

Second, if the passport is stated in such a form that we are unable to recognize the type of the geometric figure immediately, we take the long road to solution of the problem. We assign values either to the x or to the y, generally to the letters (often called the "variable," because it may take on different values) that is raised to a lower power and which does not appear in any higher power. After these values are assigned to one letter (or variable), we solve the equation for the other letter. Thus we obtain for x and y pairs of values which represent coordinates of points on the geometric figure. After a sufficient number of points is thus obtained in terms of their coordinates, these points are plotted on graph paper. Finally these points are joined by a smooth line.

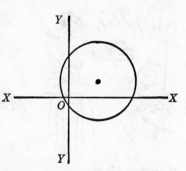

This line is the required geometric figure whose passport is given.

For example, suppose that the equation of the geometric figure is

$$y = 2x^2 - x + 4$$

We begin to assign values to x because y does not appear squared, while x appears squared (in $2x^2$). We thus have a table of values

x	-3	-2	-1	0	1	2	3
y	25	14	7	4	5	10	19

We plot these points on graph paper and join them by a smooth line. This geometric figure is a parabola.

PROBLEMS

Draw the geometric figures whose equations are:

14. $y = x^2 - 3x + 1$.
15. $(x + 3)^2 + (y - 7)^2 = 64$.
16. $xy = 4$ (*Hint:* divide both sides of the equation by x).
17. $y = 3x + 4$.
18. $(x + 3)^2 + \dfrac{(y - 1)^2}{4} = 1$.

°25°

Man's Servant—The Triangle

Measure Magic

Now we have reached one of the most fascinating phases of mathematics, with processes that dispel the mystery of how surveyors—from a distance—measure boundaries and heights, and of how ships at sea and planes in the air are guided on their courses. And, oddly enough, the processes basically are far from complicated and require no expensive instruments or great knowledge of mathematics. After perusal of this chapter, the reader himself may easily accomplish apparently impossible feats of measurement.

For a practical approach to this study, let us suppose we are buying a large piece of land. The deed contains a description of boundary markers, but we wish to know the land's precise limits and make sure that none of our parcel as described has been taken over by a neighbor. The job of measurement, however, appears an appallingly complicated task, and so we call in specialists in this work, the surveyors.

The surveyors come and set their instruments up on tripods and then begin to peer through their sight tubes. Every now and then they jot down numbers, turn their instruments around, look into the tubes again, and jot down some more numbers. Some of their assistants stretch out on the ground long ribbons of marked steel. These assistants, too, jot down some numbers. Finally after some work and more waiting, they give you a map and a written description of the property.

The entire procedure may seem complex and veiled in a profound knowledge of mathematics, but to understand it is not difficult. The magic wand that gives all these powers is a simple geometric figure formed by three sides: a "triangle."

The Triangle: Simple, Eternal, and Mysterious

A triangle is the simplest geometric figure. It has three sides and three angles. Thus in the figure below the triangle ABC has sides AB, BC, and AC and angles A, B, and C (these may be written also as BAC, ABC, and ACB; in this notation the middle letter denotes the vertex, the point where the two lines forming the angle intersect). Although the triangle is so simple, books have been written about its peculiar properties, and much is still to be discovered. However we shall be concerned only with its elementary properties, those known for more than two thousand years.

If we add the three angles of a triangle, the sum is exactly equal to a straight angle, or two right angles, or 180 degrees. Thus the sum of the angles A, B, and C is

$$A + B + C = 180°$$

If we have two triangles ABC and $A_1B_1C_1$ such that $AB = A_1B_1$, $BC = B_1C_1$, and $AC = A_1C_1$, then the angles of the triangles are correspondingly equal; thus

$$A = A_1, \quad B = B_1, \quad \text{and} \quad C = C_1$$

However, if we have two triangles ABC and $A_1B_1C_1$ such that their angles are equal—$A = A_1$, $B = B_1$, and $C = C_1$—it does not follow necessarily that $AB = A_1B_1$, $AC = A_1C_1$, and $BC = B_1C_1$; they may or may not be equal. The two triangles ABC and $A_1B_1C_1$ in this case have the same shape, appearing as though one were an enlargement of the other. If the angles of one triangle are correspondingly equal to the angles of another, but the sides of these two triangles are not correspondingly equal (as in the two triangles below), that is, when the two triangles have the same shape, they are known as "similar" triangles. We shall

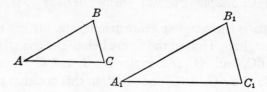

be concerned first with the properties of similar triangles, by means of which we shall be able to perform many of the measurements earlier described.

Similar triangles may be obtained when a line is drawn parallel to one of the sides of a triangle as shown below. This line may be drawn inside the triangle as well as outside, but when the line is outside two sides of the triangle must be extended in order to

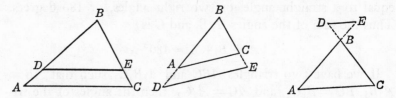

meet it. This is shown by the dotted lines in the drawing. Here we have the similar triangles *ABC* and *DBE*.

When two triangles are similar the respective magnitudes of their sides are related to one another in a manner to be stated as soon as we have learned something about the method of comparing the magnitudes of two objects.

The Bases of Comparison

When the magnitudes of two quantities are compared with one another, we may raise two questions: (1) How much does the magnitude of one object exceed the magnitude of the other, and (2) how many times is the magnitude of one object greater, or smaller, than the magnitude of the other object?

When we are concerned with the question of "how much," we subtract the smaller quantity from the larger, and the difference represents the answer. For example, if the population of one town is 5,347 and that of another 8,593, then the population of the second exceeds that of the first by $8,593 - 5,347 = 3,246$.

The question of "how many times" requires the operation of division, since we actually ask the question: If one quantity is greater than another, then how many times does the greater quantity contain the smaller? To answer this, we simply divide the number that expresses the magnitude of the greater quantity by the number that expresses the magnitude of the smaller quantity. For example, if one book contains 275 pages while another contains 550, then the second book has twice as many pages as the first book, a conclusion simply obtained by division of 550 by 275, or $550 \div 275 = 2$.

Often the answer to the question "how many times" is given in the form of a ratio. Thus the number of pages in the books is in the ratio of 2 to 1 or, as it may be written in fraction form, 2/1.

It should be noted that the same ratio may express the relationship of several pairs of quantities, although these pairs may not be correspondingly equal. For example, 15 and 25, 12 and 20, and 21 and 35 are three pairs of numbers, but each pair is in the ratio of 3 to 5, or 3/5.

If we know one quantity, and know the ratio between a second quantity and the first quantity, we can obtain the second quantity by multiplying the first quantity by that ratio. For example, if we have 15, and we know that the ratio of a second quantity to 15 is 2/3, then the second quantity is

$$15 \cdot \frac{2}{3} = 10$$

Generally, if we know the quantity a and the ratio

$$\frac{b}{a} = k, \quad \text{then} \quad b = ak$$

If we take two pairs of quantities such that their ratios are equal, we can say that the four quantities are "proportional," or that they "form a proportion." Thus, by equating the two fractions formed by the two pairs of quantities respectively we obtain a proportion

$$\frac{15}{25} = \frac{21}{35}$$

or

$$\frac{21}{35} = \frac{12}{20}$$

Similar Triangles and Their Properties

Thus far we observed that when two triangles are such that their angles are correspondingly equal the triangles may be similar (they may also have the sides correspondingly equal, but not necessarily). We also noted that similar triangles may be obtained by drawing one line parallel to one side of a triangle and, when necessary, by extending the other two sides to meet this line. Thus we have another condition for triangles being similar; that is, that in a triangle a parallel line may be drawn (or if there are two triangles such that their sides are correspondingly parallel, as in the triangles below). The reader may, if he chooses,

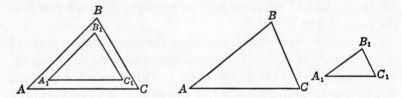

refer to a geometry textbook for proofs of these statements, since here we are concerned chiefly with application of the results.

The most important property of similar triangles is this: when two triangles are similar, their corresponding sides are proportional. This means that if we have two similar triangles, and the side of one is twice the corresponding side of the other ("corresponding side" denotes a side that is opposite an equal angle as shown in the two triangles below), then the other corresponding sides are in the same ratio. For example, the two triangles ABC

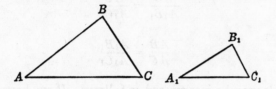

and $A_1B_1C_1$ are similar; that is, angle $A =$ angle A_1, angle $B =$ angle B_1, and angle $C =$ angle C_1. Then we have the ratios

$$\frac{AB}{A_1B_1}, \quad \frac{AC}{A_1C_1}, \quad \text{and} \quad \frac{BC}{B_1C_1}$$

and these ratios are equal. In another form,

$$\frac{AB}{A_1B_1} = \frac{AC}{A_1C_1} = \frac{BC}{B_1C_1}$$

It will be helpful now to examine some of the properties of proportions and apply them to the proportions

$$\frac{AB}{A_1B_1} = \frac{AC}{A_1C_1} = \frac{BC}{B_1C_1}$$

Suppose we have two equal ratios,

$$\frac{a}{b} = k \quad \text{and} \quad \frac{c}{d} = k$$

We then have the proportion

$$\frac{a}{b} = \frac{c}{d}$$

But we also have that $a = bk$ and $c = dk$. Dividing the first equality by the second we obtain

$$\frac{a}{c} = \frac{bk}{dk}$$

or

$$\frac{a}{c} = \frac{b}{d}$$

If we apply this result to the proportion of the sides of the similar triangles, we have that

$$\frac{AB}{A_1B_1} = \frac{AC}{A_1C_1}$$

then

$$\frac{AB}{AC} = \frac{A_1B_1}{A_1C_1}$$

This result may be interpreted as follows. If we have two similar triangles, then if two sides of one triangle are in some proportion, the two corresponding sides of the other triangle (the sides that are opposite the correspondingly equal angles) are in the same proportion. This is a result of high significance.

Now we may arrive at one more result. If the ratio of two corresponding sides of two similar triangles is 1/1—that is, the corresponding sides of two similar triangles are equal—the triangles are equal. In other words, the equality of two triangles (which is known as "congruence") is a special case of similarity of two triangles.

Two Especially Helpful Triangles

Recalling that among the many properties of a triangle there is the property that the sum of the angles of any triangle is always exactly equal to two right angles or to 180 degrees, we shall now examine, among the many triangles that may be thought of, or are in existence, two that are of particular interest.

A triangle may have three equal sides as shown in the accom-
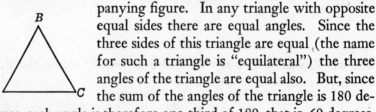
panying figure. In any triangle with opposite equal sides there are equal angles. Since the three sides of this triangle are equal (the name for such a triangle is "equilateral") the three angles of the triangle are equal also. But, since the sum of the angles of the triangle is 180 degrees, each angle is therefore one-third of 180, that is, 60 degrees. This triangle in itself offers very little help in enabling us to perform measurements of the type described above; however, if one side of this triangle is divided into two equal parts (an operation

called "bisection") and we join the point of bisection with the opposite vertex, we obtain two equal triangles, and triangles of this type are highly useful for our purpose.

Let us examine just what happens when we perform the operation described in the preceding paragraph. Let *ABC* be an equilateral triangle. The side *AC* is bisected, and point *D* is the bisection (or the middle) point of the side *AC*. We join the vertex *B* and the middle point *D* with a straight line *BD*. We thus obtain two triangles, *ABD* and *DBC*. These two triangles are equal, for reasons we can now demonstrate. We observe that the three sides of one triangle are correspondingly equal to the three sides of the other triangle; $AB = BC$, $BD = BD$, and $AD = DC$. Moreover, we now know that if two triangles are equal, opposite equal sides there are equal angles. Now angle *ADB* is opposite side *AB* (in triangle *ABD*), and angle *BDC* is opposite side *BC* (in triangle *BDC*).

But $AB = BC$. We therefore conclude that angle $ADB =$ angle *BDC*.

But these two angles are about a point on one side of a line, and their sum is thus 180 degrees. It follows then that each of the angles *ADB* and *BDC* is equal to 90 degrees, or is a right angle.

Thus, the two triangles *ABD* and *BDC* are right triangles. Moreover, since angle $A = 60$ degrees and angle $ADB = 90$ degrees, and the sum of the angles of a triangle is 180 degrees, the remaining angle *ABD* is equal to 30 degrees. A triangle of this type is known as a 30-, 60-, 90-degree triangle. We notice that in such a triangle the smallest side (*AD*) is equal to one-half of the largest side (*AB*, which is equal to *AC*). Moreover, since we know the Pythagorean relation, we can obtain the expression for the side *BD*. Since the triangle *ABD* is a right triangle we have

$$AD^2 + BD^2 = AB^2, \quad \text{or} \quad (\tfrac{1}{2}AB)^2 + BD^2 = AB^2$$

Then

$$BD^2 = AB^2 - (\tfrac{1}{2}AB)^2, \quad \text{or} \quad BD^2 = AB^2 - \tfrac{1}{4}AB^2$$

Finally,
$$BD^2 = \tfrac{3}{4}AB^2, \quad \text{or} \quad BD = \tfrac{1}{2}AB\sqrt{3}.$$

Thus if we know that we have a 30-, 60-, 90-degree triangle, and we know the largest side, we can obtain the values of the other two sides. For example, if in such a triangle the largest side is 10 inches, then the other two sides are 5 inches, and $5\sqrt{3} = 5\cdot1.7 = 8.5$ inches. If we know the smallest side, we can in a similar manner obtain the values of the other two sides. For example, if the smallest side is 8 inches, then the largest side is 16 inches, and the third side $8\sqrt{3} = 8\cdot1.7 = 13.6$ inches. If we know the side that is opposite the 60-degree angle, we can now say that the largest side is equal to

$$\frac{2\cdot\text{the side opposite the 60° angle}}{\sqrt{3}}$$

Suppose that the side opposite the 60-degree angle is 5.1 inches. Then the largest side is

$$\frac{2\cdot5.1}{1.7} = \frac{10.2}{1.7} = 6 \text{ inches}$$

The smallest side is 3 inches.

Another useful triangle is a right triangle that has two angles equal. The angles of such a triangle are then 45, 45, and 90 degrees. In such a right triangle the sides opposite the 45-degree angles are equal. The triangle in the next figure is a 45-, 45-, 90-degree triangle. If we apply it to the Pythagorean relation

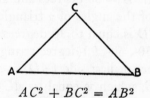

we have
$$AC^2 + BC^2 = AB^2$$

But $AC = BC$. Replacing BC by AC we have

$$AC^2 + AC^2 = AB^2 \quad \text{or} \quad 2AC^2 = AB^2$$

Finally,
$$AB = AC\sqrt{2}, \ AB = 1.4AC$$

Thus, if $AC = 5$ inches, $AB = 1.4\cdot5 = 7$ inches.

The Triangle as a Superyardstick

By constructing a simple 45-, 45-, 90-degree triangle one can easily measure heights of objects such as trees, buildings, and other structures. Remembering that in such a triangle one angle is a right angle and the sides that form this angle are equal, the reader can cut one out of cardboard; trace one on a flat piece of wood, with pins stuck into its vertices, or make one by simply folding a piece of paper, as follows:

a) Fold the paper with the crease *AB* as illustrated.

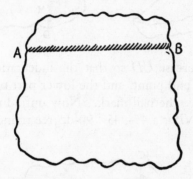

b) Fold the paper again so that one part of the crease *AB* falls on itself as shown; you now have another crease, *CD*, the two creases forming a right angle.

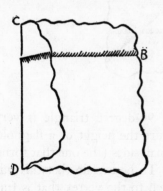
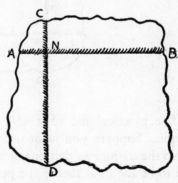

c) Keeping the paper folded twice, fold it again so that the portion of the crease *AB* falls on the portion of the crease *CD*.

Where the end *B* falls on the crease *CD* make an indentation with your nail. Now turn this fold back.

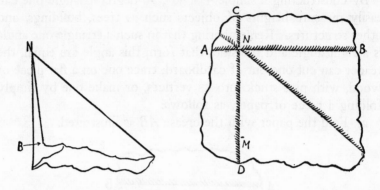

d) Fold the crease *CD* so that the indentation made by the nail becomes an end point, and the lower part of the crease falls on the part above the nail mark. Now unfold the entire paper. The triangle *MNP* is a 45-, 45-, 90-degree triangle.

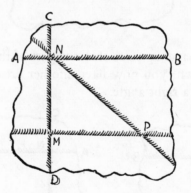

The practical use of a 45-, 45-, 90-degree triangle is very simple. Suppose you want to measure the height of a flagpole. Hold the triangle so that one of its small sides (the one that forms the right angle) is facing the pole. To be certain that this side is parallel to the pole you may attach to the vertex that is further from you, the one of the 45-degree angle, a weighted string. When this string runs so that it just touches the side of the triangle, you have this side parallel to the pole. Now, after your triangle is adjusted, look along the longer side and try to sight the top of the pole. You may have to walk to or away from the pole to see its top. As soon as you can observe the top of the pole, put the triangle down and measure your distance from the foot of the pole. Add to this distance your own height, and the resultant sum is the height of the pole.

This drawing illustrates the procedure in measuring the height of the pole BM.

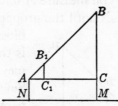

AN denotes the person who measures the distance. When this person directs the 45-, 45-, 90-degree triangle toward the pole as indicated in the drawing, the top B of the pole is seen along the line AB_1 so that AB_1B is a straight line. Moreover, the lines B_1C_1 and BC are parallel. We then have two 45-, 45-, 90-degree triangles, ABC (the large triangle) and AB_1C_1 (the small triangle). And since the triangle ABC is a 45-, 45-, 90-degree triangle, the side AC is equal to the side BC. Then the height of the pole BM is equal to the sum of the lengths BC and CM. Now we note that the length CM is equal to the height of the eyes of the person who measures the height of the pole, and the length BC is equal to AC, which in turn is equal to the length NM, or the distance of the person from the foot of the pole. Thus we have the following simple rule for measuring the height of the pole, or of any other object:

Stand away from the object whose height you want to measure so that the top of the object can be seen along the larger side of a 45-, 45-, 90-degree triangle. Measure your distance from the foot of the object, being certain that the ground is level, and add to this distance your height to your eyes. The resultant sum is the height of the object.

Should you be unable to employ a 45-, 45-, 90-degree triangle, you may use the following method for measuring heights of objects. There are several variations of the method but the principle is essentially the same.

Take a stick of wood equal in length to the height of your eyes, and place it vertically, either held by an assistant or stuck into the ground. To check the stick's position, attach to it a weight tied to a string. When the weight does not deviate from the stick and the string runs along the stick, you may be certain that the stick is placed vertically. This stick must be placed so that when you lie down on the ground with your feet against the stick, you see the top of the stick and the top of the object whose height you measure at one point. This process may require several trials until the proper position is found. The next drawing

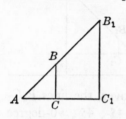

illustrates this method of measuring. BC is the stick. AC denotes the person who measures the height of the object B_1C_1. Since the stick is placed vertically, it is parallel to the object B_1C_1. Thus we have two similar triangles ABC and AB_1C_1. Moreover, $AC = BC$. Thus the two triangles are 45-, 45-, 90-degree triangles. Hence AC_1 must be equal to B_1C_1. In other words the distance AC_1 is equal to the height of the object B_1C_1.

It is not absolutely necessary to have a large stick, compelling you to stretch yourself on the ground flat on your back. Instead you may crouch or rest on your knees, but this may require looking sidewise and you will still have to keep your head on the ground. The drawing below illustrates this method of measuring. BC is the stick (now it is of any length). AC denotes the distance of the observer's eye to the lower end of the stick. The stick BC

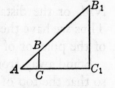

is placed so that the observer's eye A, the upper end of the stick B, and B_1, the top of the object whose height is measured, are all on the same line ABB_1. Moreover, the distance AC is selected in such a manner that $AC = BC$. This can be accomplished by attaching a string at C, which is as long as BC. We then have two 45-, 45-, 90-degree triangles, ABC and AB_1C_1. We therefore are able to measure the height of the object B_1C_1. This height is equal to the distance AC_1 to the bottom of the object B_1C_1. Naturally the entire procedure is based on the assumption that the ground is level and the object B_1C_1 is perpendicular to it.

How to Measure Distant Heights

Often an object is inaccessible to these processes. However, there are several methods by means of which such a measurement can be performed. Some of these involve computations, but the result can be accomplished by an instrument that anyone can construct. Take two strips of wood or cardboard and put them together, as in the accompanying figure. The strips should be perpendicular to one another 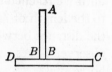 (forming right angles) and should be attached so that AB is equal to BC and DB is equal to one-half of AB (1/2 AB).

To measure the height of an inaccessible object hold the instrument so that the short end (DB) is directed downward. The upper part of the instrument is then a 45-, 45-, 90-degree triangle. Sight the top of the object to be measured so that point A, point C, and the top of the object M are on the one line ACM as shown in the next figure. When this is attained place a marker (T) on

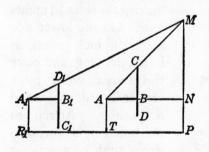

the ground where this takes place. Then turn the instrument around so that the short end (DB) is now directed upward. Walking away from the object, sight until the top of the object (M), point D, and point A are on the same line. When this is attained, put another marker (R) on the ground. Be sure, however, that the two markers and the bottom of the object are also on the same line, as shown in the figure. Now the distance between the two markers, together with the height of the observer's eyes, is the height of the object. We may convince ourselves of this from the following considerations. The two right triangles

A_1NM and $A_1B_1D_1$ are similar because B_1D_1 is parallel to MN. Therefore, we have the proportion

$$\frac{MN}{NA} = \frac{B_1D_1}{B_1A_1}$$

But we know that B_1D_1 is equal to one-half of B_1A_1. Therefore MN is equal to one-half of NA_1. From the first operation (when we applied the 45-, 45-, 90-degree) we obtained a length equal to MN. Therefore when we walked away from the object until we reached the second position, we covered a distance equal to the length of MN. To obtain the height of the object we add the distance between the two markers R and T and height of the observer's eyes. Again, here we also assume that the ground is horizontal.

An Instrument for Measuring Any Height

A universal instrument for measuring heights can be constructed by anyone. This does not require any special skill or any special knowledge of mathematics; all that one must remember is the property of similar triangles, that in two similar triangles any two corresponding sides are in the same ratio.

On a piece of paper draw a square, for practical purposes

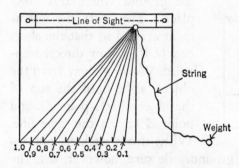

making the sides 10 inches long. On the lower side mark the inch points, as in the drawing, and paste this square on a piece of cardboard, or wood if possible. Attach to the upper-right corner a string with a weight at one end. It is advisable also to attach two pieces of cardboard to the top of the instrument for sighting purposes as shown in the drawing. Now the instrument is ready for use.

To measure the height of an object, hold the instrument so that the top of the object is observed through the two sighting attachments on top of the instrument. The weight will stretch the string to represent a straight line. Moreover, the string will cross the lower side of the square where the inch divisions are marked (sometimes it is advantageous to have the spaces between these marks divided into tenths). Where the string crosses the lower side of the square we can read a number. This number (decimal fraction) gives the ratio of a part of the horizontal side to the vertical side of the square and gives us all the information required to obtain the height of the object. The procedure is illustrated in the accompanying figure. The object is *MP*. The height of the corner of the instrument is *AD*, which is equal to *NP*. The observer directs his instrument so that he can see the top of the object through the two small holes on the upper part of his device. When this is attained he notes that the string crosses the lower edge of the instrument at point *C*. Thus there

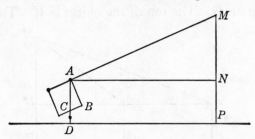

are two right triangles, *ANM* and *ABC*. These triangles are similar because the angles of one are equal to the angles of the other (a pair of right angles; one set of angles *CAB* and *MAN* have their sides perpendicular). Since the triangles are similar, we can write the proportion

$$\frac{MN}{CB} = \frac{AN}{AB}$$

and from this we obtain

$$MN = AN \cdot \frac{CB}{AB}$$

The ratio *CB/AB* represents the ratio of the portion that the string cuts off of the lower side of the square to the adjacent side of the square. But all such ratios are given on the instrument directly. The reader will observe that all the markings are given as decimal fractions, and if the distances between these markings are also divided into tenths, the ratios can be read to hundreds. The value of AN represents the distance of the observer from the bottom of the object whose height is measured. Thus, if this distance DP is known, it should be multiplied by the number read off the instrument. To this product should be added the value of the height of the corner of the instrument. The sum thus obtained is the height of the object.

Heights of inaccessible objects also can be easily measured with the same instrument as in the following drawing. In this case the top of the object must be sighted twice, and the two points at which the observations are made must be on the same line with the bottom of the object. Too, the operator must write down his observations because he will have to perform a few computations. The top of the object is M. The height of

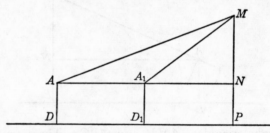

the corner of the instrument above the ground is AD (which is equal to A_1D_1 and NP). Suppose that at the point A_1 it was found that $MN = 0.6A_1N$ and that at the point A it was found that $MN = 0.3AN$. Then

$$A_1N = \frac{MN}{0.6}, \quad \text{and} \quad AN = \frac{MN}{0.3}$$

Then the distance D_1D, which is equal to

$$AA_1 = AN - A_1N = \frac{MN}{0.3} - \frac{MN}{0.6}$$

If we perform the subtraction we find that

$$AA_1 = \frac{MN}{0.6}, \quad \text{and} \quad MN = 0.6AA_1$$

Measuring Heights with a Mirror

It may surprise the reader, perhaps, to learn that the vanity mirror that almost every woman carries in her pocketbook is an instrument that may be put to work in measuring the heights of objects. Its working principle is based on light reflection, and its physical law is very simple.

Light falling on a flat mirror is so reflected that the angle of reflection is equal to the angle under which the light falls on the mirror. This property enables us to observe certain objects not directly in the line of our vision, as illustrated below. Suppose an objects sends out from S a ray of light that falls on a flat mirror MM. The ray falls at the point O, then is reflected in the direction OR. Now the angles MOS and ROM are, according to this property, equal. If we happen to be in the direction OR we can see the object S in the mirror as S_1, and the distance SD is equal to S_1D. By means of this property

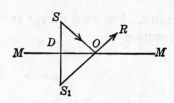

we can measure heights of objects. Suppose that we want to measure the height of the object MP. We place a mirror on the ground and walk away from it until we see the top of the object. We then have two right triangles that are similar because the angles of one are equal to the angles of the other. The follow-

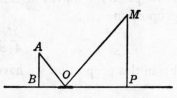

ing drawing illustrates this type of problem. The similar triangles AOB and OMP lead to the proportion

$$\frac{MP}{AB} = \frac{OP}{OB}$$

This means that the height of the object is as many times taller than the observer as the distance of the mirror from the object is greater than the distance of the mirror from the observer. The height of the observer as well as the distances of the mirror from the object and the observer can be measured. When the respective values are obtained we find that

$$MP = \frac{AB \cdot OP}{OB}$$

The mirror may be applied to measuring the heights of inaccessible objects also, as follows.

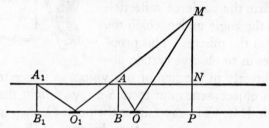

Suppose that the object MP is inaccessible. Place the mirror at O. For this position we have the proportion

$$\frac{MP}{AB} = \frac{OP}{OB}$$

and from this we obtain that

$$OP = \frac{OB \cdot MP}{AB}$$

Now place the mirror at O_1, and for this position we have the proportion

$$\frac{MP}{A_1B_1} = \frac{O_1P}{O_1B_1}$$

From this proportion we have that

$$O_1P = \frac{O_1B_1 \cdot MP}{A_1B_1}$$

Subtract OP from O_1P. We have then (remember that $A_1B_1 = AB$)

$$O_1P - OP = O_1O = \frac{O_1B_1 \cdot MP}{AB} - \frac{OB \cdot MP}{AB}$$

or

$$O_1O = \frac{MP}{AB} \cdot (O_1B_1 - OB)$$

and finally,

$$MP = \frac{AB \cdot O_1O}{O_1B_1 - OB}$$

In other words, the height of the object is equal to the product of the height of the observer's eyes from the ground by the ratio of the distance between the mirror positions to the difference between the distances of the mirror from the observer.

Measuring Distances between Inaccessible Objects

Distances between inaccessible objects may be measured in a manner very similar to that used in measuring heights of inaccessible objects. The basic principle is the reduction of the measurement to the determination of some other distance that is equal to the required distance.

The simplest of all methods calls for use of the 45-, 45-, 90-degree triangle, preferably traced on a flat piece of wood, with pins stuck at the vertices of the triangle, shown in the illustration below. These pins enable us to sight distant objects. Variations in this method of measuring distances are:

a) Suppose that we have two points A and B, one of which is inaccessible. Select a point C such that when you sight A and

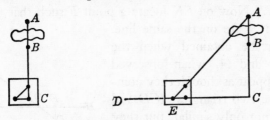

B along the shorter side of the 45-, 45-, 90-degree triangle the two pins at the vertices of the triangle and points A and B are seen as one point. Place a marker on the ground to indicate this point C. Then, while holding your instrument firmly, turn and sight some object D along the other short side of the triangle. Thus the directions AC and CD will be perpendicular to one another. Walk in the direction of *CD* so that the point *C* and the two pins on the instrument line up in one point. While walking in this manner, backward, sight the point *A* along the larger side of the triangle. When the point *A* lines up with the two pins along the larger side of the triangle in one point, you have a right triangle *ECA* whose sides *EC* and *AC* are equal because *ECA* is a 45-, 45-, 90-degree triangle similar to the triangle on the instrument. Now the distances *EC* and *BC* can be measured and the distance between the points *A* and *B* is equal to the difference between the distances *EC* and *BC*.

   b) Two variations in application of this triangle to measurement of the distances between two points, one of which is inaccessible, are illustrated below.

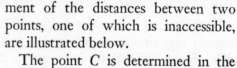

   The point *C* is determined in the same manner as in *a*) above, but from here on the procedure is different. At *C*, which is perpendicular to *AC*, the direction *CH* is determined. Along *CH* measure off equal distances *CD* and *DE*. *CD* need not be equal to *AC*. In other words, the triangle *ADC* is just a right triangle and not necessarily a 45-, 45-, 90-degree triangle. At *E* determine the direction *EK*, which is perpendicular to *CH*. Now on *EK* locate a point *F* such that the points *F*, *D*, and *A* are on the same line.

This may be obtained when the points *D* and *A*, when observed from *F*, appear as though they coincide. The two triangles *ACD* and *FED* are not only similar, but they are equal (congruent), because they have equal angles and equal sides.

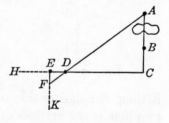

Then *EF* = *AC*, and from *EF* we subtract *BC*. The difference thus obtained is the required distance *AB*.

   In the second variation of this method, instead of making the distances *DC* and *ED* equal we may find it practicable to make the distance *ED* smaller, say one-fifth of *DC*, as shown in the accompanying drawing. In all other respects the procedure is the same as in the first variation. After the distance EF is determined we consider the two triangles EFD and ADC. This time the triangles are similar, and we have the following proportion

$$\frac{EF}{AC} = \frac{ED}{DC}$$

But, as we know,

$$\frac{ED}{DC} = \frac{1}{5}$$

Therefore,

$$\frac{EF}{AC} = \frac{1}{5}$$

and from this we have that

$$AC = 5EF$$

Multiply the value of the distance EF by five, subtract from this product the value of the distance BC, and the difference obtained is the distance between the two points A and B.

c) We may make similar use, too, of the 30-, 60-, 90-degree triangle. The reader will recall that in such a triangle the shortest side is equal to half the longest side, and the longest side is opposite the right angle. On a piece of heavy cardboard draw an equilateral triangle (one whose three sides are equal), bisect one of the sides, and join the midpoint thus obtained with the opposite vertex of the triangle. This will result in two 30-, 60-, 90-degree triangles. We make use of only one. After this triangle is traced place pins in the vertices and instrument is ready for use. The procedure for measurement of the distance between two points, one of which is inaccessible, is illustrated below. Sight the points A and B by means of the instrument so that the pins E and F and the points A and B are on the same line, and they 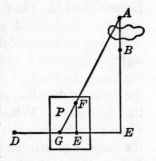 appear to you as one point. At the same time sight along the line EG some point D. This will give a line ED, which will form with the line EA a 90-degree angle. Finally, while walking along the line *ED*, sight through the instrument the points *A* and *F*. This will be possible when you reach the point *P*. Thus another 30-, 60-, 90-degree triangle *AGE* is obtained, and the distance *EG* is equal to $\sqrt{3} = 1.73$ the distance *AE*. Thus, to obtain the distance *AE*, multiply the distance *EG* by 1.73. From this product subtract the distance *EB*, and the difference is the required distance *AB*.

Measuring between Two Inaccessible Points

To measure the distance between two inaccessible points without approaching them, for example the length of a small island in the middle of the river, is a large order. Let us limit it and measure such a distance with a measuring tape and a right angle only.

Surveyors might use special and very costly instruments, but the problem can be solved without them in a few very simple steps, the following drawing illustrating the method employing only a tape and a right angle.

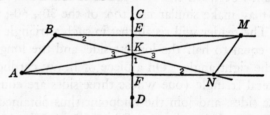

Suppose that *A* and *B* are both inaccessible. Take any two points *C* and *D*. On the line *CD* determine two points *E* and *F* such that the lines *BE* and *AF* are perpendicular to the line *CD*. This can be accomplished by means of the right angle when sighting the point *C* and the point *B* at the same time while walking along the line *CD*. Point *C* will be sighted along one side of the right angle while point *B* is sighted along the other side of the right angle. When this occurs, the point *E* is determined. Place a marker at point *E*, and perform the same operations for the purpose of determining the point *F*. Place a marker at point *F* also. Divide the distance *EF* into two equal parts, and place a marker at *K*, the midpoint of *EF*. Walk along the line *AF*

(when it is extended) until a point N is reached such that the point B and the marker K, when observed from it, seem to merge into one point. Repeat the same process while walking along the extended line BE. This will give the point M such that the point A and the marker K, when observed from it, seem to merge into one point. Measure the distance MN; this is equal to the distance between points A and B.

The correctness of this result can be established from the following considerations. The right triangles BEK and FKN are congruent (equal) because the sides EK and FK are equal to one another. Moreover, the angles of the two right triangles are correspondingly equal to one another. There is a pair of right angles (recall that we make use of a right angle), and the other pairs of the angles are also equal as indicated in the drawing. Angles 1 and 1 are formed by two intersecting straight lines BN and EK, and they are known as vertical angles (all vertical angles are equal). Likewise, angles 2 and 2 are equal because the sum of the angles of a triangle is 180 degrees. We found that two pairs of angles are equal and therefore the same holds true for the third pair. A similar reasoning may be applied to the right triangles AKF and EKM. These triangles also are congruent.

Now in congruent triangles the corresponding sides (those opposite the equal angles) are equal. Therefore BK (opposite a right angle) is equal to KN (opposite a right angle), and AK (opposite a right angle) is equal to KM (opposite a right angle). The triangles ABK and KMN have two pairs of correspondingly equal sides and a pair of equal angles 3. This is sufficient for the triangles to be congruent and this conclusion leads directly to the fact that MN is equal to AB.

Another Method for Inaccessible Points

In this chapter we described an instrument which consists of two perpendicular strips of cardboard or wood and with which heights of objects can be measured. This same instrument may be successfully used for measuring distances between two inaccessible points, as in the drawing on p. 444.

Let A and B be two inaccessible points. Hold the instrument horizontally so that the smaller strip CP is directed to the right. Sight point B along the strip Cn and walk away from B (or toward it) until the point A can be sighted along the line mn. When this takes place, put a marker D on the ground. Now turn over the instrument so that the smaller strip CP is directed to the left while the larger strip Cm is directed to the right. Continue to sight the point B while walking away from the point C and at the same time try to sight the point A through the end P_1 of the smaller strip CP. When this finally takes place put a marker D_1 on the ground. The distance $D_1 D$ (that is, the distance between the markers D and D_1) is equal to the distance between the two inaccessible points A and B. The reader may refer to an earlier section to establish the validity of the result.

What the Surveyor Does When He Surveys

The methods for measuring distances or heights that were described in this chapter are similar to those employed by surveyors, but our instruments are extremely simple and crude in comparison with theirs. When great precision is required, instruments as a rule are complicated and expensive, and their handling requires skill which can be attained only after special training and considerable practice.

In almost all our instruments the right angle was used, but the instruments employed by surveyors (as well as by navigators on ships and airplanes) are so constructed that any angle can be measured, enabling them to proceed with measurements in any location and at any position. Moreover, while our simple instruments allow only crude measurements, those used by the technicians provide extremely fine measurements; with them a navigator can at any time locate himself within a fraction of a mile, and a surveyor can measure boundaries to within an inch.

In all other respects the measurements performed by surveyors reduce (or can be reduced) to determining right triangles in which one side is the distance that is required to be measured. A surveyor is not content to measure an angle to degrees and as a rule obtains minutes, but finer measurements do not involve any new or special mathematical procedures. The finer measures lead to finer results; the fundamental principles remain the same. Some of these fundamentals will be described next.

The Triangle—Man's Master

The Triangle Key to Measurement

In Chapter 24 we became acquainted with three ratios of the coordinates of a point on a circle. These ratios, as here illustrated, were

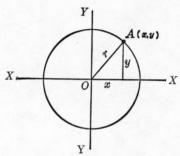

and

$$\frac{y}{r} = \sin A$$

$$\frac{x}{r} = \cos A$$

$$\frac{y}{x} = \tan A$$

The reader will observe, however, that the radius of the circle and the lines that represent the two coordinates of a point form a right triangle. We may then derive similar ratios for any right triangle. Let us take any right triangle *ABC*, where angle *C* is a right angle. The side *AC* corresponds to the *x* coordinate in the case of a point of a circle, the side BC to the y coordinate, and the side AB to the radius. In a right triangle the side opposite the right angle is the largest; and mathematicians call it the "hypotenuse."

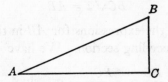

We then have the following ratios:

$$\frac{BC}{AB} = \sin A, \quad \text{which is} \quad \frac{\text{side opposite the angle } A}{\text{hypotenuse}}$$

$$\frac{AC}{AB} = \cos A, \quad \text{which is} \quad \frac{\text{side adjacent the angle } A}{\text{hypotenuse}}$$

$$\frac{BC}{AC} = \tan A, \quad \text{which is} \quad \frac{\text{side opposite the angle } A}{\text{side adjacent the angle } A}$$

Some Values of the Trigonometric Trio, Sin, Cos, and Tan

We discussed in detail in Chapter 25 the 45-, 45-, 90-, and 30-, 60-, 90-degree right triangles; we shall now obtain the three respective ratios for them.

The 45-, 45-, 90-degree triangle, besides being a right triangle, possesses another interesting property: two sides of this triangle are equal—that is, it is an "isosceles" triangle. Thus in the triangle ABC, the sides AC and BC are equal. If we apply the Pythagorean relation to this triangle we have

$$AC^2 + BC^2 = AB^2$$

But $AC = BC$. Therefore we can write

$$AC^2 + AC^2 = AB^2$$

or

$$2AC^2 = AB^2$$

Extracting the square root on both sides of the equation, we have

$$AC\sqrt{2} = AB$$

And since $AC = BC$, we also have

$$BC\sqrt{2} = AB$$

Let us substitute the expressions for AB in the expressions for the ratios in the preceding section. We have

$$\sin A = \frac{BC}{AB} = \frac{BC}{BC\sqrt{2}}, \quad \text{or} \quad \sin A = \frac{1}{\sqrt{2}}$$

If we multiply both the numerator and denominator of the fraction

$$\frac{1}{\sqrt{2}} \quad \text{by} \quad \sqrt{2}$$

we have

$$\frac{\sqrt{2}}{(\sqrt{2})^2} = \frac{\sqrt{2}}{2}, \quad \text{or} \quad \sin A = \sin 45° = \frac{\sqrt{2}}{2}$$

In a similar manner we obtain the value of

$$\cos A = \frac{\sqrt{2}}{2}$$

or

$$\cos 45° = \frac{\sqrt{2}}{2}$$

The value of tan A is then obtained:

$$\tan A = \frac{BC}{AC} = \frac{BC}{BC} = 1 \quad (AC = BC)$$

Thus, tan $45° = 1$.

From the table of the values of square roots in the Appendix we find that $\sqrt{2} = 1.414$.

Then

$$\frac{\sqrt{2}}{2} = 0.707.$$

We have then that

$$\sin 45° = 0.707$$

$$\cos 45° = 0.707$$

and

$$\tan 45° = 1$$

Let us now examine the 30-, 60-, 90-degree triangle. In the preceding chapter we observed that in this triangle the shortest side is equal to half of the longest side (the hypotenuse, which is opposite the right angle), that is, $BC = \frac{1}{2}AB$. If we apply the Pythagorean relationship to this triangle, we have

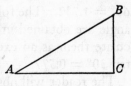

$$AC^2 + BC^2 = AB^2$$

or, bringing BC^2 to the right side of the equation and changing its sign, we obtain

$$AC^2 = AB^2 - BC^2$$

But, since $BC = \frac{1}{2}AB$, $BC^2 = \frac{1}{4}AB^2$, we have

$$AC^2 = AB^2 - \frac{1}{4}AB^2 = \frac{3}{4}AB^2$$

Extracting square roots on both sides of the equation, we have

$$AC = \frac{1}{2}\sqrt{3}AB$$

Let us substitute the expressions for AC and BC in the expressions for the ratios in the preceding sections. We have

$$\sin B = \frac{AC}{AB} = \frac{\frac{1}{2}\sqrt{3}AB}{AB} = \frac{\sqrt{3}}{2}$$

In a similar manner we obtain the value of $\cos B$:

$$\cos B = \frac{BC}{AB} = \frac{\frac{1}{2}AB}{AB} = \frac{1}{2}$$

The value of $\tan B$ is

$$\tan B = \frac{AC}{BC} = \frac{\frac{1}{2}\sqrt{3}AB}{\frac{1}{2}AB} = \frac{\frac{1}{2}\sqrt{3}}{\frac{1}{2}} = \sqrt{3}$$

Now, the angle B is a 60° angle. We then have

$$\sin 60° = \frac{\sqrt{3}}{2}$$

$$\cos 60° = \frac{1}{2}$$

and

$$\tan 60° = \sqrt{3}$$

From the tables of values of square roots we find that $\sqrt{3} =$ 1.732. We then have sin 60° = 0.866, cos 60° = 0.5, and tan 60° = 1.732. The following values of the ratios of the 30-degree angle are obtained in a similar manner, and the reader may calculate them as an exercise: sin 30° = 0.5, cos 30° = 0.866, and tan 30° = 0.577.

The reader will observe that sin 30° = 0.5, and cos 60° = 0.5, and 30° + 60° = 90°. The values of the sine and cosine are equal, and the sum of the respective angles is 90 degrees (a right angle). This is true not only for the 30-, 60-, 90-degree triangle but for any other right triangle. The reader may convince himself of this by writing the respective ratios of the two angles of a right triangle. Thus if we know the value of the sine of a certain angle, we know at once that this is also the value of the cosine of the angle which is 90 degrees minus that angle. However, this is only one of the many interesting properties of the ratios of angles which belong to a branch of mathematics known as trigonometry. The values of the ratios (known as trigonometric ratios) are given in a self-explanatory table in the Appendix.

How to Measure Angles

In the preceding chapter we stated that to measure distances and heights, to navigate a ship, or to locate one's self either on water or land, it is necessary to measure angles. For this purpose surveyors as well as navigators use specially constructed

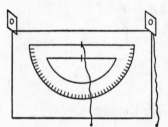

and very costly instruments. However, anyone can construct a simple instrument for measuring angles at cost of a few cents.

In the preceding chapter (page 434) an instrument for measuring the heights of objects was described. To turn this instrument into one that will measure angles, a simple protractor may be purchased for a few cents. Paste this protractor on a rectangular piece of cardboard as shown above. At one end of the cardboard attach a string with a weight. When the cardboard is held up and the weight pulls on the string so that the string runs along the edge of the cardboard, the straight line which forms the edge of the protractor will be horizontal. At the midpoint of this straight line (the edge of the protractor), which is usually indicated either by a small hole or a line mark, attach another weighted string. In all other respects this instrument is used exactly as the one for measuring heights.

For example, if we wish to sight the top of an object to determine the observed angle that it makes with the horizon, we turn the upper edge of the instrument so that the top of the object can be observed through the two holes of the sight line. While the instrument is being turned, the string attached to the center of the edge of the protractor will cross the semicircle of the protractor at some point, the weight attached to the string serving to keep it vertical. The reading at that point will give the angle (known as the "angle of elevation") in degrees. The accompanying drawing illustrates the procedure.

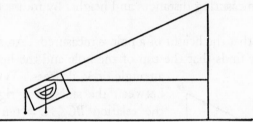

To measure an angle that is formed by two objects—that is, when the two objects as well as the observer are all in the same plane—the instrument must be placed as nearly level as possible. For this purpose a small table is useful, and the instrument is placed on it so that the straight-line edge of the protractor points to one object. After this the string attached to the midpoint of the 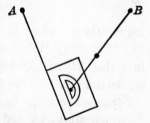 straight-line edge of the protractor is pulled tight, while the instrument is held with one hand, until the other object can be sighted along this string. Where the string crosses the protractor the number will indicate the number of degrees in the required angle. The drawing above illustrates this procedure.

Naturally, however, such an instrument is not very perfect and its measurements are crude, but they serve for many practical purposes.

Angles and Their Ratios

Every angle has a set of ratios corresponding to it. In the Appendix table these ratios are for degrees and minutes but this will be found sufficient for simple measurement. The reader will recall that the ratios that correspond to the angles were obtained when right triangles were examined. Thus the simplest application of these ratios may be found when a right triangle is obtained. The right triangle was used in Chapter 25, but for simplicity only special cases of right triangles were considered. Now we shall make use of any right triangle. From the following illustrations the reader will note how simple is the principle applied to measuring distances and heights by means of the right triangle.

Suppose that the height of a pole is measured. At, say, 30 feet, an observer finds that the top of the pole and the horizon make

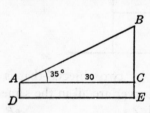

an angle of 35 degrees. We then have between the sides of a right triangle the relation $BC/AC = \tan 35°$. But AC is the distance from the pole, and $AC = 35$ feet. From the table of trigonometric ratios in the Appendix we find that $\tan 35° = 0.57$. Substituting these values in the expression we have the equation $BC/35 = 0.57$. We know how to solve this equation, and we find that $BC = 0.57 \cdot 35 = 19.95$ or about 20 feet. If the observer is 6 feet tall, the height of the pole is $20 + 6 = 26$ feet.

Suppose we want to find the distance between points A and B, which are so located that it is impossible to measure this distance directly. We locate another point C such that the angle ACB is a right angle. The distance AC is measured and then from A the angle BAC is measured with the instrument described in the preceding section, the instrument to be held horizontally

in this case. The triangle below illustrates the procedure. In
the right triangle ABC the distance AC is measured. Suppose
that it is 45 feet, and that angle BAC is 38 degrees. We then
have the relationship $AC/AB = \cos A$
(angle A is the angle BAC). Substituting
the values of AC and A in the above expression we have $45/AB = \cos 38°$. From
the table of trigonometric ratios we find
that $\cos 38° = 0.79$. We then have the
equation $45/AB = 0.79$, which we know how to solve. We then
have that $AB = 45/0.79 = 56.9$ or about 57 feet. Instead of measuring the distance AC we might measure the distance BC. We
then would have to work with the expression $BC/AB = \sin A$.

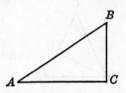

The Ratio That Does Everything

We shall now try a few problems in measuring distances that,
to one unfamiliar with our preceding studies, would seem more
complicated, because their solution presupposes very meager information.

Suppose we wish to measure the distances from two accessible
points to an inaccessible point, for example a point on an island
and two accessible points on shore.
Let us denote the two points on the
shore by A and B, and assume that the
distance between these two is 100
feet. But we are interested in the
two distances AC and BC, the point C being on the island, and
have to measure these two distances without rowing out.

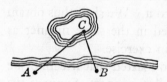

At point A we measure the angle CAB (let it be 48 degrees)
and at point B we measure the angle CBA (let it be 64 degrees).
We may then construct a diagram of the three points which in
the diagram will be the vertices of a triangle ABC, and recall
that the sum of the angles of a triangle is 180 degrees. Since we
know the magnitudes of the angles A and B, we have

$$A + B + C = C + 48° + 64° = 180°$$

and from this we obtain that

$$C = 180° - 48° - 64° = 180° - 112° = 68°$$

Draw a line *AD* which would form a right angle (that is, will be perpendicular to) with the side *BC* of the triangle *ABC*, as illustrated. We thus obtain two right angles, *ACD* and *ADB*, and we may write the expressions

$$\frac{AD}{AB} = \sin B, \text{ or } AD = AB \sin B$$

and

$$\frac{AD}{AC} = \sin C, \text{ or } AC = \frac{AD}{\sin C}$$

In this latter expression we may substitute the expression for *AD*, and we have

$$AC = \frac{AB \sin B}{\sin C}$$

We obtain from the table of trigonometric ratios in the Appendix that $\sin 64° = 0.90$ and $\sin 68° = 0.93$. We then have (since $AB = 100$ feet) that

$$AC = \frac{100 \cdot 0.90}{0.93}$$

Performing the computations we find that

$$AC = 96.8 \quad \text{or} \quad \text{about 97 feet}$$

To obtain the value of the distance *BC* we must draw a line from *B* to the side *AC* perpendicular to it. We shall thus obtain two other right triangles, and proceed in the same manner as above. This is left to the reader as an exercise.

The distance between two points so located that it cannot be measured directly is obtained in a similar manner. Suppose we wish to measure the width of a lake between two given points on the shore. We locate some other point on the shore and thus obtain a triangle as shown in the illustration below. Let the two

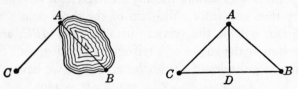

points on the shore be *A* and *B*. We select any other point *C*. At *A* we measure angle *BAC* and at *C* we measure angle *ACB*.

We also measure the distance AC. Suppose it is 150 feet. Let angle A (or BAC) be 82 degrees and angle C (or ACB) be 77 degrees. Since the sum of the angles of a triangle is 180 degrees we have

$$A + B + C = 180°, \quad \text{or} \quad 82° + B + 21° = 180°$$

and from this we compute the value of the angle B,

$$B = 180° - 82° - 77° = 180° - 159° = 21°$$

Let us make a diagram of this problem. In the triangle ABC we draw a line AD perpendicular to the BC of the triangle. We then have two right triangles, ABD and ADC. From the right triangle ADC we have the ratio

$$\frac{AD}{AC} = \sin C, \quad \text{or} \quad AD = AC \sin C$$

From the right triangle ABD we have the ratio

$$\frac{AD}{AB} = \sin B, \quad \text{or} \quad AB = \frac{AD}{\sin B}$$

Substitute the expression for AD (obtained from the right triangle ADC) in the expression for AB. We have then

$$AB = \frac{AC \sin C}{\sin B}$$

Finally, substituting the values of AC and of the angles C and B, we have

$$AB = \frac{150 \sin 77°}{\sin 21°}$$

From the table of trigonometric ratios in the Appendix we find the values of $\sin 21°$ and of $\sin 77°$. We finally obtain

$$AB = \frac{150 \cdot 0.97}{0.36}, \quad \text{or} \quad AB = 441.6 \quad \text{or} \quad \text{about 442 feet}$$

All the problems of the type described may be solved so that the results may be represented by more precise measures, but for this purpose finer instruments and greatly amplified ratios would be required.

Circles, Angles, and an Age-Old Problem

The Circle: Sphinx to the Mathematicians, Old Saw to the Carpenter

There are in mathematics three classic problems that laymen for countless years have tackled in spite of the fact that (or because) the mathematicians declare they cannot be solved by simple methods. Periodically—and this may be expected to continue indefinitely—there pops up another "solution" which may puzzle the trained mathematician because it is so ingenious, however faulty it may be. But the goal is so hopeless that more than a hundred years ago the French Academy of Sciences publicly announced that neither its members nor its officers would waste their time trying to discover the mistakes in these supposed solutions.

Let us examine the famous problem of the circle: How to construct a square that is equal in area to the area of a given circle, the construction to be performed with only a straight edge and compasses, two instruments used by draughtsmen. In many cases this problem may be modified to the construction, with the same instruments, of a straight line equal in length to the length of the circumference of a given circle. The reader is forewarned: what is proposed in these two problems (which are identical in nature) cannot be accomplished. Mathematicians have proved this fact, but the proof is far beyond the scope of even college mathematics; it is a pity that there is no proof so simple that it could be understood by everyone.

Another form of the same problem associated with the circle is arithmetical. First, however, let us explain the meaning of the expression "a given circle." When we mention a given circle we imply that its position (although this is not always necessary) and its radius are known to us. Now, let us assume that we have a circle and, instead of constructing a straight line whose length will be equal to the length of the circumference of the circle, it is proposed to obtain the length of the circumference in terms of some unit of measure—say, inches, centimeters, feet. In other words, it is proposed to measure the length of the circumference of the circle. An easy problem it may seem, but it is not so simple.

Let us dispense with the condition that a straight line, whose length should be equal to the length of the circumference of a given circle, be constructed with a straight edge and compasses; let us try to measure it with a tape. Suppose the radius of our circle is 5 inches long. We make a mark on the circumference of the circle, then wind the tape around the circle once. If we are careful enough in measuring, we may find that the length of the circumference is not quite 31½ inches long. If our tape is graduated to tenths of an inch, we may note that the circumference is more than 31.4 inches long but less than 31.5 inches long.

In other words, the circumference is just a little longer than three times the diameter of the circle (the diameter is twice as long as the radius of the circle). This is a fact known to every carpenter, but mathematicians are not content with the statement of this fact in the form just given. Moreover, a mathematician will not accept the validity of a measurement performed as an experiment; a mathematician demands that a problem be solved on paper, in mathematical terms.

The fact that the circumference of a circle is a little more than three times as long as the diameter has been known for thousands of years. In the Bible's *Kings* and *Chronicles* we find a statement that when King Solomon built his temple the circumference of the great cistern in the court was three times as long as its diameter. The Egyptians knew that the circumference of the circle was 3.16 times as long as its diameter. Asked to measure the circumference of a circle with a radius 5 inches long, they would measure the diameter, find that it is 10 inches long, and then stop measuring, concluding that the circumference is 31.6 inches long. In Ancient Rome the circumference was considered 3.12 times as long as the diameter of the circle, and a Roman would say the circumference of our circle is 31.2 inches long.

Why all these discrepancies? The reason lies in the fact that the problems concerning the circle cannot be solved exactly by any means (not speaking of elementary processes, as we shall learn later).

The Elusive Pi

The arithmetical solution of the problem of the length of the circumference of a circle reduces to the finding of a number to be used as a multiplier. If we know of such a number, we can multiply the value of the diameter of a circle by it and thus obtain the length of the circumference. But what is this number?

An Arab mathematician, Mohammed Ibn Musa, who lived about a thousand years ago, wrote in his book on algebra: "The best method to obtain the circumference of a circle is to multiply the diameter by $3\frac{1}{7}$. This is the quickest and easiest method. God knows of a better one." This number $3\frac{1}{7}$ was first computed by the ancient Greek mathematician Archimedes, whom we mentioned in discussing number giants.

In mathematics, this number associated with the circle is truly outstanding in its value; apart from mathematics it is closely associated with gambling, banking, saving money, and many other activities of men both useful and destructive. Its symbol is the Greek letter π (pi).

Its exact value is not known. It is impossible to write in numerical form the value of π: an industrious computer once labored to establish the ultimate value until he obtained over seven hundred decimals—an extravagant waste of time and energy. Here is the approximate value to thirty-six decimal places (just a curiosity; so many decimal places have no practical use-fulness):

$$3.14159265358979323846264338327995 0288 \ldots$$

For our purposes 3.14 will suffice. For many advanced engineering and technical problems 3.14159 is good enough.

If you have difficulty in remembering this number, there is a simple sentence which may aid your memory. This sentence is made up of words the number of letters in each of which corresponds in the same order to some digit of the value of π given as correct to four decimal places:

3.	1	4	1	6⁻
Yes,	I	have	a	number.

Taking the Girth of a Circle

Now we can write the formula for the length of the circumference of a circle. We know the diameter of the circle must be multiplied by the number π. Thus if the symbol for the diameter of a circle is d, and the symbol for the length of the circumference is C, we have the formula $C = \pi d$. But we also know that the diameter of a circle is twice as long as the radius. Thus if the radius is denoted by r, we know that $d = 2r$. Then we have another way for finding the girth of a circle, $C = 2\pi r$. For example, if the radius of a circle is 35 inches, then the circumference of the circle is $C = 2 \cdot 3.14 \cdot 35 = 219.8$ or about 220 inches. The reader will observe that as a rule there is no sense in using many decimal places in the value of π. Let us consider some problems:

It is known that the distance of the earth from the sun is about 93,000,000 miles, correct to a million miles. Suppose that the earth moves around the sun in a circular path (this may be assumed because the ellipse, which is the actual path of the earth, is very close to being circular). What is the distance that the earth covers in a year, or 365 days?

Before we plunge headlong into computation of the circumference of this circle we shall examine the information we have on hand. The distance of the earth from the sun is given as

93,000,000 miles, but this information is correct only to a million miles, so we cannot rely on more than two figures in this number. Now we know (as shown in Chapter 7) that at best we can obtain two significant figures in any product of this number by any other one. Thus our value of π may contain two or three figures—that is, two decimal places. We have then the distance covered by the earth in one year,

$$2 \cdot 3.14 \cdot 93,000,000 = 58,304,000,000 \text{ or about } 58,000,000,000 \text{ miles.}$$

PROBLEMS

1. Assuming that the moon moves around the earth in a circular path, compute the distance covered by the moon in 28 days (the distance of the moon from the earth is about 240,000 miles, correct to a thousand miles).

2. What is the speed per minute of the earth in its motion around the sun?

3. What is the speed per second of the moon in its motion around the earth?

4. If the radius of the earth is 4,000 miles (correct to ten miles) what is the length of the circumference of the earth around the equator?

5. The earth, rotating on its axis, completes one revolution in about 24 hours. What is the speed per second of a point on the equator?

6. Suppose that a man six feet tall walks around the earth on the equator and around the equator of the sun (the radius of the sun is about 400,000 miles, correct to a thousand miles). During either of the trips the top of his head will describe a circle whose circumference will be longer than the circle described by his feet. Will the difference between the lengths of the circumferences of these two circles be greater on the sun than on the earth, and by how much?

7. Suppose a string is wound around the equator of the earth and then 50 feet of string is added to make a longer circle. If this circle is stretched around the equator there will be some space between the equator and the string. Will a six-foot-tall man be able to crawl under the string?

8. A pocket watch has a seconds dial ¼ inch in diameter. What is the distance covered by the seconds hand in one day, in a week, in a month, in a year?

Trig without Tables

Tables of trigonometric ratios are very handy when we perform measurements with the aid of angles, but lacking them, we can now compute them easily and quickly through a method for the calculation of sine ratios for all angles. Calculation of the cosine and the tangent ratios, as it will be shown, depends on the calculation of the sine ratios; moreover, most of the problems in the measurement of heights and distances may, as the reader has observed, be performed by means of the sine ratios.

First, to be able to calculate the values of the sine ratios we must have on hand some sine ratios whose values are known to us. We have worked with the 30-, 60-, 90- and the 45-, 45-, 90-degree triangles, and we also know that the sine ratio represents the ratio of the side opposite the angle to the hypotenuse of a right triangle. Let us recall some of the properties of these triangles:

In a 30-, 60-, 90-degree triangle the side opposite the 30-degree angle is equal to ½ the hypotenuse while the side opposite the 60-degree angle is equal to $\frac{1}{2}\sqrt{3}$ times the hypotenuse. Thus we know that

$$\text{sine } 30° = \tfrac{1}{2} = 0.5$$

and

$$\text{sine } 60° = \frac{\sqrt{3}}{2} = 0.866$$

In a 45-, 45-, 90-degree triangle the side opposite the 45-degree angle is equal to $\frac{1}{2}\sqrt{2}$ times the hypotenuse. Thus, we know that

$$\text{sine } 45° = \frac{\sqrt{2}}{2} = 0.707$$

Moreover, if we recall that we examined the trigonometric ratios in connection with the coordinates of a point moving along the circumference of a circle, and that the sine ratio was obtained as the ratio

$$\frac{y \text{ coordinate of the point}}{\text{radius}}$$

we can obtain more ratios. If the angle is 0 degree (that is, when the point is at the intersection of the circle with X-axis) the y coordinate is zero (0). Then the sine ratio is also 0 because zero divided by any number is always zero. If the angle is 90 degrees (that is, the point is at the intersection of the circle with Y-axis), the y coordinate is equal to the radius. Then the sine ratio is 1. Thus we know the following sine ratios:

sin 0° = 0, sin 30° = 0.5, sin 45° = 0.707, sin 60° = 0866, and sin 90° = 1

This is the information with which we may begin our work in calculating the sine ratios of other angles measured in degrees.

To proceed with the calculation we shall make use of a simple principle which will enable us to calculate the ratios of angles that are very small. This principle is: When we have a small angle (that is, the point that is moving along the circle is so located that its y coordinate is very small in comparison with the radius of the circle), we may replace the y coordinate in the sine

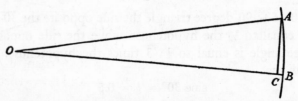

ratio with the arc of the circle that corresponds to that small angle as shown in the figure above. However, we may convince ourselves of this fact by calculating, for instance, the sine ratio of the 1-degree angle.

A circle contains 360 degrees and the circumference of a circle, whose radius is r, is $2\pi r$. Then for the angle of 1 degree we have an arc

$$\frac{2\pi r}{360} = \frac{\pi r}{180}$$

The sine ratio of the angle of 1 degree is then

$$\sin 1° = \frac{\pi r}{180r} = \frac{3.14}{180} = 0.0175$$

This value, if verified with a table of sine ratios, may be found to be correct.

In a similar manner we may calculate

$$\sin 2° = 0.0349$$
$$\sin 3° = 0.0524$$
$$\sin 4° = 0.0698$$
$$\sin 5° = 0.0873$$

Can this process be continued for all the angles up to 90 degrees?

Let us check by calculating sin 30°, whose value is known to us. We have then, remembering that the arc that corresponds to the 30-degree angle is

$$\frac{2\pi r}{360} \cdot 30 = \frac{\pi r}{6}$$

Then

$$\sin 30° = \frac{\pi r}{6r} = \frac{3.14}{6} = 0.523$$

This result exceeds the correct value of sin 30° by 0.023. In other words, it is not applicable to a 30-degree angle.

Let us calculate sin 15°. In the drawing below the triangle ABC is a right triangle with angle $BAC = 15°$. Extend line BC to D so that $BC = CD$. Join A and D. Then angle $BAD = 30$ degrees. Draw line BE perpendicular to AD. Then the right triangle ABE is

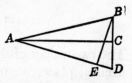

a 30-, 60-, 90-degree triangle, and AE, as we know, is equal to $\frac{1}{2}\sqrt{3} = 0.866$ times AB, that is,

$$AE = 0.866AB$$

Moreover, $AB = AD$ (because the triangles ABC and ACD are congruent; they have two sides and a pair of right angles equal. $AC = AC$, $BC = CD$, and angle $ACB =$ angle ACD). Then

$$ED = AD - AE = AB - 0.866AB = 0.134AB$$

Now, apply the Pythagorean relation to the right triangle BED. We have then

$$BD^2 = BE^2 + ED^2$$

Moreover, BE is a side of a 30-, 60-, 90-degree triangle, and it is opposite the 30-degree angle. Hence, $BE = 0.5AB$. We may now write

$$BD^2 = (0.5AB)^2 + (0.134AB)^2 = 0.25AB^2 + 0.018AB^2 = 0.268AB^2$$

From this we obtain that

$$BD = \sqrt{0.268AB^2} = 0.518AB$$

Moreover, $BC = \frac{1}{2}BD$. Therefore,

$$BC = 0.259AB$$

Now we have that

$$\sin 15° = \frac{BC}{AB}$$

or

$$\sin 15° = \frac{0.259AB}{AB} = 0.259$$

This value checks with the value of sin 15° to three decimal places.

If we calculate sin 15° by means of the arc of the circle we have

$$\sin 15° = \frac{2\pi r}{360r} \cdot 15 = 0.262$$

The two values of sin 15° differ. But if we round them to two decimal places we obtain 0.26 and 0.26. Thus, up to the 15-degree angle we may calculate the sine ratios by means of the arc of the circle, and the results obtained will be correct to two decimal places, or to hundredths.

For the interval between 15 and 30 degrees we proceed as follows. The difference between sin 30° and sin 15° is 0.50 − 0.26 = 0.24. We divide this difference into 15 equal parts, and each part will represent the step-up in the value of the sine ratio as another degree is added to 15 degrees. Then the value of the step-up is 0.24/15 = 0.016. From a strict mathematical point of view, such a procedure is not entirely correct, but since we are interested in the values of the sine ratios correct to two decimal places only, our results obtained by this method are fairly correct. Thus we obtain

$$\sin 16° = 0.26 + 0.016 = 0.276 = 0.28$$
$$\sin 17° = 0.26 + 0.032 = 0.292 = 0.29$$
$$\sin 18° = 0.26 + 0.048 = 0.308 = 0.31$$
$$\sin 19° = 0.26 + 0.064 = 0.324 = 0.32$$

Calculation of the values of the sine ratios of the angles for the interval between 30 and 45 degrees is performed in the same manner. The difference between sin 45° and sin 30° is 0.71 − 0.50 = 0.21. The step-up in the value of the sine ratio is for this interval 0.21/15 = 0.014. We then have

$$\sin 31° = 0.50 + 0.014 = 0.514 = 0.51$$
$$\sin 32° = 0.50 + 0.028 = 0.528 = 0.53$$
$$\sin 33° = 0.50 + 0.042 = 0.542 = 0.54$$
$$\sin 34° = 0.50 + 0.056 = 0.556 = 0.56$$

To calculate the sine ratios of the angles in the interval between 45 and 90 degrees we shall recall two important facts concerning the sine and cosine ratios of the angles of a right triangle. The first fact is that for any angle

$$\sin^2 A + \cos^2 A = 1, \quad \text{or} \quad \sin^2 A = 1 - \cos^2 A, \quad \text{and} \quad \cos^2 A = 1 - \sin^2 A$$

The second fact is that the sine ratio of an angle is equal to the cosine ratio of an angle with which the first angle makes 90 degrees, that is,

$$\sin A = \cos (90° - A)$$

Thus, if we wish to calculate the sin 56° we calculate cos (90° − 56°), or cos 34°, and we use the expression

$$\cos A = \sqrt{1 - \sin^2 A}$$

Thus, we have that

$$\sin 56° = \cos 34° = \sqrt{1 - \sin^2 34°}$$

or

$$\sin 56° = \sqrt{1 - (0.56)^2} = \sqrt{1 - 0.31} = \sqrt{0.69} = 0.83$$

The calculation of the cosine ratios of angles is performed by means of the relation

$$\cos A = \sqrt{1 - \sin^2 A}$$

and the calculation of the tangent ratios is performed by means of the relation

$$\tan A = \frac{\sin A}{\cos A}$$

This Lopsided World: Even Your Best Friend Is Two-Faced

Here we may look into a common and highly interesting phenomenon; with its explanation the reader may perform an amusing experiment for his friends.

There are countless reports of people who have rowed an hour or more in darkness trying to reach the opposite shore of a river or lake, only to return to the place from which they started, and of others who wandered in darkness, or fog, or snowstorm only to retrace their steps unwittingly. Animals sometimes behave similarly: Blindfold a dog and it will swim in circles. Hunters say that a wounded animal in attempting to escape will run along a curve that resembles a circle. Finally, blindfold a man and ask him to cross a street; his path will resemble a portion (an arc) of a circle. Why is this?

The solution of the riddle lies in the fact that there is no living being whose body is so perfectly constructed that it is symmetrical; that is, its left side is an exact mirror reflection of the right side or, as we may say, it is perfectly balanced. There is no human face whose right side is exactly the same as its left side, as a mirror, or a close look at your friends, will prove. But outward appearance is only half the story: the body of a human, as well as that of an animal, is not equally developed on the right and the left side. A left hand, foot, or eye may be stronger than the right one, or vice versa.

So, in walking in the dark we generally go around in circles because no human being takes (whether blindfolded or not) equal steps with the right and left foot. The difference in the strides may be very minute, but these differences accumulate. An experienced horseman when he wishes to turn does not pull on one side of the reins, but leans slightly to the side of the saddle, and this causes the horse to turn to that side. If the rider were leaning continuously, the horse would go around in circles. Watch a circus rider closely; this is exactly what he does.

Thus if a man walks so that the step taken by his left foot is $\frac{1}{16}$ inch longer than that taken by his right foot, and if he makes 4,000 steps, half of them will be with the left foot and the difference will be $2,000 \cdot \frac{1}{16} = 125$ inches. The eyes guide in the light, but let him walk in total darkness or be blindfolded and he will describe a circle because his left foot will have to cover more distance. In other words, his right foot will describe a circle inside the circle described with his left foot, and the man will always turn to the right. The diagram below shows the situation when a man walks with a left stride longer than the right one.

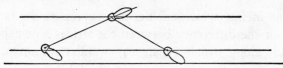

The distance between a man's heels is about 4 inches. Thus if with his right foot he describes a circle of radius r, the radius of the outer circle (described with the left foot) is $(r + 4)$. The lengths of the respective circumferences are $2\pi r$ and $2\pi(r + 4)$, and the difference between these two lengths is $2\pi(r + 4) - 2\pi r = 2\pi 4$.

It is easy to compute the radius of the circle that a man may walk around if we know the difference between the strides taken by his right and left foot. Let us assume that his stride is 3 feet, and the radius of the circle that he walks around is r, then the length of his path is $2\pi r$, and the number of steps he takes is $\dfrac{2\pi r}{36}$ (we translate everything into inches). Since half of his steps are taken by the left foot, and the other half by his right foot, the number of the longer steps (say, by the left foot) is

$$\frac{2\pi r}{2 \cdot 36} = \frac{\pi r}{36}$$

Multiply this number by the difference between the lengths of the strides (suppose that it is $\frac{1}{16}$ inch) and we have

$$\frac{\pi r}{36 \cdot 16}$$

This result must be equal to the difference between the lengths of the two concentric circles (suppose that it is 125 inches). We then have

$$\frac{\pi r}{36 \cdot 16} = 125$$

and from this we obtain the value of r, as

$$r = 125 \cdot 36 \cdot \frac{16}{3.14}, \quad \text{or about 8,600 inches}$$

which is about 720 feet.

If the radius of the circle is r and the difference between the lengths of the strides is d we have the formula

$$\frac{\pi rd}{36} = 2\pi 4$$

or $rd = 288$ inches, which enables us to compute the radius if d is known, or the difference between the strides when the radius of the circle along which a man may wander is known.

Squaring the Circle

We have observed that the length of the circumference of a circle as well as the area of a circle (more correctly, construction of a square whose area is equal to the area of a circle) cannot be determined by simple means with the use of rulers and compasses only. Such stipulation indicates that only two kinds of operations are allowed: (1) the drawing of a circle with a given radius at a given point as a center, and (2) the drawing of a straight line through two given points. These operations do not lead to solution of this problem, and whoever attempts the feat is trying to do the impossible.

The length of the circumference of a circle of radius r is $C = 2\pi r$. Solution of the problem of obtaining the length of the circumference is determined by the nature of the number π, which, as we have noted, cannot be expressed numerically since its value has an infinite number of decimals.

There are many simple expressions which enable us to calculate the value of π. None of these expressions ever ends—they are known as "expressions with an infinite number of terms." Some were discovered several hundreds of years ago. Here is a very simple one (if the reader wishes, he may curl up for a long spell of calculation, but he is forewarned that seven hundred decimals already have been obtained without definitive result):

$$\frac{\pi}{4} = 1 - \frac{1}{3} + \frac{1}{5} - \frac{1}{7} + \frac{1}{9} - \frac{1}{11} + \text{ and so on, indefinitely.}$$

28

The Mathematics of Seeing

Can You Trust Your Eyes?

The next time conversation lags, ask your friends a question: "Do you think you could cover 'cigarettes' with a dime if the word were set in average size book type?" Now, before anyone digs up a dime, make your friends guess the size of the word. Generally, most people will say that it is impossible to cover the word with a dime.

Let us examine the reason why few people can judge the size of an object. Naturally, we shall consider this inability from a purely mathematical point of view and pass over physical reasons such as faulty eyesight. Suppose you see an automobile coming toward you. You observe the car about half a mile away. Can you judge the dimensions of the car? Suppose you observe the car one-quarter of a mile away. Do the dimensions of the car appear twice as large? Would you say that the car appears to be only about a foot long? Look at the full moon. How big is it? Is it as big as a half-dollar, a quarter, or a nickel? You may have heard as a child that the moon is as large as a platter. Such descriptions may be nice and mother-goosey but do they have any meaning? Now and then you may see a newspaper report of someone who has seen a comet and who described it as having a tail *two yards* long plainly visible to the naked eye. Such reports should be taken with a carload of salt.

In order to judge the magnitude and size of an object we must fully comprehend the correct procedure—what takes place and what we are meant to do. This will be the topic of the present chapter.

Actual and Apparent Sizes

There is a distinction between the apparent size of an object and its actual size. Suppose you observe an airplane passing in the distance. If the airplane is far away, it may appear as a speck not much larger than a fly. On the other hand, if you observe the same airplane at close hand—or even a fly if it's on your own nose—you may be amazed at its size. Thus, the apparent size of an object depends primarily on the distance of this object from you. The actual size of an object is something that cannot be observed at all, because in order for our eyes to focus upon that object it must be at some distance from the observer.

The act of seeing consists in observing the outlines of an object. This necessitates observation of the extremities of the figure. Now, it is quite obvious, and the reader may convince himself by examining the drawing below that any two extrem-

ities of an object and the eye of an observer form a triangle. The eye of the observer is located at the vertex of this triangle. The two extremities of the object and the eye of the observer in the drawing are joined with two straight lines which are the sides of the angle. The farther we remove the object from the observer the smaller is the angle thus formed. In other words, there is a definite angle that is associated with the act of seeing. This is an important angle because it determines the apparent magnitude of the object. It is known as "the angle of observation" or "the angular magnitude of an object at a distance." The actual magnitude of an object, when this object is removed some distance from the observer, remains unchanged. But the angular magnitude of this object changes (and becomes smaller) when the object is moved away from the observer. On the other hand, should the object be moved toward the observer the angular magnitude of this object would increase.

The reader must have noticed that during the processes of measuring heights and distances of objects with the instruments described in Chapter 26 the angles that were measured were actually the angular magnitudes of the objects (or the angular magnitudes of the distances between objects). However, those angles were comparatively large. But, whatever the magnitudes of those angles were, they had to be appreciably large for the observer to be aware of them. In many situations the angular magnitudes of objects are so small that we fail to take notice of them. Let us consider several common examples of very small angular magnitudes.

The Circle Family: Meet Cousin Chord

We have already seen that the circumference of a circle is divided into 360 parts and that every part is a degree. Moreover, we also know that when we have very small angles we may use a procedure whereby the y coordinate of a point may be replaced by the arc of a circle, or vice versa. We shall now introduce another member of the circle family.

If we take any two points on the circumference of a circle and join these two points with a straight line, we obtain a special line segment. This line segment is known as "the chord" of the circle and is the diameter's first cousin. In any circle there is an infinite number of chords. They may be of any size, provided they do not exceed the magnitude of the diameter of the circle. There is also an infinite number of diameters in any circle, because the diameter passes through the center like the spoke of a wheel, and through any point an infinite number of straight lines may be passed.

Now, if an angle is very small, say 1, 2, 3, or perhaps 4 degrees, but never greater than 5 degrees, it is permissible at times to make use of the arc of the circle (the smaller one) that joins the end points of the chord. The difference between the lengths of the chord and its arc in such cases is so small that it may be considered as imperceptible. If we make this agreement, we may then consider that the distance between the two extremities of an object, when its angular magnitude is very small, is an arc of a circle.

This agreement enables us to determine the angular magnitude of an object whose actual size is known to us. For example, suppose a six-foot man is about 350 feet away. The angular magnitude of this man is determined as follows: The radius of the circle in this case is 350 feet. The length of the circumference of this circle is $2 \cdot 3.14 \cdot 350 = 2,198$ feet. What part of this circle is an arc 6 feet long? To answer this question we divide 2,198 by 6. We then have $2,198/6 = 366.3$, and this indicates that a six-foot arc in a circle whose radius is about 350 feet corresponds to about 1 degree. If the man were some 175 feet away, his angular magnitude would be about 2 degrees; 700 feet away, it would be about ½ degree.

Don't Eclipse the Moon with a Match

The farther an object is removed from an observer the smaller is its angular magnitude. This fact is actually an explanation of the phenomenon that objects at a distance seem to be smaller than when they are nearer to an observer.

Let us reverse the question proposed in the preceding section. At what distance from an observer must a six-footer stand so that he can be observed at an angle of 1 degree? We proceed as follows: The circle is divided into 360 degrees and 1 degree is therefore ⅟₃₆₀th part of a circle. Now, if 6 feet is the magnitude that is observed as 1° it must be an arc that is a ⅟₃₆₀th part of a circle, and thus the circumference of the circle in this case is $6 \cdot 360 = 2,160$ feet. In other words, we know the length of the circumference of a circle, and we must determine the radius of the circle (which is the distance of the man from the observer). The formula for the length of the circumference of a circle with a radius r is

$$C = 2\pi r = 2 \cdot 3.14r = 6.28r$$

Then $r = \dfrac{C}{6.28}$, and, since $C = 2,160$ feet, we have

$$r = \frac{2,160}{6.28} = 343.9$$

or about 344 feet.

How far must a six-foot man be from an observer in order for his angular magnitude to be ½ degree? In this case the arc of the circle is also 6 feet, but it corresponds to ½ degree or $\frac{1}{720}$th part of a circle. The circumference of this circle is then $6 \cdot 720 = 4,320$ feet long, and the radius $\frac{4,320}{6.28} = 687.9$ or about 688 feet.

The above computation can be simplified. Let us consider the following problem. At what distance will an object 1 foot long be observed at an angle of 1 degree? In this case the circle will have a circumference 360 feet long, and the radius is then $\frac{360}{6.28} = 57.3$ or about 57 feet. In other words, the object is removed from the observer a distance that is about 57 times as great as its own length.

At what distance from an observer would a dime have the same angular magnitude as the moon (½ degree)? In other words, how far from our eyes must we keep a dime in order that it should not appear any larger than the moon? We compute this distance as follows (the diameter of a dime is about $\frac{11}{16}$ or 0.6875 inch): $0.6875 \cdot 2 \cdot 57 = 78.375$ or about 78 inches (or 6.5 feet).

The reader may check the following results: In order that a quarter appear not larger than the moon it must be about 9 feet away from the observer. A ten-inch phonograph record must be about 95 feet away from the observer in order that it appear not larger than the moon. The head of a match is about ⅛ inch (0.125 inch) in diameter and must be held at least 14 inches away from the eyes, or it may appear to eclipse the moon. This may seem surprising, but the results of the reader's computations should convince him.

PROBLEMS

1. A man 5 feet, 8 inches tall is observed at an angle of 20 minutes. How far is the man from the observer?

2. At what height must an airplane, whose wing span is 120 feet, be observed at an angle of 20 minutes?

3. At what angle is the earth observed from the moon? (The radius of the earth is about 4,000 miles, and the distance of the earth from the moon is about 240,000 miles.)

4. Three miles away a building is observed at an angle of 24 minutes. What is the height of the building?

5. How far off would you have to be to observe a six-foot man at an angle of 1 minute?

How Good Is Your Eyesight?

At one time or another most of us begin to wonder whether our eyesight is weakening. We then decide to visit an eye specialist, and the chances are that most will need treatment, for it is generally agreed that few men ever have perfect eyes.

When we refer to perfect eyesight we have in mind normal eyesight, that is, a type of vision that need not be corrected by glasses and that is not impaired in any way or manner. There are people that have unusually good vision. They can see and discern objects that even a person with a normal vision cannot see. However, a normal eyesight is now fairly well determined, and anyone can test his own eyes (satisfactorily enough, but, naturally, not as well as an optometrist, who has special instruments for this purpose) in his own home. For this purpose we shall need only a very simple instrument.

On a piece of paper draw a square whose sides are 1½ inches long. In this square draw 20 lines, each of which should have the thickness of a paper match. The drawing on the left illustrates the construction of this instrument. The thickness of a paper match is about 0.04 inch (1 millimeter).

Pin this paper at the height of your eyes to a well-illuminated wall and, while looking at it, walk away from it until the entire square appears to you as a solid gray piece of paper. Then step forward until you can distinguish the black lines once more. Measure your distance from the wall. If it is about 11.5 feet, then your eyesight is normal, or if it is more than 11.5 feet, better than normal. If, however, your distance from the wall is less than 11.5 feet, then your eyesight is below normal.

The reason for all this is directly tied up with the fact that we may use the arc of the circle whenever the angle corresponding to that arc is very small. According to standards set by optometrists a person has normal eyesight if he can distinguish an object whose angular magnitude is 1 minute. We know how to com-

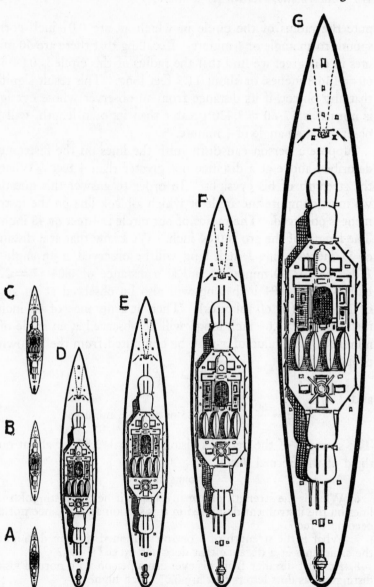

HOLD THIS PAGE 12 INCHES AWAY FROM YOUR EYES

A battleship 500 feet long will appear to an aviator flying *A*—10,000 ft.;
B—7,000 ft.; *C*—5,000 ft.; *D*—2,500 ft.; *E*—2,000 ft.; *F*—1,500 ft.; *G*—1,000 ft. above
the surface of the sea.

If you hold this page 2 feet away from your eyes, the above distances will
be doubled.

pute the radius of the circle in which an arc 0.04 inch corresponds to an angle of 1 minute. Recalling that there are 60 minutes in a degree, we find that the radius of this circle is $0.04 \cdot 57 \cdot 60 = 136.8$ inches, or about 11.5 feet long. This result signifies that any object, if its distance from an observer whose eyesight is normal is $57 \cdot 60 = 3,420$ greater than its own length, will be observed at an angle of 1 minute.

Suppose a person can distinguish the lines on the instrument described above at a distance not greater than 4 feet. What is the strength of his eyesight? In order to answer this question we must compute the angle at which a black line on the instrument is observed. The radius of our circle is 4 feet or 48 inches. The length of the arc is 0.04 inch. We know that at a distance of 57 inches a line 1 inch long will be observed at an angle of 1 degree (or 60 minutes), and at a distance of $0.04 \cdot 57 = 2.28$ inches a line 0.04 inch long will also be observed at an angle of 1 degree (or 60 minutes). Then at a distance of 48 inches the same line (0.04 inch long) will be observed at an angle of x minutes. The value of x may be computed from the following proportion

$$\frac{x}{60} = \frac{2.28}{48}$$

and

$$x = \frac{60 \cdot 2.28}{48} = 2.85 \text{ or about 3 minutes}$$

The strength of the person's vision is then 1/2.85, or about one-third of the normal vision.

PROBLEMS

6. What is the strength of a man's vision if he can distinguish the lines on the instrument described in this section at a distance not exceeding 6 feet?

7. What is the strength of a person's vision if she can distinguish the same lines at a distance that does not exceed 9 feet?

8. At what distance from his eyes can a person with normal vision distinguish as dots letters that are 0.075 inch high?

9. The letters on an electric sign are all 1 foot high. At what distance can a person with 0.1 normal vision read the sign? (*Note:* This means that no letter must appear as a dot.)

10. At a distance of 3,000 feet from an electric sign a person can distinguish the letters (each 3 feet high) as dots only. What is the strength of his vision?

The Glass Eye: Sees All, Knows All

One of man's greatest inventions is the magnifying glass. Through it, man first glimpsed the elements of modern science and became familiar with "invisible" (to the glassless eye) worlds. By means of the magnifying glass we are thus able to observe and study objects that are too small to be seen with the naked eye. A common variation of the magnifying glass is the eyeglass.

There are many different instruments in which magnifying glasses (or, as they are generally called, lenses) are used, such as the microscope, the telescope, eyeglasses, the photographic camera, binoculars, and many others. The magnification power of these instruments differs with the purpose set before them. Some microscopes magnify 100 times, others 200 times or more. The magnifying power of telescopes varies with their size. Average binoculars have a magnification of about 8 times. Let us examine what happens when we observe an object through binoculars that magnify 8 times.

Suppose a person, observing with his naked eye, sees an object at an angle of 30 minutes and at a distance of 1 mile. When he observes this object through binoculars that magnify 8 times he sees this object at an angle of 240 minutes or 4 degrees. We mentioned above that the size of the object remains unchanged. An object that is observed at a distance of 1 mile at angle of 30 minutes is $\frac{5,280}{114} = 46.3$ feet long. Now, the same object will be observed at angle of 4 degrees at the distance $\frac{5,280}{114} \cdot \frac{57}{4}$ $= 660$ feet. But 660 feet is equal to one-eighth of a mile. In other words, the observation of an object through binoculars that magnify 8 times enables the observer to see the object as though the distance between him and the object is reduced 8 times. Thus, the magnification of the angle at which an object is observed results in the apparent reduction in the same ratio of the distance between the observer and the object.

The largest telescopes in the world are in the astronomical observatories in the United States. Their magnifying power is

very great. Let us assume, however, that we observe a celestial
object through a telescope that magnifies 1,000 times. Suppose
that this object is the moon, whose distance from the earth is
about 240,000 miles. By means of this telescope the distance is
reduced to 240 miles. The diameter of the moon is about 2,160
miles, and the full moon is observed at angle of 30 minutes. A
person with normal vision will thus see any object on the moon
whose diameter is 2,160/30 = 72 miles only as a dot. With a
telescope that magnifies 1,000 times any object whose diameter
is greater than 72 × 5,280/1,000 = 380 feet may be clearly seen
by our observer. If there were factories of the average size on
the moon, they could be observed through a 1,000 magnification
telescope.

The Historical Eye: Don't Look Now, Boys

During the Battle of Bunker Hill General Prescott is said to
have issued to his soldiers the following order: "Don't fire until
you see the whites of their (the British) eyes." The minutemen
then supposedly unclenched their trigger fingers until they could
literally look the enemy in the eye. Let's see where all the shooting began.

The average distance between the eyes of a man is about 1.2
inches. Thus, for a soldier with normal eyesight to distinguish
the eyes of his foe, the soldier must be less than 1.2·3,420 = 4,140
inches, 342 feet, or 114 yards distant. A soldier with about 0.7
of normal vision will be able to distinguish the whites of the
enemy's eyes less than 342·0.7 = 239.4 feet, or about 80 yards
away.

If we observe a man through binoculars that magnify 8 times,
the whites of a man's eyes could be observed as far as 342·8 =
2,736 feet, or 912 yards, provided our vision is normal. However, if our vision is about 0.7 of normal, then this man must be
less than 2,736·0.7 = 1,915 feet, or about 638 yards distant.

If anyone tells you that he can recognize the face of a man at
a distance of two city blocks (a city block is about 300 feet), he
must have an unusually strong vision or an embarrassingly fertile
imagination.

∠ 29 ∠

The Lost Horizon

If the Earth Were Flat

Have you ever walked along a railroad track? If you have, you must have noticed that the rails seem to meet far away in a point.

After you have read the preceding chapter you have a better understanding why the rails seem to converge on a straight stretch of railroad track. If the track curves, you may observe that the distance between the rails also diminishes as the rails recede from you. As the rails recede from you, the angle at which you see the distance between the rails becomes smaller and smaller. This angle diminishes until it is equal to 1 minute. At this point you no longer observe the distance between the rails, and they seem to meet in one point.

Let us suppose that the earth is flat. Also let us suppose that in this flat surface of the earth there is a railroad track that runs in a perfectly straight line.

If we stand on this railroad track and watch the rails converge in the distance we may observe (or we may think that we do) the point where these rails seem to meet in a point. We know now how to compute the distance from the observer to such a point. For the time being we shall assume that the vision of the observer is normal. In order to compute this distance we must multiply the distance between the rails by 3,420 (an object observed at an angle of 1 degree is at a distance 57 times as great as its diameter, and at angle of 1 minute is at a distance 57·60 = 3,420 times as great as its diameter).

479

The distance between the rails of a railroad track (also known as the standard gauge of railways) is 4 feet 8½ inches (or 56.5 inches). The place where the rails seem to converge (under the conditions stated above, the earth being flat, the track a perfectly straight line, and the vision of the observer normal) is

$$56.5 \cdot 3,420 = 193,230 \text{ inches}$$

or about 3.0 miles.

Do we actually see this point?

In order to answer this question we must remove the first condition imposed, that is, that the earth is flat. When we assumed the flatness of the earth, we introduced an artificial situation. This was done in order to simplify the discussion. When we consider the actual situation, however, we must dispense with any artificial condition that might have been imposed by us. In the following section we shall see how the fact that the earth is spherical in shape influences our seeing of objects at a distance.

PROBLEMS

At what distances will men, whose vision is, respectively, (1) 0.5, (2) 0.7, (3) 0.3, (4) 0.1, and (5) 1.2 normal, see the rails meet in a point?

How Far Is Faraway?

If the earth were flat and there were no obstructions to the vision, anyone could see as far as "the ends of the earth." But the earth is not flat. It is a huge globe (approximately a sphere) with a radius about 4,000 miles long. The surface of the earth "bends," that is, it follows the curved outline of the sphere, or as we say, it follows the curvature of the earth. On the other hand, we see in straight lines and not in curves. We do not readily secure the impression that the earth is spherical in shape because the earth's radius is very large in comparison with ourselves. The fact that there are very tall mountains on the earth's surface does not necessarily require any modification in our statement concerning the sphericity of the earth. Even the tallest mountain range is an insignificant wrinkle on the earth's surface when the earth is viewed as a whole.

In order to understand what happens to the line of vision on the surface of the earth, we shall need some additional information concerning the properties of a circle and some lines that are drawn in connection with it. We can learn all that we need to know about seeing on the surface of the earth by making a drawing of a sphere (see below), assuming that this is the drawing of the earth's globe

In this drawing AB denotes an observer, whose height is h. OB is the radius of the earth's sphere. AR is the line of vision of the observer. We note that the line AR touches (or, in mathematical language, is tangent to the sphere) the sphere. This line touches the sphere in one point only. It cannot touch the sphere in two points because it would then cut the sphere, and this would happen at a point that is nearer to the observer than the point D (where it is tangent); the other point, the one farther than D, is of no interest to us. Moreover, the observer can turn around, and his line of vision at every position of the turning of the observer will touch the sphere in one and only one point. Thus the observer may consider himself as standing in the center of a circle, and the points of that circle are the points where his lines of vision touch the earth's sphere. This circle is called "the horizon."

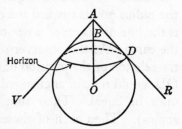

If the observer were standing in a trench so that his eyes were exactly on the surface of the sphere (that is, at B), his line of vision would touch the sphere in point B, and he would be unable to observe anything. However, since the surface of the earth in the vicinity of an observer is irregular in shape, this rarely happens. On the other hand, this can take place on a large expanse of water, provided the surface is calm.

In order to compute the visible horizon distance from an observer, we must know how to compute the distance BD, or, since there is very little difference between the length of the line AD and the arc BD (which is an arc of a circle), we may compute

the length of the line *AD*. For this purpose we must know one
very important property concerning the circle and a line that is
drawn tangent to it. This property can be established by proof,
but we shall state it without going through all the steps necessary
to prove it. *If a line is drawn tangent to a circle, and a radius of
the circle is drawn to the point of tangency, then the tangent line
and the radius are perpendicular to one another.* In other words,
these two lines form a right angle. We may convince ourselves
of the correctness of this fact if we consider the following: The
radius makes some angle with the tangent line on either side of
the radius. These two angles should be equal because at point *D*
the radius points toward the center of the earth and the line *DR*
is the line of vision of a person whose eyes are on the surface of
the earth. As the observer so located at *D* would turn around,
the relation of the position of the line *DR* in regards to the radius
OD would remain unchanged. Thus the angles *ADO* and *ODR*
must be equal. Their sum is a straight angle (or two right
angles). Then each of these two angles is a right angle.

We now have a right triangle *ADO* with a right angle at *D*
and the hypotenuse *AO*. Let us denote the radius of the circle
(which is also the radius of the earth) by *r*. Moreover, we denoted the height of the observer (to be more correct, the height
of his eyes, but the difference is so insignificant that we may talk
of the height of the observer) by *h*, which is *AB*. Then

$$AO = AB + BO = h + r$$

Let us now apply the Pythagorean relation to this right triangle.
We have then

$$AO^2 = AD^2 + OD^2$$

or

$$AD^2 = AO^2 - OD^2$$

or

$$AD^2 = (h + r)^2 - r^2 = h^2 + 2rh + r^2 - r^2 = h^2 + 2rh$$

The expression

$$AD^2 = h^2 + 2rh$$

may be modified if we consider the following. The radius of the earth's sphere is measured in miles, and, as we now know, is about 4,000 miles. The height of the observer, although it is measured in feet, in order to be consistent, must also be expressed in terms of miles. Thus the height of the observer will be a very small fraction of a mile. If, for example, the observer is 6 feet tall, he will be $\frac{1}{880}$th of a mile in height. Now, if we square this fraction we obtain a still smaller fraction,

$$\left(\frac{1}{880}\right)^2 = \frac{1}{774,400}$$

We may as well disregard h^2 altogether, because this term will not contribute anything numerically important in our result. Then, we have the distance of the horizon computed from the expression

$$AD^2 = 2rh$$

or

$$AD = \sqrt{2rh}$$

Since $r = 4,000$ miles, we have

$$AD = \sqrt{8,000h} = 89.443\sqrt{h}$$

where h is always expressed in terms of a mile.

Thus, if the observer is 6 feet tall, the distance of his horizon is

$$\frac{89.443}{\sqrt{880}} = \frac{89.443}{29.67} = 3.14 \text{ miles}$$

If the observer is 5 feet 8 inches tall, the distance of his horizon is computed as follows:

$$5 \text{ feet } 8 \text{ inches} = 5\tfrac{2}{3} \text{ feet} = \frac{17}{3} \text{ feet}$$

and his corresponding h is

$$\frac{\frac{17}{3}}{5280} = \frac{1}{932} \text{ mile}$$

Then the distance of this horizon is

$$\frac{89.443}{\sqrt{932}} = \frac{89.443}{30.53} = 2.93 \text{ miles}$$

Seeing Is Not So Simple

The air we breathe is important for us to keep alive, but it does not help us much in order to see straight. The air consists of tiny particles, invisible to us, but which affect the line of vision, or, it would be correct to say, the paths of rays of light. One important phenomenon that results in light traveling along a curved path is the bending of light owing to the thickness of air. For although air seems imperceptible it has thickness. In order to understand what takes place in the air, let us perform a little experiment.

Place a spoon in a glass of water. If you look down into the glass, you may notice that the part of the spoon in the water is somewhat raised toward you. If you look at the side of the glass, the spoon will seem as though it is bent at the surface of the water. This is illustrated in the drawing below. The same thing happens when light travels through air. If we look straight ahead of us, light goes through layers of air, and these act on light in the same manner as the surface of the water acts on the spoon. The light is therefore bent somewhat.

This effect enables us to see somewhat farther under certain conditions than under others. On the average, the greatest lengthening of the horizon distance is about 0.06 of the distance computed according to the methods described in the preceding section.

The horizon distance is lengthened under the following conditions:

1. On the sea.
2. When it is cold.
3. In the morning and in the evening.
4. When the air is dry.
5. When the air pressure is above normal.

The horizon distance is shortened under the following conditions:

1. On land.
2. When it is warm.
3. During the day.

4. When it is humid.
5. When the air pressure is below normal.
6. As the observer rises above the ground.

Thus, the horizon distance of a man 6 feet tall may be, under very favorable conditions, equal to

$$3.14(1 + 0.06) = 3.14 \cdot 1.06 = 3.33 \text{ miles}$$

The horizon distance of a man 5 feet 8 inches tall may be, under very favorable conditions, equal to

$$2.93(1 + 0.06) = 2.93 \cdot 1.06 = 3.11 \text{ miles}$$

With the above information in our heads let us have another look at the railroad: If the vision of a man is normal will he be able to see the point where the rails of a railroad track seem to meet?

The reader will recall that in the first part of this chapter we computed the distance from the observer to the point where the rails seem to meet. We found that it is about 3.0 miles. But this distance is less than the greatest possible horizon distance a six-foot man could see but a man 5 feet 8 inches tall could not. Thus, only the taller of these two men is really able to see (if their vision is normal) this point. According to the usually accepted form of speech, this point is "below the horizon" for the 5 feet 8 inches man.

PROBLEMS

6. What fraction of normal vision should a man 6 feet tall possess in order that he could see the rails converge at a distance of 3.14 miles?

7. What fraction of normal vision should a man 5 feet 8 inches tall possess in order that he could see the rails converge at a distance of 2.93 miles?

8. What fraction of normal vision should a man 5 feet 10 inches tall possess in order that he could see the rails converge at a distance of 2.75 miles?

9. What fraction of normal vision should a man 5 feet 7 inches tall possess in order that he could see the rails converge at a distance of 2.85 miles?

10. What fraction of normal vision should a man 5 feet 11 inches tall possess in order that he could see the rails converge at a distance of 3 miles?

How Far Can You See?

As the observer rises above the ground the distance of his horizon increases. This can be seen from the formula $AD = \sqrt{2rh}$. As h increases, so does the product $2rh$. This statement should not be construed as contradictory to the list of conditions that lead to the shortening of the horizon distances given above. The shortening of the horizon distances owing to those conditions is a small fraction of the computed distance and is considered as a correction only.

Thus, a pilot of an airplane that flies 10,000 feet above the ground can see $89.443 \sqrt{\dfrac{10,000}{5,280}} = 89.443 \sqrt{1.89} = 89.443 \cdot 1.37 = 123$ miles; and a pilot of an airplane that flies 3 miles above the ground can see $89.443 \sqrt{3} = 89.443 \cdot 1.73 = 155$ miles. A person who stands on the observation platform of the Empire State Building in New York City, which is about 1,240 feet above the ground, can see

$$89 \cdot 443 \sqrt{\frac{1,240}{5,280}} = 89 \cdot 443 \sqrt{\frac{1}{4.26}} = \frac{89.443}{2.06} = 43.43 \text{ miles}$$

In the above computations we may introduce the correction for the shortening of the horizon distances under the most favorable conditions. Then we have:

a) For the pilot flying 10,000 feet above the ground

$$125 \cdot 0.94 \ = \ 117.5 \text{ miles}$$

b) For the pilot flying 3 miles above the ground

$$155 \cdot 0.94 \ = \ 145.7 \text{ miles}$$

c) For the observer standing on the platform of the Empire State Building

$$43.43 \cdot 0.94 \ = \ 41 \text{ miles approximately}$$

PROBLEMS

11. What is the horizon distance of a man who stands on a tower 200 feet high?

12. What would be the horizon distance of a six-foot man on the moon? The radius of the moon is 1,080 miles.

13. What would be the horizon distance of a six-foot man on the sun? The radius of the sun is 400,000 miles.

14. What is the horizon distance of a man who rows a canoe? Let his elevation above the water level be 3 feet.

15. What is the horizon distance of a pilot flying 5 miles above the ground?

Distance Observations in Sea Warfare

The periscope of a submarine is 1 foot above the water. What is the horizon distance of the submarine (assuming that the sea is calm)?

We then have a horizon distance of

$$89.443 \sqrt{\frac{1}{5,280}} = \frac{89.443}{72.7} = 1.2 \text{ miles}$$

Correcting for the most favorable conditions, we have

$$1.2 \cdot 1.06 = 1.3 \text{ miles}$$

If the periscope of the submarine is 2 feet above the water, the horizon distance of the submarine (assuming that the water is calm) is

$$89.443 \sqrt{\frac{2}{5,280}} = \frac{89.443}{51.38} = 1.75 \text{ miles}$$

and with the correction for the most favorable conditions we have

$$1.75 \cdot 1.06 = 1.86 \text{ miles}$$

Suppose that a ship whose funnel rises 100 feet above the water is observed by the submarine whose periscope rises 1 foot above the water. How far from the ship can the submarine observe this ship?

In order to solve this problem we must compute the horizon distances of the submarine as well as the horizon distance of the top of the ship's funnel. The reason for this double computation is in the fact that the ship (as it can be seen from the drawing below) is below the horizon for the submarine if it is farther from it than 1.3 miles. The ship's funnel (that is, its top) has a horizon distance of its own, and a point located on the horizon of the ship's funnel must at the same time be located on the horizon of the submarine's periscope. In other words, the top of the ship's funnel, a point on its horizon (which is also a point on the periscope's horizon), and the periscope must all be on the same straight line. The sum of the two horizon distances is the

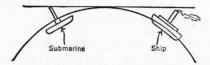

answer to our problem. We know the periscope's horizon distance is 1.3 miles. The horizon distance of the top of the ship's funnel is

$$89.443 \sqrt{\frac{100}{5,280}} = 89.443 \left(\frac{10}{72.7}\right) = 12 \text{ miles}$$

and with the correction for the most favorable conditions it is 13 miles. Then our required distance is

$$1.3 + 13 = 14.3 \text{ miles}$$

When the distance between the submarine and the ship is less than 14.3 miles, the submarine commander can clearly see the ship.

A lookout on the crow's nest of a battleship is 110 feet above the water line. He observes an enemy battleship the top of whose funnel is 130 feet. What is the distance between the two warships?

The distance between the two warships is the sum of the horizon distances of the lookout and top of the funnel of the second warship. We then have

$$89.443 \sqrt{\frac{110}{5,280}} + 89.443 \sqrt{\frac{130}{5,280}} = 89.443 \left(\frac{10.49}{72.7} + \frac{11.40}{72.7}\right) =$$

$$89.443 \left(\frac{21.89}{72.7}\right) = 26.27 \text{ miles}$$

Correcting for the best favorable conditions, we have

$$26.27 \cdot 1.06 = 27.8 \text{ miles}$$

Reaching Out for the Horizon

Thus far we were concerned with the horizon distance of an observer whose elevation above the ground was known. This horizon distance was computed by means of the formula

$$AD = \sqrt{2rh}$$

where r was the radius of the earth's sphere (4,000 miles), and the elevation h of the observer was always given in miles.

This problem may be reversed. If the horizon distance is given, we can determine the elevation of the observer which will enable him to see that far. In other words, we compute the value of h from the above expression. To perform this computation, we square the two sides of the above expression, and we obtain

$$AD^2 = 2rh$$

and from this we obtain

$$h = \frac{AD^2}{2r}$$

or, since $r = 4,000$, we have

$$h = \frac{AD^2}{8,000}$$

It may happen the given horizon distance has been corrected for the best favorable conditions. In other words, the value of AD was given as corrected, that is, if the uncorrected distance is d, then $AD = 1.06d$. From this we have $d = \frac{AD}{1.06}$. Should this be the case, we must compute the value of d from the given value of AD. For example, if the given horizon distance is 23.5 miles, and it is known that it was corrected, then

$$d = \frac{23.5}{1.06} = 22.17 \text{ miles}$$

At what height must an airplane pilot fly his craft in order to see Washington, D. C., and New York City at the same time? The distance between these two cities is about 230 miles.

We may assume that the horizon distance in this case is given as uncorrected for the best favorable conditions. In order to be able to see both cities at the same time, the airplane at the midpoint between the two, that is, his horizon distance must be about 115 miles. We have then

$$h = \frac{115^2}{8,000} = \frac{13,225}{8,000} = 1.65 \text{ miles}$$

PROBLEMS

16. To what height must one rise in order to be able to see an object 25 miles away?

17. How high above the water should the crow's nest of a battleship be in order for the lookout to be able to observe at a distance of 20 miles the top of a funnel of a warship 60 feet high above the water? Account for corrections.

18. To what height should one rise on the moon in order to be able to see 50 miles away?

Celestial Illusion: Sunrise and Sunset

Anyone who has observed sunrise or sunset or the rising or setting moon must have noticed that these two celestial objects seem to be considerably larger than when they are observed higher in the sky. Could it be that these objects change their size, or that they approach the earth when rising or setting?

We know, of course, that neither the sun nor the moon moves toward and away from the earth each day. Moreover, measure of the angular magnitude of the sun and the angular magnitude of the moon shows that, whether the sun or moon is at the horizon or high in the sky, the angular magnitude remains about the same, ½ degree. Then what is the cause of this phenomenon?

The answer to this riddle cannot be completely given. However, some explanation which is sufficiently satisfactory may be offered. The visible, but not true, change in the angular magnitude of these two celestial objects is caused by the appearance of the sky.

The sky does not appear to us as a half sphere. It appears to us as though the part of the sky above us is somewhat flattened out and is nearer to us than the portion at the horizon. The drawing below illustrates the appearance of the sky as we see it. As the sun and the moon move along the sky, their respective angular magnitudes remain unchanged. But, since they seem to be located as shown in the drawing, they appear to us larger when they are at the horizon than when they are high in the sky.

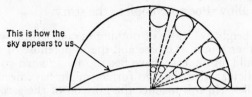

This is how the sky appears to us

This drawing is self-explanatory. The reader will observe that for every position of the sun (or the moon) the angular magnitude remains the same. Actual measurements confirm this fact.

The Soaring Horizon: Another Illusion

Whoever has watched the horizon as he climbed a tall building or tower has noted that the horizon seemed to rise with him at the same time and was always at the same level with his eyes. This impression is completely incorrect. This can be detected by fine instruments that measure angles. However, the angle that the line of vision of a person rising above the ground makes with the horizon is very small, and homemade instruments are not powerful enough to measure it. The fact that such an incorrect impression actually takes place was well described by Edgar Allan Poe in his "The Amazing Adventure of One Hans Pfaall," from which this passage is quoted below:

"What mainly astonished me in the appearance of things below, was the seeming concavity of the surface of the globe. I had thoughtlessly enough, expected to see its real convexity become evident as I ascended; but a very little reflection sufficed to explain the discrepancy. A line dropped from my position perpendicularly to the earth would have formed the perpendicular and a right angled triangle, of which the base would have extended from the right angle to the horizon, and the hypotenuse from the horizon to my position."

The drawing below illustrates what Poe's hero expected to see. His hero went up in a balloon, the position of which is

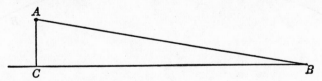

indicated by the letter *A*. The line of vision was to be the hypotenuse of the right triangle *ABC* with the right angle at *C*. But, let us allow Poe to complete the story.

"But my height was little or nothing in comparison with my prospect. In other words, the base and the hypotenuse of the supposed triangle would, in my case, have been so long, when compared with the perpendicular, that the two former might have been regarded as nearly parallel. In this manner the horizon of the aeronaut appears always to be upon a level with the car. But as the point immediately beneath him seems, and is at a great distance below him, it seems, of course, also at a great distance below the horizon. Hence the impression of concavity; and this impression must remain, until the elevation shall bear so great a proportion to the prospect, that the apparent parallelism of the base and the hypotenuse disappears."

The following drawing illustrates what his hero saw. The point *A* indicates the position of the balloon. The line of vision is *AB*, and the base line is *BC*. Note that the horizon line *AB* is

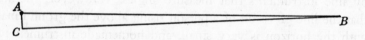

on the same level as the observer, although the observer is high above the ground. This results in a false impression that the surface below the balloon is concave.

However, when the balloon ascends to a greater height above the ground this optical illusion disappears, as may be seen from the drawing below. In order to obtain the correct impression the balloon must rise to a very great height so that the pilot may observe the curvature of the earth's surface.

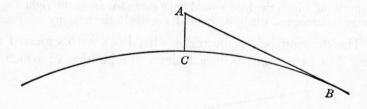

BEAUTY CONTEST

JUDGE'S STAND

√ 30 √

The Shape of Things

Foundation for a Figure

The reader is equipped now to proceed more searchingly into the mathematical origins and laws of the heretofore-puzzling geometric figures of our two-dimensional world, to learn more of the ageless problems of "infinity," and to be initiated into some of the "trade secrets" of the professional mathematician— all growing out of the carpentry of lines and angles.

First in Chapter 25 we examined "similar" triangles and their properties. We found that when two triangles have corresponding equal angles they are similar, and their respective sides (those that are opposite equal angles) are proportional, but that if these sides are equal, the triangles are congruent, that is, identical in size and shape.

In geometry we are concerned with the properties of figures composed of points, lines (straight and curved), and angles. The study of these is usually reduced to the properties of their lines and angles, and the conclusions are generally stated in terms of these properties.

Two of the fundamental properties of geometric figures that occupy the interest of mathematicians are those associated with the shape and size of figures. We shall now examine the plane geometric figures of the space of two dimensions, such as those made up of lines and angles. Any figure made up of lines and angles may contain any number of these, but we shall see now that there is a definite relation between the number of lines and angles in any geometric figure.

493

Essentially the shapes of geometric objects are determined by their elements, the lines and angles that go into their making. Thus a figure made up of three lines is a triangle, but there are many different triangles; some are smaller than others, although they have the same shape. We know now that such triangles are classed as similar because they have the same shape, a situation such as that in the enlargement of a snapshot. In addition there are geometric figures made up of more than three lines, and those of curved lines, such as the circle, the ellipse, and the parabola. In the main, then, the shapes of geometric figures are based upon the number of lines and angles that make them up, the size of these lines and angles, and, finally, the kind of lines, straight or curved.

Tailoring with Straight Lines and Angles

A geometric figure is made up of only a few elements, and thus far we have mentioned two of them, lines and angles. These elements, in themselves, also are geometric figures, and a line may be thought of as originated by yet another geometric figure, the point. The line, we know, has length but has neither width nor thickness.

To form an angle, we take two straight lines and make them intersect; two intersecting straight lines then form four angles. Sometimes all these four angles are equal, and we now know that in such a situation each is a right angle (an angle of 90 degrees), and the two straight lines are perpendicular to one another. Whether these two straight lines are perpendicular to one another because the angles formed are right angles, or the four angles are right angles because the two straight lines that form them are perpendicular to one another, depends on how we look at the situation; one statement depends on the other. However, we need not be deeply concerned here with the nature of these statements; this is more the province of a textbook of geometry.

When the four angles formed by two intersecting straight lines are not right angles they are not all equal to one another, but they are equal in pairs. This can be easily established by the following considerations: In the accompanying figure the two straight lines *AB* and *CD* intersect in O. We then have four angles, $\angle 1$, $\angle 2$, $\angle 3$, and $\angle 4$ ($\angle$ is the symbol for an angle).

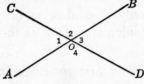

Note, however, that on any of the two straight lines, on either side of them at the point O we have a straight angle which is equal to 180 degrees. Thus

$$\angle 1 + \angle 2 = 180°, \quad \text{and} \quad \angle 2 + \angle 3 = 180°$$

From these two equations we obtain

$$\angle 1 = 180° - \angle 2, \quad \text{and} \quad \angle 3 = 180° - \angle 2$$

We then conclude that

$$\angle 1 = \angle 3$$

and this is not an accident; we make use of a very simple truth that if we have two things (in this case $\angle 1$ and $\angle 3$) and each of them is equal to the same thing (in this case $180° - \angle 2$) then these two things ($\angle 1$ and $\angle 3$) are equal to one another.

Angles $\angle 1$ and $\angle 3$ are called "vertical angles," and their equality is true for any of their kind and for any two intersecting straight lines. The reader may establish, as an exercise, that the angles $\angle 2$ and $\angle 4$ are equal.

We may also have two straight lines so drawn that they never intersect, however far they are extended. These are known as "parallel straight lines." The upper and lower edges of this page may be considered as an illustration of two parallel lines.

We have in earlier chapters come across some situations in which parallel lines were involved. In one we mentioned that the rails of a railroad track "seem" to meet at a point in the distance; now, we must impress the importance of the word "seem." The rails, of course, do not intersect, but they only appear to do so owing to peculiarities of our vision which diminish the angular magnitude of objects as they become more distant. So in the geometry that concerns us, parallel lines neither intersect nor meet, however far they are extended. We may imagine another geometry in which parallel lines would intersect (mathematicians have developed such a geometry), but this latter would serve only to confuse us here. We can best progress now by combining straight lines to see what geometric figures result.

Three Straight Lines and Three Angles

The only geometric figure that can be made up with three straight lines and three angles is the triangle ("tri" means three). We have examined some special types and know that a triangle with three equal sides has also three equal angles. This one is called the "equilateral (equal-sided) triangle." Since the sum of the angles of a triangle is two straight angles, or 180 degrees, every angle of an equilateral triangle is equal to 60 degrees.

If two sides of a triangle are equal, the angles opposite the equal sides are also equal. Such a triangle is called "isosceles."

We have examined some right triangles and know also that in a right triangle there is a relation between the numerical values of the sides known as the Pythagorean theorem. This relation states that the sum of the squares of the numerical values of the two sides forming the right angle of a right triangle is equal to the square of the numerical value of the side opposite the right angle, the hypotenuse. Thus in the right triangle *ABC* (*C* is the right angle)

$$AC^2 + BC^2 = AB^2$$

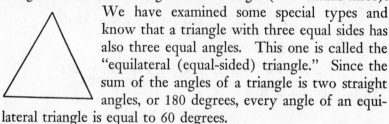

On this relation are based most of the greatest discoveries in mathematics and related fields.

However, this Pythagorean relation may be generalized to apply to any triangle, not necessarily a right triangle. Let us examine any triangle *ABC*. From the vertex *B* draw a perpendicular *BD*. Thus within the triangle *ABC* we have another triangle (a right one) *BDC*. Note that all the angles of the triangle *ABC* are all less than 90 degrees. Now we may apply the Pythagorean relation to the right triangle *BDC*. We have then

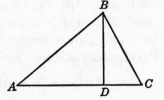

$$BC^2 = BD^2 + DC^2$$

We note also that the triangle *ABD* is a right triangle, because *BD* is perpendicular to *AC*. We have a Pythagorean relation also for this triangle,

$$AB^2 = BD^2 + AD^2$$

From this last relation we obtain that

$$BD^2 = AB^2 - AD^2$$

Also note that

$$AD + DC = AC, \quad \text{or} \quad DC = AC - AD$$

Then

$$DC^2 = (AC - AD)^2 = AC^2 - 2AC \cdot AD + AD^2$$

Now we have the expressions for BD^2 and DC^2. Substitute these expressions in the relation

$$BC^2 = BD^2 + DC^2$$

We then have

$$BC^2 = AB^2 - AD^2 + AC^2 - 2AC \cdot AD + AD^2$$

And from this we have

$$BC^2 = AB^2 + AC^2 - 2AC \cdot AD$$

Similar expressions may be obtained for the sides *AB* and *AC*. We may derive AB^2 by taking $AD = AC - DC$ and using the expression $AB^2 = BD^2 + AD^2$. To derive the expression for AC^2 we must draw a perpendicular line to the side *AB* (or *BC*) and follow the same method as above. This is left to the reader as an exercise.

Suppose that one of the angles of the triangle is greater than 90 degrees (such an angle is called "obtuse"). We have then the triangle ABC (and the angle C is obtuse). We draw BD perpendicular to AC (when AC is extended through C). We then have two right triangles ABD and BDC. We may write two Pythagorean relations for the two respective right triangles,

$$AB^2 = AD^2 + BD^2, \quad \text{and} \quad BC^2 = CD^2 + BD^2$$

From the last relation we have that

$$BD^2 = BC^2 - CD^2$$

From $AC + CD = AD$ we have that

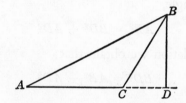

$$AD^2 = (AC + CD)^2 = AC^2 + 2AC \cdot CD + CD^2$$

Substitute the expressions for BD^2 and AD^2 in the expression $AB^2 = AD^2 + BD^2$. We have then

$$AB^2 = AC^2 + 2AC \cdot CD + CD^2 + BC^2 - CD^2$$

or

$$AB^2 = AC^2 + BC^2 + 2AC \cdot CD$$

Observe that when the angle opposite the side AB is less than 90 degrees, the term $2AC \cdot CD$ is negative, but when the angle opposite AB is greater than 90 degrees (obtuse) the $2AC \cdot CD$ is positive. Moreover, if the angle C is a right angle we obtain the relation $AB^2 = AC^2 + BC^2$, and this relation is only a particular case of the general Pythagorean relation derived above. When the triangle is a right triangle, CD vanishes; that is, it has the value zero, and the product $2 \cdot AC \cdot CD$ is also equal to zero.

There are countless other interesting properties of triangles and much is still to be discovered, but before we leave them we must recall one more important property: The sum of the angles of a triangle is always 180 degrees (or two right angles). Moreover, we must clarify the notion concerning the three straight lines and the three angles that go into the making of triangles. If we have any three straight lines and any three angles (whose sum is 180 degrees) it does not follow that we can construct this figure. The three lines that go into a triangle are subject to a definite limitation: The length of any one of them must be less than the sum of the lengths of the other two. For example, if we have three straight lines 3, 5, and 9 inches long, we cannot construct a triangle, as 3 + 5 is less than 9.

On the other hand we can make one, if we have three straight lines of 3, 5, and 7 inches.

The triangle and its angles are determined when its three sides (which represent the given three straight lines) are stated, but if only the angles are given we may have an infinite number of triangles and all will be similar. To avoid confusion, we shall not associate the problem of determining a triangle  with six elements, three straight lines and three angles. In brief, a triangle is determined when three sides are given, or when two sides and an angle are given, or when one side and two angles are given.

Note that when one side and two angles are given we may as well consider that the three angles are given, and when we know two angles, we can easily compute the third. For example, if the two given angles are 47 and 71 degrees, the third angle is $180° - (47° + 71°) = 180° - 118° = 62°$. But the three angles would not determine the triangle although they determine its shape, because with three angles we may have an infinite number of triangles, all similar. But once we have a side given, in addition to the three angles, the triangle is definitely determined.

Adding Another Line and Angle

Four straight lines go into the making of a four-sided figure, but the problem of what determines them requires considerable knowledge of geometry. We may mention, however, one definite requirement: The sum of any three sides of a four-sided figure is always greater than the fourth side. This means that when four straight lines are given, and the sum of any three of them is greater than the fourth straight line, then a four-sided figure may be constructed with these four straight lines. This fact may be observed from the figure below; if the sum of the sides *AB*, *BC*, and *CD* were equal to or less than the side *AD*, we could not have a four-sided figure.

There are many types of these figures. Mathematicians call them "quadrilaterals" (the Latin "quadratus," for square, and "lateris," for side). Any four-sided figure has four angles. We may therefore use an easier name, "quadrangle" (four-angled). In its most general form a quadrangle is such that no two of its sides are equal. It is just a four-sided figure.

To identify the various types of quadrangles we shall start with the most specific and familiar, the "square." This is a four-sided figure; its sides are equal, its four angles are equal, and each of them is a right angle. In other words, in a square every two adjacent sides are perpendicular to one another. Moreover, the opposite sides are parallel to one another. It is established that two lines perpendicular to a third are parallel to one another; in the drawing the lines *CD* and *EF* are both perpendicular to the line *AB* and, therefore, *CD* and *EF* are parallel to one another.

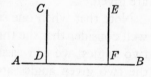

The figure below is that of a square *ABCD*. The four sides *AB*, *BC*, *CD*, and *AD* are equal; that is,

$$AB = BC = CD = AD$$

Moreover,

$$\angle A = \angle B = \angle C = \angle D = 90°$$

A square has two diagonals, straight lines drawn from one vertex to an opposite vertex. Thus in the square *ABCD* the straight lines AC and BD are diagonals and equal, as well as perpendicular to one another.

If the side of a square is, say, a and we consider the geometric figure that is formed by two sides and a diagonal, we have a special right triangle, a 45-, 45-, 90-degree triangle. This needs no special proof. The reader may observe that in this right triangle two sides are equal: therefore, two angles are equal. The sum of the angles of a triangle is 180 degrees; subtract from this the 90-degree angle and we have 90 degrees. Dividing this difference by two we have 45 degrees. Now if we apply to the triangle ABD the Pythagorean relation, we have

$$AB^2 + AD^2 = BD^2$$

But $AB = a$. We then may write

$$a^2 + a^2 = BD^2$$

or

$$BD^2 = 2a^2$$

Extracting square roots on both sides of the equation we have $BD = a\sqrt{2}$. The square root of 2 ($\sqrt{2}$) cannot be obtained exactly; there is no number whose square is exactly equal to 2.

Now we shall leave the square and consider a type of a quadrangle in which some of the limitations that are imposed on a square (the equality of the sides, the parallelism of the opposite sides, the equality of the angles, the equality of the diagonals, or the perpendicularity of the diagonals) are removed. We shall prune these limitations one at a time.

Suppose that first we remove the equality of the sides, making those of our new quadrangle equal in the pairs of the opposite sides. But they must be perpendicular to the adjacent side, and the two diagonals must be equal. The new quadrangle is called the "rectangle." Are the diagonals of the rectangle perpendicular to one another?

The reader, if he will examine a square, will be able to convince himself that the two diagonals of a square bisect (divide into two equal halves) one another, and will observe that the diagonals form four right 45-, 45-, 90-degree triangles. This is enough of a hint. In the case of a rectangle, however, the two

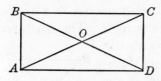

diagonals, although they bisect one another, do not form right triangles. This can be established by examining first the two congruent right triangles *ABD* and *ACD* and showing that some angles are equal; then the two triangles *AOD* and *BOC* can be shown to be both isosceles and congruent; this will lead to the equality of *BO* and *OB* and *AO* and *OC*.

Should we retain the equality of the four sides of a quadrangle but remove the perpendicularity of the adjacent sides, we have another type of a four-sided figure. This is called the "rhombus." In such a figure the diagonals still bisect one another, and are also perpendicular to one another. Also the parallelism of the opposite sides is preserved. We may imagine the sides of a square hinged at the vertices; we then take the square and hold it at the opposite vertices and pull slightly. The square will thus be deformed and the result will be a rhombus, as illustrated.

Note that if we define a rhombus as a quadrangle all of whose sides are equal and whose opposite sides are parallel, then a square falls under this classification and all squares are "rhombi" (the plural of rhombus). On the other

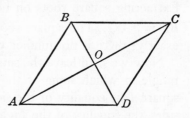

hand, not all rhombi are squares; only those rhombi whose angles are all right angles are squares.

We may also define a rhombus as a quadrangle all of whose sides are equal and whose diagonals are perpendicular to and bisect one another. Nothing is said here about the equality of these diagonals. If we have a quadrangle of this type and it happens that the diagonals are equal, then this rhombus is a square.

Instead of retaining the limitation that all the four sides of a quadrangle be equal, we may retain the limitation that all the four angles of a quadrangle be equal, which means that the angles of the quadrangle be all right angles. Someone may suggest that the limitation that all the angles be all right angles should be modified so that they all be equal but not necessarily right angles. In other words, let all the angles be 60-degree angles, for example. To determine whether this is possible we must find the sum of the angles of a quadrangle; is this sum the same for any quadrangle? Let us take any quadrangle ABCD. In it we draw a diagonal, say AC. We then have two triangles ABC and ACD. Since we have two tri-

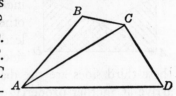

angles, the sum of their angles is 360 degrees, and this is the sum of the angles of the quadrangle. Now if any quadrangle has four angles, and if all these four angles are to be equal, every one of them must be $\frac{360°}{4} = 90°$; that is, a right angle. Thus we cannot have any but right angles under the above condition.

Since imposition of this limitation does not make any specific statement concerning the sides of the quadrangle, we may assume that there is no limitation on these. However, since the angles of a quadrangle under the imposed condition are all right angles the sides enclosing them are perpendicular to one another. Since we know that two straight lines perpendicular to a third are parallel to one another, the sides are parallel to one another. In other words in the new quadrangle the opposite sides are parallel to one another.

Here we shall mention another property of straight lines: Parallel straight lines enclosed between parallel straight lines are

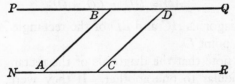

equal. Thus the two parallel straight lines AB and CD enclosed between the two parallel straight lines PQ and NR are equal.

Since there is no limitation concerning the magnitude of the sides of our new quadrangle, except that we know that the opposite sides are parallel and equal, the figure contains two unequal pairs of sides, as illustrated. Note that if we draw the diagonals we have two right triangles *ABD* and *ACD*. These are congruent because two sides and the included angle (a right angle)

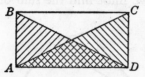

of one are equal to two sides and the included angle (a right angle) of the other. This congruency of the triangles leads to the conclusion that the third sides (the hypotenuses) are equal. But these third sides are the diagonals of the quadrangle; thus we arrive at another property of this new type of quadrangle: the diagonals are equal. This is our "rectangle," or quadrangle, all of whose angles are right angles.

This emphasizes that the rectangle is a more general figure than the square. The only difference is that in a rectangle the two perpendicular sides may not be equal, while in a square they must be equal. Thus a square is a rectangle also, but a special one whose sides are equal.

The reader may also convince himself that the diagonals of a rectangle bisect one another. For this purpose he will note that the two diagonals of a rectangle (as in the earlier figure) form four triangles, *AOB*, *BOC*, *COD*, and *AOD*. From the two congruent right triangles *ABD* and *ACD* we have that the angles *ADB* and *CAD* are equal. Then the triangle *AOD* is an isosceles triangle from which it follows that the lines *AO* and *OD* are equal. In a similar manner it may be established that the triangles *AOB*, *BOC*, and *COD* are also isosceles triangles. We then may show that

$$AO = OD = CO = OB$$

or that the diagonals *AC* and *BD* of the rectangle *ABCD* are bisected at the point *O*.

However, note that the diagonals of the rectangle *ABCD* are not perpendicular to one another. If they were, the triangles *AOB*, *BOC*, *COD*, and *AOD* would all be 45-, 45-, 90-degree triangles, and all would be congruent to one another. If they were congruent to one another, then their respective sides *AB*, *BC*, *CD*, and *AD* would be equal. But we know that this can happen only when the rectangle is a square. In the case of a rectangle that is not a square, only the opposite sides are equal. Thus *AB* and *BC* are not equal. This means that the condition for the 45-, 45-, 90-degree triangle is not fulfilled, and the diagonals of a general rectangle are not perpendicular to one another.

Squashing the Rectangle

Let us imagine that the four vertices of a rectangle are hinged, that we hold the figure at the opposite vertices and pull slightly to deform our rectangle.

We shall still have a quadrangle (a four-sided figure), but none of its angles will be right angles. In some respects this figure reminds us of the rhombus, and in other respects of the rectangle. But it is neither a rhombus (all its sides are not equal) nor a rectangle (all its angles are not right angles).

In the case of this quadrangle the condition of right angles is removed. However, the limitation that the opposite sides be parallel to one another is still retained, but this is the only limitation imposed. The accompanying figure illustrates this new type of a quadrangle, known as the "parallelogram." Its two diagonals are not equal (this is related to the property of the rhombus) but bisect one another (this is related to the

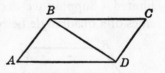

rhombus and the rectangle). That its diagonals bisect one another may be established by the procedure followed when those of a rectangle were examined. In the next figure we may see that the triangles *ABD* and *BDC* are congruent. This leads to the equality of the angles denoted by numbers 1 and 3. Then we can show similarly that the triangles *ABC* and *ACD* are congruent. This leads us to the equality of the angles denoted by

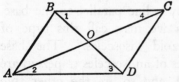

2 and 4. That the triangles are congruent in pairs is established if we remember that two triangles are congruent when the three sides of one are equal to the three sides of another. Then, recalling that two triangles are congruent when one side and two angles of one are equal to a side and two angles of another, we can show that the triangles *AOD* and *BOC*

are congruent, as is also the case with the two triangles AOB and COD. From this we finally obtain $AO = OC$ and $BO = OD$, which signifies that the diagonals of a parallelogram bisect one another.

Now we may note that a rectangle and a rhombus as well as a square possess all the properties of a parallelogram. Thus a parallelogram is a generalization of a rectangle, of a rhombus, and of a square. In other words, all rectangles, all rhombi, and all squares are parallelograms, but not all parallelograms are rectangles, or rhombi, or squares. Impose on a parallelogram certain limitations (all the angles must be right angles) and you obtain a rectangle. Require that the four sides of a parallelogram be equal, and you have a rhombus. Now if we impose the conditions that the sides of a parallelogram be equal, and all the angles of the parallelogram be equal (that is, right angles), we have a square.

The limitation that a quadrangle's opposite sides be parallel leads to a parallelogram, but this requirement still may be delimited. Suppose we decide that only one pair of the opposite sides of a quadrangle be parallel, and no specific condition is im-

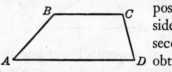

posed on the second pair of opposite sides. Naturally, we avoid making the second pair of sides parallel. We then obtain a geometric figure whose drawing is shown above. Now this figure is still a quadrangle, but it is no longer a parallelogram. Its name is "trapezoid." Its parallel sides are not and cannot be equal, but its nonparallel sides may or may not be equal. If the nonparallel sides are equal, we are reminded of an isosceles triangle whose upper part is sliced off by a line parallel to the base. Thus we may call this type of trapezoid "isosceles." The base angles of an isosceles trapezoid are equal, and so are the other two angles. The reader may see that the diagonals are also equal by examining the two triangles ABD and ACD. He may note that

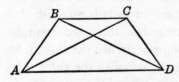

these are congruent because $AB = CD$, $AD = AD$, and the angles BAD and CDA are equal. Then $BD = AC$. The diagonals of a trapezoid never bisect one another, however.

The trapezoid is a generalization of a parallelogram. If the trapezoid is delimited—that is, if the opposite sides are made parallel—we obtain a parallelogram, so a parallelogram is a special case of a trapezoid, and all parallelograms are also trapezoids. From this it follows that, since the parallelograms include rhombi, rectangles, and squares, these are all special trapezoids.

Finally, if we remove the last limitation on a quadrangle, that one pair of opposite sides be parallel, we then obtain a quadrangle whose description contains no specific information concerning its sides or (and) its angles. Its sides may all be unequal, and so may its angles. The accompanying figure illustrates such a quadrangle.

The general four-sided figure, the quadrangle, represents a complete class of four-sided figures. It contains trapezoids, parallelograms, rhombi, rectangles, and squares. Not every quadrangle is a trapezoid, a parallelogram, a rhombus, a rectangle, or a square, but every one is a quadrangle. Further, a quadrangle is so general that no specific limitation is imposed on it since any specification may lead to a trapezoid, a parallelogram, a rhombus, a rectangle, or a square. However, we may devise some other limitations that will lead to forms of a quadrangle other than these. For example, the kite is patterned after a quadrangle whose adjacent sides are equal in pairs, as in the following figure. The reader may convince himself that one diagonal of this quadrangle bisects the other, but it in turn is not bisected. Moreover, the diagonals are perpendicular to one another. He will observe that the triangles ABD and BDC are congruent (the three sides of one are equal to the three sides of the other). Then, since $AB = BC$, the triangle ABC is isosceles. The results show that

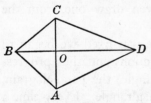

AOB and *BOC* are not only congruent but are right triangles.

There are many other forms of general quadrangles. Some of them are shown here.

There's Method in Their Math

The reader has now been introduced to one of the most important and fundamental procedures used by professional mathematicians in their work. To many this work seems a dark mystery, perhaps because mathematicians employ unfamiliar symbols—they often go so far that many are unable to fathom the work of their own brethren in trade. Others find difficulty in comprehending their work because a great number of mathematicians' studies have little or no practical application at present. We use the expression "at present," because many times through the ages mathematics has offered discoveries which then had no practical or scientific application, but which, years later, industry and the sciences found of vital importance.

When mathematicians study certain objects or situations, they follow the course (which, as we shall observe presently, is a method not confined to their use alone) that enables them to obtain as soon as possible most of the information pertinent to their study. This method was illustrated when we set out to study the types of quadrangles and their properties. We started out with a specific quadrangle and its properties were so precisely stated that the reader could even draw one from the worded description.

After our square type of quadrangle was fixed we began to remove, one by one, the various restrictions and thus progressively obtained the rhombus, the rectangle, the parallelogram, the trapezoid, and finally the general quadrangle. Every time a restriction was removed we obtained a type that included the previously studied type of a quadrangle—when the rhombus was obtained, we found that the square could be thought of as a rhombus; when the parallelogram was obtained, we found that the square, the rhombus, and the rectangle could be thought of as parallelograms. Our complete investigation may be represented schematically as follows:

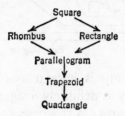

This procedure may be completely inverted. We may start with the general quadrangle and impose restrictions, one by one, on the properties of the quadrangle, each time arriving at a more specific geometric figure until finally we reach a dead end that is marked by a square. Schematically this development may be represented as follows:

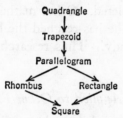

We may illustrate the properties of four-sided figures by means of a drawing. In this drawing (see below) the general quadrangle, being the most inclusive figure, contains within it the trapezoid. The trapezoid, being more general than the parallelogram, includes within it the parallelogram. Further, the parallelogram, being a quadrangle more general than either the rectangle or the rhombus, includes these two figures within itself. Finally, either the rectangle or the rhombus is more general than the square. Therefore the rectangle includes within itself the square, and so does the rhombus.

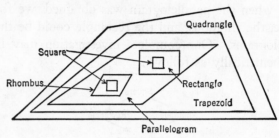

This method of study is known as classification. By this method every property is definitely assigned, and all the known types of geometric figures (in this case, quadrangles) are placed in their proper locations. This same method is applied to all other advanced studies in the field of mathematics. A mathematician examines particular cases, studies all the possible elements that may identify the type of the situation that confronts him, and also watches for whatever leads may occur in his study. Then he allows his imagination to generalize. Finally, when he reaches (in his own opinion) the most general situation, he considers his study completed. Other mathematicians may not accept his opinion that he has reached the limit of generality and may continue the study. Thus research and study of mathematics goes on.

Math's Trade Secret Applied to Other Fields

Classification is the fundamental process, the first step, in systematic study in mathematics. Before anything definite about the general properties of the object or situation may be examined, every possible related object or situation must be classified and placed in its proper relation to the study. This same method of classification is used in almost all human activity, but some of us may not realize it.

For example, someone has a headache. It might have been caused by business worries, or it might have been caused by overeating. Should it persist, a doctor is called. He seeks various symptoms that enable him to locate the disease. Actually when a doctor diagnoses an illness he classifies it according to the symptoms he observes.

Another illustration: The population of the United States consists of citizens and noncitizens. Citizens who have reached the age of twenty-one are eligible to vote. Those who have reached the age of twenty-five and have been citizens seven years may be elected to the House of Representatives. Those who have reached the age of thirty and have been citizens nine years may be elected to the United States Senate. But only those who are natural born citizens, who have reached the age of thirty-five, and who have resided in the United States fourteen years may be elected President.

In other sciences classification is widely used. All living beings may be divided into groups according to the kind of blood they have, the kind of food they eat, the way they move around, and so on, as the scientists may require. Another example of classification was given in Chapter 1, where the numbering of books in libraries is discussed. The reader may, as an exercise, find other examples of classification, whether on a broad scale or of limited scope.

How to Wrap a Circle

If we have five straight lines joined so that they form five angles, we obtain a five-sided figure. A six-sided figure is formed with six lines and contains six angles. We may now assume that if a figure has a certain number of sides, it has the same number of angles. The names for these figures are coined by adding to the Greek word "gon" (side) the Greek words denoting the specific number of the figure's sides. Thus, a five-sided figure is called "pentagon"; a six-sided figure "hexagon"; a seven-sided figure "heptagon"; an eight-sided figure "octagon," and a ten-sided figure "dekagon." For figures with a greater number of sides we write the number of sides and add "gon" on the right. Thus, a twelve-sided figure is called a "12-gon." To indicate that a figure has many sides we use the Greek word "poly," and thus we have "polygon."

Of all the polygons, those that may be of most interest to us
are those whose sides are all equal, and whose interior angles are
all equal. Thus far we became acquainted with two such polygons, the equilateral triangle and the square. There is a reason
for this special interest; by means of these polygons it was possible to calculate the value of the number π that is used as a
multiplier when the length of the circumference of a circle
whose radius is known is computed. Such polygons are known
as "regular" polygons.

If a polygon is regular—that is, has all its sides equal—all its
interior angles are also equal. This fact may be established from
consideration of a circle. We recall that in any circle equal arcs
are joined by equal chords. A straight line that joins the end
points of an arc of a circle is called the chord that corresponds
to that arc. Now we may divide the circumference of a circle
into any desired number of equal parts and obtain that number
of equal arcs. If we draw the chords of these arcs, we obtain a
polygon, and it is a regular polygon because all the chords (which
also form the sides of the polygon) are equal. The drawing
below shows such a polygon. The reader should note that we

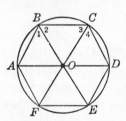

used the expression we "may" divide the
circumference of a circle into any desired
number of parts and avoided the use of
"can." The circumference of a circle may
be divided, but in some cases we cannot
divide it into a certain number of parts if
only a ruler and compasses are used.

Let us draw a few radii from the center of the circle to the
end points of the arcs, the vertices of the regular polygon. We
then obtain isosceles triangles (the radii of the same circle are
all equal because the circle is a figure all of whose points are
equally distant from its center). Now all these triangles are
congruent because all the sides of one are equal to the sides of
the other. Thus the two triangles *AOB* and *BOC* in the figure
above are congruent, and so are the triangles *BOC* and *COD*.
From the fact that the triangles are congruent we conclude that

the base angles of all these three triangles are all equal. Then by adding two equal angles we have

$$\angle 1 + \angle 2 = \angle 3 + \angle 4$$

or

$$\angle ABC = \angle BCD$$

This fact can be established for all the angles of a regular polygon.

Note that the greater the number of equal parts into which the circumference of a circle is divided, the smaller is each equal arc of the circle, and likewise each chord. Moreover, the greater the number of chords the closer does the regular polygon hug the circumference of the circle. Now we shall have to call up our imagination. If we continue to increase the number of the equal parts into which the circle is divided, the closer will the sum of the lengths of the sides of the regular polygon approach the length of the circumference of the circle. This gives us a clue as to how to compute the length of the circumference. All that we have to do is to continue to compute the sum of the lengths of the sides of the regular polygon when the number of these sides increases, and finally we may obtain the length of the circumference of the circle as closely as we may please.

This was the reasoning employed by the Greek mathematician and scientist Archimedes. He computed the sum of the lengths of the sides of a regular 96-gon, and reasoned that a regular polygon may be "wrapped" (or, as mathematicians say, "circumscribed") around a circle. And when a regular polygon is wrapped around a circle, and the number of the sides of such a polygon increases indefinitely, this polygon seems to hug the circumference of the circle also. In other words, whether we work with the polygon inside or outside the circle, we shall come as closely as possible to the circumference of the circle. This was the second part of the reasoning of Archimedes.

Finally, he reasoned (we translate it into modern language), the formula for the circumference of the circle is

$$C = \pi d$$

where C is the length of the circumference of the circle and d is the diameter. Then

$$\pi = \frac{C}{d}$$

Archimedes assumed that it is sufficient to consider the sum of the lengths of the sides of the 96-gon both inside and outside the circle. He then calculated π to be greater than $3^{10}/_{71}$ and at the same time less than $3\frac{1}{7}$. Nowadays some take the value of π as $3\frac{1}{7}$, which in decimals is 3.142857 (we know that a better approximation is 3.14159).

Before we leave the polygons, let us consider one question: If we have a polygon of a certain number of sides (this polygon need not necessarily be regular), can we determine the sum of its interior angles? We shall recall that in the case of a quadrangle we found that the sum of the interior angles of a quadrangle is always 360 degrees, and of a triangle, 180 degrees. Let us examine this question and, if possible, obtain an answer. The polygon illustrated is a representation of any polygon. We take

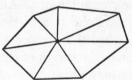

a point within it and draw straight lines to the vertices. We then obtain the same number of triangles as there are sides in the polygon. Suppose that the polygon has n sides. Then we have n triangles, we then have $n \cdot 180$ degrees as the total sum of the interior angles of all the triangles. But we must not overlook that the angle around the point within the polygon (where all the vertices of the triangles come together) is 360 degrees, or $2 \cdot 180$ degrees. If we subtract this angle from the sum of the interior angles of all the triangles, we obtain the sum of the interior angles of the polygon of n sides. This sum is

$$n \cdot 180° - 2 \cdot 180°$$

or

$$(n - 2)180°$$

This formula gives the general expression for the sum of the angles of any polygon. Thus in the case of a triangle we have three sides ($n = 3$), and the formula gives

$$(3 - 2)180° = 180°$$

In the case of a quadrangle, we have $n = 4$, and the formula gives

$$(4 - 2)180° = 2 \cdot 180° = 360°$$

In the case of a pentagon, we have $n = 5$, and the formula gives

$$(5 - 2)180° = 3 \cdot 180° = 540°$$

In the case of a dekagon, we have $n = 10$, and the formula gives

$$(10 - 2)180° = 8 \cdot 180° = 1,440°$$

Jumping Off into Infinity

In Chapter 25 we became acquainted with the circle, the ellipse, the parabola, and the hyperbola. These figures were de-

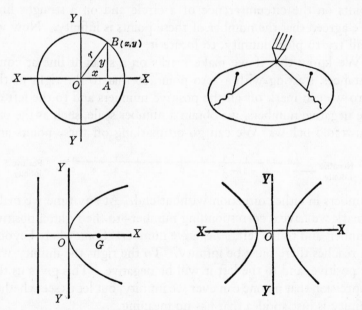

fined in terms of a point-world being moving in the same plane according to definite rules: (1) When the point-world being moves so that it is always at the same distance from one point, it describes a circle. (2) When it moves so that the sum of its distances from two points is always the same, it describes an ellipse.

(3) When it moves so that its distances from one point and a straight line are equal, it describes a parabola. (4) When it moves so that the difference of its distances from two points is always the same, it describes a hyperbola. The drawings of these four curved figures appear on page 515.

We shall now examine these figures to discover whether there is any relationship between them, and if so, what it is that causes the difference in their respective shapes.

To be able to analyze their nature we shall need an important idea—the notion of "infinity"—that we came across when we discussed trigonometric ratios of angles. We found that the tangent ratio of a 90-degree angle is greater than any known number, that it is not a number, and we named it infinity. We also made use of this notion when we considered the number of points on the circumference of a circle and on a straight line. We agreed that the number of these points is infinity. Now we shall try to place infinity, to locate it.

We know that if we make marks on a straight line at equal distances, starting with a zero point, so that to the right of the zero we can mark off all the positive numbers and to the left all the negative numbers, we obtain a number scale, such as the one illustrated below. We can go on marking off these points and

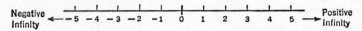

Negative Infinity ← −5 −4 −3 −2 −1 0 1 2 3 4 5 → Positive Infinity

numbers in either direction without end. At any time we make a mark we have a corresponding number—to the right, a positive number, and to the left, a negative number. Somewhere beyond all reaches there must be infinity. To the right the infinity will be positive, and to the left it will be negative. This gives us the impression that no one can ever see infinity, but let us see whether infinity is just an idea that has no meaning.

For our purpose we shall consider numbers obtained from the division of 1 by any other number, for example $\frac{1}{3}$, $\frac{1}{15}$, $\frac{1}{146}$. Such numbers are called the reciprocals of the original numbers. Thus $\frac{1}{3}$ is the reciprocal of 3, $\frac{1}{15}$ is the reciprocal of 15, $\frac{1}{146}$ is the reciprocal of 146. Now let us construct a directed number scale in which, instead of the original numbers, the points will be marked by their reciprocals. We shall remember also that the reciprocal of a fraction, say $\frac{1}{20}$, is

$$\frac{1}{\left(\frac{1}{20}\right)} = 20$$

the reciprocal of

$$\frac{1}{1,500} \text{ is } \frac{1}{\left(\frac{1}{1,500}\right)} = 1,500$$

In other words, the reciprocal of a very small fraction is a very large number, and, conversely, the reciprocal of a very large number is a very small fraction, for example, the reciprocal of 1,000,000 is

$$\frac{1}{1,000,000}$$

To simplify our method we shall have the original number scale above the new scale as shown below. Note that in the

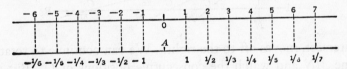

number scale of the reciprocals the marks have decreasing values as the points move to the right (and to the left) of the point that corresponds to the zero point of the upper scale. We have assigned no number to this point on the number scale of the reciprocals. Now we shall assign a value to it. As the points to the right of the upper scale (the number scale) approach the zero point, their corresponding values become smaller and smaller. But their reciprocals then become larger and larger, and the original numbers and their reciprocals both remain positive. To the left of the zero point on the number scale the same holds, except that the numbers and their corresponding reciprocals are negative. The point on the reciprocal scale that corresponds to the zero point on the number scale must have some value, but this value must necessarily be larger than any number. So this point on the reciprocal scale must be marked infinity. For infinity we have a symbol ∞, as illustrated in the drawing below.

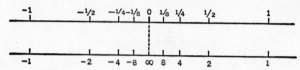

Now, approaching this point from the right, the infinity's sign is positive, and from the left, negative. But there is only one point that corresponds to infinity, and there is only one infinity. The sign therefore refers to the direction of approach to that single infinity.

Now suppose we have two intersecting straight lines *AB* and *MN*, and *MN* is pivoted at the point *P* so that it can be rotated. Then as we rotate it the point *C*, where the two straight lines

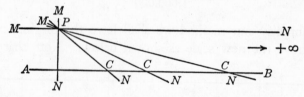

intersect, moves off to the right. We can continue to rotate the line *MN* and watch the consecutive positions of *C*. But when *MN* is parallel to *AB* the two straight lines do not intersect. What happens to the point *C*? We say that it jumps off to infinity and, to be consistent, add that the two parallel straight lines intersect at infinity.

Let us continue to rotate the straight line *MN* in the same direction. We note that it will intersect *AB* on the left. So

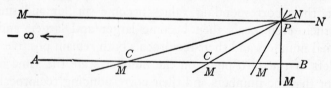

our description will be complete and consistent, we say that *C* jumped off to infinity, "passed through" it, and now is coming back from the negative side. The positive and the negative infinities are located in the same place.

Now let us return to our curved geometric figures. In the case of the circle we have one point, the center. Suppose this point splits into two. No sooner than this takes place, the curved figure ceases to be circular and it becomes elliptic. This continues as long as the distance between these two points can be expressed by any number, however large. We may also think of one point as staying fixed and the other point as moving off, whether to the left or to the right, is immaterial. As long as the moving point does not reach infinity the curved geometric figure remains an ellipse, but as soon as this point jumps off to infinity, the ellipse splits open, and the curve becomes a parabola. We may think of the parabola as being a closed curve whose closing is done at infinity.

After a point has moved off to infinity and passed through it, that point has to come back from the left (if it has moved to the right); thus its path ceases to be a parabola and becomes an hyperbola. We have two curved parts of an hyperbola before us, but both ends move off and we have the impression that we have two curves. Nothing can be further from the true situation; we really have only one curve, split open indeed, but closing up at infinity.

Thus we do not have four different curves. We have one curve, the circle that is being variously "tortured." We simply change the shape of the circle by imposing certain conditions on it.

31

The Size of Things

Birth of a World

When we examined the behavior of the point-world or line-world being or the properties of Flatland, or the method of measuring distances between two points in a world of five dimensions (five degrees of freedom), we did not question the existence of such worlds. Now we shall see whether they really exist. However, regardless of our findings, we should remember that physical nonexistence is not necessarily a handicap to the mathematician. Mathematics often deals with imaginary elements, but, if mathematical rules are applied, the results are not only consistent and correct but *real*.

We live in a world of three dimensions (degrees of freedom). If we are given three coordinate axes (think of a corner in a room where two walls and the floor meet), we know that we need three measures in order to locate a point. Most of us (except perhaps the Thin Man or your favorite neighborhood ghost) accept the notion of a three-dimensional world as a matter of fact. Likewise, we are familiar with the properties of a two-dimensional world (think of a table top or a motion-picture screen). For the one-dimensional world, we must finally resort to imagination because this world has only one property, length —no thickness, no width, no height to catch our physical eye. In the same way, we can think of a world that has been deprived of even this one property, a point-world—a world of no dimensions and no degrees of freedom.

We also have learned that we may start out with the point-world and develop worlds of any number of dimensions by introducing one dimension at a time. However, once we master this method, we may skip all the intermediate worlds and deal with the world of the particular number of dimensions that interests us. When we derived the formula for measuring distances between two points, we hit upon the method that should be used in our world-leaping. We found that the square of the value of the desired distance was equal to the sum of the squares of the differences between the respective coordinates and that the number of coordinates was exactly the same as the number of the degrees of freedom (dimensions) of the world under consideration. Thus, for example, the distance between two points in a six-dimensional world whose coordinates are $A(x_1, y_1, z_1, w_1, t_1, u_1)$ and $B(x_2, y_2, z_2, w_2, t_2, u_2)$ is given by the formula

$$d = \sqrt{(x_2-x_1)^2+(y_2-y_1)^2+(z_2-z_1)^2+(w_2-w_1)^2+(t_2-t_1)^2+(u_2-u_1)^2}$$

We knew that all these coordinates were measured along straight lines, but how these straight lines—that is, coordinate axes—were arranged could be described but could not be drawn. We learned that all six of these coordinate axes had to be perpendicular to one another and that every one of them had to be perpendicular to the remaining five. With little difficulty we can draw a picture of three coordinate axes that comply with such a description (they are perpendicular to one another and any one of them is perpendicular to the remaining two). We can see such an arrangement if we go stand in a corner. When it comes to 4, 5, 6, 15, 45, 100, or any other number of coordinate axes greater than three, pictures fail us and we have to retreat to thought.

Thus far our discussion was confined to coordinate axes and we have avoided the problem of worlds of many dimensions. How can we grasp such worlds in our imaginations?

Let us start with a world of no degrees of freedom. We can draw a picture, although a very crude one, of such a world. It is a point-world. It has no other property but that of position. A point made by a piece of chalk or by a pen or pencil gives us only an exaggerated picture of such a world. Nevertheless, this point-world will be very useful to us in our development, as we shall see presently.

Let us move a point and imagine that it leaves a trace, which will be a straight line. As we have seen, a straight line has length only. Now a straight line generated by a point has no ends on either side and can be extended indefinitely. That portion of the straight line measured—that is, whose magnitude is expressed in some definite manner (usually in terms of a number of known units)—is known as "the line segment."

Now let us move the straight line that was generated by the moving point. Here we had better interpose a word as to the manner in which all these motions are performed. Whenever we move a straight line, we assume that every point of it is subject to the same motion. Thus every point moves in the same manner as the point that generated the straight line. For the sake of convenience we shall use such a motion that the path of every point will be perpendicular to the straight line. We may have moved all the points of the straight line along parallel slanted lines, but we generally agree to follow the perpendicular lines because they happen to be more convenient.

When the straight line moves as described above, it generates a world of two dimensions which we call "a plane." Since the straight line has no ends, and since the distance through which it can be moved also has no ends, the plane generated by a straight line is limitless. Likewise, it can be observed that in any part of a plane a straight line will thus necessarily lie with all its points. If any part of the straight line sticks out (bulges), then the straight line does not lie with all its points on that surface, and the surface is therefore not a plane. The generation of the plane may be roughly approximated by a wide paint brush. When such a brush is moved along a flat surface, it leaves a wide trace, seemingly flat and uniform.

The drawing below illustrates the motion of a straight line. Only a few points are picked, for it is impossible to use all the points of the straight line since there is no gap between any two neighboring points. Before leaving the plane, we should note that the motion of a straight line perpendicular to itself adds to length another dimension—width. We should also bear in mind that a plane has no thickness. The generating line, of course, had no thickness, and the motion just performed was so limited that it could not add thickness to the plane.

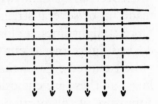

If, in turn, this plane is moved perpendicularly to itself by being lifted up and moved always parallel to its original position, we introduce thickness—or, as we usually say, we add height. This motion therefore results in a world of three dimensions. By means of this motion a Flatlander is hoisted out of his thin world into our fat one. Its dimensions are length, width, and height (or thickness). A homemade example of the birth of this three-dimensional world may be had by building up a stack of thin playing cards one at a time. Soon you will become aware of definite thickness. The entire pile occupies three-dimensional space. Again, since this world of three dimensions is generated by a plane that is boundless by virtue of a straight line that is endless, it is itself boundless and endless. This is a mathematician's world; we have no way of illustrating it in its entirety.

We need not stop with a world of three degrees of freedom. We now know a simple method for creating a world of one, two, and three dimensions: *Take the world you have and move it perpendicularly to itself so that it always remains parallel to itself.* In this way, we may go on creating worlds of four, five, or any other number of dimensions we may choose. So you see, Colonel Stoopnagle is not always right in his radio assumption: Mathematicians (not "people") have more fun than anybody. If they don't like this world, they build another.

Measurements in Flatland

We know that the line-world allows only one type of measurement, that of the length of a portion of a straight line. Generation of the world of two dimensions (Flatland) expands the nature of measurement. First, more freedom in measuring line segments is allowed here than in the line-world, where we have only one straight line. In Flatland we can have an infinite number of straight lines which may be placed in any manner we wish. Moreover, in Flatland we have learned that we can have figures made up of several straight lines. A figure formed by three or more straight lines, a closed curved figure, a portion of a closed curved figure that is cut off by a straight line, or a portion of a closed curved figure—that is, its arc and two or more straight lines—all these are enclosing a portion of Flatland. Can we have a measure of this portion of Flatland, the plane enclosed by such a figure?

To arrive at some definite method of measuring a portion of a plane we shall attempt to discover whether there is a unifying method in measuring the magnitude of objects. We shall start with the simplest magnitude, the length of straight-line segments. We shall agree that a straight line is generated by a moving point and that the distance through which a point moves is the length of the line segment.

We also know that the world of two dimensions is generated by a straight line moving perpendicularly to itself so that it always remains parallel to itself. Now suppose that we have decided upon a unit distance, that is, a unit length of a line segment such as one inch. Suppose this unit is marked off on the straight line. Then we move this line and generate the two-dimensional world. Let us measure off a unit length along the direction through which the line was moved. The line segment then will have moved through a unit distance perpendicularly to itself. It will have covered a portion of the plane (of the two-dimensional world) whose shape is a square, as illustrated. This portion of the plane we agree to use as a unit measure of the plane.

Let us examine what actually happens as the straight line moves to generate a plane, and assume that the line sweeps along so that it occupies every position as it moves. We know that a straight line has neither width nor thickness, but

that as it moves it generates width. The portion of the plane so generated by a line segment of unit length after this segment has moved through a distance of one unit may be thought of as the result of placing segments one near the other.
There will be an infinity of such segments because a straight line has the thickness of a point and there is an infinity of points in any line segment. We may represent this crudely in a drawing such
as shown at right. Now, to obtain a numerical value for that portion of the plane, we multiply the value of the unit of length by the value of the unit of width. Thus we have

$$\text{unit} \cdot \text{unit} = (\text{unit})^2$$

according to the method of algebra.

Thus the unit measure of the portion of the plane accepted by us is that portion which is enclosed within a square whose side is a unit of length. The unit of measure is a square unit, and is known as the unit of measure of "areas."

This explanation does not represent the historical development of the method of measuring areas, since men introduced this method for some reason unknown to us perhaps because most areas are either squares or rectangles. It would be quite reasonable to use triangular, pentagonal, or circular units, or units of any other shape, but their practical applications would be extremely inconvenient.

Since we have agreed upon a unit of measure for areas, we may apply the method we used in computation of the area of any rectangular figure. We may use a segment that is several units long, and move it through a distance of a certain number
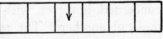
of units. The portion of the plane so generated by the moving line segment has the shape of a rectangle, as illustrated. The area of the rectangle may be computed as follows. If our line segment is *a*
units long and is moved through the distance of one unit, it would generate a rectangle whose area
would be *a* square units, as shown in the accompanying drawing. If we move this line segment through the distance of another

unit, we obtain another rectangle whose area is again *a* square units. Thus we conclude that every time we move a line segment *a* units long through a distance of one unit we obtain a rectangle whose area contains *a* square units. Now, if we move the same line segment through the distance of two units, we obtain a rectangle whose area contains 2*a* square units. If we move this line segment through the distance of three units we obtain a rectangle whose area contains 3*a* square units. Generally, if we move this same line segment through the distance of *b* units, we obtain a rectangle whose area contains *ab* square units.

This result gives us the rule for the computation of areas of rectangles, quadrangles all of whose angles are right angles: *Multiply the number of units of length in the width of the rectangle by the number of units of length in height* (or length, if we care to call it so) *of the rectangle*. The product represents the number of square units, or units of area, in the area of the rectangle.

For example if we have a rectangle that is three inches wide and five inches long, then the area of the rectangle is $3 \cdot 5$, or fifteen square inches. In general practice, the square inch is written as inch^2. We may then write the area of our rectangle as 15 inches^2. Once the rule for the computation of areas of rectangles is established, the rules for the computation of areas of other geometric figures follow from it.

Algebra to the Rescue of Geometry

Now we can obtain rules for the computation of areas of geometric figures that are quadrangular in shape. The derivation of these rules, which is a part of geometry, may be considerably simplified if we use algebra freely to avoid complicated discussions and lengthy examination of geometric figures.

When we examined the various types of quadrangles, we were not concerned with the magnitude of their figures. We were concerned, however, with the relations of one type of figure to those of another. The reader will recall that a parallelogram could be obtained if we assumed that the vertices of a rectangle were pivoted on hinges, and we were to pull on two opposite vertices so the rectangle would be distorted. Let us examine the area of a parallelogram to discover whether there is any relation between the rule for the computation of the area of a parallelogram and the area of a rectangle. To avoid much discussion let us recall, too, that congruent triangles were found equal in shape and could be considered identical. If two figures are identical, they must be equal in areas, and we may therefore agree that congruent triangles as well as other congruent geometric figures have equal areas.

With this last result in mind we can thus obtain the rule for the computation of areas of parallelograms. In a parallelogram $ABCD$ draw a line BE perpendicular to AD, and another line CF also perpendicular to AD (we extend AD beyond the point D. We then have two triangles ABE and CDF that are congruent. And $AB = CD$ because they are the opposite sides of a parallelogram, and the opposite sides of a parallelogram are equal. $BE = CF$ because they are both

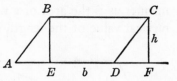

perpendicular to AD, and therefore they are parallel (two lines perpendicular to a third are parallel), and parallel lines between parallel lines (BC and AD) are equal. Obviously the quadrilateral $BCFE$ is a rectangle. To compute the area of a rectangle we multiply the number of the units in the length and height, respectively.

Since the triangles ABE and CDF are congruent and equal in area, we may transport the triangle ABE so that it occupies the place where the triangle CDF would be. This will not change the magnitude of the area of the parallelogram, as the areas of the parallelogram $ABCD$ and the rectangle $BCFE$ are equal. This means that we may compute the area of the rectangle $BCFE$, and the result is the value of the area of the parallelogram.

Thus we have the rule for computing the area of a parallelogram: *Multiply the number of the units of length in the base* **AD** *of the parallelogram by the number of the units of length in the height* **BE** *of the parallelogram, and the product thus obtained is the numerical value of the area.* Thus, if the base has *b* units of length, and the height contains h units of length, the area of the parallelogram is

$$A = bh$$

For example, if the base of a parallelogram is 10 inches long and the height of the parallelogram is 5 inches, then the area is $10 \cdot 5$, or 50 inches².

Since all rectangles are also parallelograms, we may consider that one side of a rectangle is its base and the other side is its height. Then the formula $A = bh$ is also valid for rectangles. Whatever was said concerning the rectangle can be equally applied to squares. In this case the base and the height are equal in length. Thus, if the side of a square is a then the area is

$$A = a^2$$

The area of a rhombus in square units is obtained in the same manner as is the area of a parallelogram by multiplying the numerical value of the length of its side by the numerical value of the height.

That a diagonal of a parallelogram divides it into two congruent triangles may be restated in terms of the area of the parallelogram. If in the parallelogram $ABCD$ we draw the diagonal AC, we obtain two triangles, ABC and ACD. The sides of these are correspondingly equal,

$$AB = CD, \quad BC = AD, \quad \text{and} \quad AC = AC$$

and the two triangles are congruent, thus equal in areas. This leads to the conclusion that the area of the parallelogram $ABCD$ is divided into two equal halves by the diagonal AC. The same would happen if the diagonal BD were drawn, but more about this later. Now the area of the parallelogram is given by the formula $A = bh$, where A is the area, b is the base, and h is the height (also called altitude) of the parallelogram. Since the area of one of the triangles ABC or ACD is equal to half the area of the parallelogram, we have the formula for the area of the triangle

$$A = \tfrac{1}{2}bh$$

where A is the area, b is the base (or a side of a triangle), and h is the height of the triangle drawn as a perpendicular from the vertex opposite the base b, as illustrated.

If a triangle is a right triangle, its area is obtained as half of the product of the numerical values of the two sides that include the right angle. The reader may convince himself of this in two ways: (1) He may take a rectan-

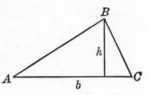

gle and draw one diagonal, then having two right triangles by the method used in the case of a parallelogram; or (2) he may consider one of the sides that includes the right angle as the altitude of the triangle when the other side that includes the right angle is the base.

Let us consider the parallelogram $ABCD$ further. We shall draw the two diagonals AC and BD. When we draw the diagonal AC we obtain two equal-in-area (and congruent) triangles ABC and ACD. Also when we draw the diagonal BD we ob-

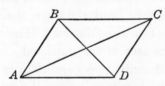

tain two triangles ABD and BCD which are also equal in areas (and congruent), and these two triangles have areas each equal to half the area of the parallelogram. Now, if we examine the triangles ABD and ACD, we observe that they have the same base and the same altitude. However, these two triangles are not congruent because AC is not equal to BD. The diagonals of a parallelogram are not equal unless the parallelogram is a rectangle or a square. However, since the altitudes are equal, this equality signifies that the vertices are at the same distance from the base, located on a line that is parallel to the base. This is so because they are on the line BC, which is parallel to the base AD. Thus we have an important property of triangles: *If two or more triangles have the same base, and all the vertices opposite the base are located on a straight line that is parallel to this base, then all these triangles have the same area.* For example, in the drawing below the triangles ABC, ADC, AEC, AFC, AHC, AKC have the same areas, since the vertices

B, D, E, F, H, and *K* are on the straight line *BK*, which is parallel to the base *AC*.

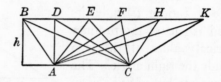

Computation of the area of a trapezoid is performed also by means of a formula. We shall make use of the method employed above, since whenever we cannot obtain a formula directly we may attempt to cut up the figure into other figures for whose areas we have formulas. Since any quadrangle can be cut up into two triangles by a diagonal, let us draw the diagonal *AC* of the trapezoid *ABCD*. We have then two triangles *ABC* and *ACD*. These two triangles are not congruent because their sides are not cor-

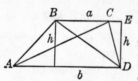

respondingly equal to one another. Thus we shall have to compute the areas of the triangles separately, and then we shall have to add the two areas obtained. Their sum will be the area of the trapezoid.

The trapezoid is a quadrangle with only two parallel sides. The other two sides are not parallel; they may be equal (the trapezoid is then isosceles), but they need not be equal. Since two sides of a trapezoid are parallel, a line drawn perpendicular to one parallel side will be perpendicular to the other side, as two straight lines that are perpendicular to a third straight line are parallel. Thus, if we draw such a perpendicular line, we can use it as the altitude of the triangles *ABC* and *ACD*. Since we have the altitudes we may, using the two parallel sides of the trapezoid as the respective bases, compute the areas of the triangles. The sum of these two is the area of the trapezoid. Let $BC = a$, $AD = b$, and ED (the altitude of the trapezoid, which is also the altitude of the triangles) $= h$. We know the formula for the area of a triangle, then the area of triangle $ABC = \frac{1}{2}ah$, and the area of triangle $ACD = \frac{1}{2}bh$. The area of the trapezoid

is equal to the area of triangle ABC + the area of triangle ACD which equals
$$\tfrac{1}{2}ah + \tfrac{1}{2}bh$$

The expression on the right has the factor h in every term (ah and bh). We have then the formula for the area of the trapezoid,

$$A = \tfrac{1}{2}(a + b)h$$

This is a universal formula; by assigning various numerical values to the values of the sides a and b we can obtain the formulas we have derived in this section.

If $a = b$, that is, when we have a parallelogram or a rhombus, we have
$$A = \tfrac{1}{2}(b + b)h \quad \text{or} \quad A = bh$$

When the quadrangle is a rectangle, $a = b$, and h, the altitude can be taken as the width w of the rectangle, that is, $h = w$. We then have
$$A = \tfrac{1}{2}(b + b)h \quad \text{or} \quad A = bh$$

Also, the base b may be taken as the length l of the rectangle. Thus finally we have the formula written with other letters, $A = lw$; that is, the area of the rectangle = length·width.

Finally, if we have a triangle, the upper side a of the trapezoid may be considered as if it had shrunk to a point, or $a = 0$. Then we have
$$A = \tfrac{1}{2}(0 + b)h \quad \text{or} \quad A = \tfrac{1}{2}bh$$

This is the formula for the area of the triangle we obtained earlier.

This derivation of formulas for the areas of the parallelogram, rectangle, rhombus, triangle (and also the square, which is a special case of a rectangle with all sides equal) shows that all these geometric figures are special cases of a trapezoid. The application of algebra, it may be noted, in the process of our examination of the trapezoid enabled us to arrive at this conclusion.

The Area of a Circle

To obtain the formula for the area of a circle we shall keep in mind two facts of which we made use previously. The first is the formula for the area of a triangle, $A = \tfrac{1}{2}bh$, where b is the base of the triangle and h is the perpendicular drawn from the vertex opposite the base to the base. The second fact is that when we have an arc of a circle that is very small in comparison with the entire length of the circumference of the circle, we may, instead of this arc, use the chord that joins the ends of this arc. This same statement may be worded also as follows. If in a circle two radii form a very small angle (we found by computation that such an angle may not exceed 5 degrees), then the arc of the circle that corresponds to this angle may be replaced by the chord that joins the end points of the chord. The accompanying drawing illustrates this fact.

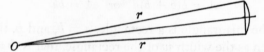

To obtain the formula we may attempt to slice the circle into triangles. If this can be done, our problem can be solved. Suppose we divide the circumference of the circle into a great number of equal parts, assuming that this division is performed. Let the drawing below illustrate such a division. Now, if the arcs

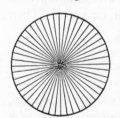

of the circle are very small (and we can make them as small as we please, provided we have the proper instruments and plenty of patience), every two radii and the chord that joins the ends of an arc form an isosceles triangle (since the radii are equal, two sides of the triangle are thus equal). Now we need to have the altitude of the triangle, and we shall draw it from the center of the circle to the chord that joins the ends of the arc. Here again we shall make one assumption: If the arc of the circle

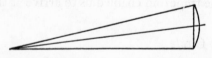

is very small, the altitude of the triangle differs very little from the radius of the circle, and we may replace the altitude by the radius of the circle.

For example, suppose that the radius of the circle is 1 inch and that the angle that the two radii form is 1 minute; that is, the arc of the circle is $\left(\dfrac{1}{360\cdot 60}\right) = \dfrac{1}{21,600}$th part of the circle, or (since the length of the circumference of the circle is given by the formula $C = 2\pi r$)

$$\frac{2\cdot 3.14\cdot 1}{21,600} = \frac{3.14}{10,800}\ \text{inch}$$

or about 0.0003 inch. Thus, if we use this length for the length of the chord that joins the ends of the arc, we have an isosceles triangle whose sides are 1 inch, 1 inch, and 0.0003 inch. When we draw the perpendicular from the vertex opposite the 0.0003 inch side, we obtain a right triangle in which we know that the hypotenuse is equal to 1 inch and that one side is equal to $\dfrac{0.0003}{2} = 0.00015$ inch. If we denote the other side by x, we have the Pythagorean relation

$$x^2 + (0.00015)^2 = 1^2$$

or

$$x^2 = 1 - 0.0000000225$$

and

$$x = \sqrt{1 - 0.0000000225}$$

In Chapter 15 we obtained an approximate formula for the extraction of square roots,

$$\sqrt{1 - a} = 1 - \frac{a}{2}$$

By means of this we compute that (since we may take $a = 0.0000000225$)

$$x = 1 - \frac{0.0000000225}{2} = 1 - 0.00000001125$$

or

$$x = 0.99999998875\ \text{inch}$$

which differs by less than one ten-millionth of an inch. We may as well take $x = 1$ inch. In other words, the altitude of such a triangle may be taken equal to the radius of the circle. With this fact at our command we obtain the area of this small triangle as: area = 1/2 · radius of the circle · small part of the circumference of the circle.

Now suppose that we divide the circumference of the circle into a great number of equal parts. Let this number be n. Then each arc is equal to

length of the circumference of the circle divided by n

or, in symbols,

$$\frac{2\pi r}{n}$$

We shall take this length as the length of the base of our small triangle. Then the area of this triangle is

$$\frac{1}{2} \cdot \frac{2\pi r}{n} \cdot r = \frac{\pi r^2}{n}$$

We multiply the area of this triangle by n, we obtain the area of the circle

$$A = \frac{\pi r^2}{n} n, \quad \text{or} \quad A = \pi r^2$$

For example, if the radius of the circle is 5 inches long, then the area of the circle is

$$A = 3.14 \cdot 25 = 78.5 \text{ inches}^2$$

The Area of Any Figure

To compute the areas of any figure, as, for example, the one

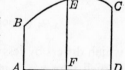

shown here, we may use a formula that gives very close results when the figure enclosing the area is irregular in shape. This is obtained from a simpler formula $A = \frac{1}{6}(a + 4c + b)h$ which is applied to the computation of the area of a figure as shown at right. In this figure $AB = a$, $CD = b$, $EF = c$, and $AD = h$, AB and CD are both perpendicular to AD, and so is EF. Moreover, F is the midpoint of AD. This is only an approximate formula when it is applied to figures as shown above, but it is not when applied to quadrangles and triangles. Of this last fact we can convince ourselves by the following considerations.

Let us apply this formula to a trapezoid $ABCD$. In it $AD = b$, $BC = a$, $EF = c$ (where E is the mid-point of AB, and F is the midpoint of CD), and $MN = h$ (h is perpendicular to AD and BC, it is the altitude of the trapezoid). Here we shall have to establish some relationship between a, b, and c. With this in mind let us draw a line PR perpendicularly to AD and BC and passing through E and a similar line TS passing through F. We then have a rectangle $RPTS$, and from it we can obtain the relation

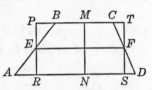

$$c = \tfrac{1}{2}(a + b)$$

That this is so can be established from the fact that the triangles PBE and AER are congruent (because $AE = EB$, and the two angles at E are vertical angles and, therefore, they are equal). Besides, the two triangles are right triangles; therefore, since we know one of the acute angles of a right triangle, we know the remaining two (one is a right angle, and the other is obtained from the fact that the sum of the angles of a triangle is 180 degrees). The same reasoning applies to the two right triangles CTF and FDS. Then $EF = PT = RS$ (the reader can observe several rectangles in the drawing). But $PT + RS = AD + BC = a + b$. From this we have that

$$c = \tfrac{1}{2}(a + b)$$

Now if we substitute this expression for c in the formula

$$A = \tfrac{1}{6}(a + 4c + b)h.$$

we have

$$A = \tfrac{1}{6}[a + 4 \cdot \tfrac{1}{2}(a + b) + b]h$$

Performing all the work with the letters in this formula, we have

$$A = \tfrac{1}{6}(a + 2a + 2b + b)h$$

or

$$A = \tfrac{1}{6}(3a + 3b)h = \tfrac{1}{2}(a + b)h$$

which is the formula for the area of the trapezoid known to us.

One important result just obtained is the fact that a line that joins the midpoints of the nonparallel sides of a trapezoid is

$$c = \tfrac{1}{2}(a + b)$$

that is, it is equal to half the sum of the parallel sides. The same fact may be applied to a triangle. In the case of a triangle we

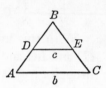

set $a = 0$ (because the upper parallel side of the trapezoid has shrunk to a point). We then have a line that joins the midpoints of the sides of a triangle is

$$c = \tfrac{1}{2}b$$

that is, it is equal to half the third side. We shall make use of this result presently when we obtain formulas for volumes.

Applying the above result to the formula

$$A = \tfrac{1}{6}(a + 4c + b)h$$

we have

$$A = \tfrac{1}{6}(a + 4\cdot\tfrac{1}{2}b + b)h$$

Finally, since $a = 0$, we have

$$A = \tfrac{1}{6}\cdot 3bh = \tfrac{1}{2}bh$$

and this is the formula for the area of a triangle.

Thus we see that the formula

$$A = \tfrac{1}{6}(a + 4c + b)h$$

gives exact results for quadrangles. For all other figures it gives approximate results. If we wish to compute the area of a figure as shown next, we cut it up into several figures which resemble in shape (they need not be necessarily similar) the figure to which such a formula is applied. The areas of the various portions are computed and then added.

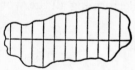

1. Compute the area of a right triangle whose sides (which include the right angle) are 10 inches and 15 inches.

2. Compute the area of an equilateral triangle whose side is 10 inches.

3. Compute the area of an isosceles triangle whose sides are 10, 10, and 6 inches.

4. Compute the area of a parallelogram whose base is 25 inches and whose altitude is 10 inches.

5. Compute the area of a trapezoid whose parallel sides are 15 and 25 inches, and whose altitude is 10 inches.

32

Escape from Flatland

Measuring in Three Dimensions

When we flee from Flatland, we soon find ourselves in a fascinating new environment in which, with the help of some imaginary rubber bands, we shall meet an important unit of measure, strike up an acquaintance with cubes, cones, pyramids, prisms, and parallelopipeds, and be able at last to measure the inside of the earth.

We know now how to generate a limitless world of three dimensions, or degrees of freedom, but to be able to measure the size of objects that possess the properties of this world (now they have, in addition to length and width, another dimension—that of height), we need a special unit of measure. The unit that served in the world of two dimensions is inadequate, unless we are interested in measuring areas only. Note, too, that in the world of two dimensions, or Flatland, we could measure distances (lengths) as well as areas; a straight line could be placed in any manner we pleased, but a plane is fixed because the plane is the world of two dimensions. In the world of three dimensions a straight line is allowed more freedom; it can be allowed to stay in the plane, but it may also be placed so that it pierces, or passes through, the plane. Also there may be an infinite number of planes, placed in any manner we choose. But in this world of three degrees of freedom (it should be remembered

538

that "freedom" refers to the freedom of movement of a point) there can be only one space of three dimensions.

The units of measure for distances and areas are the same as those we used in the line-world and in Flatland, but the unit we are now looking for must conform to the three properties of three-dimensional space—it must measure length, width, and height as if these three are united into one measure. In other words, just as in the case of the unit of measure for area, the length and width are united, the single unit eliminating the necessity of stating the dimensions of a figure; besides, to give the length and width of a figure is sometimes impossible. If we have a rectangle we can give its dimensions, as, for example, 9 feet wide and 12 feet long, and the area is then 108 square feet, or 108 feet^2. But suppose we have a triangle: what is its width, and what is its length? There is no answer to this. On the other hand, if we have the area of the triangle, say 48 feet^2, we can form some idea of its magnitude; it is equal to the area of a rectangle 12 feet long and 4 feet wide (or 6 feet long and 8 feet wide, or any other combination of two numbers whose product is 48).

The unit of measure for objects that occupy the space of three dimensions—objects that are neither points, nor lines, nor planes—must possess the same property as the unit for areas. It must be so common that it can be used for all objects that are three-dimensional in nature, and it must allow us to judge their magnitude in comparison with other objects of the same type, regardless of their shape. This unit we seek is known as the unit of measure for "volumes," that is, the quantity of three-dimensional space that these objects enclose.

To obtain this unit let us consider the generation of a space of three dimensions. This is accomplished by the motion of a two-dimensional world along a straight line perpendicular to itself so that the plane remains always parallel to itself. We have pointed out that a crude illustration of this may be the stacking of cards in a single pile. Now suppose that we take a unit-portion of the two-dimensional world, the portion enclosed within a square all of whose sides are a unit long. We know that this square encloses one (unit)^2 area of the two-dimensional world. If we move this unit-portion of the two-dimensional world through the distance of one unit-length in the manner used in the generation of a three-dimensional space, this square will be at a distance of one unit from the place it originally occupied, and it will be parallel to its original position.

Now let us imagine that the unit-portion of the two-dimensional world is attached at its vertices in its original position with rubber strings, and that the entire plane remains fixed. Only the unit-portion of the plane (the two-dimensional world) is subject to the motion through the distance of one unit of length. As the square that encloses his unit-portion is lifted out of the plane as described, the rubber strings begin to stretch, and this continues until the square reaches its destination, a distance of one unit of length from its original position. Also we shall assume that there is a trace of the square left on the plane from which it was lifted. We thus obtain a figure that is not a plane figure any longer; this figure has one square on the plane, and another square above it at a distance of one unit of length. Moreover, there are four more squares on the sides of the new figure.

The reader can observe that these figures are squares because the rubber strings are perpendicular to the plane from which the original square was lifted, since the unit-portion of the area was moved along a line perpendicular to the plane and remained always parallel to the plane from which it was lifted. Thus each string is perpendicular to (makes a right angle with) the sides of the square traced out on the plane to which the string is attached. Moreover, the sides of the figures that are framed by the strings and the sides of the square and its trace are all equal.

A figure that consists of four sides that are parallel in pairs is a parallelogram, but, if the angles of a parallelogram are right angles and all the sides are equal, the quadrangle is a square. Thus our new figure has six squares as its sides and is three-dimensional. Its name is the "cube" (the reader's attention is called to the fact that the cube illustration below utilizes a two-dimensional plane to represent a drawing of a three-dimensional object; thus the parts of the object that are farthest from us cannot actually be seen, and their outlines are drawn in broken lines).

The magnitude of the unit of measure for volumes is not difficult to obtain. We know that the plane has no thickness, but that after we move the plane or a unit-portion of it we obtain thickness. We may again recall an infinite number of portions of a plane, each of the form of a square with a unit area, stacked one upon the other; thus, to obtain our new unit, we multiply the old unit (the unit of measure for areas) by the unit distance—that is, we have

$$(unit)^2 \cdot unit = (unit)^3$$

Thus the unit-measure of the portion of the three-dimensional space, or the unit-measure of volume accepted by us, is that portion which is enclosed within a cube whose edge is a "cubic measure," and is known as "the unit of measure of volume."

This explanation, of course, does not represent a historical development of the method of measuring volumes. Originally volumes were measured in terms of content of the substances put into the various hollow three-dimensional objects which serve as containers. Later the foregoing method was introduced. How and why this was done is a secret lost in the ages, but perhaps it was stumbled upon and then found to be the more convenient.

Now that we have agreed upon a unit of measure we shall develop the main principle applied to the measurement of volumes of those three-dimensional objects, also known as "solids," or "solid objects," that are akin in many respects to rectangles. We may use for this purpose a square portion of a plane with a unit area. If we move this unit-area through the distance of a units of length in the manner described above we obtain a volume containing a cubic units. Now we may also take, instead of a square with a unit-area, a rectangle that contains, say, a units of area and move it through the distance of one unit of length. Each of the a square units of area of the rectangle generates in this case one unit of volume, and the a units of area will then generate a units of volume. If we move this rectangle through another unit-distance of length we obtain another *a* unit of volume. Thus, after the two trips, the rectangle will have generated 2*a* units of volume. Now if the rectangle moves through *b* units of distance it will generate *ab* units of volume. In other words, the volume is obtained in this case as the product of the numerical value of the area of the rectangle (which is here equal to *a* square units), and the numerical value of the distance through which the rectangle was moved (in this case equal to *b* units of length). The numerical result is then *ab* cubic units.

The geometric figure generated by the rectangle in this illustration is known as the "prism" or the "rectangular prism," because all its faces are rectangles. It is also called "rectangular parallelopiped."

Since the area of a rectangle is obtained as the product of the numerical values of its length and width, and the volume of the rectangular prism is obtained as the product of the numerical

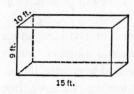

value of the area of the rectangle and the distance through which it was moved, we may write the rule for the computation of volumes of rectangular prisms (we shall call the last distance "height of prism": volume = length·width·height. Thus a room 15 feet long, 10 feet wide, and 9 feet high contains 15·10·9 = 1,350 feet³ (cubic feet).

What's in a Figure?

In the preceding chapter we employed a formula convenient in computing the areas of various figures. This formula was

$$A = \tfrac{1}{6}(a + 4c + b)h$$

where *A* was the area,

a and *b* were two parallel sides,

h the line perpendicular to *a* and *b*,

c a line drawn through the midpoint of *h* parallel to *a* and *b* (see the accompanying drawing).

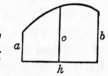

We shall apply this formula, with a change in the notation, to computation of volumes of various solid figures commonly known to us, and will find that it is almost universal in application. For certain solid figures it will give exact rules and results, and for other solid figures whose shape is rather irregular it will give approximate, but sufficiently satisfactory results. Our formula will read:

$$V = \tfrac{1}{6}(A + 4C + B)H$$

where V is the volume,

H the height of the solid figure,

A the area of the upper base of the solid figure,

B the area of the lower base of the solid figure,

C the area of the section of the solid figure passed through the midpoint of H parallel to the bases A and B.

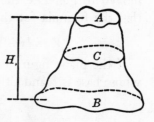

Let us obtain the formula for the volume of a rectangular prism. We now know that such a prism is obtained after a rectangle is moved through a certain distance in a direction perpendicular to its plane. Now the distance, as we also know, may be considered as the height of the solid figure. The area of the rectangle does not change throughout the entire process. Thus we have, if the area of the rectangle is A, $A = B = C$, and the volume of the rectangular prism is

$$V = \tfrac{1}{6}(A + 4A + A)H$$
$$V = \tfrac{1}{6}\, 6AH = AH$$

This is the formula we obtained in the preceding section.

Should the rectangular prism be a cube whose edge is a, then the area of the face of the cube is a^2, and the height, or altitude, is a. Finally, the volume of the cube is

$$V = a^2 \cdot a = a^3$$

Suppose that instead of a rectangle, a parallelogram, a rhombus, or a trapezoid is moved in the direction perpendicular to its respective plane. We then obtain prisms that are not rectangular any longer. We may also move in the same manner a circle, an ellipse, or any other closed curved figure. In this case we obtain solid figures known as "cylinders" ("right cylinders," when their altitudes are perpendicular to their bases). While all these figures are moved in the direction perpendicular to their respective bases, the figures, as well as their areas, remain unchanged. Thus, in each case, if A is the area of the figure moved, then

$$A = B = C$$

and H is the distance through which the original plane figure is moved to generate the respective solid figure. We then have that the formula for the volume of the solid figure is

$$V = \tfrac{1}{6}(A + 4A + A)H, \quad \text{or} \quad V = AH$$

If the plane figure moved is a parallelogram (or a rhombus) whose base is b and altitude is h, then the volume of the prism is

$$V = bhH$$

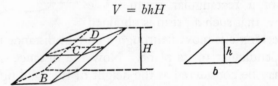

where H is the altitude of the prism.

If the plane figure moved is a trapezoid whose parallel bases are a and b, and altitude is h, then the volume of the prism is

$$V = \tfrac{1}{2}(a + b)hH$$

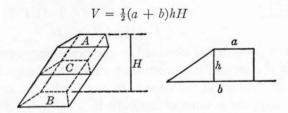

where H is the altitude of the prism.

If the plane figure moved is a triangle whose base is b and altitude is h, then the volume of the prism is

$$V = \tfrac{1}{2}bhH$$

where H is the altitude of the prism.

∝

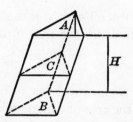

If the plane figure moved is just any quadrangle whose area is *A*, then the volume of the prism is

$$V = AH$$

where *H* is the altitude of the prism.

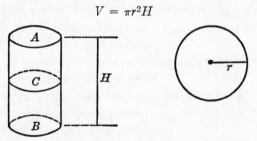

If the moved plane figure is a circle whose radius is *r*, then the volume of the right circular cylinder is

$$V = \pi r^2 H$$

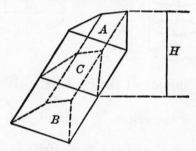

where *H* is the altitude of the cylinder.

The formula for the area of an ellipse is similar to that for the area of the circle. In a circle we have only a radius, while in an ellipse the value of the radius changes. The reader will recall that the equation of the ellipse is

$$\frac{x^2}{a^2} + \frac{y^2}{b^2} = 1$$

where $2a$ is the smallest (or the largest) and $2b$ is the largest (or the smallest) diameter. The formula for the area of the ellipse is

$$A = \pi ab$$

Note that if a is equal to b the ellipse turns out to be a circle, and we have $A = \pi a^2$, and this is the area of a circle whose radius is a. With this information we can obtain the formula for the volume of a right elliptical cylinder, which is

$$V = \pi abH$$

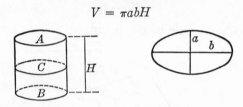

where H is the altitude of the cylinder. Many tank cars are elliptical cylinders.

The formula for the volume of a solid figure,

$$V = \tfrac{1}{6}(A + 4C + B)H$$

may be applied to derivation of the formula for the volume of a sphere. We will recall that a sphere is a surface such that all its points are at the same distance from a point inside it, known as the center, and this distance is called the radius of the sphere.

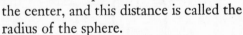
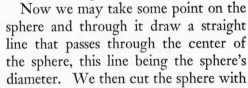

Now we may take some point on the sphere and through it draw a straight line that passes through the center of the sphere, this line being the sphere's diameter. We then cut the sphere with a plane that is perpendicular to this diameter (see the drawing above). This plane will trace out a circle on the surface of the sphere, and the radius of this circle is the same as the radius of the sphere. Let the radius of the sphere be r. We have then the three areas that are required in the foregoing formula. A is the area of the point P (where the diameter PT cuts the surface of the sphere), C is the area of the circle that is perpendicular to the diameter PT, and B is the area of the point T (where the diameter PT cuts the surface of the sphere).

Now we know that a point has no dimension and therefore its area is zero. Thus we have that $A = B = 0$, and $C = \pi r^2$. Finally, if we substitute these values in the formula for the volume of a solid figure, we have that

$$V = \tfrac{1}{6}(0 + 4\pi r^2 + 0)2r$$

where $H = 2r$ (the length of H is the length of the diameter PT of the sphere), and thus the formula for the volume of the sphere of radius r is
$$V = \tfrac{4}{3}\pi r^3$$

For example, if we have a ball an inch in diameter, its volume is (the radius is 0.5 inch)

$$V = \tfrac{4}{3} \cdot 3.14 \cdot (0.5)^3$$
or
$$V = 1.33 \cdot 3.14 \cdot 0.125$$

or, the volume is 0.52 inch³ (cubic inch).

The Refugee Returns to His Land of Flight: Flatland Again

To complete the derivation of formulas for the various solid geometric figures, we must return to Flatland and recover a very important property of two-dimensional figures. The reader will find that the general procedure in mathematics is to fall back on simple relations and facts before making new advances. We could continue along our present path and complete the derivation of the necessary formulas, but such a procedure would result in a circuitous discussion involving much unnecessary (and difficult) mathematical development. Moreover, the facts we are about to obtain will prove useful in some additional discussions in which the applications of geometry are important.

In the preceding chapter we found that a straight-line segment drawn through the midpoints of two sides of a triangle is equal to one-half the third side of the triangle. Now suppose we attempt to discover whether this fact may be generalized. Suppose we divide the two sides of a triangle into three equal parts, and let us join the points that mark off the thirds of these sides by a straight-line segment. What would be the relation of this line-segment to the third side of the triangle? We have the triangle ABC, and $BD = \frac{1}{3}AB$, and $BE = \frac{1}{3}BC$. Thus, we have the proportion

$$\frac{BD}{AB} = \frac{BE}{BC}$$

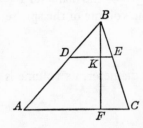

Now the two triangles ABC and DBE are similar. This is so because, as we now know, two sides of one are proportional to the two sides of the other (they form two equal ratios) and the angles that these two pairs of sides are including are equal ($\angle B = \angle B$). Moreover, if we draw from the vertex B the perpendicular BF (which cuts the line DE in the point K) we can show that $BK = \frac{1}{3}BF$. This can be established from the fact that the two triangles ABF and ABK are similar. Since the triangles ABC and DBE are similar, $\angle A = \angle D$. Thus the angles of the triangle ABF are respectively equal to the angles of triangle DBK. Therefore the relation $BK = \frac{1}{3}BF$ is correct.

At this point we may generalize. Instead of dividing the sides of the triangle into three equal parts we shall use, say, n equal parts. We may use the above drawing, assuming that $BD = \frac{1}{n} AB$ and $BE = \frac{1}{n} BC$. The procedure in examining the property of the line-segment DE is exactly the same as before. Thus we find that the two triangles ABC and DBE are again similar, and from this we can establish that their respective altitudes are also in the same ratio, $\frac{1}{n}$.

Thus we have a general fact: Whenever two triangles are similar, their altitudes are in the same ratio as the respective sides. This fact may be stated in another way.

If two triangles ABC and $A_1B_1C_1$ are similar, then their sides a, b, and c (of the triangle ABC) are a_1, b_1, and c_1 (of the triangle $A_1B_1C_1$) and the respective altitudes of h and h_1 (drawn to the sides b and b_1, respectively) form the proportions

$$\frac{a}{a_1} = \frac{b}{b_1} = \frac{c}{c_1} = \frac{h}{h_1}$$

Now the respective areas of the two triangles are:

Area of triangle $\quad ABC = A = \tfrac{1}{2}bh$

Area of triangle $A_1B_1C_1 = A_1 = \tfrac{1}{2}b_1h_1$

Then

$$\frac{A}{A_1} = \frac{bh}{b_1h_1}$$

But $\dfrac{h}{h_1} = \dfrac{b}{b_1}$. Replace then $\dfrac{h}{h_1}$ by $\dfrac{b}{b_1}$. We have then

$$\frac{A}{A_1} = \frac{b^2}{b_1^2}$$

So, when two triangles are similar, their areas are in the ratio of the squares of their corresponding sides.

For example, if the sides of one triangle are twice as large as the respective sides of another triangle, then the area of the first is four times as large as that of the second triangle. Suppose the side of one triangle is $2a$ and the side of the other is a, then the areas of the two triangles are in the ratio

$$\frac{(2a)^2}{a^2} = \frac{4a^2}{a^2} = \frac{4}{1}$$

Moreover, the same fact that the areas of two similar triangles are in the ratio of the squares of their corresponding sides may be extended to the areas of any two similar figures. The reader may establish this by considering any two similar figures and then breaking these figures up into similar triangles. He should remember that similar plane figures all have equal angles, arranged in the same order, and that their corresponding sides are proportional.

The same thing holds for circles. Suppose we have two circles whose radii are R and r, respectively. The areas of these circles are

$$C = \pi R^2$$
$$C_1 = \pi r^2$$

We then have the proportion

$$\frac{C}{C_1} = \frac{R^2}{r^2}$$

This signifies that the areas of two circles are to one another as the squares of their respective radii. For example, if the radius of one circle is 15 inches, and the radius of another circle is 5 inches, then the areas of the circles are in the ratio

$$\frac{225}{25} = \frac{9}{1}$$

that is, the area of the first circle is nine times as large as that of the second. Note that the radius of one circle is three times as large as the radius of the second circle. Squaring 3, we obtain 9. Thus we have a simpler procedure for establishing the same fact.

Comes the Revolution: Cones and Pyramids

The solid figures examined thus far, with the exception of the sphere, were generated by a plane geometric figure of some definite area that was moved parallel to itself along a line perpendicular to the plane of this figure; thus this line was actually the altitude of the solid figure so generated. However, the restriction that the line of motion be perpendicular to this plane may not be enforced, provided the parallelism of the consecutive positions of the moving plane is preserved. Then the volume of the solid figure so generated is obtained as the product of the numerical value of the area of the plane figure that was moved, and the numerical value of the altitude of the solid figure. The situation here is similar to computation of the area of a parallelogram. The parallelogram may be thought of as having been generated by a line that was moved parallel to itself along a slanted line.

However, there are some solid figures in the formation of which the size of the area diminishes, although throughout the entire process their shape remains the same. This may remind us of a triangle: If we take a triangle and draw any number of lines parallel to its base, we may think of it as having been generated by a straight line that was moving parallel to itself and always decreasing in size until it finally vanished into a point at the vertex of the triangle, as shown in the accompanying figure.

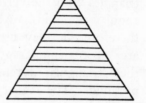

A counterpart of such a situation is found in the case of solid figures. Such solid figures are known as "pyramids" if the moving plane figures are polygons, and "cones" if the moving plane figures are closed curved ones, such as circles or ellipses. If we apply the formula $V = \frac{1}{6}(A + 4C + B)H$ to the pyramid (let us take a pyramid with a triangular base), then the midsection of the pyramid as shown in the drawing below is

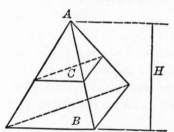

also a triangle. Moreover, this triangle is similar to the base triangle, since its sides are respectively equal to half of the sides of the base triangle. This can be established by observing that the pyramid has three triangular faces, and in each of these the midpoints of two sides are joined by a straight-line segment. This line-segment, as we now know, is equal to one-half the third side of the triangle. Now since these two triangles are similar and their sides are in the ratio of 2 to 1, their areas are in the ratio of 4 to 1. In other words, if the area of the base is B, then the area of the midsection $C = \frac{1}{4}B$. Moreover, the area at the vertex of the pyramid is zero, because the vertex is a point. Thus $A = 0$. If we substitute these values in our formula, we obtain the formula for the volume of the pyramid:

$$V = \tfrac{1}{6}(0 + 4\cdot\tfrac{1}{4}B + B)H$$

or

$$V = \tfrac{1}{6}\,2BH$$

or

$$V = \tfrac{1}{3}BH$$

If the area of the base of the pyramid is any polygon it may be broken up into triangles, and by joining the vertices of these triangles with the vertex of the pyramid we obtain several triangular pyramids. All these have the same altitude H, and, therefore, we may use the above formula which gives us the area of a triangular pyramid. The sum of the volumes of all these triangular pyramids gives us the volume of our general pyramid. The reader can see that the formula holds for any pyramid and, moreover, that there is no need to restrict the moving plane so that it moves along a line perpendicular to it; the only restriction is that the plane be always parallel to itself.

If the base of the solid figure is a circle whose radius is r, and the vertex of this figure is a point, we have a cone. To compute the figure's volume we start out with the expression

$$V = \tfrac{1}{6}(A + 4C + B)H$$

where A is the area at the vertex (that is, $A = 0$), B is the area at the base ($B = \pi r^2$), C is the area of the midsection, and H is the altitude of the cone. Now we can readily see that the midsection of the cone is also a circle, but its radius is equal to $\tfrac{1}{2}$ of the radius of the base. Thus

$$C = \tfrac{1}{4}B$$

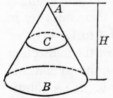

Substitute these values in the earlier expression and we have

$$V = \tfrac{1}{6}(0 + 4\cdot\tfrac{1}{4}B + B)H \quad \text{or} \quad V = \tfrac{1}{3}BH$$

Since $B = \pi r^2$, we have for the volume of a cone

$$V = \tfrac{1}{3}\pi r^2 H$$

If the altitude of the cone whose base is a circle ("circular cone") when it is drawn from the vertex, passes through the center of the base circle, such a cone is known as "the cone of revolution." One may be obtained as the result of the revolution of a right triangle about one of the sides including the right angle. If the right triangle is revolved around its hypotenuse, we obtain two cones of revolution with a common base whose radius is the perpendicular drawn from the vertex of the right angle to the hypotenuse, as shown in the accompanying figure.

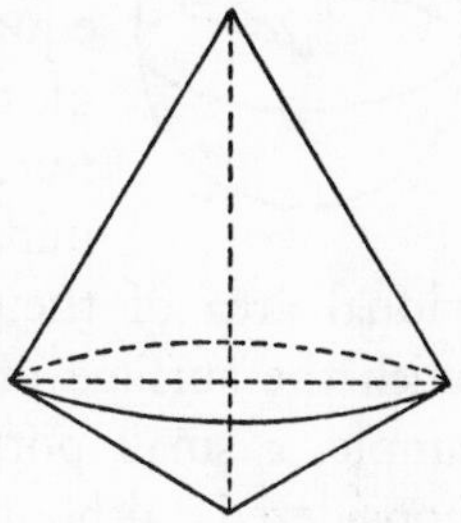

As an exercise the reader may compute the volume of the Great Pyramid whose dimension we mentioned earlier: a square base 763.79 feet on each side and an altitude of 486.23 feet.

Just How Big Is the Earth?

If we assume that the earth is a sphere whose radius is about 4,000 miles, we can now easily compute its volume. It is

$$\tfrac{4}{3} \cdot 3.14 \cdot (4,000)^3 \text{ cubic miles}$$

or

$$1.33 \cdot 3.14 \cdot 64 \cdot 10^9 \text{ cubic miles}$$

or, finally, about

$$2.67 \cdot 10^{11} \text{ miles}^3 \text{ (cubic miles)}$$

Now, what is the area of the surface of the earth? To answer this we must have the formula for the area of the surface of a sphere, and to develop it shall recall one important fact concerning the relationship between a small angle formed by two radii of a circle, the arc that corresponds to it, and the chord that joins the end points of this arc: If this angle is very small so that its corresponding arc is very small in comparison with the length of the circumference of the circle, we may use the length of this arc and the chord that joins its ends interchangingly.

Let us take a sphere whose radius is r. Its volume is given by the formula
$$V = \tfrac{4}{3}\pi r^3$$

Now suppose that the volume of the sphere is divided into a great number of pyramids, all equal in volume, whose vertices are all the center of the sphere. Suppose that there are n such pyramids. Now if the number of these pyramids is very great, we may consider the individual area of their respective bases very small in comparison with the surface of the sphere and as flat as a plane. For example, a small portion of the surface of the earth may be so considered, although the earth is approximately spherical in shape. Suppose that one base has an area equal to B. We take the altitude of the pyramid as equal to the radius of the sphere; it is r. Then the volume of the pyramid is

$$V = \tfrac{1}{3}Br$$

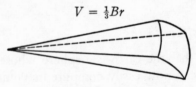

Now, since the volume of the sphere was divided into n equal parts, each part has a volume equal to

$$\frac{1}{n} \cdot \frac{4}{3}\pi r^3$$

and this is equal to the volume of the pyramid obtained. We equate these two expressions and have

$$\frac{1}{n} \cdot \frac{4}{3}\pi r^3 = \frac{1}{3} \cdot Br$$

Cancelling out the $\tfrac{1}{3}$ and r on either side of this equation we obtain
$$\frac{4}{n} \cdot \pi r^2 = B$$

which is the surface of $1/n$th part of the surface of the sphere. From this we obtain that the area of the surface is

$$A = nB = 4\pi r^2$$

Thus, the area of the earth's surface is

$4 \cdot 3.14 \cdot (4,000)^2$ square miles, or, about $2.01 \cdot 10^8$ miles^2

Speaking of Volumes: It's a Small World

We found that the areas of similar figures are to one another as the squares of their corresponding sides or elements, as, for example, the squares of their altitudes, because the altitudes of similar plane figures are in the same ratio as the corresponding sides. If we have two similar figures whose areas are A and A_1, respectively, and their corresponding sides are b and b_1, or their altitudes are h and h_1, we may have the proportions

$$\frac{A}{A_1} = \frac{b^2}{b_1^2}$$

or

$$\frac{A}{A_1} = \frac{h^2}{h_1^2}$$

The property of similarity is not restricted to plane figures; two cubes are similar, and two spheres are similar, and it is easy to detect their similarity. As a matter of fact, all cubes are always similar to one another and so are all spheres, because all the edges of a cube are always equal, and all the radii of a sphere are also always equal. If we have two cubes, we can obtain the ratio of the edge of one to the edge of the other. The same type of relation may be established between the radii of two spheres.

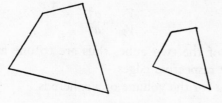

Similar Polygons

The similarity of other solid figures depends on several conditions. We recall that the similarity of plane figures depends on the equality of angles and for polygons with more than three sides (triangles)—quadrangles, pentagons, and others with many more sides—the equal angles must be in the same order in the two figures and the corresponding sides must be proportional. This is illustrated on page 555 in the drawing of similar polygons. When two solid figures are similar, their edges as well as their faces must be proportional. Now the faces are plane polygons, and we know now under what conditions they are proportional. A simple case of similar solid figures is attained when one is cut by a plane parallel to its base. The reader will observe that this was done when the formulas for the volumes of the

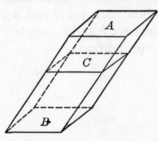

various solid figures were derived. The midsection [whose area was denoted by the letter C in the formula $V = \frac{1}{6}(A + 4C + B)H$ for the volume of a solid figure] was such a plane; that is, it was drawn parallel to the base. A drawing of a prism with such a plane is illustrated here.

The formula for the volume of a cube is

$$V = a^3$$

where a is the edge. Now suppose that we have two cubes, the edge of one being a_1, and the edge of the other a_2. Then the volumes of these two cubes are

$$V_1 = a_1^3 \quad \text{and} \quad V_2 = a_2^3$$

From this we have the proportion

$$\frac{V_1}{V_2} = \frac{a_1^3}{a_2^3}$$

The volumes of the two cubes thus are to one another as the cubes of their respective edges.

The formula for the volume of a sphere is

$$V = \frac{4}{3}\pi r^3$$

where r is the radius of the sphere. Now suppose that we have two spheres, the radius of one being r_1, and the radius of the other r_2. Then their volumes are

$$V_1 = \frac{4}{3}\pi r_1^3 \quad \text{and} \quad V_2 = \frac{4}{3}\pi r_2^3$$

From this we have the proportion (the reader will observe that the two expressions contain $\frac{4}{3}$ as a factor, and this is canceled out)

$$\frac{V_1}{V_2} = \frac{r_1^3}{r_2^3}$$

This signifies that the volumes of two spheres are to one another as the cubes of their radii. Moreover, since the radius of a circle (or of a sphere) is equal to one-half the diameter, that is, $r = 0.5d$, we have

$$\frac{V_1}{V_2} = \frac{(0.5d_1)^3}{(0.5d_2)}$$

or

$$\frac{V_1}{V_2} = \frac{d_1^3}{d_2^3}$$

that is, the volumes of two spheres are to one another as the cubes of their diameters.

For example, the radius of the earth is about 4,000 miles, and the radius of the sun about 400,000 miles. Then the volumes of the sun and the earth are in the ratio

$$\frac{(400,000)^3}{(4,000)^3} = \frac{4^3 \cdot 10^{15}}{4^3 \cdot 10^9}$$

or

$$\frac{10^{15}}{10^9} = \frac{10^6}{1}$$

The sun, then, is about one million times as large as the earth.

We found that the volume of a prism, pyramid, or cone is given by the formulas: for the prism,

$$V = BH$$

for the pyramid and the cone,

$$V = \tfrac{1}{3}BH$$

where B is the area of the base, and H is the altitude of the solid figure.

We know that the areas of similar figures are to one another as the squares of their corresponding sides. In other words, if these corresponding sides are b_1 and b_2, respectively,

$$\frac{B_1}{B_2} = \frac{b_1^2}{b_2^2}$$

Moreover, the altitudes of similar figures (solid or plane) are to one another as the corresponding sides of these figures,

$$\frac{H_1}{H_2} = \frac{b_1}{b_2}$$

Multiply these two proportions, which are also two equalities. We then have

$$\frac{B_1 H_1}{B_2 H_2} = \frac{b_1^3}{b_2^3}$$

and this proportion represents the relationship of the two volumes of similar solids V_1 and V_2. Thus the volumes of two similar solids are to one another as the cubes of their corresponding sides or edges.

We may well recapitulate now the relationship of various geometric figures as follows:

a) Lengths are to one another as their measures.
b) Areas of similar plane geometric figures are to one another as the squares of the lengths of their corresponding sides.
c) Volumes of similar solid geometric figures are to one another as the cubes of the lengths of their corresponding sides.

Amplifying these rules, the ratios are raised to the power indicated by the number of the dimensions of the geometric figures in question. For lengths we have the first power; for areas we have the second power (the square); for volumes we have the third power (the cube). It is quite reasonable to expect that for similar solid geometric figures in the fourth dimension we shall have the ratio of the fourth powers of the corresponding sides, and so on.

The diameter of the red star Betelgeuse in the constellation Orion is four times as large as the average distance from the earth to the sun, about 93,000,000 miles. The diameter of the sun is about 800,000 miles, and that of the earth about 8,000 miles. So we have the ratios

$$\frac{\text{Volume of Betelgeuse}}{\text{Volume of the sun}} = \frac{(4 \cdot 93 \cdot 10^6)^3}{(8 \cdot 10^5)^3}$$

$$\frac{\text{Volume of Betelgeuse}}{\text{Volume of the earth}} = \frac{(4 \cdot 93 \cdot 10^6)^3}{(8 \cdot 10^3)^3}$$

The reader in performing these computations will find that Betelgeuse is about 100,000,000 times as large as the sun and that it would take about

$$100,000,000,000,000 \text{ earth spheres}$$

to make up a volume to equal it.

In Chapter 4 it was mentioned that Archimedes computed the number of grains of sand in the universe as 10^{63}. He arrived at this number as follows. He assumed that there were 10^4 (a myriad) grains of sand in a sphere the size of a poppy seed. Then he assumed that the diameter of a poppy seed was about 0.025 of a Greek inch long. Then in a sphere whose diameter was a Greek inch long there were

$$40^3 \cdot 10^4 = 64 \cdot 10^7$$

grains of sand.

The Greek unit of length was the stadium = 9600 Greek inches. Then in a sphere whose diameter was a stadium long there were

$$9600^3 \cdot 64 \cdot 10^7 = 57 \cdot 10^{20}$$

grains of sand. To play safe, Archimedes decided that it would be reasonable to expect that there were not less than 10^{21} grains of sand in such a sphere.

The diameter of the universe, he assumed, was not greater than 10^{14} stadia long. Then in a sphere with such a diameter there would be

$$(10^{14})^3 \cdot 10^{21} = 10^{63}$$

grains of sand.

PROBLEMS

The following problems are based on the "Travels into Several Remote Nations of the World by Lemuel Gulliver," by Jonathan Swift.

The reader will recall that in the Land of the Lilliputs everything was one-twelfth of the normal size, while in the Land of the Brobdingnags everything was twelve times the normal size.

1. Gulliver's daily ration in the Land of the Lilliputs was equal to 1,728 average Lilliputian rations. Why was this number selected?

2. Gulliver relates that the content of a Lilliputian barrel did not exceed our half-pint. An American barrel contains 32 gallons, an English barrel contains 42 gallons. Were Gulliver's calculations correct?

3. The mattress that Gulliver was provided by the Lilliputians to sleep on was made up of 600 Lilliputian mattresses. One hundred and fifty of them were sewn into one layer, and then four layers were sewn one on the top of the other. Was this mattress comfortable in comparison with an average mattress? Explain.

4. In the Land of the Brobdingnags Gulliver was once hit by a falling apple. He related that this apple flattened him out. Was this description correct?

5. The Queen of the Brobdingnags gave Gulliver her ring. Gulliver wore this ring as a necklace. Was this possible? What were the dimensions of this ring?

Name Your Figure

We have described the method for the generation of spaces of various dimensions. We started with a point, which represented the space of zero dimensions, and moved it so that it generated a straight line and resulted in a space of one dimension. Then the straight line was moved, creating the space of two dimensions, and this plane, moved, produced the space of three dimensions. This process, as we have already indicated, can be carried on indefinitely. Each time one space is moved along a straight line perpendicular to it, but remaining always parallel to itself, a space of a higher dimension by one is generated. Let us now examine in detail what happens when these motions are performed so that the objects moved, as well as the distances through which they are moved, are of definite size, say of one unit of measure.

When a point is moved through a unit of length it generates a straight-line segment whose length is represented by that unit. This segment consists of two end points and a length, but for reasons that will become obvious presently, we shall say that this segment has two vertices and a length. Thus, the straight-line segment AB has two vertices, A and B, and a length, the distance between A and B.

$$A \text{———————} B$$

When the straight-line segment AB is moved, perpendicularly to itself, a distance equal to its own length, it generates the square $ABCD$ and the motion may be described in detail. Note that the vertex A when it is moved traces out a straight-line segment AD and so does the vertex B. It produces the straight-line segment BC. But each point, when moved, produces two vertices and a length, therefore the two vertices produce twice as many of them. Now the straight-line segment AB produces the area of the square and also the straight line CD, the final position of AB.

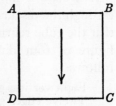

Introducing algebra in the description of the number of the various parts of the square generated by the moving straight line, we shall denote a vertex by v, a straight-line segment (the side) by s, and the area by A. Then a straight-line segment may be represented as $2v + s$. Now, when a square is generated, a vertex v produces $2v + s$, and a line produces $s + A$. Hence the square may be described as follows:

Two vertices produce.......... $2(2v + s) = 4v + 2s$
The line in the original position. s
The line produces............. $s + A$

Adding these, we have....... $4v + 4s + A$

In other words, a square has four vertices, four sides and one area; the reader may check this with the drawing of the square above.

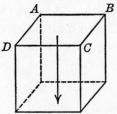

When the square is moved through the distance of one unit in the direction perpendicular to itself, but so that it remains always parallel to itself, it generates a cube. We know that v produces $2v + s$, s produces $2s + A$ (the original position of s stated above should be included), and A (the area) produces $2A + V$ (the original and final positions of the area and the volume of the cube).

The cube may be then described as follows:

Four vertices produce... $4(2v + s) = 8v + 4s$
Four sides produce..... $4(2s + A) = $ $8s + 4A$
One area produces...... $2A + V$

Adding all these, we have $8v + 12s + 6A + V$

In other words, a cube (in three dimensions) has eight vertices, twelve sides (or edges), six areas (or faces), and one volume.

Now we shall proceed with higher dimensions with the method of algebra.

If a cube is moved along a straight line perpendicular to it through the distance of one unit of length, and in such a manner that the cube remains always parallel to itself, it generates a solid figure of four dimensions. This figure may be described as follows:

Eight vertices generate . $8(2v + s) = 16v + 8s$
Twelve edges generate . $12(2s + A) =$ $24s + 12A$
Six faces generate . . . . . $6(2A + V) =$ $12A + 6V$
One volume generates . . $2V + H$

Adding these, we have $16v + 32s + 24A + 8V + H$

When the volume of a cube is moved it generates a four-dimensional volume (we denote it by H) and two volumes (one in the initial position and the other in the final position).

Thus a four-dimensional cube has sixteen vertices, thirty-two edges, twenty-four faces, eight (three-dimensional) volumes and one four-dimensional volume. The four-dimensional cube is usually called a "cuboid," or "tesseract."

Now if a cuboid is moved along a straight line perpendicular to itself through the distance of one unit of length, and in such a manner that the cuboid remains always parallel to itself, it generates a five-dimensional cube. This solid figure may be described as:

Sixteen vertices generate. . . . . $16(2v + s) = 32v + 16s$
Thirty-two edges generate. . . . . $32(2s + A) =$ $64s + 32A$
Twenty-four faces generate. . . . . $24(2A + V) =$ $48A + 24V$
Eight (three-dimensional) volumes generate. . . . . $8(2V + H) =$ $16V + 8H$
One (four-dimensional volume) generates. . . . . $2H + G$

Adding these, we have. . . . . $32v + 80s + 80A + 40V + 10H + G$

When the volume of a four-dimensional cube is moved it generates a five-dimensional cube (we denote it by G) and two four-dimensional cubes (one in the initial position and one in the final position). Thus a five-dimensional cube has thirty-two vertices, eighty edges, eighty faces, forty (three-dimensional) cubes, ten cuboids (four-dimensional cubes), and one five-dimensional cube. There is no special name for a five-dimensional cube; the reader may give it any name he wishes.

With the same procedure as above it is possible to obtain the various parts that will describe a cube in any number of dimensions. Here again the reader may name his own figure.

PROBLEMS

6. Gulliver related that while sojourning in the land of the Brobdingnags he was once struck by a falling apple. The only damage he reported was a slight bump on the head. Was his report correct? [Answer: No. Assuming that an apple weighs one third of a pound, an apple in the land of the Brobdingnags would have weighed 1,728 times as much. Thus the apple which struck him should have weighed 576 pounds. Such an apple should have killed him.]

7. Describe a six-dimensional cube. Start with a five-dimensional cube. [Answer:

32 vertices generate....	$32(2v+s)$	$=64v+32s$
80 edges generate......	$80(2s+A) =$	$160s+80A$
80 faces generate......	$80(2A+V) =$	$160A+80V$
40 three-dimensional volumes generate...	$40(2V+H) =$	$80V+40H$
10 four-dimensional volumes generate...	$10(2H+G) =$	$20H+10G$
1 five-dimensional volume generates...		$2G+K$

$$64v+192s+240A+160V+60H+12G+K]$$

33

*How Algebra Serves
Geometry*

200 Men and an Egg

Now that we have escaped from Flatland, let us swing around
Africa to Madagascar. Here we may stir up, from a single egg,
an omelet we can properly measure for 200 persons—and this
feat, actually not so fantastic as it may seem, will serve both as
a graphic review for our latest learning and as an introduction
to our next adventures.

There actually have been such eggs, but even mathematicians
have failed to figure out which came first, the egg or the bird
that laid it—the aepyornis. This nightmarish creature, far larger
than the ostrich and now happily extinct, is known to have laid
eggs about a foot and a half long, as against the common chicken
egg, which is only about two and a half inches long. Now to
our omelet and the mathematical nourishment, if not the flavor,
that it promises.

We have learned that the volumes of similar objects (objects
whose angles are equal and are in the same order, and whose
sides are proportional) are to one another as the cubes of their
corresponding sides, or elements. Thus the volumes of the eggs
of an aepyornis and a chicken are in some ratio, and this is

$$\frac{\text{the egg of an aepyornis}}{\text{the egg of a chicken}} = \frac{18^3}{2.5^3}$$

We translated the length of the aepyornis egg, originally given
in feet, into inches because the length of the chicken egg is given

in inches, and when a ratio or proportion is obtained all the measures involved must be stated in the same unit.

We then find that the above ratio is

$$\frac{5,832}{15.625} = \frac{373}{1}$$

approximately, and that the aepyornis egg is about 373 times larger. So two hundred strong-stomached men, accustomed to two-egg American omelets, could have breakfasted well on the one egg of an aepyornis.

The Lesson of the Shrinking Dime

When we compare two numbers and say that one is twice as large as the other, we can form a definite picture of the relations of the measures they represent. For example, if we say that one foot is twice as long as six inches, we have some notion of the length of a foot and from this we can easily infer the other length.

In geometry, however, the comparison of two magnitudes goes beyond the comparison of linear, or length, measurements; here we often have the problem of comparing areas and volumes, and the mere statement that one object is twice as "large" as another is inadequate. We must specifically state whether we refer to lengths, areas, or volumes.

We often hear that a microscope "magnifies 1,000 times." We have found how a magnifying glass simply magnifies the angle under which the object is observed, and how, when an object is moved away from us, it appears smaller because the angle depends on the distance of the object from the observer. To illustrate, hold up a dime. When it is very close to your eyes, it may obscure a building, but as you move it farther from you the dime soon appears much smaller than the building. The microscope, too, only brings the object closer to your eyes in a process impossible with unaided vision.

But suppose that an object is really magnified 1,000 times. First its linear measures may be magnified 1,000 times. We know that the volumes of two objects are to one another as the cubes of their corresponding linear measures. Thus, when the length of an object is magnified 1,000 times, the volumes of such objects are magnified $1,000^3$ times. This means that the volumes are $1,000^3 = 1,000,000,000$, or one billion times larger.

In this case "one billion times larger" refers to volumes. Moreover, since equal volumes of the same substance have the same weight, magnification of the volume a certain number of times will result in magnification the same number of times of the weight of the object.

A dime is about $\frac{11}{16}$th of an inch in diameter. Suppose we have a silver coin of the same composition as a dime, all of whose measurements have been magnified 1,000 times. The volume of such a coin will be 1,000,000,000 times as large as the volume of the dime. It will contain as much silver as there is in one billion dimes, and be worth a hundred million dollars. The diameter of this coin will be $1,000 \cdot (\frac{11}{16}) = 687.5$ inches or 57 feet 3.5 inches long. A dime is about $\frac{1}{24}$th of an inch thick. The new coin will be $1,000 \cdot (\frac{1}{24}) = 41.7$ inches (approximately) thick.

Tin-Can Economy

Canned foods are generally packed in cans that are right cylinders and that show the content in weight. The formula for the volume of a right cylinder is

$$V = \pi r^2 h$$

where r is the radius of the circle that forms the base of the can, and h is the height of the can. Now we know that the diameter of the circle is twice the radius— that is, $d = 2r$, or

$$r = \frac{d}{2}, \quad \text{and} \quad r^2 = \frac{d^2}{4}$$

Then the formula for the volume of the can is

$$V = \frac{\pi d^2 h}{4}$$

The sizes of food cans are so varied nowadays that one has difficulty determining whether the same product is purchased advantageously in one or another size. To determine which contains more of the product it is necessary to compare the volumes of the cans, and this can be accomplished by means of the preceding formula for volume. Suppose we have two cans whose dimensions are as follows:

	Diameter of Base	*Height*
First can.......	D	H
Second can.....	d	h

The sizes of cans usually vary both in the diameters of the bases and the heights. It is necessary, therefore, to consider the two measurements. We have then the two volumes

$$V_1 = \frac{\pi D^2 H}{4}, \quad \text{and} \quad V_2 = \frac{\pi d^2 h}{4}$$

The ratio of the two volumes is

$$\frac{V_1}{V_2} = \frac{D^2 H}{d^2 h}$$

For example, suppose we have the measurements $D = 3\frac{1}{2}$ inches and $H = 4$ inches, and $d = 2\frac{3}{4}$ inches and $h = 3\frac{1}{2}$ inches. We then have the ratio

$$\frac{(\frac{7}{2})^2 \cdot 4}{(\frac{11}{4})^2 \cdot (\frac{7}{2})} = \frac{(\frac{7}{2}) \cdot 4}{\frac{121}{16}} = \frac{224}{121} = 1.85 \text{ approximately}$$

In other words, the first can is a little less than twice the size of the second can.

Square vs. Rectangle

Which of the two quadrangles, a square or a rectangle, contains a larger area? Or, modifying the question, suppose you have a certain quantity of wire fencing, to be placed around a piece of ground that is to be quadrangular; what should be the form of this quadrangle?

Suppose this fencing is k units of length. If the quadrangle is to be a square, then according to the properties of the square, all of whose four sides are equal, each side will be $\frac{k}{4}$ units long, and the area of the square will be

$$\left(\frac{k}{4}\right)^2 = \frac{k^2}{16} \text{ square units}$$

If the quadrangle is to be a rectangle, then according to the properties of the rectangle the opposite sides of this quadrangle are equal in pairs. Since the sum of the sides of our quadrangle is definite, k units of length, and the side of a square is $\frac{k}{4}$, we may shorten one side of the square, say by a units, and lengthen another side by the same number of units. We then will have two sides, each $\left(\frac{k}{4} - a\right)$ units long, and two sides $\left(\frac{k}{4} + a\right)$ units long. The area of this rectangle is then

$$\left(\frac{k}{4} - a\right)\left(\frac{k}{4} + a\right) = \frac{k^2}{16} - a^2 \text{ square units}$$

Let us examine which of the quantities $\frac{k^2}{16}$ and $\left(\frac{k^2}{16} - a^2\right)$ is greater.

To simplify our work we shall introduce a symbol widely used in mathematics. When two quantities are compared as to their magnitudes, they may be equal to one another or one may be greater than the other. To designate equality of two quantities we use the symbol $=$, as for example, $A = B$. If A is greater than B, we write it symbolically as $A > B$. If A is less than B, we write it symbolically as $A < B$.

The operations with the symbols $>$ and $<$, which are known as the symbols for inequality, and with expressions connected by them are subject to the same rule as operations with expressions connected by the symbol for equality. In the case of expressions connected with the symbol for equality, which is known as the "equation," we may add, or subtract, from each side of the equation the same quantity, without producing any change in the values of the terms in the expressions involved. For example, if we have the equation

$$3x + 5 = 14$$

we can subtract 5 from both sides of the equation and have

$$3x + 5 - 5 = 14 - 5$$

or

$$3x = 9$$

and

$$x = 3$$

We note that if we substitute the value of x in the equation $3x + 5 = 14$, we obtain

$$3 \cdot 3 + 5 = 14$$

or

$$14 = 14$$

which is an identity.

The same rule may be applied to inequality relations. For example, if we have the relation

$$3x + 2 < 14$$

we may subtract 2 from both sides of the inequality. We then have

$$3x + 2 - 2 < 14 - 2, \quad \text{or} \quad 3x < 12$$

We may also divide both sides of the inequality in the same manner as in the case of the equation, provided, however, that we do not divide by zero or by a negative number; the latter is a special restriction for inequalities. We have then $x < 4$. If we substitute a value for x less than 4, say 3.5, in the foregoing inequality, we have

$$3 \cdot 3.5 + 2 < 14, \quad \text{or} \quad 10.5 + 2 = 12.5$$

and

$$12.5 < 14$$

which is an inequality in the same sense as before. However, should we substitute the value $x = 4$, we obtain an equality (identity)

$$14 = 14$$

In other words, our inequality is thus destroyed.

Now let us determine the sign by which the two expressions $k^2/16$ and $(k^2/16 - a^2)$ should be connected. Let us write

$$\frac{k^2}{16} ? \frac{k^2}{16} - a^2$$

with the question mark to be replaced by the proper sign when this will be decided upon.

Any positive number is considered as greater than zero, for example $5 > 0$. A negative number is then considered less than zero; it cannot be greater than zero (this is reserved for positive numbers), and it cannot be equal to zero. The expression

$$\frac{k^2}{16} ? \frac{k^2}{16} - a^2$$

is either an equality or an inequality. We therefore can subtract $k^2/16$ from both sides. We then have

$$0 ? -a^2$$

Now a^2 is positive, and $(-a^2)$ is negative. Therefore we can write $0 > -a^2$.

Thus we have established the sign that must connect the two expressions, and we have

$$\frac{k^2}{16} > \frac{k^2}{16} - a^2$$

In other words, this expression tells us that the area of the square is greater than the area of the rectangle when the sums of the sides of the two quadrangles are the same (k units of length).

The reader should note that in the above discussion no special values were considered; all the work was done with letters. This procedure implied that the conditions set and the results obtained would hold for any given value. This is the method of algebra, and such a generalized approach enables us to examine properties under consideration without regard to any special case.

Suppose that the length of the fencing is 100 yards. If we enclose a square with it, the side of the square is $\frac{100}{4} = 25$ yards, and the area is $25^2 = 625$ square yards. Suppose we take a rectangle 24 yards by 26 yards. Its area is then $24 \cdot 26 = 624$

square yards. The reader may examine a rectangle 24.5 yards by 25.5 yards; its area will be less than 625 square yards.

Squares, Circles, and Suds

We have found, then, that of all the rectangles (the same may be said of quadrangles) the sum of whose sides is the same, the square will enclose the largest area. Now suppose we have fencing of a given length; what will be the shape of the geometric figure such that the fencing around it will enclose the largest possible area?

Suppose we take the area as circular. Then the length of the circumference of the circle is k units of length. If the radius of this circle is r, we have then that

$$2\pi r = k, \quad \text{or} \quad r = \frac{k}{2\pi}$$

The area of the circle is given by the formula

$$A = \pi r^2$$

Substituting in this formula the expression for the radius

$$r = \frac{k}{2\pi}$$

we have

$$A = \frac{\pi k^2}{4\pi^2}$$

and finally

$$A = \frac{k^2}{4\pi}$$

Now we shall compare the value of the area of a square, the sum of whose sides is k, with the area of a circle the length of whose circumference is also k. The area of the square is

$$\frac{k^2}{16}$$

and the area of the circle is

$$\frac{k^2}{4\pi}$$

We then form the relationship

$$\frac{k^2}{16} \; ? \; \frac{k^2}{4\pi}$$

Multiply both sides of the relationship by $(16 \cdot 4\pi)$. We then have

$$\frac{16 \cdot 4\pi \cdot k^2}{16} \; ? \; \frac{16 \cdot 4\pi \cdot k^2}{4\pi}$$

Finally, we have

$$4\pi \cdot k^2 \; ? \; 16k^2$$

Now, the value of π, given as correct to six places, is 3.14159. Obviously π is less than 4, that is,

$$\pi < 4$$

and

$$4\pi < 16$$

Therefore,

$$4\pi \cdot k^2 < 16k^2$$

Now, since we have established the type of the relationship, we shall divide both sides of the inequality by $16 \cdot 4\pi$. We then have

$$\frac{4\pi \cdot k^2}{16 \cdot 4\pi} < \frac{16k^2}{16 \cdot 4\pi}$$

or

$$\frac{k^2}{16} < \frac{k^2}{4\pi}$$

So the area of the circle is greater than the area of the square.

To illustrate, suppose we have 100 yards of wire fencing. For a square, each side of this figure will require $\frac{100}{4} = 25$ yards, and the area of the square will be 625 square yards. The area of the circle whose circumference is 100 yards is computed as follows. The circumference is $2\pi r$, then

$$2\pi r = 100, \quad \text{and} \quad r = \frac{100}{2\pi}, \quad \text{or} \quad r = \frac{50}{\pi}$$

The area of the circle is then

$$A = \frac{\pi 50^2}{\pi^2} = \frac{2,500}{3.14}$$

or $A = 796$ square yards, approximately.

The same problem of the circle and the square may be approached from a different point of view. Suppose we have a circle and a square whose areas are equal; which of the two will be smaller, the circumference of the circle or the sum of the sides of the square?

Let the radius of the circle be r and the side of the square be a. Then, since the area of the circle is equal to the area of the square, we have

$$a^2 = \pi r^2, \quad \text{and} \quad a = r\sqrt{\pi}$$

The sum of the lengths of the sides of the square is then

$$4a = 4r\sqrt{\pi}$$

The length of the circumference of the circle is $2\pi r$. We must then compare the quantities $4r\sqrt{\pi}$ and $2\pi r$. We have

$$4r\sqrt{\pi} = 4r\sqrt{3.14} = 4 \cdot 1.77r = 7.08r$$

and

$$2\pi r = 2 \cdot 3.14r = 6.28r$$

Thus the length of the circumference of the circle is smaller than the sum of the lengths of the sides of the square when the areas of these two figures are equal. Many natural phenomena illustrate that for some reason this economy (the largest area with the smallest length of circumference) is practiced by nature. The reader may perform the following experiment at home. Form a square by bending a wire as shown below. Dip

this wire in suds so that a film of soap is left on the wire. Tie together the ends of a small piece of silk string and place it gently on the film of soap. This string, when the film inside it is pierced, will immediately take the shape of a circle.

Sawing Out the Biggest Log

The question as to whether the rectangle or the square, the sum of whose sides is the same, contains the larger area, indirectly uncovers another important property of numbers. Suppose we have a number, say 24, and it is required to obtain two numbers whose sum is 24, but whose product will be the greatest. Now instead of taking the sum of all four sides of the rectangular quadrangle we may take the sum of the two sides whose product will give the area; that is, we may consider only half of the sum of the sides of the quadrangle. We may immediately draw the conclusion that the number 24 should be split into two equal addends—that is, into 12 and 12. The product of 12 and 12, which is equal to 144, is the greatest possible product. For example,

$$11 \cdot 13 = 143$$
$$11.5 \cdot 12.5 = 143.75$$

This result may be applied to a problem that often arises in the work of a sawmill. Given a circular log of definite length, it is required to cut out of it a beam with a rectangular cross section so that the least quantity of wood is wasted; in other words, the largest (in volume) beam is sought.

Since the length of the log will be preserved, and it is assumed that its thickness is uniform throughout (if it is not, we consider the smaller circular cross section), we shall be concerned with the circular cross section. The reader will recall that the volume of a prism is obtained as the product of the area of its base and its altitude. Since altitude is not changed, everything depends on the area of the base. Our problem may then be restated as

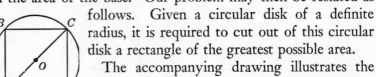

follows. Given a circular disk of a definite radius, it is required to cut out of this circular disk a rectangle of the greatest possible area.

The accompanying drawing illustrates the restated problem. In the circle is inscribed a rectangle. The diagonal of the rectangle is also the diameter of the circle. It is well known in geometry that when a right triangle is inscribed in a circle, its hypotenuse is the diameter of the circle.

In a circle with center O, the diameter AB is drawn (see the following figure). Take any point C on the circumference and join this point with the end points A and B of the diameter AB. We thus obtain a triangle ABC. Now if we join C to the center O by a straight line, we obtain two triangles, ACO and OCB. These two triangles are isosceles triangles, because they have two sides (AO and CO in the triangle ACO, and CO and OB in triangle OCB) that are equal to one another. We also know

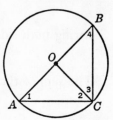

that the base angles (lying opposite the equal sides) of an isosceles triangle are equal. We then have

$$\angle 1 = \angle 2, \quad \text{and} \quad \angle 3 = \angle 4$$

but we also know that the sum of the angles of any triangle is 180 degrees. Thus

$$\angle 1 + \angle 2 + \angle 3 + \angle 4 = 180°$$

But this is the sum of the angle of the triangle ABC. Moreover, since

$$\angle 1 = \angle 2 \quad \text{and} \quad \angle 3 = \angle 4$$

we can write

$$2(\angle 2) + 2(\angle 3) = 180°$$

and (dividing both sides of the above expression by 2)

$$\angle 2 + \angle 3 = 90°$$

This result signifies that angle C is a right angle and the triangle ABC is a right triangle, and its hypotenuse is AB. But AB is also the diameter of the circle.

Now, in the right triangle ABC $AB = 2r$ (AB is the diameter) and $AC = x$. Then from the Pythagorean relation

$$AC^2 + BC^2 = AB^2$$

we have that

$$BC^2 = AB^2 - AC^2$$

or

$$BC^2 = 4r^2 - x^2$$

and

$$BC = \sqrt{4r^2 - x^2}$$

The area of the rectangle $ABCD$ is

$$AC \cdot BC$$

or

$$A = x\sqrt{4r^2 - x^2}$$

Squaring both sides of the last equation we have

$$A^2 = x^2(4r^2 - x^2)$$

The sum of the two factors x^2 and $(4r^2 - x^2)$ is

$$x^2 + 4r^2 - x^2 = 4r^2$$

Thus for any circle of the radius r, the sum of these two factors is constant, that is, $4r^2$. Therefore, in accordance with the arithmetic property established at the start of this section, the product of these two factors, A^2, will be the greatest possible when these two factors are equal—that is, when

$$x^2 = 4r^2 - x^2$$

From this we obtain that

$$x^2 = 2r^2$$

and

$$AB = x = r\sqrt{2}$$

and

$$BC = \sqrt{4r^2 - x^2} = \sqrt{4r^2 - 2r^2} = \sqrt{2r^2} = r\sqrt{2}$$

that is,

$$AB = BC$$

In other words, the rectangle is a square, and this square is inscribed in the given circle. Under these conditions the volume of the beam will be the largest and the least wood will be wasted.

Cutting Corners from a Triangle, or How to Get the Most Out of a Garret

Suppose you have a triangular piece of cardboard or wood, and you wish to cut out from it the largest-in-area rectangle so that one of the sides of the rectangle lies on one of the sides of the triangle. Will you choose the smallest side of the triangle or the largest? Will you decide to take the side that is the far-

thest from a vertex or the nearest? What would be your procedure in selecting the proper side?

Let us attack this problem from the general point of view.
We shall examine any triangle *ABC*. The rectangle that will
be cut out is *DEFH*. Since the fig-
ure *DEFH* is a rectangle, the side
DE is parallel to the side *HF* and
therefore parallel to the side *AC* of
the triangle *ABC*. Now we know
that if in any triangle we draw a
line parallel to a side, we obtain
two similar triangles. Therefore the

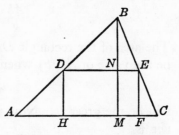

triangles *ABC* and *DBE* are similar, and their corresponding sides
are proportional, as are their corresponding altitudes. We have
then the proportion

$$\frac{BM}{BN} = \frac{AC}{DE}$$

and from this we obtain that

$$DE = \frac{BN \cdot AC}{BM}$$

Let us denote the side *DE* of the triangle *DBE* by *x*, and the
altitude *BN* of the same triangle by *y*. Also let us denote the
side *AC* of the triangle *ABC* by *b*, and the altitude *BM* of the
same triangle by *h*. We have then (after making the substitutions in the expression for *DE*) that

$$x = \frac{by}{h}$$

The area of the rectangle *DEFH* is given by the expression
DE·EF. But *EF = NM = BM − BN*. Therefore

$$EF = h - y$$

Then the area of the rectangle *DEFN* ($A = DE \cdot EF$), after the
expressions for *DE* and *EF* are substituted in it, is

$$A = \frac{by}{h}(h - y)$$

Now for any triangle the side b and the altitude h are definite in size. Therefore they cannot influence the magnitude of the area A when the dimensions of the rectangle are determined. We may therefore rewrite the last expression as

$$\frac{Ah}{b} = y(h - y)$$

The area of the rectangle $DEFH$ will be the largest (and so will be the value of Ah/b) when the product

$$y(h - y)$$

will be the greatest. Now the sum of the factors of this product is

$$y + h - y = h$$

that is, it is constant. Therefore, as we now know, this product will be the greatest when the factors are equal, that is, when $y = h - y$. From this we have that $2y = h$, or

$$y = \tfrac{1}{2}h$$

The last result indicates that the side DE of the rectangle $DEFH$ must cut the altitude BM into two equal parts; that is, the altitude BM is bisected at the point N. Moreover, we now also know that this leads to the conclusion that the side DE must be equal to one-half the side AC to which it is parallel. In other words,

$$x = DE = \tfrac{1}{2}b$$

Thus, since we may apply the same procedure to any side of the triangle ABC and obtain similar results, we may ask whether the area of the rectangle will vary with the selection of the side of the triangle. Now, the area of the triangle ABC is

$$\tfrac{1}{2}bh$$

The area of the rectangle $DEFH$ is

$$\tfrac{1}{2}b \cdot \tfrac{1}{2}h = \tfrac{1}{4}bh$$

and this indicates that the area of the rectangle is equal to one-half the area of the triangle. In other words, it is immaterial which side of the triangle we select. The result will always be the same.

How to Make Money in the Box Business

Suppose that you have a square piece of cardboard whose side is 48 inches long, and want to make an open box (without a top) of the largest possible volume. The corners of the cardboard will have to be cut out and then the outside strips must be bent as shown in the drawings. Now this presents a double problem:

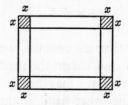 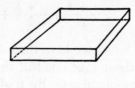

the volume of the box must be the largest possible, the area of cardboard wasted must be the least possible.

Suppose the corners that are cut out are squares whose sides are x inches long. Then the dimensions of the box will be: length, $(48 - 2x)$ inches; width, $(48 - 2x)$ inches; and height, x inches. The volume of the box is then

$$V = (48 - 2x)(48 - 2x)x$$

The volume is thus a product of three factors. We know under which conditions the product of two factors will be the greatest (the factors must be equal when their sum is given), but we do not at this moment know under which conditions the product of three factors will be the greatest when the sum of these factors is given.

Suppose we have three numbers a, b, and c, whose sum is given as $a + b + c = K$. Let us assume that a, b, and c are unequal to one another. Now if we consider two numbers, say a and b, take their sum, and divide it by 2, we have two numbers

$$\frac{a + b}{2} \text{ and } \frac{a + b}{2}$$

whose product will be the greatest.

Thus we have the product

$$\frac{a + b}{2} \cdot \frac{a + b}{2} \cdot c$$

and this product, since

$$\frac{a+b}{2} \cdot \frac{a+b}{2} > ab$$

will be greater than abc. However, the sum of the three factors of the above product is

$$\frac{a+b}{2} + \frac{a+b}{2} + c = a + b + c = K$$

Thus when we have three factors that are unequal, we select two of them, take one-half their sum and obtain the product of three new numbers. By trial and error we may finally obtain the greatest product possible. On the other hand, if the three factors are all equal, such a change is unnecessary. It follows then that if the three factors are equal their product will be the greatest, when their sum is given. In other words, if three numbers are given, their sum is divided by 3, and the cube of this quotient will be greater than abc, and the greatest possible product will thus be obtained.

Now let us return to the expression for the volume of the box

$$V = (48 - 2x)(48 - 2x)x$$

The sum of these three factors is

$$48 - 2x + 48 - 2x + x = 96 - 3x$$

Now, this sum is not definite because it changes with the change in the value of the x; in other words, the sum of the three factors must be free from the x. Note that we have the following expressions containing x: $-2x$, $-2x$, and $+x$. To eliminate x the sum of the positive and negative terms must be equal to zero. This could be possible if we had a term such as $+4x$. Now we may multiply both sides of the expression for the volume of the box by 4. We have then

$$4V = (48 - 2x)(48 - 2x)4x$$

The sum of the factors of the product in this case is

$$48 - 2x + 48 - 2x + 4x = 96$$

The product of these three factors will be the greatest when

$$48 - 2x = 4x$$

or

$$6x = 48 \quad \text{and} \quad x = 8$$

Thus when $x = 8$ inches the volume of the box will be the largest. This is so even if under these conditions $4V$ will be the largest. But if $4V$ is the largest, then V, itself, also will be the largest. We have then the dimensions of the box in inches as length, 32; width, 32; and height, 8. The volume will thus be

$$32 \cdot 32 \cdot 8 = 8{,}192 \text{ inches}^3$$

Any other dimensions will not give a volume as large. For example, if we cut out squares whose sides are 7 inches, remembering that we must not waste cardboard, we have then the dimensions: length, 34; width, 34; height, 7. The volume will thus be $34 \cdot 34 \cdot 7 = 8{,}092$ inches^3.

Nature Study: Why Is a Sphere?

We have noted that nature often likes to assume a spherical form, as evidenced in the earth (if we disregard the flattening at the poles), the sun, the moon, and the stars. If we mix alcohol and water and drop in a small quantity of olive oil, the oil drop will float as though suspended in the liquid and its shape, too, will be spherical.

There must be some definite reason for this. A clue may be obtained from the following considerations. Suppose we have a cube whose edge is a units long. Then the area of the surface of this cube (it will have six squares) will be $6a^2$. Which of the two figures, a cube having the surface $6a^2$ or a sphere having the same surface, will contain the larger volume?

The formula for the surface of a sphere whose radius is r is $4\pi r^2$. Then we have

$$4\pi r^2 = 6a^2 \quad \text{and} \quad r^2 = \frac{6a^2}{4\pi}$$

From this we obtain

$$r = \frac{a\sqrt{6}}{2\sqrt{\pi}}$$

The formula for the volume of a sphere is $V = \frac{4}{3}\pi r^3$. Substitute in this expression the expression for r as obtained. We have then

$$V = \frac{4}{3}\pi \cdot \frac{a^3 6\sqrt{6}}{8\pi\sqrt{\pi}}$$

which, when simplified, becomes

$$V = a^3 \frac{\sqrt{6}}{\sqrt{\pi}}$$

Now $\sqrt{6} = 2.45$ (approximately), and $\sqrt{\pi} = \sqrt{3.14} = 1.77$ (approximately). Then

$$\frac{\sqrt{6}}{\sqrt{\pi}} = \frac{2.45}{1.77} = 1.4 \text{ (approximately)}$$

Then $V = 1.4a^3$. The volume of a cube whose edge is a is a^3. Then

$$1.4a^3 > a^3$$

Thus we see that a sphere having the same surface area will contain a larger volume than the cube. Or, from another point of view, if a cube and a sphere have the same volume, the sphere will have a smaller surface than the cube.

As nature tends to be thrifty with her substance, we can now see why she likes the sphere. This spherical economy is very important in industry and science when smaller surface and larger volume are necessary.

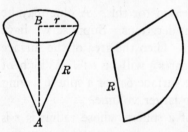

Fashion Your Own Funnel

A funnel can be made of a circular piece of paper or tin by cutting out a portion of the material as illustrated and folding the remaining portion into a cone.

The problem that arises in the process of construction is to waste as little material as possible and yet obtain a funnel that will contain the largest possible volume.

To solve it, we denote the radius of the circular piece of material by R and the radius of the base of the conical funnel by r;

then the circumference of the base of the funnel is $2\pi r$. The length of this circumference will be the length of that portion of the circumference of the circular piece of material that will be left after a part was cut off. Let this part be x. Then

$$2\pi r = x, \quad \text{and} \quad r = \frac{x}{2\pi}$$

The altitude of the cone (if we apply the Pythagorean relation to the right triangle ABC in the drawing) is

$$AB^2 = H^2 = R^2 - r^2 = R^2 - \left(\frac{x}{2\pi}\right)^2$$

from which we have that

$$H = \sqrt{R^2 - \left(\frac{x}{2\pi}\right)^2}$$

The formula for the volume of a cone is

$$V = \tfrac{1}{3}\pi r^2 H$$

We substitute the expression for H in this formula, and we have

$$V = \frac{1}{3}\pi\left(\frac{x}{2\pi}\right)^2\sqrt{R^2 - \left(\frac{x}{2\pi}\right)^2}$$

We shall have the largest possible volume when the expression

$$\left(\frac{x}{2\pi}\right)^2\sqrt{R^2 - \left(\frac{x}{2\pi}\right)^2}$$

will be the largest in value. To be able to examine the conditions under which this expression will be the largest in value we must get rid of the square root by squaring. We then have

$$\left[\left(\frac{x}{2\pi}\right)^2\right]^2\left[R^2 - \left(\frac{x}{2\pi}\right)^2\right]$$

This expression contains three factors whose sum is

$$\left(\frac{x}{2\pi}\right)^2 + \left(\frac{x}{2\pi}\right)^2 + R^2 - \left(\frac{x}{2\pi}\right)^2 = R^2 + \left(\frac{x}{2\pi}\right)^2$$

This sum is not free from x and to free it we shall multiply the expression

$$R^2 - \left(\frac{x}{2\pi}\right)^2 \quad \text{by 2}$$

We have then

$$\left(\frac{x}{2\pi}\right)^2 + \left(\frac{x}{2\pi}\right)^2 + 2R^2 - 2\left(\frac{x}{2\pi}\right)^2 = 2R^2$$

Now, so that this product (and, therefore, the volume of the conical funnel) be the largest possible, the three factors must be equal to one another. We then have

$$\left(\frac{x}{2\pi}\right)^2 = 2R^2 - 2\left(\frac{x}{2\pi}\right)^2$$

From this we obtain that

$$3\left(\frac{x}{2\pi}\right)^2 = 2R^2, \quad \text{and} \quad \left(\frac{x}{2\pi}\right)^2 = \frac{2}{3}R^2$$

Finally, we have that

$$\frac{x}{2\pi} = \frac{\sqrt{2}}{\sqrt{3}}R, \quad \text{and} \quad x = \frac{2\pi\sqrt{2}}{\sqrt{3}}R = 5.13R$$

To determine the number of degrees that must be in the arc of the circumference of the circular piece of material, let the number of the degrees in the arc whose length is $5.13R$ be y. The circumference of a circle is $2\pi R = 6.28R$, and the number of degrees in the circumference of a circle is 360. We have then

$$\frac{y}{360} = \frac{5.13}{6.28}$$

From this we obtain

$$y = \frac{360° \cdot 5.13}{6.28} = 294°, \text{ approximately}$$

This means that about $(360° - 294°) = 66°$ must be cut out of the circle. When this is done, the remaining portion of the circular piece of material will fold into the largest possible conical funnel that can be made from the original material.

The reader may check the result by computing the volume of the cone, assuming that the radius of the circular piece of material is 10 inches when 66 degrees of the circular piece is cut out, then compute for a smaller number of degrees, say 60, 50, and 40 degrees.

Cork-Screw Geometry

But, the Earth Isn't Flat . . .

With the help of a somewhat odd assortment of tools—an ocean liner, an airplane, a scheming spider, a fly, our rubber bands, and the North and South Poles—we are equipped now to approach the mathematics of navigation, to climb the screw's "spiral" stairway, to calculate the measurement of distances on nonflat surfaces, and, incidentally, to learn the rudiments of efficient fly-catching.

For many practical purposes we assume that the earth is flat. If we wish to learn the area of a piece of ground, say of rectangular shape and of dimensions known to us, we multiply the numerical values of its width and length. The fundamental assumption is that this plot of ground includes a portion of a plane. Actually the surface of the earth is not a plane but is approximately spherical in shape, and the rectangular piece of ground is a portion of the surface of the sphere. So computation of the area of this plot of ground as if it were a rectangular portion of a plane introduces an error, but one so small in comparison with the magnitude of the area that it may be disregarded in ordinary problems.

Furthermore, the familiar expression "The shortest distance between two points is a straight line" is incorrect. What is actually meant is that the shortest distance between two points, when these points are unattached to any geometric figure, is measured along a straight line.

Any side of a triangle is, as we have learned, less than the sum of its other two sides; thus in the triangle ABC (nothing is specified in this triangle) $AB < BC + AC$. We may have the vertex C of this triangle far distant from the side AB, or we may have it as close to it as we please, but as long as we have a triangle ABC,

$$AB < BC + AC$$

We chose the side AB, although this was entirely arbitrary; the same relation holds for the side BC and the side AC. The drawing below illustrates that it is immaterial how far from the side AB the vertex C may be removed.

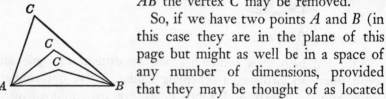

So, if we have two points A and B (in this case they are in the plane of this page but might as well be in a space of any number of dimensions, provided that they may be thought of as located in some plane at the same time) and we wish to travel from A to B (or from B to A), our one shortest route is along the straight line that joins these points.

But is this property of a straight line reserved for the plane only? And what are the means for measuring the shortest distances between two points on surfaces other than the plane? Let us see if we can answer these questions in the following sections.

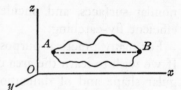

Shortest Distances in Three Dimensions

The shortest distance between two points when they are not on a plane, but in the space of three dimensions—that is, when they are not attached to any geometric figure—also is measured along a straight line because we can pass through these two points a plane, and the distance between two points in a plane is measured along the straight line that joins the points.

The plane is not the only surface possible. There are many others: some of them are combinations of two or more planes (we encountered them when we examined such solid geometric figures as the cube, the prism, and the pyramid); others are curved (for example, the surface of a sphere), and still others are combinations of curved and plane surfaces (such as the cylinder and the cone).

Now if two points are on some surface other than a plane (this surface may be a combination of two or more planes; it may be a curved surface, or it may be some combination of these), how shall we determine the shortest distance between them? Or, similarly, since the earth is approximately a sphere, if we propose to travel, say by airplane, from one point on the earth's surface to another, how shall we determine the shortest route? First, let us suppose we have two adjoining planes (such as two walls of a room, or two faces of a prism) and there are two points, one on each plane; what is the method for proceeding from one point to the other by the shortest route?

In the geometry of two dimensions, two intersecting straight lines form an angle. By analogy we may think of two intersecting planes in the world of three dimensions as forming some kind of an angle. To visualize such an angle, begin to open a closed book. At the start the opening will be small, but it becomes larger. Such a three-dimensional angle is known as a "dihedral" angle ("di"—two, "hedron"—face). The dihedral angle may be measured by the angle that is traced on another plane when at some point on the edge of the angle (this edge corresponds to the vertex of the plane angle) this plane is passed perpendicularly to this edge. If we stand an opened book on a table, the plane of the table will be perpendicular to the edge of the book; the drawing illustrating a dihedral angle as well as the method of measuring such an angle is shown at right.

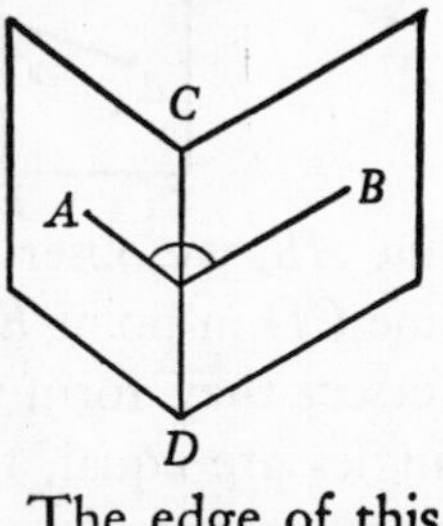

Suppose we have a point A on the face P of a dihedral angle, and we also have a point B on the face Q of the same dihedral angle. The edge of this dihedral angle is CD (CD is a straight line). We may travel from point A to point B along the faces of the dihedral angle in many different ways; the problem is to find the shortest route.

Will it be a curved path, a straight line, or a combination of straight lines?

If the plane *P* and the plane *Q* are continuations of one another, that is, when the dihedral angle is measured by an angle of 180 degrees, the two planes are actually one plane. We know the shortest route from one point to another when the two lie in the same plane will be a straight line that joins the points *A* and *B*.

On the other hand, if the plane *P* is not a continuation of the plane *Q*, when the dihedral angle is measured by an angle that is less than 180 degrees, the points *A* and *B* can be joined by a straight line, but this straight line *AB* will not lie in either of the two planes *P* or *Q*. If you have a dihedral angle made of a folded cardboard, you may join the two points *A* and *B* by a rubber string tightly drawn.

For a simple experiment, flatten out the dihedral angle so that the planes *P* and *Q* form one continuous plane. Then the line *AB* (which is represented by the tightly drawn rubber string) will stretch out along the new plane. It will represent a straight line in that plane, and represent also the shortest route from *A* to *B* when these points lie in the same plane.

While the planes *P* and *Q* are flattened and the shortest distance between the points *A* and *B* is measured along the straight

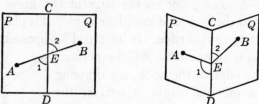

line *AB*, we observe that the straight line *AB* now intersects the line *CD* in point *E*. We know that when two straight lines intersect they form two pairs of vertical angles, and that vertical angles are equal; thus $\angle 1 = \angle 2$. If the rubber string leaves a trace on the planes *P* and *Q* when they are flattened out, this trace is the straight line *AB*.

Now let us fold back the planes *P* and *Q* to their original positions. The trace of the rubber string, the straight line *AB*, will be folded also and will be broken up into two parts which will be joined in the point E. The part AE will lie in the plane P and the part EB will lie in the plane Q. Since the straight line AB was the shortest route from A to B when the planes P and Q were flattened out, the sum of the parts of the straight line AB, AE, and EB will still be the shortest route from A to B along the planes P and Q. Moreover, the angles $\angle 1$ and $\angle 2$ remain the same and equal when P and Q are brought back into their original position. Thus we have the method for the determination of the shortest route from A to B along the planes P and Q, and it should be remembered that, in summary, the shortest route between two points A and B, each lying on one of the faces of a dihedral angle, is a broken straight line, AEB, such that its point E lies on the edge CD of the dihedral angle. Moreover, the two angles AED ($\angle 1$) and CEB ($\angle 2$) are equal.

With this method for determination of the shortest route between two points on two connected planes established, we shall be able to find the methods for surfaces of other types.

A Tip for the Spider

In a room on one wall sits a fly, and on the opposite wall sits an ill-intentioned spider: What is the shortest route the spider can take to reach the fly?

The accompanying drawing shows the locations of the fly and of the spider, assuming that both are nearer the ceiling than the floor. Let us draw a plan of the room in which we shall

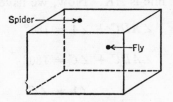

disregard the floor, and keep the planes of the walls and ceiling

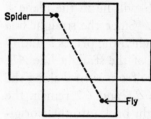

in one continuous plane. Then the fly and the spider will be in the same plane. The shortest distance from the spider to the fly will be along a straight line that joins their respective positions, as indicated in the drawing of the plan.

Now, suppose the spider is 2 feet below the ceiling and 3 feet away from the wall, and the fly is 3 feet below the ceiling and 1 foot away from the wall. The width of the room is 15 feet, and the length is 19 feet. We then have a right triangle whose hypotenuse is the shortest route from the spider to the fly. By means of the Pythagorean relation we find that the spider, if he employed the same process, traveled

$$\sqrt{20^2 + 15^2} = \sqrt{625} = 25 \text{ feet}$$

for his dinner.

How to Know Your Way around a Prism

To determine the shortest route along the faces of a prism we shall need to employ a property of parallel lines, one that we came across briefly when we examined parallelograms. We know that in any parallelogram the opposite angles are equal. Moreover, since the sum of the angles on the same side of a parallelogram is 180°, or, as in the accompanying parallelogram, $\angle A + \angle ADC = 180°$. But the sum of the angles about the point D is also 180 degrees, because the angle about D on one side of the straight line is AK. Now, we have

$$\angle ADC + \angle 1 = 180°$$

and

$$\angle ADC + \angle C = 180°$$

Therefore,

$$\angle 1 = \angle C$$

The straight lines BC and AD are cut by the line CD (this line is called the "transversal"). Moreover the straight lines BC and AD are parallel. Thus we see that when two parallel lines are cut by a transversal so that a figure similar to the letter Z is formed, the angles (known as the "alternate interior" angles) in the corners of the letter Z are equal.

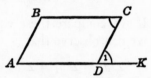

Now, to proceed with determination of the shortest route along the faces of a prism, suppose that we have a right prism, one such that its edges are perpendicular to the bases (any other prism will lead to the same results). The faces of the prism are marked by numbers in the following drawing, and we shall let point A be on face 1 and point B on face 5.

If we slit the prism along the edge EF and flatten the faces so that their planes form a continuous plane, the shortest distance

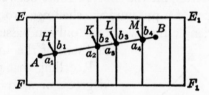

between A and B is determined along the straight line that joins them. This straight line cuts the edges of the prism in the points H, K, L, and M. Moreover, the entire surface of the flattened out faces is a rectangle the length of whose base is equal to the sum of the lengths of the sides of the faces, and whose altitude is the edge of the prism. Note also that the angles that the line AB makes at the points H, K, L, and M with the edges of the prism are equal as indicated on the drawing,

$$\angle a_1 = \angle b_1, \ \angle a_2 = \angle b_2, \ \angle a_3 = \angle b_3 \ \text{and} \ \angle a_4 = \angle b_4$$

On the other hand, the edges of the prism are parallel to one another and all are perpendicular to the same line, the base of the rectangle obtained after the faces are flattened into one plane.

All these parallel lines are cut by a transversal AB. Therefore we have the following equalities of angles:

$$\angle b_1 = \angle a_2, \quad \angle b_2 = \angle a_3, \quad \text{and} \quad \angle b_3 = \angle a_4$$

If we compare these equalities with those obtained previously, we can observe that

$$\angle a_1 = \angle b_1 = \angle a_2 = \angle b_2 = \angle a_3 = \angle b_3 = \angle a_4 = \angle b_4$$

Thus we see that the broken line along which is the shortest route between two points on the faces of a prism makes equal angles with the prism's edges. Should the two points lie on the same face of a prism, then the shortest route between these is the same as that between two points in a plane—a straight line.

Journey across a Pyramid

To determine the shortest route between two points on different faces of a pyramid we shall need to make use of a property of a triangle that we noted only in passing when we considered the sum of the angles of a triangle.

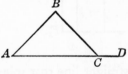

Recalling that this sum is equal to 180 degrees, or a straight angle, suppose we take a triangle ABC and extend the line AC beyond the point C. Now, about this point C on each side of the line ACD, there is a straight angle, which is also a 180-degree angle. We therefore have the equalities

$$\angle A + \angle B + \angle C = 180°, \quad \text{and} \quad \angle C + \angle BCD = 180°$$

We then have that

$$\angle A + \angle B = 180° - \angle C, \quad \text{and} \quad \angle BCD = 180° - \angle C$$

This leads to the conclusion that

$$\angle A + \angle B = \angle BCD$$

which signifies that in any triangle an exterior angle is equal to the sum of the interior angles nonadjacent to it.

Suppose we have a pyramid, and on two of its faces, which

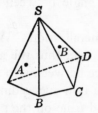
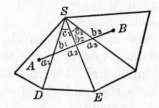

are triangles, are two points A and B. The shortest route between them is one of the infinite number of broken lines that join these points. Let us examine the angles that the shortest route makes with the edges of the pyramid.

In the accompanying drawing we denote the angles of the various triangles whose vertices all are coinciding with the vertex S of the pyramid and whose bases are the parts of the broken line that is the shortest route between A and B. We have then

$$\angle a_1 = \angle b_1$$
$$\angle a_2 = \angle b_2$$
$$\angle a_3 = \angle b_3$$

Let us examine one of the triangles formed by the edges of the pyramid and a part of the broken line, say the triangle on the face SDE. According to the property of the exterior angle of a triangle derived by us above, we have

$$\angle a_2 = \angle b_1 + \angle c_1$$

From this we have

$$\angle a_2 - \angle b_1 = \angle c_1$$

But we found that

$$\angle a_1 = \angle b_1$$

then we have

$$\angle a_2 - \angle a_1 = \angle c_1$$

We can prove in a similar manner (this is left to the reader as an exercise) that

$$\angle a_3 - \angle a_2 = \angle c_2$$

which shows the relation between the angles made by the broken line of the shortest route with the respective edges of the pyramid and the angle between those edges. The difference between two succeeding angles is equal to the angle between the two corresponding edges.

Note how this fact is actually a generalization. When we have a prism, its edges do not intersect, and thus the angle between them is zero. Then the difference between two succeeding angles is zero and, therefore, these two succeeding angles are equal. Should the two points A and B lie on the same face of the pyramid, the shortest route between these two points (since they lie in the same plane) is a straight line.

Points about a Glass

In order to simplify our examination of the shortest route along the cylinder we shall consider a right circular cylinder (one whose base is a circle) such as a glass.

A cylinder has no edges, which puts us to some disadvantage unless we can find means to rectify this lack. The side surface of a cylinder is a smooth, round surface. In the case of a right circular cylinder this surface is perpendicular to the upper and lower circular bases. Now we may draw any number of straight lines on the side surface of a right circular cylinder so that each line will lie with all of its points in that surface. But these lines will follow one direction only; they will all be parallel to one another, and all will be perpendicular to the upper and lower circular bases of the cylinder. Some of these lines are shown in

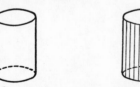

the drawing. Mathematicians call these lines "generators," and with good reason. For the right circular cylinder may be thought of as having been generated by one of such lines when this line was moved along the circumference of the base circle. As this line moves, it traces out (generates) the side surface of the cylinder, hence the name.

We may as well dispose here of one special case, when two points are both on the same generator, as shown below. The shortest route is then measured along the straight line joining them, and this straight line is the generator. No other straight line but a generator can be drawn on the side surface of a cylinder, since any other straight line in any other position will touch the side surface of the cylinder in one point or will be tangent to it. Any other line drawn on the surface of a cylinder (that is not a generator) is not straight, it is a curved line, curved not in the sense of a circle, or of an ellipse, or of any other curve we have been confronted with so far.

Suppose we have two points on the side surface of a cylinder, and these points, *A* and *B*, do not lie on a generator. Then, to reach from one point to the other by the shortest route possible, we must traverse a curved line, and this line must lie with all its points on the side surface of the cylinder. Let these points be joined by such a line of the shortest route, and draw a few generators on the side surface of

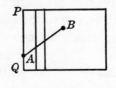

the cylinder so that they intersect the line. Then slit the cylinder open along some other generator which does not intersect the line *AB* of the shortest route. Finally flatten this slit-opened side surface. We thereby obtain a rectangle whose altitude is the generator of the solid and whose base is the circumference of the circular base of the figure. Since the points *A* and *B* lie in the plane of the side surface that was flattened, and since the line *AB* is the line of the shortest route and this line is now in the plane, it must be a straight line. From this point on we are confronted with a situation exactly the same as in the case of a right prism. It becomes evident to us that, since the generators are all perpendicular to the base of the rectangle and therefore are parallel, the shortest route makes equal angles with the generators.

There is one more special case that must be mentioned. Suppose A and B are at equal distances from the base of the cylinder. Then the line of the shortest route will lie along a circle parallel to the circular base of the cylinder. When the side surface is slit open and flattened out, this line will be a straight-line segment parallel to the base of the rectangle as shown below.

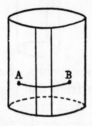 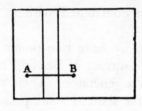

It All Depends on Your Direction

When we have two points in a plane and are interested in the shortest route from one to the other, we are not concerned with the direction in which we travel. In a plane, whether we go

from A to B, or from B to A, we shall be traveling along the same line of the shortest route. This is because the plane is an open surface. You may start out along a straight line at some point in the plane and never return to the point.

This is not the case, however, on the surface of the earth. You may start from New York and travel eastward until you return to New York, or you may start from New York and travel westward until you return to New York. Moreover, if you travel from New York to India, you may take the western or the eastern route; one of these two may be longer than the other, and it may happen that they may be equal in distance.

The same case occurs on the side surface of a cylinder, a prism, a pyramid, or any other figure of a similar type. Suppose we have two points A and B on the side surface of a cylinder

We may proceed from A to B in the direction indicated by an arrow in the accompanying drawing. On the other hand, we may go from A to B in the opposite direction. The straight line which joins the centers of the two circular bases of the cylinder is known as the "axis" of the cylinder. Thus, when we move in the direction indicated by the arrow we may say that we move

around the axis in one direction (from left to right), and, if we go from right to left, it is in the opposite direction. Which of the two directions shall we choose for the shortest route between A and B on the side surface of the cylinder?

Suppose we have two points and wish to join these points, A and B, with two lines. One must be the line of the shortest route from A to B (or from B to A). Then slit the cylinder open along a generator that passes through the point A and

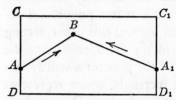

flatten out the surface of the cylinder. The flattened-out surface becomes a plane rectangle as shown at left. The point A is represented twice on this rectangle because it lies on the generator CD, and the side surface of the cylinder was cut along this generator; also this line or section is represented twice, once as the side CD and also as the side C_1D_1 of the rectangle. Now either the straight line AB is shorter than the straight line BA_1, or AB is longer than BA_1, or the two straight lines are equal in length.

If the straight line AB is equal to the straight line BA_1 in length, the generator that can be passed through the point B will

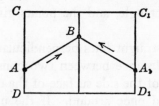 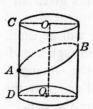

cut the rectangle CC_1D_1D in half. In other words, a plane passed through A and B will cut the cylinder in half also, as illustrated. We may think of the plane as a dihedral angle whose edge is the axis OO_1 of the cylinder and whose opening is measured by an angle of 180 degrees.

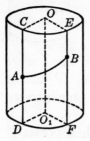

If, however, the line AB is shorter than the line BA_1 (as shown in the first drawing of the rectangle) the 180-degree dihedral angle becomes folded; that is, the points A and B lie on the faces of a dihedral angle that is less than 180 degrees, as shown in the drawing at left.

The above illustrations thus show the method for determination of the shortest route on the cylinder surface.

The Screw: Industry Spirals Up Its Stairway

Let us perform a simple experiment. Around a cylinder wind a sheet of paper several times, puncture it at two points, and denote these points by A and B. Then unravel this paper, letting its width be equal to the generator of the cylinder. After the paper has been unraveled, the traces of the punctures will appear at equal intervals in the plane of the rectangle, which represents the paper that was wound around the cylinder. Denote these

B_1	B_2	B_3	B_4
A_1	A_2	A_3	A_4

traces by A_1, A_2, A_3, and A_4, and also by B_1, B_2, B_3, and B_4. The points given an A notation will all lie on a straight line parallel to the base of the rectangle, and the points given a B notation will lie similarly.

Pass through the A points straight lines perpendicular to the base of the rectangle. The distance between two consecutive lines will designate the extent of the side surface of the cylinder each time the paper is wound once around. If the unfolded paper were wound once more around, the perpendicular lines would all fall on the other.

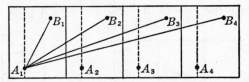

Join the point A_1 and all the B points with straight lines, these representing the lines of the shortest route between A_1 and B_1, B_2, B_3, and B_4 respectively. This statement may seem strange, since, after all, the points B_1, B_2, B_3, and B_4 are all traces of the same point B, and were obtained when the paper on which the point was marked was punctured. How can there be four lines of the shortest route? We shall now remove this inconsistency.

When the paper is wound back on the cylinder the straight line A_1B_1 between the straight lines P_1S_1 and P_2S_2 will become the line A_1B_1—a curved line. The area of the rectangle $P_1P_2S_2S_1$ is the area of the side surface of the cylinder; that is, it represents the amount of paper that was used to wind it around the cylinder once only.

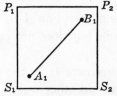

Let us continue winding the paper around the cylinder. After this is done twice, the straight line A_1B_2 becomes the curved line A_1B_2, which goes around the cylinder in a complete revolution but does not complete the second revolution, as is shown by the drawing below.

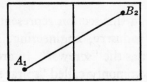

With winding of the paper three times around the cylinder, the straight line A_1B_3 becomes the curved line of the shortest route between the points A_1 and B_3 which goes around the

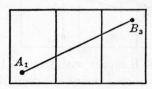 

cylinder in two complete revolutions, but it does not complete the third.

The reader will now realize that the straight line A_1B_4 changes into a curved line A_1B_4 which goes around the cylinder in three complete revolutions but does not complete the fourth. The

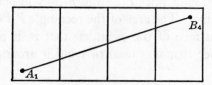

straight line A_1B_5 changes into the curved line A_1B_5 which goes around in four complete revolutions but does not complete the fifth.

In the above illustration, the movement from the points A to the points B were from left to right. In other words, the respective lines of the shortest route represent the paths of points revolving around the axis of the cylinder while moving along the side surface of the cylinder from left to right. However, this does not exclude the revolution of a point along the side surface from right to left. The drawing of these illustrations is left to the reader as an exercise.

The curved lines described in this section represent a type of line extremely important in industry, engineering, and many other fields. They are known as the "screws." In architecture, these lines represent what is commonly called "spiral staircases," but the correct word is "winding."

Coming around the Cone: Helix, the Spiral Screw

To examine the lines of the shortest route along the side surface of a cone, we may recall the results obtained when we examined the shortest route around a pyramid. The cone is a solid geometric figure closely related to the pyramid; in a pyramid the base is a polygon, while in a cone it is either a circle or an ellipse or, generally, some other closed, curved-plane geometric figure. We shall confine our discussion to a cone whose base is a circle, and our cone will be also a right circular cone—a cone such that a line from its vertex, when drawn perpendicularly to the base, will pass through the center of the base circle.

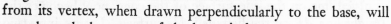

We found that in the case of the shortest route on the side surface of a pyramid, the difference between the angles made by this line with the two neighboring edges of the pyramid is equal to the angle between these edges. In the following drawing, the side surface of the pyramid is flattened out. The straight line AB is the line of the shortest route, and the two neighboring edges are SD and SE. We then have $\angle a_2 - \angle a_1 = \angle c_1$.

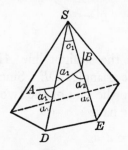
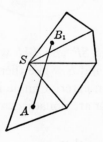

We can imagine the cone as being generated by a line SR that is hinged at a point S above a circle (the line from S to the center O of the circle is perpendicular to the plane of the circle) while this line SR slides along the circumference of the circle. We then may call the line SR the "*generator*" of the cone equivalent to the cylinder generator.

Suppose we have on the side surface of the cone two points
A and *B*. These may be joined with any number of lines, and
among them will be only one which will be the line of the short-

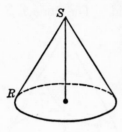

est route from *A* to *B*. Let us slit open the
side surface of the cone, but along a generator that does not intersect the line of the
shortest route from *A* to *B*. Then let us
flatten out the side surface of the cone; we
have a portion of a circle whose center is
the point *S* (formerly the vertex of the
cone) and whose radius is the generator of
the cone. The line of the shortest route from *A* to *B*, which is
a curved line on the side surface of the cone, now becomes the
straight line *AB* on the flattened side surface. Let us draw two

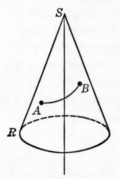
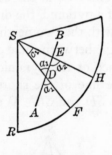

generators *SF* and *SH* which cut the straight line *AB* in the
points *D* and *E*. We then have the triangle *SDE*. Since in any
triangle an exterior angle is equal to the sum of the two interior
angles that are nonadjacent to it, we have

$$\angle a_1 + \angle c_1 = \angle a_2$$

and from it that

$$\angle a_2 - \angle a_1 = \angle c_1$$

The result signifies that for a line of the shortest route on a
cone the difference between the angle that this line makes with
two consecutive generators of the cone is equal to the angle between these generators. This result is similar to the one obtained
in the operation with the pyramid.

In the same way we may learn the line of the shortest route traversed by a point around the side surface of a cone. In the case of the cylinder this motion is described as "double motion," the rotation about the axis and the upward motion along the generator. In the case of the cone it may be described as a combination of the rotation about the axis and of the upward motion along the direction of the generator. The result is a spiral screw which mathematicians call "helix." The reader will now see why winding staircases should not be described as "spiral."

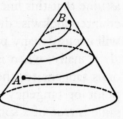

The Shortest Route on Earth

We can now consider a trip on the surface of the earth, which, we may assume, is approximately the surface of a sphere. What is the shortest route from one point to the other? This problem is closely associated with navigation and would determine, for example, the shortest route of a ship or an airplane from the American continent to Europe or Asia.

In the case of a right circular cylinder or a right circular cone, a straight line may be placed so that it will lie with all its points on their side surfaces, when this line is the generator of the cylinder or cone. This, however, is impossible in the case of a sphere; a straight line can touch its surface in only one point. When a straight line touches the surface of a sphere, the line is said to be tangent to the sphere. If a straight line is in contact in more than one point, it cuts through the surface. However, no straight line can have more than two points of contact with the surface of a sphere. We can illustrate the relation between a straight

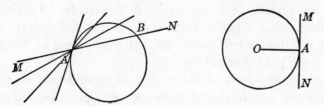

line and a sphere with that between a straight line and a circle. Any straight line cuts the circle in two points. Suppose the straight line *MN* cuts the circle in the points *A* and *B*. Let us assume that this line is pivoted on the point *A* and rotated in the counterclockwise direction (to left). Then the straight line *MN* will occupy many positions, during which *B* will be approaching *A*. Finally, when *B* coincides with *A*, the straight line touches, or is tangent to, the circle. A radius of a circle drawn to the point of tangency is perpendicular to the tangent line. The same is true of a sphere. When a line is tangent to a sphere, we may think of the line as the edge of a knife; if we follow the direction of the radius drawn from the center of the sphere to the point of tangency of the line, we shall cut the sphere into halves, and the section will be circular in shape. The circle ob-

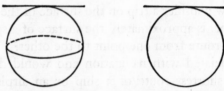

tained after the sphere is cut into halves is known as the "great circle." Its radius is equal to the radius of the sphere, and its circumference is the greatest of all the circumferences of the circles that may be obtained by cutting the sphere. The line that is tangent to a sphere is tangent to the great circle at that point also. Naturally there are many great circles possible on any sphere.

A sphere differs from a right circular cylinder and a right circular cone in many respects, but we shall note particularly this important difference: We easily flattened the side surfaces of the right circular cylinder and the right circular cone, but with the surface of a sphere this is impossible. To illustrate, puncture a rubber ball so that the air escapes and then try to cut it (in any number of parts) so that the surface of the ball is spread out flat. It can't be done.

Through any point on the surface of a sphere any number of great circles may be passed, as through any point on a plane any

number of straight lines may be passed. On a globe representing the earth's sphere the meridians that pass through the poles
are great circles. A radius of a sphere that is drawn to a point
where several great circles pass is thus perpendicular to the tangents to all these circles
(which all lie in one plane that is tangent to
the sphere). We may then think of the great
circle as performing the functions of the
straight line in a plane, but would it then be reasonable to expect that the line of the shortest
route between two points on the surface of a sphere should be a
part, or arc, of a great circle that passes through these two points?

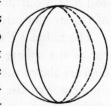

Yes. The line of the shortest route between any two points
on a sphere is an arc of the great circle that passes through the
two points. This is the reason a navigator, when he charts his
course on a flat map, indicates the shortest course not as a straight
line but as a curved line which is a part of a great circle. However, we must remember that the earth is not perfectly spherical
in shape; it is flattened out at the poles and bulges somewhat at
the equator. Thus on the surface of a sphere we actually have
only one shortest route between two points, while on the surface
of the earth we also have only one, but it will differ somewhat
from the actual great circle of a sphere. However, this is a very
fine point which need not be dwelt
upon here.

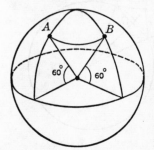

To convince ourselves of the correctness of our observation concerning the
shortest route along the sphere, suppose
that we have two points, A and B, on
the surface of a sphere located 60 degrees above, or north of, the equator.
The arc AB of the small circle (which
is parallel to the great circle of the equator) corresponds to an
angle of 90 degrees. We chose 60- and 90-degree angles to simplify our computations but the reader may use any other angles.
The facts concerning the points A and B correspond to the statement of their latitude (north of the equator) and the difference

of their longitudes, our example thus corresponding somewhat
to an actual situation on the surface of the earth.   Note that in
the drawing we also have the great circle that passes through A
and B; it is our problem to determine which of the two arcs, that
of the smaller circle or that of the great circle, is the shorter.

The radius ST of the small circle (the one parallel to the equator of the sphere) is determined as follows.   The point S is 60
degrees above the equator.   Then the right triangle OST (O is
the center of the sphere) is a 30-, 60-, 90-degree triangle.   The
angle SOT is equal to 30 degrees.   We know that in a 30-, 60-,
90-degree triangle the side opposite the 30-degree angle is equal
to half the hypotenuse.   The hypotenuse of this right triangle is
the radius of the sphere.   If we let this radius be R, then the
radius ST of the small circle is 0.5R.

To have a clear picture of the next step in our computations,
we shall take the two circles that contain the points A and B and
flatten them out on a plane.   They then appear as shown in the
figure below.   The triangle ATB (in the small circle) is a 45-,
45-, 90-degree triangle.   The sides AT and BT are each the
radius of the small circle, which is equal to 0.5R (where R is the

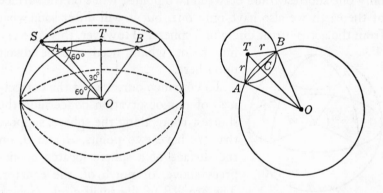

radius of the great circle.   Thus, by means of the Pythagorean
relation, we have

$$AB = \sqrt{AT^2 + BT^2}$$

or

$$AB \sqrt{(0.5R)^2 + (0.5R)^2} = \sqrt{2 \cdot 0.25R^2}$$

and, finally,

$$AB = 0.5R\sqrt{2} = 0.5 \cdot 1.414R = 0.707R$$

To determine the length of the arc AB of the great circle, we must know the angle AOB formed by the radii AO and OB of the great circle. Consider then the right triangle ACO: in it we know that $AO = R$, and $AC = 0.5AB$. But $AB = 0.707R$; therefore

$$AC = 0.5 \cdot 0.707R$$

or

$$AC = 0.3535R$$

We then have the ratio

$$\frac{AC}{AO} = \sin AOC, \quad \text{or} \quad 0.3535\frac{R}{R} = \sin AOC.$$

By means of the table of trigonometric ratios we find that the angle AOC is about 21 degrees. Then the angle AOB is about 42 degrees.

The circumference of a circle is given by the formula $C = 2\pi r$, where r is the radius of the circle, and there are 360 degrees in a circle.

Then the length of an arc of 1 degree is

$$\frac{2\pi r}{360}$$

and the length of an arc of k degrees is

$$\frac{2\pi r \cdot k}{360}$$

Then the length of the 90-degree arc of the small circle is

$$\frac{2\pi(0.5R)90}{360}, \quad \text{or} \quad \frac{3.14R}{4} = 0.785R, \text{ approximately}$$

The length of the 42-degree arc of the great circle is

$$\frac{2\pi R \cdot 42}{360}, \quad \text{or} \quad \frac{2 \cdot 3.14R \cdot 42}{360} = 0.733R, \text{ approximately}$$

Thus we see that the arc of the great circle is shorter than the arc of the circle parallel to the equator of the sphere. By following the method used above, the reader may take any other values for the positions of the points *A* and *B*, and check this statement. He is cautioned, however, that the foregoing illustration is not a technical proof. The actual proof requires the use of involved tedious mathematical processes which are of minor importance in our study of essentials. The reader will have noticed that we computed the value of the sine ratio of the angle *AOC*, and from this ratio computed the value of the angle. This is a procedure that may be considered as "reverse" work with trigonometric ratios of angles; that is, we have the sine ratio, for example, and find the angle that corresponds to it. Computational work of this type is no more difficult than direct work (having the angle find its particular ratio), but a mathematical manipulation with the reverse process in a proof is far more complicated and, in our work, unnecessary. This is one of the curiosities of mathematics; proof of the almost obvious is often very difficult, and sometimes impossible.

~ 35 ~

Mathematics, Interpreter
of the Universe

Railroading among the Stars

It is a long jaunt from our infantile crawling along the line of
the plane world, but now we are equipped to take a brief journey
among the planets as we advance to examination of two fundamental measures—distance and time—and the mathematical laws
that concern them in their relation to familiar but little understood natural phenomena.

And we may well note here, as we approach the vastnesses of
these fields, that the word "law" for our mathematical expressions must be considered only as the best available term for an
actual approximation; exact formulation of such expressions is
impossible. Also, to establish our program, we must realize that,
although every object can be definitely fixed in our world by
means of these fundamental measures, distance and time, even
the philosophers and master mathematicians have failed to provide a simple definition of them. We have already noted that it
is more difficult to define an apparently simple familiar term than
one that is strange and seemingly complex, so we shall profitably
continue here to view these terms in their generally accepted
meanings.

The fixing of an object in the world around us, the determination of its location in terms of distance and time, reminds us
of our use of the method of coordinates to determine the position
of a point in space. Thus the fixing of an object in the world

around us actually consists of the selection of proper coordinates to give a complete description of this object, not only in space but in time as well. When we say that someone was seen standing at the intersection of two certain streets, such a statement does not represent a complete description of the incident; to make the description complete it is necessary to include a statement concerning the time when this occurred.

Thus it becomes obvious that the world we live in is not only a world of spatial dimensions, it includes time as well. Our world is a space-time combination, and any statement concerning the location of an object in such a world must contain information giving the position of this object in space as well as in time. In brief, the coordinates (or a point, as we usually state them) must be augmented by one more coordinate, that of time.

So a point-world being that has no spatial coordinates will now have the coordinate which will give information concerning its place in time, the line-world being to whom is generally assigned one coordinate, which denotes his distance from some agreed-upon origin, will now have two coordinates, (x,t); the plane-world being, the Flatlander whose spatial coordinates are (x,y), will now have three coordinates, (x,y,t), and finally, a being of the three-dimensional world whose coordinates are stated as (x,y,z) will now have the four coordinates (x,y,z,t).

When we talk about a point (whether it is in a world of one, two, three, or of any other number of dimensions) and we refer to its spatial coordinates, we refer to something tangible. We can measure the required distances and can represent them by straight-line segments. When we introduce a coordinate that refers to time we introduce something that is intangible, since time cannot be measured with a yardstick. We measure time with specially devised instruments, but our measurements are not direct; we look at the dial of a watch and note some number, but we cannot think of it as a distance. This number refers to some interval of duration. We have the same point as before, but when we state its time coordinate we complete the information concerning it.

To distinguish between a point whose spatial coordinates are given and one whose spatial coordinates are augmented by a time coordinate, we shall introduce a special name for the point located in the space-time world—we shall call it the "event."

The representation of events by means of coordinates does not differ in any respect from the representation of points when their spatial coordinates are given. Thus a point-world being will have one coordinate axis, the axis of time, since a point-world being cannot move. For example the event A whose coordinate is t is represented as

and the event A whose coordinate is $-t$ is represented as

The event in a line world has two coordinates assigned to it; thus an event A whose coordinates are (x,t) is represented as shown below:

This arrangement of the coordinate axes, of the axis OT (of time) horizontally and of the axis OX vertically, may appear arbitrary, but we shall note presently that it offers advantages for examination of the problems to follow.

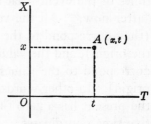

When we have three points on a straight line (no regard is paid to the time element; these are points, not events), one of them is located between the other two, and on the right of one there is a point, as well as on the left of another, as shown here:

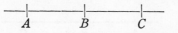

Thus the point B is between the points A and C; to the right of the point A is the point B, and to the right of the point is the point C; to the left of the point C is the point B, and to the left of the point B is the point A.

When we have a straight line made up of events we are confronted with a similar situation. To avoid confusion we shall call the straight line that is made up of events the "time line" (some mathematicians call it the "world line"). We shall denote the time of the event "now" by 0. Thus $t = 0$ denotes that the time of the event is now, and in a similar manner that the event takes place "here" by 0. Thus the location "here" is denoted by the coordinate $x = 0$. If this takes place in Flatland, then the coordinates of "here" are

$$x = 0 \text{ and } y = 0$$

in the three-dimensional space "here" is denoted by the coordinates

$$x = 0, \quad y = 0, \quad \text{and} \quad z = 0$$

Thus in the line world the event "here now" is denoted by the coordinates (0,0), and it will always be represented as the origin of the coordinate axes. All the times of the events that have already passed are thought of as "before now," and all the times of the events that are still to take place are thought of as "after now." All the values of the "befores" will be negative (they correspond to the values of the t's that are to the left of the origin), and the values of the "afters" will be positive (they correspond to the values of the t's that are to the right of the origin). In other words, the past has negative time coordinates, the present has a zero time coordinate, and the future has positive time coordinates.

Thus, if we have three events and they are not simultaneous (their time coordinates are not the same), then one of them must have taken place before the third one, and after the first one. This fact is represented on the time-coordinate axis as

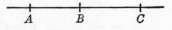

A took place before *B* and *C*
B took place after *A* but before *C*
C took place after *A* and *B*

There are no situations other than these three. The sequence of all the events accounted on the time-coordinate axis thus is

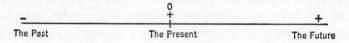

Portrait of a Timetable

The casually accepted railroad timetable is really a very complicated work containing information of the time and place of the arrival and departure of trains and, often, information of the distances between towns and cities as well as other pertinent aids for the traveler.

But there is more to a railroad timetable than the convenient and compact collection of information for the traveler: it symbolizes the backbone of the organization that solves traffic problems, provides safety in travel, and is generally a mirror of efficiency in operation. Of what use is a timetable if the trains depart and arrive in contradiction to it? So the numbers that appear in the timetable represent only the final stage of its purpose and preparation.

Primarily such a table presents information concerning certain positions of a train as it moves from one place to another, and for practical purposes we may consider that the train moves along a straight line, that the universe of the train is a line world. Since information concerning the positions of the train involves also the time, for each position of the train there must be two coordinates, its distance from the point of departure and the time. Thus for the construction of a railroad timetable we may utilize the coordinate axes OX, which will give the distances from the point of departure, and OT, which will give the time. For practical purposes (and this is customary with railroads) the zero for the time is midnight, and the hours of the day are counted from 0 to 24 (24 is again midnight).

Before we proceed with the technique of making up a railroad timetable we shall examine the application of space-time coordinates to illustration of the motion along a straight line, and here we shall consider the simplest kind of motion, that of equal distances traversed in equal periods of time. Moreover, one important restriction must be imposed here: The direction in which this motion takes place does not change; if in our illustration we consider the motion of a point along a straight line, this point can move either forward or backward. If we choose the forward motion, we shall pay no attention to backward motion (as a matter of fact, for the present such motion will not be allowed).

We shall assume that the point under consideration covers one unit of distance in a unit of time, and for the moment shall defer selection of the units. Let us suppose that the point starts out from the place on the straight line whose coordinate is $x = 0$, and the time when this takes place registers also 0, or $t = 0$. Then, since the point traverses one unit of distance in one unit of time, we may have the following:

t	0	1	2	3	4	5	6	7	8
x	0	1	2	3	4	5	6	7	8

In this table the time t denotes in terms of time intervals equal in duration the positions occupied by the moving point. We may show this information on the line that represents the path along which this point moves. Thus we have nine straight lines, each giving the successive position of the point:

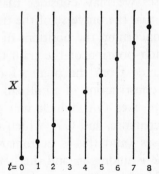

However, in drawing individual straight lines we may make use of the method of coordinate axes and locate the various points whose coordinates are given in the above table as the pairs of the numbers (x,t). Then the various positions of the point moving along a straight line will be represented as events in the time plane:

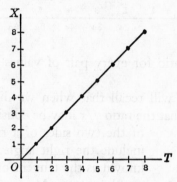

When the point moves along a straight line, its various positions pass through every point of this line. In other words, the events shown in the coordinate diagram above are just a very few of the infinite number of events that can actually be shown. If we decrease the length of the interval of time for which the recording was made, we can obtain many more pairs of (x,t), each of these pairs representing an event. In the final stage of making the time interval smaller (we can only think of it; it cannot be accomplished physically) we obtain a continuous sequence of events, and all of them make up the time line of the moving point. Its graph is a straight line.

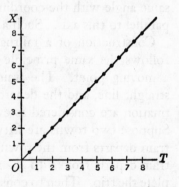

That it is a straight line can be seen from the following; for every event the ratio of its coordinate is x/t. From the table above we note that this ratio is always the same. If we object to the use of this, we may have any other table of pairs of numbers giving the coordinates of the successive events that correspond to the positions of a point that moves along a straight line so that in equal periods of time the same dis-

tances are covered. Such a table may be represented generally as

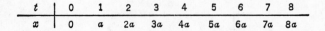

t	0	1	2	3	4	5	6	7	8
x	0	a	$2a$	$3a$	$4a$	$5a$	$6a$	$7a$	$8a$

Here again the ratio for every pair of values of x and t is the
same; it is a.

But the reader will recall that when we discussed right triangles we found that the ratio y/x may be considered as the ratio

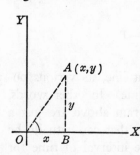

of the two sides of a right triangle that
include the right angle, and this ratio is
known as the tangent of the angle opposite the side y. Moreover, we found that
all angles having the same tangent ratio
(this holds true for other trigonometric
ratios) are equal; we limit our discussion
to angles less than 90 degrees. Thus the
time line of the moving point makes the
same angle with the coordinate axis OT as well as with any line
parallel to this axis. Such a line must then be a straight line.

Construction of a railroad timetable when done graphically
follows the same principle of drawing the time-line graph of
a moving point. The train is assumed to be moving along a
straight line, and the departure, stopover, and arrival at its destination are considered as events. We proceed then as follows.
Suppose two towns are fifty miles apart, and that every hour a
train departs from the town A to the town B, also every hour a
train departs from B to A. It takes one hour and a half to complete the trip. Then to construct the graph we draw two parallel
lines, the distance between them representing the distance between the two towns. Since the distances are represented by the
coordinate axis OX which is vertical, the two parallel lines are
drawn horizontally. On these two lines at equal intervals the
hours are denoted. Thus a train that leaves A at midnight (the
hour is denoted by 0) will arrive at B at 1:30 A.M. If a train
leaves B at 12:30 A.M., it will arrive at A at 2 A.M. However it

may be noted from the graph that the second train will meet the first train at 1 A.M. about seventeen miles from B. If a train makes a stopover, this is denoted on the graph by a break in the time line of the train, and the interval of time spent on the stop-

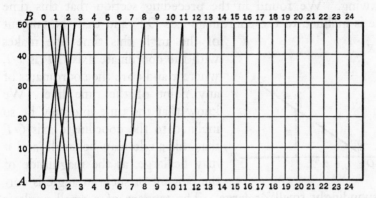

over is shown by a line parallel to the horizontal lines. Thus the 6 A.M. train from A is shown on the graph to make a thirty-minute stopover fourteen miles from A.

The drawing above is only an abbreviated sample of what is done when a railroad timetable is constructed: this is why only a few time lines are drawn in the graph.

The reader will note that the 10 A.M. train covers the distance between A and B in one hour and that its time line is steeper than the time line of a train that covers the same distance in one and one-half hours. The reason for this will be discussed in the next section.

Timing Straight-Line Motion

The time line of a point that moves along a straight line can tell us a complete story of this motion. We recall that under the conditions that govern the motion of the point the point moves along a straight line, traverses equal distances in equal periods of time, and moves in the same direction. A straight-line motion under these three conditions is known as a "uniform straight-line motion." In other words, uniform straight-line motion rules out a change in direction, and at the same time imposes the restriction that in equal periods of time equal distances should be traversed. Presently we shall obtain a simple term for this kind of motion.

Let us consider a time line of a moving point, as in the drawing. We found in the preceding section that this time line is inclined to the coordinate axis *OT*, and that the tangent

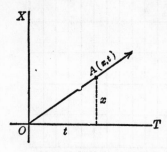

of the angle this time line makes with the coordinate axis *OT* is x/t, where *x* and *t* are the coordinates of any point of the time line. We know that the time line may be so inclined to the coordinate axis *OT* that this angle may be small, and it may be large, as the magnitude of the tangent of such an angle is cor-

respondingly small or large. The tangent of a small angle is small, and if the angle is larger its tangent also will be larger. The values of *t* (of the intervals of time) do not change, but the values of the corresponding *x*'s may change. If the value of *x*, the distance that the point traverses in equal periods of time, is small, the value of x/t is also small. But the distances traversed in equal periods of time are large, the value of x/t will be very large. Thus in the drawing below the time lines *OA*, *OB*, *OC*, and *OD*

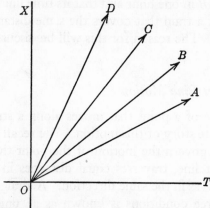

correspondingly represent points whose x/t are arranged in the order of increasing magnitude.

If a point is stationary, then its time line is parallel to the coordinate axis OT unless this point is "here" at the origin; in this case the coordinate axis OT would be its time line.

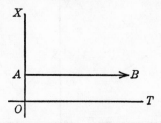

If a point is stationary for a while, then suddenly begins to move, its time line is a combination of two lines, the first portion parallel to the coordinate axis OT and the second inclined to this axis.

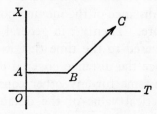

If a point moves so that for a certain period of time it traverses during equal periods certain distances, all equal, and then suddenly these equal distances either increase or decrease, the time line of such a point is also a broken line as shown below.

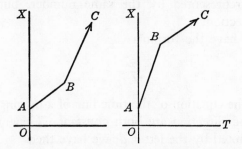

A point may move first forward and then backward to break the direction of its motion. This may also be coupled with a change in the length of the distances traversed in equal periods of time. The time lines representing such a motion are shown below.

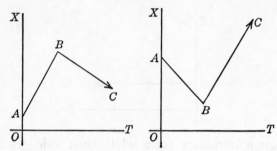

If we consider the expression x/t where x is the coordinate of the moving point and t is its corresponding value of time, we also note that for every value of t the value of x that corresponds to it represents the distance of the moving point from the origin, its point of departure. Then x/t in general represents the ratio of the distance covered to the time that it took to cover that distance. Also, since the distance covered during some known time interval is the same for any other equal time interval, division of the numerical value of the distance covered by the numerical value of total time gives us the magnitude of the distance covered during one unit of time. This new value is known as the "speed" of the moving point per unit length of time. If we consider also the direction of the motion, we have the "velocity" of that point. In other words, speed and velocity are represented by the same number, but velocity is speed + direction.

We then have the formula

$$\frac{x}{t} = v$$

and this is the equation of the time line of a moving point when its speed and direction are both constant. Generally, the distance is denoted by the letter d; we have then

$$\frac{d}{t} = v, \quad \text{and} \quad d = vt$$

By this formula we may compute the distance covered if we
know the velocity per unit of time and the time that it took
to cover that distance. For example, if an automobile travels
at the rate of thirty miles an hour, in two hours it will cover
$30 \cdot 2 = 60$ miles.

The equation

$$d = vt$$

corresponds to the time line of a point whose starting place is
the origin. If the starting place of the point is not the origin,
but a point whose distance from the origin is a units of length,
the equation is

$$d - a = vt$$

and its graph is

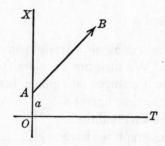

If the moving point starts from the origin, but b units of
time after the recording of time was begun, the equation is

$$d = v(t - b)$$

and the graph of the time line is

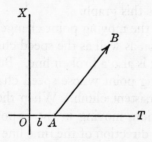

There is only one line in the plane of the coordinate axes OX
and OT that is meaningless. As the velocity of the moving point

increases, the time line becomes more steep, but it never can be-

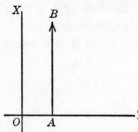

come perpendicular to the coordinate axis OT. A time line that is perpendicular to the axis OT represents an infinitely large velocity. However, it is known that no velocity can be greater than the velocity (or speed) of light, which is about 186,000 miles a second. Thus the line AB that is perpendicular to the coordinate axis OT does not represent anything that is physically possible.

The Algebra of Speed

Suppose a point moves along a straight line so that its speed changes frequently. We shall not consider for the moment the law under which such changes take place, but rather let us ex-amine the shape of the time line of a point moving under such conditions. In the accompanying graph we have a broken line. Each of the straight lines composing it represents a time line of the moving point for which the speed is the same, or constant. The reader may observe the various changes in the speed of the moving point as he examines this graph.

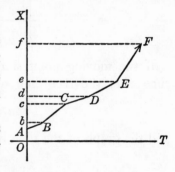

If the velocity of the moving point changes from time to time —that is, the direction as well as the speed changes—the time line of the moving point is also a broken line. But in contrast to the time line of a moving point whose speed changes, this time line does not show a persistent climb. When the point changes the direction of its motion, moving in the opposite direction along the straight line, the direction of the time line changes also. This is shown in the drawing below. The direction of the time line CD indicates that from c the point moves backward. The direction of the time line *DE* indicates that from *d* the point resumes its forward motion.

If the velocity of the moving point changes continuously, the broken time line is represented by an infinite number of very short straight lines which finally smooth out into a curve, as illustrated below.

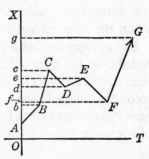

Originally we imposed a restriction on the motion of a point along a straight line; we insisted that its speed be constant. Then we introduced the notion of velocity, but still, even if the direction of the motion of the point were allowed to change, we did not remove the restriction concerning the magnitude of the speed. Now let us assume that the speed is allowed to change but only so that for every equal interval of time (in duration) the change is the same. Thus, if the speed of the point during the first second is one inch per second, then we may allow this speed increase at the beginning of each succeeding second, say by two inches. Thus we have the following speeds at the beginning of each succeeding second:

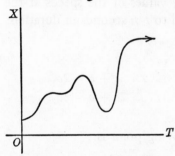

t	0	1	2	3	4	5	6	7	8
v	1	3	5	7	9	11	13	15	17

The increase in speed is known as "acceleration." If the magnitude of the acceleration is the same for intervals of time of equal duration, the speed is said to be "uniformly" accelerated.

The increase in speed (or velocity) as illustrated above is generally artificial. The table of values implies that the increase takes place suddenly at the beginning of each interval of time; actually the acceleration takes place continuously. To derive an expression that would state the relationship between the distance traversed by a point moving along a straight line with uniformly accelerated speed and the time it would take to cover this distance, it is necessary to examine what happens to this point when the time intervals become very small.

Let us suppose that a point begins to move (it is first at rest), and moves for t seconds; at the end of $t = 1/n$ seconds the acceleration is c units of distance. Also let us suppose that each second is divided into n intervals and that the acceleration for each interval (which is $1/n$ seconds in length) then is c. The total acceleration is

$$c = a \cdot \frac{t}{n}$$

for t intervals when the acceleration for each interval is a. Thus each change in speed is c for each period, and since the point starts at rest we have the following values of the speeds at the end of each small period, each equal to t/n seconds in duration: the speed is:

After the first period of time...... c

After the second............... $c + c = 2c$

After the third................. $2c + c = 3c$

until we reach the last period of time.

The distance traversed by the moving point is:

After the first period of time (which is $\frac{t}{n}$ seconds long)......................... $c\left(\frac{t}{n}\right)$

After the second period................... $2c\left(\frac{t}{n}\right)$

After the third period.................... $3c\left(\frac{t}{n}\right)$

Finally, after the nth period of time........ $nc\left(\frac{t}{n}\right)$

Then the total distance traversed by the moving point is

$$d = c\left(\frac{t}{n}\right) + 2c\left(\frac{t}{n}\right) + 3c\left(\frac{t}{n}\right) + \ldots + nc\left(\frac{t}{n}\right)$$

$$= [1 + 2 + 3 + \ldots + n]\, c\left(\frac{t}{n}\right)$$

The sum in the brackets can be obtained by means of the formula

$$\frac{n(n + 1)}{2}$$

because 1, 2, 3, . . ., n is a sequence known to us as the "how-much" ladder.

Then

$$d = \frac{n(n + 1)}{2} \cdot \frac{t}{n} c$$

But we have

$$c = a\frac{t}{n}$$

Then we have finally that

$$d = \frac{n(n + 1)}{2} \cdot \frac{t}{n} \cdot a \cdot \frac{t}{n}$$

or

$$d = \frac{at^2}{2} \cdot \frac{(n + 1)}{n}$$

But

$$\frac{(n + 1)}{n} = 1 + \frac{1}{n}$$

Now, if n is allowed to become infinitely large, $1/n$ becomes very small, and it may be discarded. Then we have finally that the distance traversed by a point moving with a uniformly accelerated speed is given by the expression

$$d = \tfrac{1}{2}at^2$$

The value of a is then obtained from this formula as

$$a = \frac{2d}{t^2}$$

This signifies that the acceleration is measured as per the square of the time, and we usually state that the acceleration is so many units of length per second square, or per second per second.

If we know the magnitude of the acceleration, we may compute the velocity at any given time, as well as the distance traversed during a given interval of time. Thus if the acceleration is $a = 4$ feet per second square, then in the first second the distance covered is 2 feet, and during the second second, 8 feet.

The graph of the time line of a point moving with a uniformly accelerated speed is a parabola. The reader will recall that we obtained the equation of the parabola as $y^2 = 4ax$ (see Chapter 24).

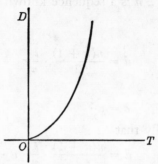

Speed on the Curves

Now we shall remove the restriction that a point can move along a straight line only.

Suppose a point moves freely within a plane in Flatland. It may move along a straight line and its path may be some curved line—a circle, an ellipse, or any other curve. To account for the time we must have three coordinates for every point on the time line; thus we have a counterpart of the three-dimensional coordinates. Two of these coordinates are x and y, and the third is t. We need not dwell on examination of the new kinds of time lines; since everything that was said concerning the time lines and their properties thus far is equally applicable to time lines for motions in Flatland.

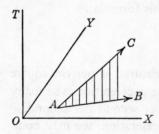

If a point moves along a straight line in Flatland its actual path is a straight line in the plane of the coordinate axes OX and OY. But the time line of this moving point is a straight line (if the motion is with a uniform speed or velocity) that is inclined to this plane, as shown in the drawing at left.

Thus the straight line AB is the path of the moving point, usually called the "orbit," and the straight line AC is its time line.

If the orbit of a moving point is a curved line, however, then its time line is also a curved line as shown in the accompanying drawing.

Uniform speed implies a motion with constant speed along a straight line. If a point moves along a curved line, even if its speed is always the same, the direction of the motion changes, and such a motion also is known as accelerated. The reason for this classification is that the motion along a curved path is usually considered as a combination of two separate motions along two straight lines parallel to the coordinate axes OX and OY.

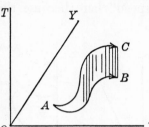

When a point moves along a curve it seems to have a tendency to continue along a straight line and fly off the curved path, but there always is something that pulls it back onto the curved path. The breaking up of this straight-line tendency into two motions along the two parallel lines shows that the magnitude of this straight-line fly-off speed changes from place to place on the curve. This is seen from the drawing below. The velocity at the point A is shown by the line tangent to (touching) the curve. Then there are two velocities, one parallel to the coordinate axis OX (it is denoted by v_x) and the other parallel to the coordinate axis OY

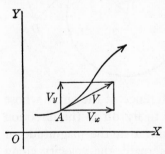

(denoted by v_y). These two velocities are known as the "components" of the velocity along the curve, which is assumed to be the velocity of the tendency to fly off. Since the two component velocities are represented by two perpendicular lines (we should remember that the coordinate axes are perpendicular to one another), we have by means of the Pythagorean relation that

$$v = \sqrt{v_x^2 + v_y^2}$$

Why Don't We Fly Off into Space?

Of the many possible motions along curved orbits in a plane, we shall consider the motion along a circle with a constant velocity. The reader should note that we do not use the word "speed" here because the direction of the motion constantly changes. Study of this motion along a circle reveals a hint to one of the most important theories of natural phenomena, Newton's theory of gravitation.

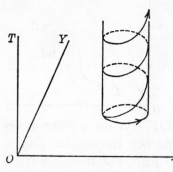

First we shall note that the time line of a point moving along a circle with a constant velocity is a winding screw-curve, such as we examined in Chapter 34.

When a point moves along the circumference of a circle, it has a tendency to leave its path and continue to move along a straight line that is tangent to the circumference of this circle. Since the point continues to move along the circumference of the circle, there must be something that causes it to "stay put" on its orbit. This situation is very similar to the motion of the earth around the sun, that of the moon around the earth, and even that of ourselves as the earth rotates on its axis.

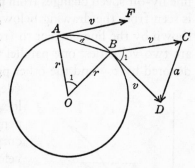

As a point moves along the circumference of the circle whose center is O, at some point A it tends to fly off in the direction shown by the arrow. We shall assume that the magnitude of this intended velocity is v (which is actually the velocity along the circumference of the circle, as it soon will be shown). At another point B the same tendency is observed. Now let us suppose that the arc AB corresponds to an angle 1. We may assume that we can draw the velocity at the point A from the point B (we retain the same direction; that is, BC is parallel to AF). Then we may explain the fact that at the point B the direction of the tendency to fly off is BD because BC is pulled by $CD = a$. As we make the angle 1 smaller this may and does happen; the moving point is pulled. Moreover, as the angle 1 becomes very small the direction of the pull is toward the center O of the circle. We also know that as the angle 1 becomes very small we may replace the arc AB by the straight line $AB = d$.

We also note that the two triangles ABO and BCD are both isosceles and are similar because AF is perpendicular to AO, and BC is perpendicular to AO, and BD is perpendicular to OB, and therefore the angles marked 1 are equal. Then we have that

$$\frac{CD}{BC} = \frac{AB}{AO}$$

Recalling that $CD = a$, $BC = v$, $AB = d$, and $AO = r$, we have

$$\frac{a}{v} = \frac{d}{r}$$

Now the distance d may be supposed to be covered in t seconds; then $d = vt$, $a = bt$, the total acceleration (this is the name for the pull), and we have

$$\frac{bt}{v} = \frac{vt}{r}, \quad \text{or} \quad b = \frac{v^2}{r}$$

where v is the velocity along the circumference of the circle and r is the radius of the circle along the circumference of which the point moves. This expression gives us the "centripetal acceleration," the pull toward the center of the circle which prevents the point from flying off along a tangent.

If this centripetal acceleration were suddenly eliminated, or if the earth were suddenly to stop revolving on its axis, we would fly off into space along with every-

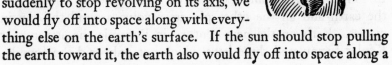

thing else on the earth's surface. If the sun should stop pulling the earth toward it, the earth also would fly off into space along a tangent to its own orbit. On the other hand, if the sun were still pulling the earth but the earth stopped moving around the sun on its orbit, we would immediately hurtle headlong into the sun and perish. How all this operates, what is the magnitude of the pulls, and how they are measured will be discussed now.

What Makes the Universe Hang Together?

The universe, to which are related the sun and its planets (including the earth), the stars, meteors, comets, and all other objects filling it, is quite empty. It has no up, no down, no right side, and no left side. Still this universe as a whole represents a very orderly collection. The objects that fill it seem to hang in space, although they have no visible supports that would help them to keep their places. These objects do not fall suddenly into the bottomless abyss that is the universe. There is something, however, that prevents such disasters; what is this mysterious power that keeps all these objects where they are?

Moreover, if each star and each planet were considered separately, we might ask the same question justifiably. We know that the earth has a solid core (what is inside underneath this core is anybody's guess), but the sun and the stars are all made up of gases. A gas is a very flimsy substance, although in the case of some stars one cubic inch of it may weigh several tons. We may also refer to the earth's atmosphere, but this, too, is a gas. Why doesn't the gas that makes up the sun, the stars, and the earth's atmosphere fly off into space? What keeps the sun or the stars together? We know that a whiff of smoke rising from a chimney or from a smoker's pipe quickly disappears; if it is impossible for us here on earth to have a ball of smoke, would it be possible somewhere in space outside the earth?

To answer these questions, we must go back several centuries. In 1543 a Polish monk, Copernicus, announced his theory that the earth and all the other planets revolve around the sun in circles. Early in the next century in Bohemia the astronomer Kepler formulated three laws which not only laid the foundation of theoretical astronomy but are so general that (as far as the statements of relationship connected with them are concerned) they have influenced other branches of pure science. These laws are, in a simpler formulation, that the planets move in circles, and the sun is at the center of the circle; that the radius drawn from the sun to a planet sweeps equal areas in equal periods of time, and that the cubes of the diameters (or radii) of the circles are proportional to the squares of the periods of revolution (of the planets). These laws are applicable not only to the stars, the sun, and the planets, but, for one example, to the motions of electrons in atoms, though with some modifications.

According to this second law the planets are assumed to move around the sun in circular paths (orbits) with a constant speed. We have obtained a very important relationship concerning the motion along the circumference of a circle, namely

$$g = \frac{v^2}{r}$$

which is the centripetal acceleration that holds the point on the circular path. In this formula the v represents the speed of the point, and r, the radius of the circle.

If it takes t units of time for the point to complete one revolution, then the speed is

$$v = \frac{2\pi r}{t}$$

where $2\pi r$ is the circumference of the circle. Substitute this value of v in the formula for the centripetal acceleration and we have

$$g = \frac{4\pi^2 r^2}{rt^2} = \frac{4\pi^2 r}{t^2}$$

According to the third law of Kepler, by which the ratio of the cube of the radius of the circle to the square of the time of revolution, r^3/t^2, is the same for all the planets; that is

$$\frac{r^3}{t^2} = k$$

or

$$\frac{r}{t^2} = \frac{k}{r^2}$$

The reader may check this relationship by the table below, giving the values in terms of the average distances from the earth to the sun and of a period of one year.

Planet	Distance from the Sun	Period of Revolutions about the Sun
Mercury..............	0.387	0.24
Venus................	0.723	0.62
Earth................	1.000	1.00
Mars.................	1.524	1.88
Jupiter...............	5.203	11.86
Saturn...............	9.539	29.46
Uranus...............	19.191	84.02
Neptune.............	30.071	164.8
Pluto................	39.000	249.2

The reader is warned, however, that the formula $r^3/t^2 = k$ is not an exact statement of the law, nor is the law as stated above exactly expressed. At best it is an approximation, and at no time will the reader obtain the value of $k = 1$ (which should be expected since for the earth $1^3/1^2 = 1$). However a value of k sufficiently close to 1 is a fairly good check on the correctness of the third law of Kepler.

Substitute k/r^2 for the value of r/t^2 in the expression

$$g = \frac{4\pi^2 r}{t^2}$$

and we have

$$g = \frac{4\pi^2 k}{r^2}$$

This result shows that the centripetal acceleration, the pull toward the sun, does not depend on the speed or size of the planet. It does depend, however, on the nature of the sun; the value of k may be somehow related to it. It depends on the distance of the planet from the sun, and it decreases with the square of this distance. This decrease with the square of the distance is an interesting phenomenon; for example, a similar decrease is in effect when we examine the strength of illumination. Illumination decreases with the square of the distance of an object from the source of light.

The last result gives us a hint concerning what holds the planets in their orbits. Two separate factors contribute to this: (1) the fact that the planets move around the sun and (2) the fact that the sun pulls the planets toward it. But this is only a hint. In the next section we shall delve into this more deeply.

The Democracy of a Tumble

It would take us too far afield if we attempted to examine all the laws and relationships that express the natural phenomena of weight, but we can progress far by accepting some of the fundamental facts. It is about three hundred years since the Italian scientist Galileo discovered that a body dropped from a height does not fall all the way the same speed. Its speed increases as it falls; the motion of a falling body is thus a uniformly accelerated motion in a straight line. Galileo discovered that all objects dropped from the same height, regardless of their size, shape, or any other characteristic, reach the ground simultaneously (there may be some discrepancy due to air resistance but, if the resistance of the air is eliminated, Galileo's observation is correct). In other words, falling bodies are affected only by the pull toward the earth.

However, when we raise an object from the ground, we experience something called the lifting of a definite weight. Moreover, not all objects are equally heavy; what makes one object heavier than another?

If we have some substance and then take twice as much of it, we say that the second amount weighs twice as much. Thus we may come to the conclusion that weight depends on the amount of substance. This amount of substance we call mass, and it is denoted by the letter m or M. When we lift this mass we must overcome the gravitational pull of the earth, which tugs with equal force each unit of the mass. This pull is denoted by the letter g. Now, if there are m units of mass, the pull toward the earth is the product of m and g. This product is known as the measure of weight,

$$\text{weight} = mg$$

and, when an object of mass m rests, its downward pressure, or weight, is therefore $m \cdot g = mg$. In other words, the heaviness of an object depends upon the value of the product of its mass and the gravitational pull exerted on it.

Another important measure we shall use is very similar to weight. Suppose an object is at rest; to disturb or set it in motion we must apply some external or outside force to it. If a body is moving and we apply a force to it, it may either change its direction or move faster (or slower, depending upon how this force is applied), or both. This application of force causes a change in the velocity of the object (when the object is at rest its velocity is zero). Thus force may have something to do with acceleration. Moreover, if this force is applied by means of some other object, the weight of the object controls the magnitude of the force. An object that weighs twice as much as another (that is, an object whose mass is twice the mass of another) will produce a force twice as great, and the change in the velocity of the object to which this force is applied (which is denoted by a) is thus proportional to the amount of mass. We have then the relation

$$\text{force} = f = ma$$

where f is the force.

If force is applied for some length of time, say t, we have the total amount of force used up equal to ft. This total force may be applied instantaneously, and the same effect is attained. Note, however, that

$$ft = mat$$

but

$$at = v \text{ (v is the velocity)}$$

then

$$ft = mv$$

which means that the total force used up during the time t is equal to the product of the mass of an object (which is used for the application of the force) and the velocity of that object.

A Multiplication Table for Physical Relations

To save time and labor, a multiplication table which gives us all the necessary formulas for the various physical relations is given below. This table is constructed on the same plan as that of any other mathematical table. The formula for any relationship or physical property whose name appears in a certain cell is obtained as the product of the letters that head the vertical column and horizontal row to which this cell belongs. The reader may have noticed that all the formulas obtained in the preceding sections were finally stated as products of some fundamental quantities. For example, the formula for the distance traversed by a point moving with uniform constant speed along a straight line is

$$d = vt$$

where d is the distance traversed, v is the speed (also it may be considered as the velocity), and t is the time during which the distance d was covered.

MULTIPLICATION TABLE OF PHYSICAL RELATIONS

	Distance d	Velocity v	Acceleration a	Time t	Mass m	Force f
Distance d	——	——	$\dfrac{v^2}{2}$	——	——	$K = \dfrac{mv^2}{2}$ (Work)
Velocity v	——	$2ad$	——	d	ft (Impulse)	$P = \dfrac{K}{t}$ (Power)
Acceleration a	$\dfrac{v^2}{2}$	——	——	v (Velocity)	f (Force)	——
Time t	——	d (Distance)	v (Velocity)	$\dfrac{2d}{a}$	——	mv (Amount of motion)
Mass m	——	ft (Impulse)	f (Force)	——	——	——
Force f	$K = \dfrac{mv^2}{2}$ (Work)	$P = \dfrac{K}{t}$ (Power)	——	mv (Amount of motion)	——	——

Those cells that contain no formulas or expressions indicate that the product of the headings of their corresponding columns and rows have no meaning, but generally by means of this table it is possible to solve those problems in which the various physical and mechanical relationships stated in it are involved.

Since all mechanical and physical problems (when considered from the practical point of view) involve measures, it is important to have a clear idea of what measures are involved and to select the proper unit of measure. Generally, two systems of measures are used. In one, the units are the foot and the pound; in the other, the gram and the centimeter. Any multiple of these is permissible; instead of the gram we may use 1,000 grams or the kilogram, and instead of the centimeter we may use 100 centimeters or the meter. Thus "work," $K = fd$, is the product of a distance and force. Force may be expressed in pounds and distance in feet. Thus work is measured in terms of a "foot-pound." However the reader is warned that if the fundamental unit is used in one part we do not use a multiple of the other unit. Thus force would never be expressed in terms of a foot-ton, or in terms of a mile-pound.

Some of the expressions in the above table need further explanation. If a force is applied constantly to a moving object, or throughout a certain distance, the product of the force and distance represents the work performed. Thus

$$fd = K$$

But

$$f = ma, \quad \text{and} \quad ad = \frac{v^2}{2}$$

then

$$fd = mad = \frac{mv^2}{2} = K$$

Since the work performed through the distance d requires the time t for this, the amount of work in one unit of time is K/t. and this may be considered as applied instantaneously. Thus $P = K/t$ is the measure of the rate at which work is done.

The reader will recall also that the expression for the centripetal acceleration, the pull exerted on a point moving at a velocity v along the circumference of a circle whose radius is r and is v^2/r. Since the expression for force is $f = ma$; the expression for force that keeps an object with a mass m along the circumference of a circle, when this object moves with the velocity v, is

$$f = \frac{mv^2}{r}$$

We shall now apply these facts to the final examination of "what makes the universe hang together?"

What Came First, the Chicken or the Egg?

The ancient question about the chicken and the egg has caused controversies since it was first proposed. A chicken certainly hatches from an egg, but to have a chicken we must first have an egg. On the other hand, to have an egg we must have a chicken to lay it. Thus we are in the vicious circle as to what came first. The answer to this puzzle may be: It all depends how you look at it. However, we are about to force another problem no less puzzling.

When a point moves along the circumference of a circle with the velocity v it stays on the circumference because it is prevented from flying off its path by centripetal acceleration, expressed as $g = v^2/r$, where r is the radius of the circle.

In the case of the planets which move around the sun, we found that the acceleration is

$$g = \frac{4\pi^2 k}{r^2}$$

where

$$k = \frac{r^3}{t^2}$$

which represents the statement of the third law of Kepler.

The value of k is the same for all the planets and it depends on the nature of the central object around which they move, that is, the sun. If the radius of the moon's orbit is R, and the period of the revolution of the moon about the earth is T, we have $k = R^3/T^2$, and in this case k depends on the nature of the earth. Let us substitute this value of k in the above expression for g. We have then

$$g = \frac{4\pi^2 R^3}{T^2 r^2}$$

Now for the moon $T = 27$ days, 7 hours, 43 minutes, and 12 seconds, or $T = 2{,}360{,}592$ seconds.

We may take this value as correct to three significant places, $T = 2.36 \cdot 10^6$ seconds. Also $R = 60.1r$, approximately, or the distance of the moon from the center of the earth is about 60.1 radii of the earth. The radius of the earth is about 4,000 miles, or $4{,}000 \cdot 5{,}280$ feet. Then the radius of the earth is approximately

$$r = 4{,}000 \cdot 5{,}280 = 21{,}120{,}000 \text{ feet}$$

or, rounded, $r = 2.11 \cdot 10^7$ feet.

Substitute the above values in the expression for g. We have then, after all the necessary cancellations, that

$$g = \frac{4 \cdot (3.14)^2 \cdot (60.1)^3 \, 2.11}{(2.36)^2 \cdot 10^5} = 32 \text{ feet per second}^2, \text{ approximately.}$$

In centimeters this is $g = 981$ centimeters per second^2.

The moon is kept on its orbit because the earth pulls it; that is, the moon is forced to fall toward the earth, but the moon does not fall toward the earth; it stays in its orbit because it has a motion of its own. Which of these two phenomena takes place first? If the reader can find a satisfactory answer to the question concerning the chicken and the egg, he will find no difficulty in answering this question also. Perhaps a satisfactory answer will be that the two act at the same time. However, the moon is approaching the earth and there will be a time when it will approach it so dangerously close, thousands of years hence, that the earth's forces will tear the moon apart.

Flatfoot to the Universe: Gravitation

We still have not fully disclosed "what makes the universe hang together." There is another side to this problem: If the earth pulls the moon, the moon pulls the earth also; in other words, the earth has a tendency to fall toward the moon. Witness the tides; they are caused by the moon.

We found that the earth (whose mass is M) exerts a pull on the moon with a force

$$f = M \cdot \frac{4\pi^2 k}{R^2}$$

(R is the radius of the moon's orbit, and k depends on the nature of the earth.) If the mass of the moon is m, then the moon pulls the earth with a force

$$F = m \cdot \frac{4\pi^2 K}{R^2}$$

(here K depends on the nature of the moon, and R is the same as above.) Since neither the moon nor the earth fall on one another, we may assume that these two forces f and F are equal,

$$M \cdot \frac{4\pi^2 k}{R^2} = m \cdot \frac{4\pi^2 K}{R^2}$$

or

$$Mk = mK$$

From this we have

$$\frac{K}{M} = \frac{k}{m}$$

which signifies that these ratios are the same for the sun and other bodies as well as for all the planets.

Let us denote the ratio

$$\frac{K}{M} \left(\text{or } \frac{k}{m} \right) \text{ by } \frac{c}{4\pi^2}$$

We have then

$$\frac{K}{M} = \frac{c}{4\pi^2}, \quad \text{or} \quad 4\pi^2 K = cM$$

and

$$\frac{k}{m} = \frac{c}{4\pi^2}, \quad \text{or} \quad 4\pi^2 k = cm$$

Then the expression

$$f = M \cdot \frac{4\pi^2 k}{R^2}$$

after $4\pi^2 k$ is replaced by cm, becomes

$$f = c\left(\frac{mM}{R^2}\right)$$

This expression is the mathematical statement of Newton's law of general gravitation. According to this law two bodies (they need not necessarily be planets) attract each other (pull toward the other) with a force that is proportional to the product of their respective masses, and this force decreases with (or, as we usually say, is inversely proportional to) the square of the distance between them. If the earth and the sun were twice as far away from one another, the pull they exert on one another would be four times less than it is now.

Thus objects are kept together because gravitation operates between them. Planets move around the sun for the same reason. The sun is kept in its course because it has a motion of its own. Gravitation operates throughout the entire universe and, as a result, some orderliness exists in the almost infinitely vast collection of stars. Some type of gravitation also operates inside that pigmy universe, the atom. Even here this force is such a stout champion of the established order that it takes a scientific blitzkrieg to smash the atom and release its imprisoned energy.

∞ 36 ∞

The Firing Squad
& Mathematics

What Happens When You Pull the Trigger?

In ancient times men fought with weapons that required the use of man power to make them effective. The sling, the bow and arrow, the catapult, and many other weapons that threw projectiles at a target required the application of force. The man who could throw a stone the farthest was just as valuable then as a long-range gun is now.

Since the invention of gunpowder (and this occurred not in Europe but in China where the Chinese used it more for fireworks and fun than for laying low their enemies), man power has been replaced by chemicals, and the forward march of deadly weapons has been marked by greater fire-power, longer range, and increased destructiveness. Even now, the limit to man's inventiveness is not yet in sight.

Gunpowder is an unstable chemical. Some substances are stable, that is, they resist any outside force and considerable effort is needed in order to break them up. This effort may be in the form of fire, electricity, and other means. Some chemicals or mixtures of chemicals such as gunpowder need only a slight jar or a little heat to set them off. Then they burn almost instantaneously, or "explode," and the gases that are formed expand in a terrific blast of energy. It is this bursting power of the suddenly released gases that hurls the projectile through the gun barrel.

641

The making of gunpowder (which is now generally classified as an "explosive") is nowadays an important branch of modern industry in peace as well as war. Explosives are useful in building, mining, and excavating. We shall concern ourselves mainly with the application of explosives to war machines. In passing, however, we may note that explosives actually do more constructive than destructive work even during wartime, as becomes obvious when we realize that nearly all transportation and much industry runs on the exploding power of gasoline or other fuels.

When powder explodes in a gun, the sudden expansion of a great quantity of extremely hot and active gases exert a force that gives the projectile a velocity that sometimes reaches 3,000 feet per second and a pressure that may be over 20 tons per square inch, as is the case with the six-inch gun.

Gunpowder may be converted into gas by simple explosion or by detonation. In a simple explosion the rate at which the explosive is decomposed is comparatively slow. A grain of black gunpowder, ignited in open air, will burn at the rate of about a half-inch per second. When some gunpowder is sprinkled into a thin line, it will burn in open air at the rate of about 14 inches per second. On the other hand, detonation is almost instantaneous, its speed sometimes being at a rate of 3.75 miles per second. Actual observations revealed some interesting facts concerning the power that is generated by detonation. When a rifle is fired, the powder is actually detonated. The speed that is imparted to the bullet by this detonation is considerably greater than any speed attained by the fastest airplane. The velocity with which a bullet leaves the muzzle of a rifle (known as the "muzzle velocity") is not the same for all guns. It depends on many things, such as the amount of the powder detonated, known as the "charge," the size and the weight of the projectile, and finally the length of the barrel of the gun.

Below is a table of values for the pressure, the corresponding velocities, and distances passed by a bullet in the barrel of a gun. The reader should understand that the values given here would not apply for any other gun. They are recorded numbers. However, the information that is obtained from this and other tables is very important, especially for those whose interest is gunnery and its industry.

Distance Passed in Barrel of Gun in Centimeters	Pressure in Atmospheres (1 kilogram per cm.²)	Velocity of Bullet in Meters per Second
2	1,934	139
4	2,450	245
6	2,850	361
8	2,804	414
12	2,487	518
26	1,413	694
34	1,056	751
42	812	792
50	640	823
58	520	847
67	416	865

Note that up to a certain time the pressure increases, then it begins to fall. The highest pressure is reached about 6 centimeters from the chamber. On the other hand, the velocity of the bullet increases constantly. First the increase is markedly great, but about halfway in the barrel the rate of the increase begins to diminish. However, the muzzle velocity of the bullet, which is some 865 meters per second, is equivalent to about 1,935 miles an hour. And this is not the greatest muzzle velocity of a rifle bullet, for with modern guns velocities up to 1,700 meters per second (or about 3,850 miles per hour) have been observed.

The information given in the above table is shown below in graphical form. There are two curves in this graph. From this drawing the reader will observe how the pressure and the velocity of the bullet change.

It should be understood also that the value of the initial velocity, that is, the muzzle velocity of the bullet as given in the above table, as well as all the other values for muzzle velocities given above, are for velocities in vacuum. In air, the initial velocity of the bullet is considerably less, owing to air resistance which may reduce this velocity by as much as 20 per cent.

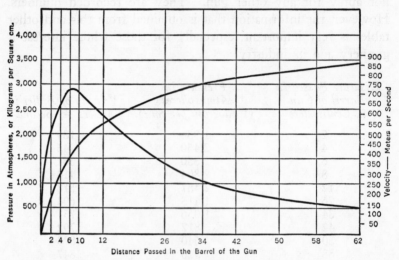

Atmospheric pressure of 1 kilogram per square cm. is equivalent to a pressure of 14.32 pounds per square inch. 1 cm. = 0.394 in., 1 meter = 3.28 ft. = 1.094 yards

How Strong Is a Bullet?

In this as well as in the following sections we shall make use of the results obtained in Chapter 35. The reader may consult the multiplication table of physical relations given in that chapter.

A flying bullet that leaves the rifle with a certain velocity (we should remember that a bullet has a weight of its own) carries a certain amount of force. The extent of this force can be judged from what a bullet can do. We know that a bullet has penetration power and can shatter some very solid materials, but just how much damage can it do?

When a bullet strikes some obstruction in its path, it uses up some, if not all, of its velocity. Thus, in order to overcome the obstruction the bullet must perform some work. Now we already know that the formula for work is

$$K = \frac{mv^2}{2}$$

By means of this formula we can compute the capacity of the bullet to perform work, that is, the amount of energy the bullet carries as it leaves the muzzle.

Suppose that the bullet weighs 10 grams. We have obtained the formula for weight in terms of the mass of an object and the value of acceleration due to gravitation ($g = 981$ centimeters per second^2): weight $= mg$ (see Chapter 35). We have then, if the weight is denoted by w,

$$m = \frac{w}{g}, \quad \text{or} \quad m = \frac{w}{981}$$

or, in terms of meters (1 meter $= 1,000$ centimeters), $m = w/9.81$. In order to simplify our computations we shall use 10 instead of 9.81, the discrepancy being too slight to affect the final result.

Then for a bullet weighing 10 grams, and whose initial muzzle velocity is, say, 1,000 meters per second, we have (keeping in mind that 10 grams $= 0.01$ kilogram)

$$K = \frac{0.01 \cdot (1,000)^2}{10 \cdot 2} = 500 \text{ kilogram-meters}$$

In terms of foot-pounds this is equal to (since 1 kilogram $=$ 2.205 pounds, and 1 meter $=$ 3.281 feet)

$$500 \cdot 2.205 \cdot 3.281 = 3,617 \text{ foot-pounds, approximately}$$

This amount of energy will move 3,617 pounds a distance of 1 foot.

A hundred-pound shell fired from a six-inch gun has the initial muzzle velocity of about 3,000 feet per second. The energy of this shell is

$$K = \frac{100 \cdot (3,000)^2}{32 \cdot 2} = 14,000,000 \text{ foot-pounds}$$

This is equivalent to 7,000 foot-ton, or enough power to drive a 7,000-ton ship 1 foot.

In practical applications there is a unit of work (and energy) known as the "horsepower." One horsepower is equal to 550 foot-pounds, approximately.

The amount of energy of a hundred-pound six-inch shell is then equal to

$$\frac{14,000,000}{550} = 25,450 \text{ horsepowers, approximately}$$

The average automobile motor generates about 100 horsepower. Thus, to set this six-inch shell in motion with a velocity of about 3,000 feet per second, it would require about 255 automobiles.

You May Not Hit the Target, but You'll Get a Kick out of This

When the charge in the chamber of a gun is detonated, the expanding gases immediately press with equal force in every direction, forward, with the bullet as well as backward along the butt of the gun in the direction of the person who fires the shot. This pressing backward delivers a kick known as the "recoil." When a cannon is fired, the recoil may be observed as the barrel of the gun moves (or rather slides) backward. When a revolver is fired, the recoil is felt in the hand of the person who holds the gun.

The recoil is thus a motion of the gun in the direction opposite to the direction of the motion of the projectile (the bullet or the shell). A gunner should be aware of the nature of the recoil because ignorance may mean injury.

To account for the energy of the recoil it is necessary to know its velocity. If this velocity is known, and the mass of the gun is also known, then the energy of the recoil can be computed by means of the formula

$$K = \frac{mv^2}{2}$$

Now, if we consult the multiplication table of physical relations of Chapter 35, we find that

$$ft = mv$$

or, in other words, that the impulse equals the amount of motion. Since the forces that are released by the detonation of the powder in the chamber take effect simultaneously and work in all directions, they are equal. Thus, since ft, that is, the impulse is the same for the gun and the bullet, the amount of motion of the gun must be equal to that of the bullet.

Let us denote the mass of the bullet by m, the velocity of the bullet by v, the mass of the gun by M, and the velocity of the gun (recoil) by V. Then,

$$mv = MV$$

and from this we have

$$V = \frac{mv}{M}$$

Since the mass is computed by means of the expression

$$m = \frac{w}{g}, \quad \text{and} \quad M = \frac{W}{g}$$

we have

$$V = \frac{wv}{W}$$

where w is the weight of the bullet, and W is the weight of the gun.

Thus, if a bullet weighs about 10 grams, and a rifle about 4.5 kilograms, and if the muzzle velocity of a bullet is about 1,000 meters per second, the velocity of the recoil is

$$V = \frac{10 \cdot 1,000}{4,500} = 2.2 \text{ meters per second}$$

The energy of the recoil is then

$$K = \frac{4.5 \cdot (2.2)^2}{10} = 1.09 \text{ kilogram-meters}$$

This energy is about 446 times less than the energy of the bullet, or about 9.5 foot-pounds. However, it is great enough to cause injury to an inexperienced person.

Let us consider the expression

$$V = \frac{wv}{W}$$

If w, that is, the weight of the bullet, is made smaller, then V, the velocity of the recoil, will become smaller. Also, if W, the weight of the gun, is made larger, then V, the velocity of the recoil, will become smaller. Thus, in order to reduce the velocity of the recoil it is advisable (1) to make the bullet lighter and (2) to make the gun heavier. Some hunters therefore add extra weight (in the form of a metal plate) to the end of the butt of a rifle.

Nowadays, however, the recoil is not considered detrimental to the operation of a gun. With the introduction of the automatic loading, the energy of the recoil is utilized and is directed into a useful operation, that of feeding ammunition into the chamber.

Another effect of the recoil is the lifting of the muzzle of a gun when it is fired. This fact is very important when one takes aim. There is some lift at the moment of detonation, but most occurs after the projectile has left the muzzle of the gun. Moreover, while the bullet travels inside the barrel of the gun, it causes the barrel (and therefore the entire gun) to vibrate, and this also contributes to the lifting of the muzzle. This vibration is usually the greatest contributing factor to lifting.

In some cases this lifting may be "negative," that is, the muzzle of the gun may point downward. The direction of the lifting depends on the manner in which the gun is held. Thus every individual must study his own method of firing and then make the necessary correction. The angle between the original position of the gun before it was fired and the position after the bullet left the gun may vary from +2 minutes (upward lifting) to −8 minutes (downward depression). Suppose a shot is fired at a target 200 yards away. The drawing below illustrates the situation in the case of lifting (or depression). AB is the distance from the gun to the target. Angle CAB is the angle of lifting. Now, since the triangle ABC is a right triangle,

$$CB = AB \tan CAB$$

If the angle of lifting is $2'$, then

$$CB = AB \tan 2' = 200 \cdot 0.00058 = 0.116 \text{ yard} =$$

4.2 inches, approximately

If the angle of depression is 8′, then

$CB = AB \tan 8' = 200 \cdot 0.00233 = 0.466 \text{ yard} =$

$$16.8 \text{ inches, approximately}$$

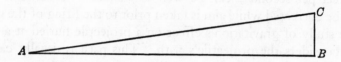

The results above show that the direct aiming at a target is not advisable. If you aim at a target directly, you will never hit it. However, this is not the only reason why a target will surely be missed if you aim straight at it. We shall find the other reasons in the sections that follow.

The Path of a Bullet

The most ideal conditions for hitting a target are those that do not exist. A person who fires a gun must remember several important facts. He must take into consideration that the bullet must travel through air. Air, however thin you slice it, offers considerable resistance to any object that speeds through it. Nowadays, engineers are fully aware of this fact, and modern designing reduces the effect of air resistance by "streamlining." We have streamlined automobiles, airplanes, ships, railroad engines—even furniture and newspaper type!—and recently streamlining overtook the design of bullets and shells.

The fact that air resistance operates in the case of projectiles thrown through the atmosphere of the earth was long known to scientists. Isaac Newton pointed out that air resistance cannot be disregarded and suggested that the resistance increases with the square of the velocity. This may be true up to certain velocities (240 meters, or about 790 feet per second), but for greater velocities this resistance seems to increase with the cube (or even with a higher power) of the velocity of the bullet (or shell). So far an exact formula for high-velocity resistance has not been found.

It would be ideal for gunnery experts if air and gravitation were eliminated and projectiles were hurled through empty space (vacuum). However, the effect of gravitational attraction (the g which is equal to 981 centimeters per second^2 or about 32 feet per second^2) can be well taken into consideration and can be corrected while aim is taken prior to the firing of the gun. The study of gravitation's effect on a projectile hurled at a target considers the projectile's path. This path is usually called "the trajectory."

When this trajectory is studied, it is examined in its relation to an imaginary plane that passes horizontally through the muzzle of a gun. Thus this plane is called "the horizon of the gun." The trajectory may be above or below this horizon. The drawings below illustrate the various positions of the muzzle of the gun and the corresponding horizons.

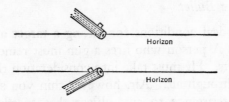

When the gun is pointed downward, the trajectory of the bullet is below the horizon of the gun. When the gun is pointed upward, the trajectory of the bullet is above the horizon.

Let us suppose that after the bullet leaves the gun no external force (we shall disregard air resistance altogether in our discussion) acts on it. Then the bullet will continue to travel along its trajectory, and this trajectory will be a straight line. The bullet will fly through the air an infinite distance. The trajectory will be a continuation of the axis of the barrel of the gun. The velocity of the bullet throughout its flight will be equal to the muzzle velocity. The flight of the bullet will be unimpeded, and it will travel with a uniform velocity. The drawing below illustrates this situation. During every second the bullet covers a distance equal to the distance passed during the first second after it has left the gun.

Such an ideal situation does not exist except in our imagination.

Let us examine what happens to the bullet when the gravitational attraction (acceleration due to gravitational attraction) of

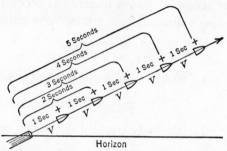

the earth acts on it as it travels through space. Let us assume for the time being that no other force, except this gravitational attraction, acts on the bullet. In other words, we shall assume that the bullet, as soon as it leaves the muzzle of the gun, loses all its initial velocity, and it begins to drop toward the earth (in the direction of the center of the earth). We thus assume that the bullet falls freely, and thus it is subject to the law of falling bodies.

We must now recall the fact that the gravitational attraction (acceleration) is a constant quantity. It is constant for every point on the surface of the earth, although it varies in magnitude for various points on the surface of the earth because the earth is not a perfect sphere.

We found in Chapter 35 that the equation for the time line of a point that moves with uniformly accelerated velocity (that is, the value of the acceleration is constant) is

$$d = \frac{at^2}{2}$$

where d is the distance traversed in t units of time, and a is the acceleration (the increase, or decrease in velocity). Since the value of g (the acceleration due to the gravitational attraction of the earth) is constant the equation for the distance through which a freely falling body passes must be of the same form. If we denote this distance by h, we have

$$h = \frac{gt^2}{2}$$

From this equation we may compute the distances through which a freely falling body will pass every succeeding second after it was allowed to fall. We shall take the value of g (981 centimeters per second^2) as 9.8 meters per second^2. We have then the following values of h for the corresponding values of t.

When $t = 0$ (the body is at rest),
$$h = 0.$$

When $t = 1$ (the body traveled the first second),
$$h = \frac{9.8}{2} = 4.9 \text{ meters.}$$

When $t = 2$ (the body traveled the second second),
$$h = 9.8 \cdot \frac{(2)^2}{2} = 9.8 \cdot 2 = 19.6 \text{ meters.}$$

When $t = 3$ (the body traveled the third second),
$$h = 9.8 \cdot \frac{(3)^3}{2} = 44.1 \text{ meters.}$$

When $t = 4$ (the body traveled the fourth second),
$$h = 9.8 \cdot \frac{(4)^2}{2} = 78.4 \text{ meters.}$$

When $t = 5$ (the body traveled the fifth second),
$$h = 9.8 \cdot \frac{(5)^2}{2} = 122.5 \text{ meters.}$$

The drawing below illustrates the respective distances passed by the falling bullet during every succeeding second after it was allowed to fall freely.

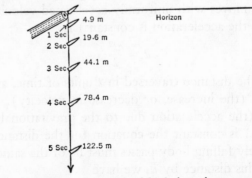

Now, if we combine these two ideal situations, we shall obtain (within the imposed limitation that the air resistance be completely disregarded) a fairly correct picture of the trajectory of the bullet. Graphically this is obtained as follows. We shall superimpose the two drawings for the ideal conditions examined by us. Then from the points on the vertical line (pointing downward) we shall draw lines parallel to the straight-line trajectory of the bullet (assuming that the gravitational attraction did not act on the bullet). Also, from the points on this straight line that mark the equal distances supposedly traversed by the bullet we shall draw lines parallel to the vertical line (pointing downward). We thus obtain a sequence of intersections of two straight lines. These points of intersections will then be joined by a smooth curve. This curve is the trajectory of the bullet.

Note that whenever we draw a vertical parallel line we indicated the direction in which the moving bullet will have to fall from its imaginary path along a straight line. The distance through which it has to fall is equal to the distance indicated on the original vertical straight line because we obtained parallelograms, and the opposite sides of a parallelogram are equal.

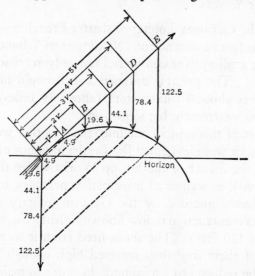

Thus, we added a series of graphs, each representing an imaginary situation, and in the final result we obtained a graph of the trajectory of the bullet. Within certain limitations, this graph gives a fairly satisfactory account of the motion of the bullet. This is a graph of a parabola. The highest point on the trajectory is known as *the vertex*. This vertex separates the trajectory into two branches. On the left of the vertex is "the ascending branch" of the trajectory and on the right, to the point of its intersection with the horizon line of the gun, is "the descending branch."

If there were no air resistance (that is, in a vacuum), these two branches would be equal. As it is, the descending branch is always shorter than the ascending one, because air resistance causes the projectile gradually to lose its velocity.

The parabolic shape of the trajectory is not artificial. The reader may observe the frequent occurrence of this shape in nature. When water is played from a hose, the stream of water assumes a parabolic shape. This is probably the best everyday illustration of the parabola.

Big Bertha's Secret

In 1918 the Germans, hoping to shatter French morale, began to shell Paris from a distance of 120 kilometers (about 75 miles). This feat in artillery was considered not only revolutionary but unbelievable. The greatest distance a shell could be hurled at that time was about 30 kilometers (about 19 miles), and that was only with extremely big siege guns.

The secret of this type of shelling, the gun that was used for this purpose (it was nicknamed Big Bertha in honor of Frau Bertha Krupp, the owner of the Krupp Works where the gun was manufactured), as well as all information pertinent to its operation was closely guarded by the German military authorities. However, its construction is now known; it had a barrel 37 meters long (about 120 feet). The shells fired from it were aimed so that most of their way they traveled high enough for air resistance to be reduced to a minimum, in order to maintain maximum velocity. Its initial velocity was about 2,000 meters per second (1.24 miles). The shells weighed 120 kilograms each (about 222 pounds).

If we refer to the drawing of the parabolic trajectory in the preceding section, we may note that one important fact in its construction was the inclination of the imaginary straight-line path of the bullet (that is, the path the bullet would travel on if there were no effect on the acceleration due to the gravitational attraction of the earth on it). This inclination of the imaginary straight line is known as the angle at which the gun is fired. If this angle is very steep, the parabolic trajectory is also very steep. If the angle is small, the trajectory will be elongated. The various types of trajectories will be examined in a subsequent section. What should be noted here is the fact that the angle of elevation of the gun controls the type and the shape of the trajectory of the projectile.

When we examined the applications of the banker's number (Chapter 19) we found that air pressure decreases with the rise above the ground and we obtained the relationship between the elevation h above the ground and the observed pressures p and P at different levels, namely,

$$p = Pe^{-kh}$$

where e is the bankers' number (2,71828 . . .), and k is the coefficient of proportionality.

As we rise above the surface of the earth the air becomes very rare, that is, its density diminishes. Up to a height of about six miles the density of the air is comparatively high. The portion of the earth's atmosphere within six miles above the ground is known as the troposphere. But as the elevation above the surface of the earth increases beyond the six-mile limit, the density of the air decreases rapidly. The portion of the air above the six-mile limit is known as the stratosphere. The fact that the air in the stratosphere is extremely rare (at the height of about twelve or thirteen miles it offers almost no resistance, even if objects move through it at high velocities) was utilized by the Germans when Big Bertha was fired. Their objective was to send the shell into the stratosphere so that it would reach it as quickly as possible and thus would lose the least amount of its initial muzzle velocity. After it had reached the stratosphere, it was supposed to travel almost unimpeded. Thus, it was not primarily the gun that enabled the Germans to hurl a shell at a target some seventy-five miles away, but use of the properties of the earth's atmosphere. Big Bertha was aimed at an angle of 55 degrees. According to their calculations, when the shell reached the stratosphere, it should begin to travel at an angle of 45 degrees, and, as we shall see presently, a projectile travels the farthest when it is hurled at this angle. Thus, the greatest part of the shell's path was in an almost vacuum. Under such conditions, when its velocity was almost the same throughout its rise into the air and only the gravitational pull acted on it, everything was almost ideal. No wonder that it traveled seventy-five miles.

The drawing below shows the trajectory of the shell fired from Big Bertha in comparison with the trajectory of an ordinary shell. Big Bertha's vertex was about twenty-five miles above the ground.

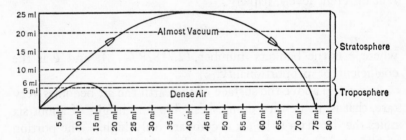

Aerial Artillery: Bigger than Bertha

The present counterpart of Big Bertha is the thousand-pound aerial bomb. Unfortunately the aerial bomb is bigger and bogey-ier than Bertha and is a living nightmare to every warring nation. Let us examine the mathematics of this nightmare's flight to earth. The trajectory of the bomb in this case represents a combination of the motion of the airplane and the gravitational pull of the earth. After the bomb has been released, it tends to continue to move along the path of the airplane. But, as soon as it is freed from contact, the pull of gravitation begins

to act, and the bomb's path is afterward neither horizontal nor
vertical, it curves below the horizon of the airplane.

This trajectory may be constructed in the same manner as the
trajectory of the bullet.

Let us assume for the time being that the pull of the gravitational attraction of the earth does not operate on the released
bomb. In other words we shall assume an ideal situation. The
path of the released bomb will then coincide with the path of
the airplane to which it was originally attached. This path will
then be a horizontal straight line. Since (it is so assumed) the
airplane travels with a constant uniform velocity, the released
bomb will continue to travel with a velocity of the same kind
and magnitude (say v). Then the trajectory of the bomb traveling under such condition is similar to the drawing below.

Now let us assume that when the bomb is released it instantaneously loses the velocity imparted to it by the moving airplane and that no other force has any influence on the bomb.
Thus, under the conditions just described the bomb becomes a
freely falling body. The distance through which this bomb will
fall is given by the equation $h = gt^2/2$, where g is the magnitude
of the gravitational attraction and equals 9.8 meters per second^2,
and where t is the time.

On page 652 of this chapter we computed the values of h for
the various corresponding values of t. These were

t (in seconds)	0	1	2	3	4	5
h (in m./sec.)	0	4.9	19.6	44.1	78.4	122.5

The drawing below illustrates the respective distances passed by
the falling bomb during every succeeding second after it was
allowed to fall freely.

Now, if we combine these two ideal situations, we shall obtain
(if the air resistance is to be completely ignored) a comparatively correct picture of the trajectory of the bomb that was
dropped from an airplane. The graph of this trajectory is ob-

tained as follows. We shall superimpose the two drawings for the ideal conditions examined by us. Then, from the points on the horizontal line that mark the equal distances supposedly tra-

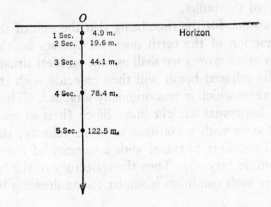

versed by the bomb, we shall draw vertical lines, each of them equal in length, denoting the total distance through which the bomb fell up to the moment corresponding to that point. Then join the lower ends of these vertical lines by a smooth curve. This curve is the trajectory of the falling bomb.

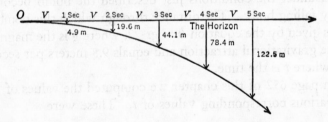

Thus, we again added two graphs, each of them a graph of an imaginary situation, and in the final result we obtained a graph of the trajectory of the falling bomb. Within certain limitations, such as the elimination of the air-resistance factor, wind velocity, this graph gives a fairly satisfactory representation of the motion of the falling bomb. This is a graph of a parabola, not an entire parabola, but one branch of it, the descending branch. Its vertex coincides with the point of the release of the bomb.

The aiming of an aerial bomb is a very complicated process. Not only the velocity of the airplane must be taken into account, but the height at which the airplane flies, the resistance of the air, the wind velocity, and many other factors must be carefully considered. However, much of this is now automatically calculated by a mechanical bombsight, and all these factors may be accounted for in a very short time, as a glance at any newsstand will remind you.

The Algebra of a Fired Shell

The trajectory of a fired shell whose graph was obtained by us represents the path through which this shell travels until it reaches its target. This trajectory is a combination of two trajectories of imaginary ideal motions, the motion along a straight line, and the motion of a freely falling body (in vacuum). Each of these two motions may be described in terms of a relationship between the path traversed and the velocity and time.

When a body moves along a straight line with a uniform velocity, the equation for this motion is

$$d = vt$$

where d is the distance, v, the velocity, and t, the time.

When a body falls freely, the distance through which it falls is given by the equation

$$h = \frac{gt^2}{2}$$

where h is the distance, g, the acceleration due to gravity, and t, the time.

It was pointed out previously in Chapter 35 that motion of a point in Flatland is represented by a time line that needs three coordinates, namely, x, y, and t. Moreover, if the path of the point is considered alone, we may think of the point's motion as a combination of the motion parallel to the axis of x's and the motion parallel to the axis of the y's as shown at right.

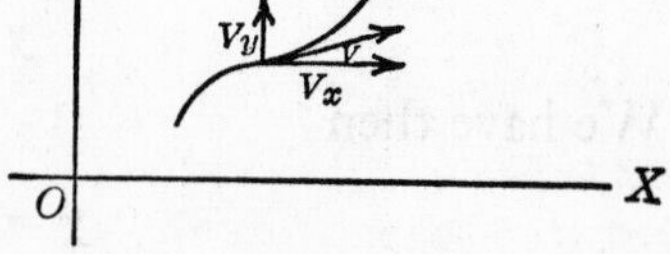

Let us examine the trajectory of a fired shell. This trajectory has its initial point at the origin of the coordinate axes XOY. For any point on this trajectory the motion along the curve may be considered as the combination of two motions, one along a line parallel to the OY axis, and the other along a line parallel

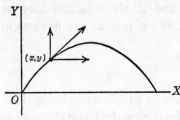

to the OX axis. The motion along the OX axis is parallel to the horizon, and thus it may be considered as a motion with a uniform velocity, say u. Thus the value of the x coordinate is $x = ut$. The value of the y co-ordinate is obtained as follows: If the motion parallel the OX axis is considered horizontal, then the motion parallel the OY axis is considered vertical. But in the vertical, that is, upward motion, the pull due to the gravity operates. Thus, if the velocity along a line parallel the OY axis is v, the position of a point on this line at the time t is vt diminished by the distance that a freely falling body will traverse during t, that is, $gt^2/2$. Then the value of the y coordinate is

$$y = vt - \frac{gt^2}{2}$$

Thus, we have the two equations $x = ut$, and

$$y = vt - \frac{gt^2}{2}$$

From the first equation we have

$$t = \frac{x}{u}$$

Substitute this value of t in the equation

$$y = vt - \frac{gt^2}{2}$$

We have then

$$y = \frac{v}{u}x - \frac{g}{2u^2}x^2$$

This is the equation of the trajectory of the fired shell as it is traced in the XOY plane. In it the time coordinate is eliminated. In other words this equation is not an equation of a time line.

As we remember, the distance a fired shell can travel depends on the angle of elevation of the gun. Let us examine how this angle of elevation is incorporated in the equation of the motion of the shell. In the drawing below this angle of elevation is formed by the tangent to the graph of the path of the shell at the point where the gun is located, at the origin of the coordinate axes and the axis OX.

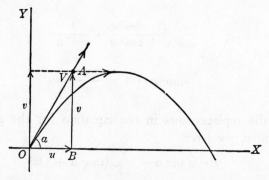

Let the initial muzzle velocity of the shell be V. This is the velocity of the shell as it leaves the muzzle of the gun, and the shell at first follows the direction in which the barrel of the gun points. Let the angle at which the gun is turned, that is, the elevation of the gun, be a. We may then think of the velocity along the path of the shell, V, as being composed of the two velocities along lines parallel to the two coordinate axes. The velocity along the line parallel the OX axis is u, and the velocity along the line parallel to the OY axis is v. We have then the right triangle AOB composed of the three velocities, that is, v, u, and V. But from the right triangle AOB we have

$$OB = u = V \cos a$$

and

$$AB = v = V \sin a$$

Let us substitute these expressions for u and v in the equation

$$y = \frac{v}{u} x - \frac{g}{2u^2} x^2$$

We have then

$$y = \frac{V \sin a}{V \cos a} x - \frac{g}{2 V^2 \cos^2 a} x^2$$

or, since

$$\frac{\sin a}{\cos a} = \tan a$$

and

$$\sin^2 a + \cos^2 a = 1$$

from which we have, by dividing both sides of the equation by $\cos^2 a$,

$$\frac{\sin^2 a}{\cos^2 a} + \frac{\cos^2 a}{\cos^2 a} = \frac{1}{\cos^2 a}$$

or

$$\tan^2 a + 1 = \frac{1}{\cos^2 a}$$

Making the replacements in the equation for the motion obtained above, we have

$$y = x \tan a - \frac{g}{2 V^2}(\tan^2 a + 1)x^2$$

By means of this equation it is possible to determine the angle of elevation of a gun when a certain desired distance (the distance from the gun to the target) is to be attained. However, it must be understood that this equation does not take care of the air resistance and, therefore, is only correct for a vacuum. If air resistance is to be taken into consideration it must be introduced as a correction. However, this will make the equation extremely complicated and will take us too far afield.

In order to show how much of a discrepancy even this equation may introduce, let us consider the flight of the shell fired from the Big Bertha. We know that the angle of elevation of this gun was 55 degrees. Let us substitute the value of tan 55° in the above equation and compute the value of V. The distance that the shell fired from this gun traveled was 120 kilometers, that is, $x = 120$ kilometers. The value of y (the height of the point above the horizon where the shell hit the target) is 0. Let us take the value of x in meters, because the value of g

will also be taken in meters, as $g = 9.81$ meters, and $x = 120,000$ meters, or $x = 12 \cdot 10^4$. We have then

$$12 \cdot 10^4 \cdot 1.428 - \frac{9.81}{2V^2} \cdot 3.040 \cdot (12 \cdot 10^4)^2 = 0$$

or,

$$1.428 - \frac{9.81}{2V^2} \cdot 3.040 \cdot 12 \cdot 10^4 = 0$$

Then

$$1.428\,V^2 = 9.81 \cdot 3.040 \cdot 6 \cdot 10^4$$

or

$$V^2 = \frac{9.81 \cdot 3.040 \cdot 6 \cdot 10^4}{1.428}$$

By means of logarithms, we may compute the value V and obtain

$$V = 1{,}120 \text{ meters per second.}$$

Thus, the velocity that would be required to hurl the shell 120 kilometers is a little more than one-half of that employed by the Germans. The air resistance and other factors required the use of a velocity equal to 2,000 meters per second.

Let us suppose that the shell from Big Bertha was fired into a vacuum with a velocity of 2,000 meters per second and that the elevation of the gun was 55 degrees. The distance the shell will travel is computed as follows. In this case $y = 0$. We have then

$$x \tan 55° - \frac{9.81}{2(2{,}000)^2}(\tan^2 55 + 1)x^2 = 0$$

or, dividing the equation by x,

$$1.428 - \frac{9.81}{2(2{,}000)^2} \cdot 3.040x = 0$$

Solving this equation for x, we have

$$x = \frac{1.428 \cdot 2(2{,}000)^2}{9.81 \cdot 3.040}$$

By means of logarithms we find that $x = 383$ kilometers, approximately.

Thus, if the velocity in vacuum is a little less than doubled (instead of 1,120 meters per second it is 2,000 meters per second), the distance is 3.2 times as great.

Bertha's Shell and Johnny's Top

An object rotated very fast on its axis becomes very stable. For example, you can make the thinnest coin stand on its edge by spinning it. Another example of this stability is a boy's spinning top. The reason the earth is not turning over while it is in motion around the sun is that the earth itself resembles a top spinning about its axis.

Many applications of the principle of the spinning top may be cited. Very large spinning tops, known as gyroscopes, are sometimes installed on oceangoing ships and battleships. The rotation of these gyroscopes reduces rolling and heaving in choppy weather. The wheels of a bicycle function as spinning tops and keep it erect. On the other hand, the principle of the spinning top can be dangerous. For instance, a fast-moving automobile will "turn turtle" if it deviates from a straight line and tries to round a corner, as the sudden turn disrupts the stability imparted by the revolving wheels. Likewise, a train will jump the track, if the engineer fails to slow down on a curve.

The stability imparted an object when it is spun on its axis can be judged from the following considerations. We shall recall that when a point moves along the circumference of a circle with a constant velocity v (the radius of the circle is r), the centripetal acceleration, that is, the pull toward the center of the circle, is $a = v^2/r$.

The velocity of a spinning top is usually expressed in terms of the number of revolutions per some unit of time. Now, let us consider a simple illustration. Suppose a top whose radius is 2 inches spins at the rate of 480 revolutions a minute. Thus a point on the circumference of the circle makes $\frac{480}{60} = 8$ revolutions a second. Since the circumference of a circle whose radius is $r = 2$ inches is $2\pi r = 4\pi$, the point covers

$$8 \cdot 4\pi = 32\pi \text{ in.}$$

in a second. This is the velocity per second of a point moving on the circumference of the spinning top. Then the centripetal acceleration of the spinning top is

$$a = \frac{(32\pi)^2}{2}$$

or

$$a = \frac{1,024(3.14)^2}{2} = 512 \cdot 9.87$$

$$= 5,053 \text{ inches per second}^2, \text{ approximately}$$

This centripetal acceleration is approximately equal to 438 feet per second^2 which is more than thirteen times as great as the acceleration due to the gravitational pull.

To prevent a bullet or shell from toppling over the barrel of the gun has elongated spiral grooves, or "rifling," bored inside. As the bullet (or shell) moves along the barrel, these grooves (which are winding inside the barrel in the same manner as the grooves of a screw) make contact with the projectile and give it a circular motion. Since the projectile moves at high velocity through the barrel, the grooves impart a high velocity of revolution (which, it should be remembered, is measured in terms of revolutions per second).

The drawing below shows the rifling in the barrel of the gun.

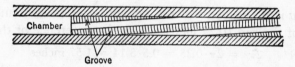

The length of the groove is expressed in terms of the length of one revolution of a groove.

If we breech a gun and look up through its barrel, we may note that the turn of the groove runs either clockwise or coun-

Clockwise   Counter Clockwise

terclockwise. Note should be taken of this because the clockwise will impart a rotary movement to the projectile which is to the right. The counterclockwise groove will impart to the pro-

666 Mathematics—Its Magic & Mastery

jectile a rotary movement which is to the left. These two types of rotation are extremely important in the process of aiming the gun at a target as it will become apparent presently.

The number of revolutions per second imparted to the projectile is computed by the expression v/k, where v is the muzzle velocity of the projectile and k, the length of the groove (that is, the length of one revolution of a groove). Thus, if the muzzle velocity of a rifle bullet is 3,000 feet per second, and the length of a groove is 10 inches, the number of revolutions per second imparted to the bullet is

$$3,000 \cdot \tfrac{12}{10} = 3,600$$

Note that since the length of the groove is expressed in inches, the velocity of the bullet must be also expressed in inches.

Suppose the radius of the bullet is 0.25 inch. Then the centripetal acceleration of a point on the rim of the lower end of the bullet is obtained according to the formula

$$a = \frac{v^2}{r}$$

where v is the velocity of the revolution of the rim and r, the radius of the rim (0.25 inch). The circumference of the rim is

$$2\pi r = 2\pi \cdot 0.25 = 0.5 \cdot 3.14 = 1.57 \text{ inches}$$

If the bullet makes 3,600 revolutions per second, then the velocity of a point on the rim is

$$v = 1.57 \cdot 3,600 \text{ inches per second}$$

Then the centripetal acceleration of this point is

$$a = \frac{(1.57 \cdot 3,600)^2}{0.25} = 127,800,000 \text{ inches per second}^2$$

$$= 11,150,000 \text{ feet per second}^2 = 2,112 \text{ miles per second}^2$$

(all numbers here are approximate)

This acceleration is about 350,000 times as great as the centripetal acceleration due to the gravitational pull of the earth.

The forward motion of the bullet and its rotary movement carry enough force for the bullet to overcome all the resistance of the air on its side surface. Moreover, this rotary motion produces a very important effect on the projectile. As the projectile moves through the air and revolves on its axis, the combination of these two motions causes the shell to change the direction of its axis so that this axis is always tangent to the trajectory of its path, as is illustrated in the drawing below.

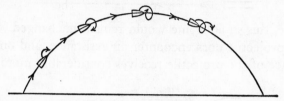

Out of the Firing Pan into the Fire

It would seem that the spinning of the bullet (or shell) should eliminate all the drawbacks caused by the resistance of the air. However, the spinning effect introduces another important element which must be taken into consideration when the aim is taken.

The spinning projectile is still being acted upon by the air through which it travels. The rotary motion of the projectile counteracts completely the force of the air pressure that tends to topple the projectile over (and backward). It should be remembered that two forces continue to act upon the spinning projectile: (1) the pressure of the air resistance which pushes upward, and (2) the downward pull of gravity. These two forces in combination with the spinning of the projectile cause the projectile to veer off sidewise. This veering is always in the direction of that side toward which the projectile turns. If the

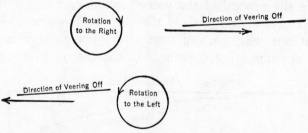

turning is clockwise, that is, to the right, the projectile veers off to the right as shown in the accompanying diagram. If the turning is counterclockwise, that is, to the left, the projectile veers off to the left also, as illustrated above.

The veering effect may be described as follows. Until this fact was mentioned, the path of the projectile, if it were viewed from above, would appear as a straight line. If there were no

resistance, this straight line would remain unchanged. But, the moving projectile does encounter air resistance, and one side of the surface of the projectile receives considerably more pressure

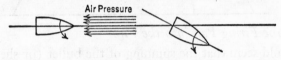

Air Pressure

than the other side. The combination of this pressure and the rotation of the projectile on its axis causes the projectile to veer off its course. The combination of the rotation of the projectile on its axis and the gravitational pull causes the projectile to turn so that its axis is always tangent to the trajectory. In the drawing above we see how the air pressure and the rotation of the projectile result in the veering off. Thus, the toppling over of the projectile is replaced by a veering-off effect.

The magnitude of the veering away from the course along the trajectory depends on the magnitude of the air pressure on the side surface of the flying projectile and the speed of revolution of the projectile on its axis. The greater either one of them is (or the two in combination), the greater is the resultant veering off.

Since the process of the veering off is continuous, the line which represents the path of the veered-off projectile is not a straight line when viewed from above but a curve as shown in the accompanying drawing. In the case of every gun the

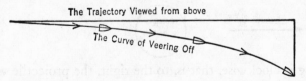

The Trajectory Viewed from above

The Curve of Veering Off

amount of veering can be determined. The equation that would give the relationship between the distance traveled by a projectile, the velocity of the projectile, the speed of the revolution of the projectile, and the air resistance is very complicated, and, for practical purposes, its use is not as advisable as a table of data computed in advance.

Thus, we see that when we dig through one problem we often come up with another one draped around our shoulders.

The Gun's Angle of Elevation

We have mentioned several times in this chapter that, when a definite initial velocity of a projectile is attained, the distance from the gun to the target—that is, the distance along a horizontal line passing through the muzzle of the gun—is determined by the angle of elevation of the gun. Naturally, this statement is based on the assumption that the projectile is hurled into a vacuum, and that there is no air resistance. It may be added here that there are other factors involved in the determination of the distance, such as the projectile's shape, weight, and initial velocity. However, we shall disregard the shape and the weight of the projectile and assume that the initial velocity V is determined.

The equation of the trajectory of the projectile is

$$y = x \tan a - \frac{g}{2V^2} (\tan^2 a + 1)x^2$$

In this equation x and y are the coordinates of some point on the trajectory, a is the angle of the elevation of the gun, g, the acceleration due to the gravitational attraction of the earth, and V, the initial (muzzle) velocity of the projectile.

Let us examine the relationship between the value of x of the target, that is, the x coordinate of the target and the value of a, the angle of elevation of the gun.

Since the target is located on the OX coordinate axis on the graph of the trajectory of the projectile, the value of the y coordinate of this point is 0 (zero). We have then

$$x \tan a - \frac{g}{2V^2} (\tan^2 a + 1)x^2 = 0$$

or, dividing both sides of the equation by y

$$\frac{g}{2V^2}(\tan^2 a + 1)x = \tan a$$

Then, solving this equation for x, we have

$$x = \frac{2V^2}{g} \cdot \frac{\tan a}{(\tan^2 a + 1)}$$

The value of $2V^2/g$ does not change, but the value of

$$\frac{\tan a}{(\tan^2 a + 1)}$$

changes in value as the value of a, and hence the value of $\tan a$, changes. Thus, this fraction controls the value of x.

The value of the tangent of an angle varies from 0 (when the angle is 0 degree) to infinity (when the angle is 90 degrees). From the table of values for the tangent ratios of angles, we find that up to, but not including, the angle of 45 degrees the value of the tangent ratio is a fraction less than 1. The value of $\tan 45°$ is 1, and the values of all the tangent ratios of angles greater than 45 degrees is each greater than 1. Thus, if we examine the tangent ratio of an angle less than 45 degrees, exactly 45 degrees, and greater than 45 degrees we may secure some hint as to how the angle of elevation of the gun influences the distance that a shell will travel (considering the horizontal distance only).

If the angle of elevation of a gun is less than 45 degrees, then its tangent is a fraction less than 1. Suppose that this fraction is $1/b$, that is, $\tan a = 1/b$. If the fraction is less than 1, then $1/b$ is less than 1, and b is greater than 1. For example, if the fraction is ⅔, then it may be written as

$$\frac{1}{\frac{3}{2}}$$

In this case $b = 3/2$. We have then the fraction

$$\frac{\frac{1}{b}}{1 + \frac{1}{b^2}}$$

This may be transformed into

$$\frac{1}{b\left(1 + \frac{1}{b^2}\right)} = \frac{1}{b + \frac{1}{b}}$$

Since b is greater than 1, the fraction

$$\frac{1}{b + \frac{1}{b}}$$

has a denominator which is greater than 2, and hence this fraction is less than $\frac{1}{2}$. Thus for all the angles of elevation of the gun a less than 45 degrees the fraction $\tan a/(1 + \tan^2 a)$ is less than $\frac{1}{2}$, and its product with $2V^2/g$ will give a value of x that is less than V^2/g.

If the angle of elevation of the gun a is 45 degrees, the tangent ratio of this angle is 1, and the fraction

$$\frac{\tan a}{(1 + \tan^2 a)} \text{ is equal to } \frac{1}{(1 + 1)} = \frac{1}{2}$$

and

$$x = \frac{2V^2}{g} \cdot \frac{1}{2} = \frac{V^2}{g}$$

If the angle of elevation of the gun a is greater than 45 degrees, then its tangent ratio is greater than 1. Let the value of $\tan a$ be $1/b$, where b is less than 1. For example, if $\tan a$ is equal to $5/2$, then it may be written as

$$\frac{1}{\frac{2}{5}}$$

Here $b = \frac{2}{5}$. Then the fraction

$$\frac{\tan a}{(1 + \tan^2 a)}$$

may be written as

$$\frac{\frac{1}{b}}{1 + \frac{1}{b^2}}$$

and this may be transformed into

$$\frac{1}{b\left(1 + \frac{1}{b^2}\right)} \quad \text{or} \quad \frac{1}{b + \frac{1}{b}}$$

Since b is less than 1, and the fraction $1/b$ is greater than 1, the fraction

$$\frac{1}{b + \frac{1}{b}}$$

has a denominator which is greater than 2, and hence this fraction is less than $\frac{1}{2}$. Thus for all the angles of elevation of the gun a greater than 45 degrees the fraction $\tan a/(1 + \tan^2 a)$ is less than $\frac{1}{2}$, and its product with $2V^2/g$ will give a value of x that is less than V^2/g.

In other words, if a shell were fired into a vacuum, it would travel the farthest if the angle of the elevation of the gun is 45 degrees. As we remember, the Germans fired Big Bertha at a 55-degree angle of elevation so that when the shell reached the stratosphere it would travel along a trajectory whose direction would make a 45-degree angle with the horizon. This change in the angle of elevation was caused, of course, by the gravitational pull of the earth.

The results obtained above may be checked with actual computations. Suppose a shell was fired with a muzzle velocity of 3,000 feet per second, and the angle of elevation of the gun was 25 degrees. Then, we have

$$x = \frac{2(3,000)^2}{32} \cdot \frac{\tan 25°}{1 + \tan^2 25°}$$

or

$$x = \frac{2(3,000)^2 \, 0.4877}{32(1 + 0.2375)}$$

By means of logarithms we find that $x = 222,000$ feet, or $x = 42$ miles, approximately.

If the muzzle velocity of the shell is 3,000 feet per second, and the angle of elevation of the gun is 45 degrees,

$$x = \frac{2V^2}{g} = \frac{2(3,000)^2}{32} = 562,500 \text{ feet, approximately}$$

or about 106.5 miles.

If the muzzle velocity of the shell is 3,000 feet per second, and the angle of elevation of the gun is 65 degrees,

$$x = \frac{2(3,000)^2 \tan 65°}{32(1 + \tan^2 65°)} = \frac{2(3,000)^2 \, 2.1445}{32 \cdot 5.599}$$

$$= 215,400 \text{ feet approximately}$$

or about 41 miles.

How to Determine the Firing Angle

The result that was obtained in the preceding section, that is, that the angle of elevation of a gun (when the velocity of the shell as it leaves the gun is given) determines how far the shell will travel holds true for all conditions. But the other part of the result, that is, that the 45-degree elevation will produce the farthest distance, is only true for a point in a vacuum. When the weight and shape of the shell as well as the air resistance are taken into consideration, the greatest distance attainable requires a different angle of elevation, and its determination involves a considerable amount of complex computation and much advanced mathematics. It may be pointed out, however, that for rifles, in general, the angle of elevation about 35 degrees will give the greatest distance, if all the conditions are taken into consideration. For other guns, the angle of elevation varies from 28 to 55 degrees.

We shall now consider the problem of determining the angle of elevation of the gun if the shell's initial (muzzle) velocity and the distance of the target from the gun are known. However, we shall have to confine ourselves to the ideal situation in which the shape and weight of the shell is not taken into consideration, and the air resistance is assumed to be absent. In other words, our shell is supposed to be fired into a vacuum.

The equation of the trajectory of the projectile is

$$y = x \tan a - \frac{g}{2V^2} \cdot (\tan^2 a + 1)x^2$$

It is our problem to solve this equation and determine the value of a. We cannot obtain the value of the angle a immediately. However, if we could solve this equation for $\tan a$, then by means of the table of the tangent ratios of angles we can determine the value of the angle a.

Let us change this equation by making some substitutions. Since x, y, g, and V are all known, we may write our equation as follows:

$$y = x \tan a - \left(\frac{g}{2V^2}\right) x^2 \tan^2 a - \left(\frac{g}{2V^2}\right) x^2$$

or

$$\left(\frac{g}{2V^2}\right) x^2 \tan^2 a - x \tan a + \left[y + \left(\frac{g}{2V^2}\right) x^2 \right] = 0$$

Now, if we write A for $(g/2V^2)x^2$, B for $-x$, C for $[y + (g/2V^2)x^2]$, and z for $\tan a$, we have

$$Az^2 + Bz + C = 0$$

If we solve this equation for z, we obtain the value $z = \tan a$, and this will enable us to determine the value of the angle a.

Now, in order to solve this equation, let us rewrite it as follows

$$Az^2 + Bz = -C$$

and, dividing both sides of the equation by A we have

$$z^2 + \frac{B}{A} \cdot z = -\frac{C}{A}$$

On the left side of the equation we have

$$z^2 + \frac{B}{A} \cdot z$$

which could be made a perfect square of the sum of two terms if some value were added to it. In other words, if we could have

$$(z + d)^2 = z^2 + 2dz + d^2$$

we would have a perfect square. Now, if we let

$$2dz = \frac{B}{A} \cdot z$$

we have, by dividing both sides by z,

$$2d = \frac{B}{A}, \quad \text{and} \quad d = \frac{B}{2A}, \quad \text{or} \quad d^2 = \frac{B^2}{4A^2}$$

Thus we have determined that value

$$d^2 = \frac{B^2}{4A^2}$$

which would make

$$z^2 + \frac{B}{A} \cdot z$$

a perfect square when d^2 is added to it. But if we add d^2 to one side of the equation, in order to keep the balance unchanged, we must add the same value to the other side of the equation. Thus we have

$$z^2 + \frac{B}{A} \cdot z + \frac{B^2}{4A^2} = \frac{B^2}{4A^2} - \frac{C}{A}$$

and the left side of the equation is a perfect square of $(z + B/2A)$. We have then

$$\left(z + \frac{B}{2A}\right)^2 = \frac{B^2 - 4AC}{4A^2}$$

Let us extract the square root from both sides of the equation. Moreover, we must take into consideration the fact that the square of a positive number is positive, and the square of a negative number is also positive; for example, $(2)^2 = 4$, and $(-3)^2 = +9$. Thus, when we obtain a square root of a number, we do not know whether this square root is positive or it is negative. To confess our ignorance, therefore, write the root with two signs $\pm$ which indicates that the root is either positive or negative. We have then

$$z + \frac{B}{2A} = \pm \sqrt{\frac{B^2 - 4AC}{4A^2}}$$

$$z = \frac{-B \pm \sqrt{B^2 - 4AC}}{2A}$$

This gives us the value of z, though actually there are two values, one taken with a positive root, the other taken with a negative root. Occasionally it may happen that the expression under the radical, that is, $B^2 - 4AC$, is negative. Although square roots of negative numbers have meaning, we do not consider a case of this sort here, since it does not arise in connection with the type of problem discussed here and such discussion would be beyond the scope of this book.

By means of the above expression for z (which is known as the formula for the roots of a quadratic equation, or the equation of the second degree in z, $Az^2 + Bz + C = 0$) we may solve the problem concerning the angle of elevation of the gun.

Suppose a target is 10 miles away from the gun, and a shell is fired with a muzzle velocity of 2,000 feet per second at a target 100 feet above the ground. We have $x = 52,800 = 528 \cdot 10^2$, $y = 100 = 10^2$, and $V = 2,000 = 2 \cdot 10^3$.

We then have the equation

$$10^2 = 528 \cdot 10^2 \tan a - \frac{32}{(2^3 \cdot 10^6)} \cdot (\tan^2 a + 1)528^2 \cdot 10^4$$

Dividing both sides of the equation by 10^2, we have

$$1 = 528 \tan a - \frac{4}{10^6} \cdot (\tan^2 a + 1) 528^2 \cdot 10^2$$

or,

$$10^4 = 528 \cdot 10^4 \tan a - 4 \cdot 528^2 \tan^2 a - 4 \cdot 528^2$$

and, finally,

$$4 \cdot 528^2 \tan^2 a - 528 \cdot 10^4 \tan a + (4 \cdot 528^2 + 10^4) = 0$$

This is a quadratic equation of the form $Az^2 + Bz + C = 0$, and $A = 4 \cdot 528^2$, $B = -528 \cdot 10^4$, and $C = 4 \cdot 528^2 + 10^4$.

By means of the expression for the roots of the quadratic equation we have

$$\tan a = \frac{528 \cdot 10^4 + \sqrt{528^2 \cdot 10^8 - 4 \cdot 4^2 \cdot 528^4 - 4 \cdot 4 \cdot 528^2 \cdot 10^4}}{2 \cdot 4 \cdot 528^2}$$

The expression under the root sign may be simplified. The square root may be rewritten as

$$528\sqrt{10^8 - 64 \cdot 278{,}784 - 16 \cdot 10^4}$$

or

$$528\sqrt{81{,}997{,}824} = 528 \cdot 9{,}055$$

Then

$$\tan a = \frac{10^4 \cdot 528 - 528 \cdot 9{,}055}{8 \cdot 528^2} = \frac{10{,}000 - 9{,}055}{4{,}224} = \frac{945}{4{,}224} = 0.2237$$

Then

$$a = 12° \ 30', \text{ approximately}$$

The other value of $\tan a$ is

$$\tan a = \frac{19{,}055}{4{,}224} = 4.511$$

and

$$a = 77° \ 30', \text{ approximately}$$

This value may be discarded because the angle is too steep.

If You Want to Hit Your Target, Don't Aim at It!

To aim at a target directly is the safest way to miss it. We have examined several reasons why this is true. Now we shall put them all together and see just how we should aim if we are to knock out the bull's eye.

First, the recoil of a gun causes the barrel either to rise or to depress, dependent entirely on the person who fires the gun. He must study the action of a gun in his hands. Then, if the gun lifts a certain angle, he should aim lower. On the other hand, if the gun depresses a certain angle, his aim should be higher.

Second, when the target is a long distance away, the gun should be elevated to a certain angle. The long flight of a projectile does not follow a straight line trajectory. Under ideal conditions (that is, when the air resistance is eliminated) the trajectory resembles a parabola, but its two branches are not equal. The ascending branch is longer than the descending.

Finally, the boring of the barrel of the gun causes the shell (or bullet) to spin. This is necessary because the spinning projectile overcomes the air resistance and the force of the air that tends to topple the projectile backward. But, because of this spinning, the projectile veers off either to the right or to the left, according to the way the boring is done. If the projectile spins clockwise (that is, to the  right) it will veer off to the right. In this case the aim should be to the left of the target. On the other hand, if the bullet spins counterclockwise (that is, to the left), it will veer off to the left, and the aim should be to the right of the target.

Thus, we see that if you aim at a target directly you will **never hit it.**

Of Math & Magic

Computing Is Believing

We too often fail to examine common experiences that, despite their apparent simplicity, would offer fascinating studies in mathematics; on the other hand, because of this inattention we often attribute to simple happenings an aura of the miraculous. For instance:

What happens when a train "takes water" from a tank as it speeds by?

Do we gain or lose weight while riding on a merry-go-round?

Is it cheaper to operate a ship eastward or westward?

How does the circus "human cannon ball" survive his stunt?

Is there any difference between an Olympic record made in Los Angeles and one made in Berlin?

These examples and others of like interest will be the meat of this chapter.

How a Locomotive Takes a Drink

When railroads were in their infancy, there was a water tower at every station. When a train stopped the locomotive usually was uncoupled and driven to the tower, where the tender was refilled with water. Nowadays the tender may be refilled while the train is moving.

At regular intervals between the rails flat, open water tanks **are** provided now. As the train passes over them a pipe, its opening facing the direction of the motion of the train, is lowered from the tender. The water is stationary, but the motion of the train forces it up the pipe and into the tender's tank.

The drawing at right shows a cross section of the tank, with the pipe from the tender lowered in it. As the train moves forward, the water rises into the pipe; there would be the same effect, of course, if the train were standing still and the water were rushing toward the train. However, the height h to which the water rises depends on the speed of the train or, in the second case, on the speed of the flow of water.

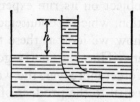

We find in the multiplication table of physical relations in Chapter 35 the relation

$$2ad = v^2$$

in which we shall replace the acceleration a by g and the distance d by the height h. We have then

$$2gh = v^2$$

and from this

$$h = \frac{v^2}{2g}$$

Suppose the train travels at a speed of 36 miles an hour, and the value of g is 32 feet per second^2. Then the train travels with the speed of

$$v = \frac{36 \cdot 5{,}280}{(60 \cdot 60)} = 52.8 \text{ feet per second}$$

The height h to which the water will rise in the pipe is

$$h = \frac{(52.8)^2}{64} = 44 \text{ feet approximately}$$

This is a height sufficient to fill the tender's tank by utilizing the motion of the train.

Gaining Weight on a Merry-Go-Round

It needn't worry stout people, but another oddity of motion is that we may gain weight by taking a ride on a merry-go-round. Suppose the merry-go-round has a radius of 15 feet and makes 10 revolutions a minute, and that a young man weighing 150 pounds and his girl friend, weighing 120 pounds, take a ride.

Since the merry-go-round makes use of circular motion, every object on its rim experiences the effect of centripetal acceleration, which is counteracted by (or counteracts, it all depends on how we look at these two effects) a centrifugal force equal to it. Thus the merry-go-rounders are affected by a centrifugal force; moreover, the weight of each rider (which is numerically equal to the product of the mass and the acceleration caused by the gravitational pull of the earth) acts as a force pulling downward. These two forces are perpendicular to one another, as shown in the drawing below.

We may construct a rectangle, the sides of which are the

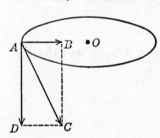

graphs of these two forces. The diagonal of this rectangle represents the combined effect of these two forces. Thus AB represents the centripetal acceleration; AD represents the force pulling toward the earth due to the weight of the rider, and AC represents the combined effect of AB and AD. The centripetal acceleration caused by the motion of the merry-go-round is obtained by means of the formula

$$a = \frac{v^2}{r}$$

Since the merry-go-round makes 10 revolutions a minute, its velocity per second is

$$\frac{10}{60} \cdot 15 \cdot 2 \cdot 3.14 = 15.7 \text{ feet}$$

Then

$$a = \frac{(15.7)^2}{15} = 16.43 \text{ feet per second}^2$$

Thus AB represents 16.43 feet per second^2.

AD represents the acceleration due to the gravitational pull of the earth, or $AD = 32.2$ feet per second^2. (Actually AB and AD represent the product of the accelerations stated above and the mass of the rider, but since the same mass is employed we may disregard this factor.)

Since triangle ACD is a right triangle, we have $(AB = CD)$

$$\frac{CD}{AD} = \tan \angle CAD = \frac{16.43}{32.2} = 0.5103$$

and from the table of the tangent ratios we find that the angle whose tangent is 0.5103 is approximately 27 degrees.

To obtain the value of AC, that of the combined two forces, we note that from the right triangle ACD we have

$$\frac{AD}{AC} = \cos \angle CAD$$

The value of cos 27° is 0.891. Then

$$AC = \frac{AD}{0.891} = 1.112AD$$

The weight of the rider, 150 pounds, is represented by AD. Then his weight AC on the merry-go-round would register, if a scale could be placed outside the machine,

$$1.112 \cdot 150 = 166.8 \text{ pounds}$$

And the weight of his girl friend would be recorded as

$$1.112 \cdot 120 = 133.44 \text{ pounds}$$

Thus we note that a gain in weight does not necessarily show an increase in mass. Weight depends on the amount of mass in an object and the gravitational acceleration due to the pull of the earth. The reader will recall that the formula for weight is $w = mg$, where m is the mass, and g is the acceleration due to the gravitational pull. If we keep the same mass but increase the gravitational pull (or the centripetal acceleration) the same mass may increase in weight.

The Cheapest Way Around the World: Go East, Old Man

When a 'round-the-world tour is organized by a travelers' agency, the cost of the trip is the same whether one chooses the eastward or the westward itinerary, but there really should be a difference in the rate despite the fact that the distance may be the same.

Let us suppose that the trip follows the forty-fifth degree of latitude and that the average rate of travel, whether by boat, train, or automobile, is 36 miles an hour. Every point on the 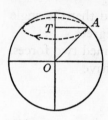 earth's surface moves about the axis of the earth with a speed that depends on the latitude of that point, as may be seen in the drawing at left. The circle with the center O shows a section of the earth's sphere. The point A is on the forty-fifth degree of latitude, and as the earth rotates this point describes a circle whose radius is AT. The triangle AOT is an isosceles right triangle. We have then (since $AT = OT$)

$$AT^2 + OT^2 = 2AT^2 = OA^2$$

Assuming that the radius of the earth's sphere is about 4,000 miles, or $OA = 4,000$ miles, we have

$$2AT^2 = 4,000^2 \quad \text{and} \quad AT = \frac{4,000}{\sqrt{2}}$$

or

$$AT = 2,000\sqrt{2} = 2,820 \text{ miles approximately}$$

Thus the point A describes every twenty-four hours a circle whose radius is 2,820 miles. The velocity of A is then

$$\frac{2 \cdot 3.14 \cdot 2,820 \cdot 5,280}{24 \cdot 60 \cdot 60} = 1,080 \text{ feet per second}$$

The speed of 36 miles per hour is equivalent to

$$\frac{36 \cdot 5,280}{60 \cdot 60} = 52.8 \text{ feet per second}$$

or, approximately, to 50 feet per second.

As the earth rotates from west to east, a person who travels in the eastern direction adds to the velocity of the rotation of his point of location the velocity of his own motion. On the other hand, a person who travels in the western direction moves against the rotation of his point of location, and the velocity of his motion must be subtracted.

Thus the velocity of rotation of a person traveling in the eastern direction is 1,130 feet per second, and the velocity of rotation of a person traveling in the western direction is 1,030 feet per second. The centripetal acceleration of these two are: for the person going east,

$$\frac{1,130^2}{2,820 \cdot 5,280} \text{ feet per second}^2$$

a person going west,

$$\frac{1,030^2}{2,820 \cdot 5,280} \text{ feet per second}^2$$

The difference between the two is

$$\frac{1,130^2 - 1,030^2}{2,820 \cdot 5,280} = 0.0145 \text{ foot per second}^2, \text{ approximately}$$

Since the centripetal acceleration of the point A is in the direction AT, and the line AT makes an angle of 45 degrees with the line AO, which is the direction of the gravitational pull of the earth, we take into consideration that the effect on the moving object at point A is the combination of these two forces. If these two accelerations are represented graphically, we may complete a parallelogram (since the angle between them is 45 degrees the quadrangle cannot be a rectangle), and the combined effect is represented by the diagonal of the parallelogram.

To compute the value of this diagonal we shall consider the triangle ABC in the above parallelogram. In it we know $AB = 0.0145$, and $AC = 32.2$, and $\angle CAB = 180° - 45° = 135°$. Let us draw this triangle separately. Then from B we shall draw a line BE perpendicular to the line AC. We then obtain the right triangles BEC and BEA (which is an isosceles right triangle).

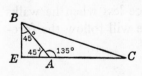

By means of the Pythagorean relation we have, from the right triangle BEA,

$$BE = EA = AB \cos 45°$$

from the right triangle BEC,

$$BC^2 = BE^2 + EC^2 = BE^2 + (EA + AC)^2 = BE^2 + (BE + EA)^2$$

or, since $BE = AB \cos 45° = 0.0145 \cdot 0.7071 = 0.01025$, approximately, and $AC = 32.2$, we have

$$BC^2 = (0.01025)^2 + (0.01025 + 32.2)^2 = (0.01025)^2 + (32.21025)^2$$

and

$$BC = \sqrt{(0.01025)^2 + (32.21025)^2} = \sqrt{1037.50032} = 32.21$$
(approximately)

Thus the acceleration of the object moving at 36 miles an hour along the forty-fifth degree of latitude is 32.21 feet per second². The ratio of this acceleration to the acceleration due to the gravitational pull of the earth is

$$\frac{32.21}{32.2} = 1.0003 \text{ approximately}$$

This indicates that an object traveling east is lighter by about 0.0003 of its weight than when it moves to the west. This is so because on the eastern trip the centrifugal force is greater than on a western trip; on a western trip the pull towards the center of the earth is greater than on an eastern trip.

For example, for a ship displacing 30,000 tons when it moves west, the difference in displacement when it travels east may be about 9 tons. Thus on an eastern itinerary the amount of fuel or energy that is used to propel a boat, a train, or any other way of travel is less than that spent on a western trip because all these means of conveyance are lighter.

It may be mentioned also that a man weighing 150 pounds and walking at the rate of 3 miles an hour at a forty-five degree latitude will weigh about 0.07 of an ounce less when he walks east. The reader may work this out if he will follow the foregoing procedure.

The 'Human Cannon Ball'

Many fairs have now added to their fire- and sword-eating performers the "human cannon ball," a performer "shot" from a huge cannon into a net. The explosion, the smoke, and the flame that the watchers see, however, are for showmanship only; the human cannon ball really is thrown out of the cannon by a spring released simultaneously with the setting of a powder charge.

Before we consider the mathematics of his flight we may recall some facts concerning the mathematics of a projectile. In the drawing below the trajectory of the projectile is shown. The initial (muzzle) velocity is v, and we know that this may

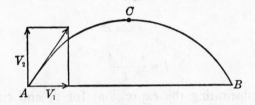

be considered the result of the combined effect of two velocities, one in the horizontal direction (v_1) and the other in the vertical direction (v_2). These velocities v_1 and v_2 are perpendicular to one another. Moreover, we must also take into consideration the angle A at which the gun is elevated, the angle made by the initial velocity v with the horizontal line AB. Let us also denote the horizontal distance between the gun and the place where the projectile hits the ground (that is, AB) by s, and denote the acceleration due to the gravitational pull of the earth by g and the time by t.

We note from the drawing that

$$v_1 = v \cos A, \quad \text{and} \quad v_2 = v \sin A$$

Since the vertical velocity will have spent itself completely when the projectile will have reached the vertex of the trajectory (the point O), and this, let us suppose, will occur t seconds after the projectile has started on its journey, we have $v_2 = gt$, and from this it follows that $t = v_2/g$, or

$$t = \frac{v \sin A}{g}$$

After the projectile reaches the vertex of the trajectory, it continues on its path and will take the same time to descend. Thus the entire trip of the projectile will last

$$2t = \frac{2v \sin A}{g}$$

The horizontal velocity v_1 will act on the projectile all the time, carrying it forward until it hits the ground. The distance in terms of the horizontal velocity will be

$$s = 2v_1 t$$

But

$$v_1 = v \cos A$$

and

$$t = \frac{v \sin A}{g}$$

therefore, substituting the expressions for v_1 and t in the expression for s, we have

$$s = 2v \cos A \, \frac{v \sin A}{g} = \frac{2v^2 \sin A \cos A}{g}$$

We shall make one substitution here to simplify the last expression, using substitutes for $2 \sin A \cos A$ the expression $\sin 2A$. We have

$$s = \frac{v^2 \sin 2A}{g}$$

Now we can apply the results to the problem of the human cannon ball. Suppose the length of the gun's barrel is 15 feet, the height of the vertex of the trajectory is 75 feet above the ground, and the angle of elevation of the gun is 70 degrees. The trajectory of the human cannon ball is shown below.

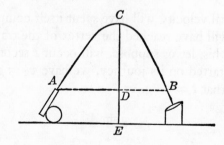

We must next compute the height CD. The horizontal line of the trajectory must pass through the muzzle of the gun. Thus we must subtract from CE, which is 75 feet, the length of DE. This may be computed from the right triangle FDE, where FD represents the length of the barrel and the angle DFE is 70 degrees. We have then

or
$$DE = FD \sin 70°$$

or
$$DE = 15 \cdot 0.9397 = 14.0955$$

$DE = 14$ feet, approximately. Then

$$CD = 75 - 14 = 61 \text{ feet}$$

The height that the human cannon ball will reach is

$$CD = H = \frac{gt^2}{2}$$

But
$$t = \frac{v \sin A}{g}$$

Then

$$H = CD = \frac{g}{2} \cdot \frac{(v \sin A)^2}{g^2} = \frac{gv^2 \sin^2 A}{2g^2} = \frac{v^2 \sin^2 A}{2g}$$

Solving the above expression for v we have

$$v^2 = \frac{2gH}{\sin^2 A}$$

and
$$v = \frac{\sqrt{2gH}}{\sin A}$$

Substitute in the last expression the values $g = 32.2$, $H = 61$. and $A = 70°$ and we have ($\sin 70° = 0.9397$)

$$v = \frac{\sqrt{2 \cdot 32.2 \cdot 61}}{0.9397} = 66.8 \text{ feet per second, approximately}$$

From the multiplication table of physical relations in Chapter 35 we have

$$v^2 = 2ad$$

where a is the acceleration and d is the distance traveled by the object. Let us compute the acceleration of the human cannon ball when he leaves the gun: The muzzle velocity, we have learned, is 66.8 feet per second, and the distance he travels through the barrel is 15 feet. Then

$$a = \frac{v^2}{2d}$$

and

$$a = \frac{(66.8)^2}{30} = 148.8 \text{ feet per second}^2$$

This acceleration is about 4.6 times as great as the acceleration due to the gravitational pull of the earth. In other words, the human cannon ball will experience an added weight of 4.6 times his original weight. Thus if he weighs 150 pounds he will experience the weight of $150 \cdot 5.6 = 840$ pounds.

How long will he have this weight? We have the formula

$$d = \frac{at^2}{2}$$

also the formula $v = at$. Then

$$d = \frac{vt}{2}$$

since

$$at^2 = at \cdot t = vt$$

And from this we have

$$t = \frac{2d}{v}$$

Substitute in this expression the values $d = 15$ and $v = 66.8$. We then have

$$t = \frac{30}{66.8} = 0.45 \text{ second, approximately}$$

While he is flying through the air he does not experience any weight at all, and this lasts

$$t = \frac{2v \sin A}{g}$$

We have then

$$t = \frac{2 \cdot 66.8 \cdot 0.9397}{32.2} = 3.9, \text{ approximately}$$

Thus his flight will take about four seconds.

When the human cannon ball hits the net, his velocity is about equal to the initial muzzle velocity (actually this velocity will be somewhat greater than the muzzle velocity because the net is not on the same horizontal line with the muzzle of the gun, but the difference is almost imperceptible). As he hits the net he sinks into it about six feet because of the impact of his body. Then, applying the formula $v^2 = 2ad$, where $v = 66.8$ feet per second, and $d = 6$ feet, we find that

$$a = \frac{(66.8)^2}{12} = 371.9 \text{ feet per second}^2 \text{ approximately}$$

This acceleration is $371.9/32.2 = 11.55$, approximately, times as great as the acceleration caused by the gravitation pull of the earth. Because of this acceleration, when the human cannon ball hits the net he will be about 12.55 times as heavy as his original weight. If he weighs 150 pounds he will experience a weight of $150 \cdot 12.55 = 1,882.5$ pounds, which is almost a ton.

He will experience this weight

$$t = \frac{2d}{v} \text{ seconds}$$

or

$$t = \frac{12}{66.8} = 0.18 \text{ second, approximately}$$

Only the short duration of such an experience saves the human cannon ball from disastrous consequences.

Want to Break a Record? Don't Go to Berlin!

There is a common notion that the only requirement for the beating of any record in an athletic competition is simply a better athlete, but the mathematics of latitude enter into this, too, with surprising results.

We have obtained the formula for the distance between the point of departure of a projectile and the point where it will hit the ground as

$$s = \frac{v^2 \sin 2A}{g}$$

Where s is the distance, v the initial velocity of the projectile, A the angle with the horizontal line that this projectile makes when it starts on its journey, and g the acceleration caused by the gravitational pull of the earth.

The formula shows that if the value of g, the value of the acceleration caused by gravitational pull, were the same all over the earth's surface, the distance that a projectile would travel would depend on two factors, (1) the angle at which it was thrown, and (2) initial velocity. In all our discussions we disregard the resistance offered by the air.

It can be seen that the greatest distance that can be attained when the velocity remains unchanged is when the angle at which the projectile is hurled is 45 degrees, because sin $2A$ is then sin 90°, and sin 90° = 1, which is the greatest value that can be attained by the sine ratio of an angle. Any other sine ratio of any angle (other than 90 degrees) is a fraction less than 1.

Let us assume now that in several events the same effort is applied to the hurling of a projectile and that its initial velocity remains the same in all, but that these events take place in different parts of the world.

If the earth were a perfect sphere the values of g, the acceleration caused by gravitational pull, would be the same for all points on the surface of the earth. However, the earth is not a perfect sphere, it is flattened out at the poles; as we travel from the equator to either of the poles we approach the center of the earth, and the value of g increases as its point on the surface of the earth is nearer its center. It was found that the value of the acceleration caused by gravitational pull may be determined by the formula

$$g = 32.173 - 0.082 \cos 2A$$

where A is the latitude of the point on the surface. For example, if the latitude of a point is 45 degrees, then

$$\cos 2A = \cos 90° = 0$$

and the value of g for this point is

$$32.173 - 0 = 32.173 \text{ feet per second}^2$$

Below is a table of the values of g for various latitudes but it should be remembered that all are only approximate, although sufficient for practical purposes.

Latitude	g	Latitude	g
0°	32.09	50°	32.19
5°	32.09	55°	32.20
10°	32.10	60°	32.21
15°	32.10	65°	32.23
20°	32.11	70°	32.24
25°	32.12	75°	32.24
30°	32.13	80°	32.25
35°	32.15	85°	32.25
40°	32.16	90°	32.26
45°	32.17		

All the values of g given above are for points at sea level where the barometric pressure is 760 millimeters (30 inches) at 0 degree Centigrade.

Since the weight of an object is obtained as the product of its mass and the acceleration due to gravitational pull, $w = mg$, an object whose mass is the same will weigh more at the poles than at the equator, and this weight increases as the object is moved northward or southward from the equator to a pole.

The heavier an object, the more the effort necessary to hurl it the same distance as a lighter object; if the same effort is applied, the heavier one will go a shorter distance. This can be checked by means of the formula

$$s = \frac{v^2 \sin 2A}{g}$$

If the effort is the same, then $v^2 \sin 2A$ remains unchanged. Let us denote $v^2 \sin 2A$ by e. Then

$$s = \frac{e}{g}$$

Let us consider, for example, the record for the javelin throw established in 1932 by Matti Jarvinen in Los Angeles. His distance was 238 feet 7 inches (2,863 inches). The 1936 Olympic Games were held in Berlin, Germany. What should be the distance for a javelin throw at Berlin that would beat the Los An-

geles record?   It is necessary first to translate the Los Angeles
record into Berlin terms.   We have for Los Angeles: $s = 2{,}863$
inches and g (Longitude 35°) 32.15 feet per second². For Berlin the value of g (Latitude 52 degrees; we shall use 50 degrees)
is 32.19 feet per second².   We have then, for Los Angeles

$$2{,}863 = \frac{e}{32.15}, \quad \text{or} \quad 2{,}863 \cdot 32.15 = e$$

and for Berlin

$$x = \frac{e}{32.19}, \quad \text{or} \quad 32.19x = e$$

Then $32.19x = 2{,}863 \cdot 32.15$, or

$$x = \frac{2{,}863 \cdot 32.15}{32.19} = 2{,}859.442 \text{ inches approximately}$$

Thus the Los Angeles record as translated for Berlin is

$$2{,}863 - 2{,}859.449 = 3.558 \text{ inches, approximately}$$

shorter.   To equalize the conditions and make competition fair,
it is necessary then to make the javelin for the Berlin Olympic
Games lighter, and it should be

$$\frac{32.15}{32.19} = 0.999876, \text{ approximately}$$

of the weight of the javelin used in Los Angeles.

The 'Devil's Ride' or Looping the Loop

Often a circus boasts a performer who "defies the law of gravitation," and rides a bicycle head downward.   The trick does

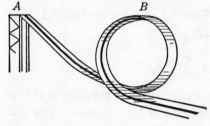

seem to be in contradiction to
natural laws, but let us do
some mathematical sleuthing.
    On the circus arena is
erected a runway such that
in the middle it twists into a
loop, as shown in the accompanying drawing.   The per-
former starts out on a bicycle from A following the darkened
track.   When he reaches the top of the loop (B) he is actually

riding with head down, and there is visible no support that would hold him up. But he does not fall headlong; he continues his ride with the familiar "greatest of ease."

Some may advance the explanation that the performer, as he descends from A, develops a velocity of such magnitude that he is just "shot" through the loop so swiftly that the gravitational pull is completely counteracted by his velocity. Let us see whether we should accept this explanation.

The drawing below shows in profile the plan of the looped path. The rider's starting point is A. AD is the height from

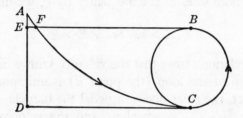

which ride starts, the elevation of the platform above the ground. Let BC be the diameter of the circular loop, that is, $BC = 2r$, where r is the radius of the loop. Then $ED = BC = 2r$.

The velocity with which the rider passes through the point B is equal to that with which he passes through the point F. As he continues from F along the track, his velocity increases, but as he begins to climb along the arc of the loop from C to B, as indicated by the arrow, all the gain in velocity is consumed for the purpose of the rise.

Now, if his velocity at B is v, which is the same as at F, and the acceleration due to the gravitational pull of the earth is g, we have the formula

$$v^2 = 2AE \cdot g$$

(the reader will find in the multiplication table of physical relations in Chapter 35 the relation $v^2 = 2ad$, and $a = g$ and $d = AE$). While the rider passes through the loop, he follows a circular path, and then develops a centripetal acceleration v^2/r.

So that he may remain on his path and not fall, this centripetal acceleration must be greater than the acceleration due to gravitational pull; that is, we must have

$$\frac{v^2}{r} > g$$

From this we have

$$v^2 > gr$$

But we obtained that

$$v^2 = 2AE \cdot g$$

Substitute this expression for v^2 in the inequality above. We have

$$2AE \cdot g > gr$$

or, dividing both sides of the inequality by g, we finally have

$$2AE > r, \quad \text{or} \quad AE > \frac{r}{2}$$

This last relation shows that the velocity with which the rider passes the top of the loop (the point B) is unimportant. As a matter of fact, the rider does not pedal the bicycle; he uses free  wheeling, and the velocity he attains depends entirely on the acceleration g. The most important factor in the entire performance is the elevation AE. This must be greater than half the radius of the loop. If it is equal to or less than half the radius, the trick will fail and the rider may be hurt. But if the apparatus is correctly planned, the trick is not dangerous at all; if the performer does not lose control of himself and retains a grip on the bicycle, his ride is as simple as one on a flat park path.

Stepping on Your Brakes

Suppose a child appears as you are driving a car at thirty-five miles an hour and you suddenly step on your brakes. How far will the car go before it comes to a complete stop, assuming that the road is ordinarily smooth?

To answer this let us recall that the formula for the distance traveled by a point moving with a uniformly accelerated velocity (that is, a velocity that increases or decreases in equal periods of time by equal amounts) is

$$d = vt + \frac{at^2}{2}$$

where d is the distance, t is the time elapsed, a is the acceleration, and v is the initial velocity.

If the initial velocity is v and the acceleration is a, then the velocity after t periods of time is

$$V = v + at$$

From this we have

$$t = \frac{(V - v)}{a}$$

Substitute this expression for t in the equation $d = vt + at^2/2$ and we have

$$d = \frac{v(V - v)}{a} + \frac{a(V - v)^2}{2a^2} = \frac{Vv - v^2}{a} + \frac{V^2 - 2Vv + v^2}{2a}$$

$$= \frac{2Vv - 2v^2 + V^2 - 2Vv + v^2}{2a}$$

Finally, we have

$$2ad = V^2 - v^2$$

and that expression will enable us to solve the problem.

With a car going 35 miles an hour as the brakes are applied, we may suppose that the loss of speed, due to friction between the road and the tires, is 30 feet per second^2. Then

$a = -30$ (the negative sign indicates that the acceleration decreases the velocity)

$$v = \frac{35 \cdot 5{,}280}{3{,}600} = 51.3 \text{ feet per second}$$

and

$V = 0$ (the car is at a complete stop)

Then

and

$$2(-30)d = 0 - (51.3)^2$$

and

$$d = \frac{(51.3)^2}{60} = 43.8 \text{ feet, approximately}$$

Thus the car will travel about 44 feet before it comes to a stop.

However, we must take into consideration the reaction time of a driver. It has been found that when a driver decides to stop his car suddenly when going at 35 miles an hour it will go about 40 feet during the average time of 1.1 seconds it actually takes to apply the brakes after the decision.

The Hammer and Anvil Circus Act

Deceptive circus showmanship is found again when a heavy iron anvil is placed on the Strong Man's chest, and an assistant pounds on it with a huge hammer. The audience fears his chest will surely cave in. It doesn't, but is it sheer strength that enables him to withstand the blows?

In examining the general case when two bodies strike each other, the backbone of the analysis is the expression for force, $f = mv$, meaning that the numerical value of the force may be obtained as the product of the mass and the velocity with which the object (whose mass is m) moves. Suppose that two objects whose masses and velocities are m_1 and v_1, and m_2 and v_2, respectively, strike one another. Then the forces that these two objects carry are $f_1 = m_1v_1$ and $f_2 = m_2v_2$, respectively.

If these objects move in the same direction, the signs of the forces (as well as of the velocities) are the same; if they move toward one another, then the signs are opposite. This, however, is provided for in the process of computation and need not have special consideration in our development.

When the two objects strike, the combined force is then the sum of the two forces, $f_1 + f_2 = m_1v_1 + m_2v_2$. Finally the velocity of each object after the collision, then obtained from the formula $f = mv$, is $v = f/m$. Then the velocity of each object is

$$V = \frac{m_1v_1 + m_2v_2}{m_1 + m_2}$$

This is the **fundamental** formula for the resultant velocity of the two objects.

For example, if one object whose mass is 2 pounds moves with a velocity of 3 feet per second and another object whose mass is 3 pounds moves in the same direction with velocity of 4 feet per second after the second object overtakes the first and collides with it the velocity of each object is

$$V = \frac{2 \cdot 3 + 3 \cdot 4}{2 + 3} = \frac{18}{5} = 3.6 \text{ feet per second}$$

If the second object moves in the opposite direction, then the velocity of the two objects after the collision is

$$V = \frac{2 \cdot 3 - 3 \cdot 4}{2 + 3} = -\frac{6}{5} = -1.2 \text{ feet per second}$$

The objects move in the direction of the second object with the velocity of 1.2 feet per second.

In this discussion we paid no attention to the fact that in some cases a collision may produce another important effect on the objects: it may deform them but if they are elastic, they return to their original shape.

When the objects are not elastic, the faster object (let its velocity be v_1) will lose some of its velocity after the collision. The amount of this loss is equal to

$$v_1 - V$$

The slower object will gain a certain velocity equal to

$$V - v_2$$

When the objects are elastic the situation is somewhat complicated. As the objects collide they compress for a while, and then resume their shapes. As the collision takes place, the faster object loses a part of its original velocity $(v_1 - V)$, but when its shape is restored it loses once more the same amount. Thus the total loss in the velocity of the first object is $2(v_1 - V)$. The slower object gains a certain amount of velocity at the collision and then gains the same amount once more when its shape is restored. Thus the second object gains $2(V - v_2)$ in velocity.

Then the resultant velocity of the first (faster) object is

$$v_1 - 2(v_1 - V) = v_1 - 2v_1 + 2V = 2V - v_1$$

or, substituting the expression for V,

$$\frac{2(m_1v_1 + m_2v_2)}{m_1 + m_2} - v_1$$

The resultant velocity of the second (slower) object is

$$v_2 + 2(V - v_2) = v_2 + 2V - 2v_2 = 2V - v_2$$

or, substituting the expression for V,

$$\frac{2(m_1v_1 + m_2v_2)}{m_1 + m_2} - v_2$$

Let us now apply this result respecting elastic objects to the problem of the anvil and the hammer in the circus act. If the mass of the anvil is m_1 and its velocity is v_1, and the mass of the hammer is m_2 and velocity v_2, and taking into consideration that the velocity of the anvil is $v_1 = 0$, we have (we shall keep in mind that the anvil receives the blow)

$$\frac{2m_2v_2}{m_1 + m_2}$$

This is the expression for the velocity of the anvil after it receives the blow.

Let us divide the numerator and denominator of the expression for the velocity of the anvil by m_1. We have

$$\frac{2v_2 \cdot \dfrac{m_2}{m_1}}{1 + \dfrac{m_2}{m_1}}$$

If the mass of the anvil is great in comparison with that of the hammer, the value of the fraction m_2/m_1 is small, and we may disregard it in the denominator of the fraction of the expression for the velocity of the anvil (after the hammer struck it). Then the velocity of the anvil is approximately equal to

$$2v_2 \cdot \frac{m_2}{m_1}$$

This result indicates that the velocity of the anvil depends on the velocity of the hammer and the ratio of the mass of the hammer to the mass of the anvil. Moreover, the lighter the hammer in comparison with the weight of the anvil, the smaller will be the effect of the blow on the anvil. For example, if the anvil is 100 times as heavy as the hammer, the velocity of the anvil is

$$2v_2 \cdot \tfrac{1}{100} = v_2 \cdot \tfrac{1}{50}$$

If the velocity of the hammer is 10 feet per second, the velocity of the anvil is 0.2 foot per second. Moreover, if the anvil weighs 200 pounds, then the force experienced by the strong man is $0.2 \cdot 200 = 40$ foot-pounds, and he experiences it only for an instant.

In circuses the audience usually is not misled as to the weight of the anvil, but the hammer is generally hollow and weighs very little in comparison with the anvil. Thus the act reduces to the ability of the strong man to support a heavy anvil, but not to his ability to withstand a heavy blow. Furthermore, the anvil is so constructed that it fits the chest and its weight is spread uniformly. In addition to this a soft padding under it protects the performer so that the blow is cushioned.

The Engineer's Dilemma

In the common collision of a train and an automobile at a crossing there are surprising arithmetical factors.

The train and the automobile are not elastic objects; therefore, we shall make use of the expression for the resultant velocity of two collided objects

$$\frac{m_1 v_1 + m_2 v_2}{m_1 + m_2}$$

Let the mass of the train be m_1, and its velocity be v_1, and let the mass of the automobile be m_2, and its velocity v_2. Moreover, since we assumed that the automobile was stalled on the tracks, $v_2 = 0$.

Divide the numerator and the denominator of the expression for the velocity by m_1 and we have

$$\frac{v_1 + \dfrac{m_2}{m_1} v_2}{1 + \dfrac{m_2}{m_1}}$$

Since the mass of the automobile is very small in comparison with that of the train, its ratio is very small and the magnitude of the fraction m_2/m_1 is so slight that it may be discarded. The velocity of the train then is v_1.

This indicates that the train, after it hits the automobile, will proceed with the same velocity, will suffer no effects of the collision, and its passengers will not be upset in any manner. But what will happen to the automobile?

It should be understood that the automobile is not a wholly elastic object, the blow deforms it and in the second stage it does not resume its original shape. Thus, recalling the preceding section, the automobile will gain a certain amount in velocity

$$(V - v_2)$$

but in the second stage will not gain the same amount but somewhat less, a fraction of $(V - v_2)$,

$$k(V - v_2)$$

Thus the total gain in the velocity will be

$$(V - v_2) + k(V - v_2) = (1 + k)(V - v_2)$$

where k is a positive fraction less than 1. We found above that $V = v_1$ as the resultant velocity of the train, also $v_2 = 0$. Thus the final resultant velocity of the automobile is

$$(1 + k)v_1$$

so it will be thrown far from the train.

Now suppose that the engineer reduces the velocity of the train so that the automboile will not receive a very strong blow. But in this case the mass of the automobile must be taken into consideration. It weighs m_2, and may derail the train. If v_1 is very small, the force of the train m_1v_1 may not overcome m_2, and the train may be thrown off its tracks.

Thus by keeping the train going at full speed the engineer throws the automobile far from the track and a more serious train wreck is prevented.

Gravitation and Flirtation

We have learned that two bodies whose masses are M and m and whose distance from one another is d are attracted to one another by a force $F = k\, Mm/d^2$, where k is a constant, known as the constant of gravitation. It was found that

$$k = \frac{1}{30.2 \cdot 10^9} \text{ pounds}$$

It is a common notion that this law of universal gravitation is applicable only to astronomical objects; this is not correct.

Suppose two oceangoing steamships are passing each other at a distance of a mile, that one displaces (weighs) 30,000 tons, and the other 25,000 tons. Then these two ships attract each other with a force equal to

$$\frac{1}{30.2 \cdot 10^9} \cdot \frac{30,000 \cdot 2,000 \cdot 25,000 \cdot 2,000}{(5,280)^2}$$
$$= \frac{3 \cdot 2^2 \cdot 2.5 \cdot 10^{14}}{30.2 \cdot (528)^2 \cdot 10^{11}} \text{ pound}$$

(Note that the weights were translated into pounds and the distance into feet.) This force is approximately equal to 0.0036 foot-pound or about 0.06 foot-ounce. If these two ships were passing at a distance of 200 feet, then the force attracting them would be about 2.5 foot-pounds. The reader may check this result by performing the computations.

Two men, each weighing 150 pounds and standing at a distance of 10 feet, attract one another with a force equal to

$$\frac{150 \cdot 150}{30.2 \cdot 10^9 \cdot 10^2} = 7.5 \cdot 10^{-9} \text{ pound, approximately}$$

If a young man weighing 150 pounds passes a young lady weighing 120 pounds at a distance of 1 foot, they are attracted to one another with a force equal to

$$\frac{150 \cdot 120}{30.2 \cdot 10^9} = 6 \cdot 10^{-7} \text{ pound, approximately}$$

So a flirtation may be only universal gravitation, if chaperons can be convinced.

Getting the Moon Rocket Started

The much-discussed problem of travel through interplanetary space continues to baffle enthusiasts. The distances to be covered are staggering; the temperature in interplanetary space is about −274 degrees Centigrade, and the means of propelling an interplanetary ship must yet be solved.

The most important question, however, is how to get started,

to overcome the gravitational attraction of the earth. We know its magnitude, the value of g which varies with the change of position on the surface of the earth. Generally this value is accepted as 32.2 feet per second.[2]

When we throw an object into the air, it rises to a certain height and then begins to fall back. If we apply a greater force, it will rise higher, but sooner or later it will come down. In artillery we achieve velocities as great as a mile per second, but still the shell comes down.

However, this gives us a hint: suppose we could attain such a velocity that the projectile would continue to go upward, what then? We know that the gravitational pull diminishes with the elevation above sea level; we could attain a velocity that would carry a projectile so far away from the earth that the gravitational pull would have no effect on it. Then the projectile could continue on into the skies unhindered.

Our nearest neighbor in interplanetary space is the moon, a mere 240,000 miles away, and proponents of interplanetary travel have even designed rocket ships for a trip to the moon and claim to have solved the problems of navigation.

Still, the most important problem—how to get away from the earth—needs complete solution, but mathematics can come to their help: it is possible by showing how to compute the velocity with which a projectile must be hurled in order that it leave the earth completely.

Suppose the mass of the projectile is m, and the velocity to be imparted is v. Then the energy of this rocket (projectile) as soon as it starts on its journey is mv^2/r. Let us denote the mass of the earth by M and the radius of the earth by r. Then, according to the universal law of gravitation, the force with which the projectile (whose mass is m) and the earth attract one another is

$$F = \frac{kMm}{r^2}$$

If this rocket were at the center of the earth, the work would be required to lift it to the surface (that is, the work necessary to overcome the force F, when the radius $r = 0$) would be infinite as any quantity divided by zero is infinity.   The formula for work is

$$K = fd$$

where f is the force and d is the distance through which the force is applied.   Now, if we wish to raise the rocket from the surface of the earth and send it into the interplanetary space, we must overcome the force of attraction

$$F = \frac{kMm}{r^2}$$

Assuming that this force is at the center of the earth we must apply it for the distance r.   We have then that the work to be performed is

$$Fr = \frac{kMmr}{r^2} = \frac{kMm}{r}$$

But this must be equal to the energy of the rocket to $mv^2/2$. Thus

$$\frac{mv^2}{2} = \frac{kMm}{r}, \quad \text{or} \quad v^2 = \frac{2kM}{r}$$

But, as it was stated above, two objects are attracted to one another according to the law of universal gravitation, and the force of attraction is on the surface of the earth,

$$F = \frac{kMm}{r^2}$$

also (consult the multiplication table of physical relations in Chapter 35)

$$f = ma$$

Since on the surface of the earth

$$f = F, \quad \text{and} \quad a = g$$

we have

$$mg = \frac{kMm}{r^2}$$

which gives

$$rg = \frac{kM}{r}$$

Now we have

$$v^2 = \frac{2kM}{r}$$

Substitute in it the expression for kM/r, or rg. We have then

$$v^2 = 2rg$$

and from this

$$v = \sqrt{2rg}$$

This formula gives the relation between the radius of the earth, the gravitational attraction of the earth, and the velocity that will send the rocket beyond its downward pull.

If we consider $r = 4,000$ miles, $g = 32.2$ feet per second[2], then

$$v = \sqrt{2 \cdot 4,000 \cdot 5,280 \cdot 32.2} \text{ feet per second}$$

and, in miles,

$$v = \frac{\sqrt{2 \cdot 4,000 \cdot 5,280 \cdot 32.2}}{5,280} = 6.985 \text{ miles per second, approximately}$$

the velocity necessary.

Thus far such a velocity per second has not been attained on the earth. Until this has been attained, and all other related problems fully solved, we need not worry about what to pack for a week-end trip to the moon, Venus, or Mars.

Where Are You?

Your Address in Two Numbers

Many cities in the world, especially the older ones, have "just grown" like Topsy. Their streets run in many directions and have names instead of numbers, or else some have names and some have numbers. However, there are some cities which have been laid out according to a systematic plan.

If you live in such a planned city you can tell where you are, or give your address to a stranger, in terms of two numbers and at most two directions. You might say that your address is 1242 7th Street, Northeast or 1242 Northeast 7th Street. To find out what this means in terms of the plan of the city, we draw a diagram (next page), and mark your address by a dot. This diagram has a rectangular grid as the overall plan, with the north-south axis intersecting the east-west one at right angles, and the avenues running north and south, while the streets run east and west. Then we mark the intersection of the N-S and W-E axes as C, and mark off the streets to the north in the north direction from C. Then North 7th Street is the seventh street so marked, and the point denoting your address must lie on a line drawn through that point and parallel to the west-east axis. Since your address is east as well as north, we mark off the avenues to the east of C along the west-east axis. Since your number on North 7th Street is 1242 east, we can locate the corresponding point between the 12th and 13th

705

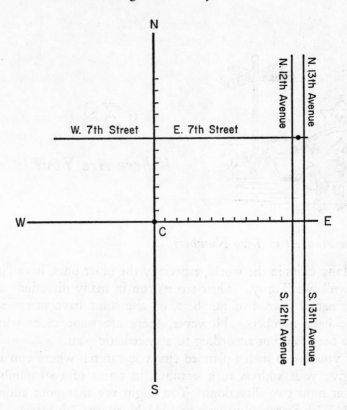

avenues. Precisely where it lies in this interval cannot be determined unless we know how many numbers there are in East 7th Street between 12th and 13th Avenues.

This lack of precision, which may be greater or less than that in this example, is usually present in an arbitrary system for designating position. It can be avoided by using the corresponding mathematical method, even though the latter would not be useful for giving your address. In the mathematical method, you would simply use the letter x to denote distance to the east of the N-S axis, using $-x$ for distance to the west. Similarly you would use y for distance to the north of the W-E axis, and $-y$ for distance to the south of it. However, in this case we could not say that the value of x,y for your address was 7, 12.42. The distances between streets and between avenues are not necessarily the same, as we have plotted them in the foregoing diagram. Instead, your address in terms of its distance from the center of town might appear as shown in the *x,y* figure drawn here, where *x* is the distance of your house

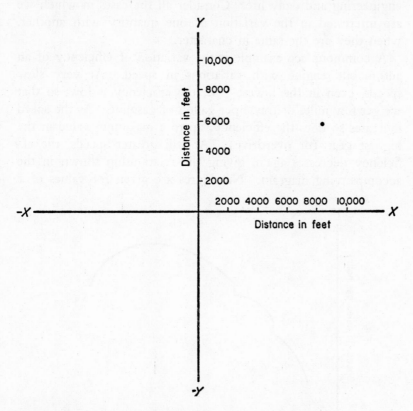

(actually some point in it) from the *Y-* *−Y* axis, and *y* is its distance from the *X-* *−X* axis.

Rectangular Cartesian Coordinates

The *x,y* system is widely used in mathematics, and in fact has appeared in many examples already given in this book. In some of them, as for instance the trajectory of a fired shell on pages 660–661, it was used as in the example just discussed in this chapter, to denote position (or rather successive positions) relative to two rectangular axes, so that both x and y represented distances. In others, however, the x and the y did not denote the same quantity, and this type of use occurs widely in science, engineering and daily life. Consider all the cases in which we are interested in the variation of one quantity with another, when they are the same in character.

A commonplace example is the variation of efficiency of an automobile engine with variations in speed. At very slow speeds, even in the lowest gear, the efficiency is low, so that we get few miles of travel per gallon of gasoline. As the speed increases so does the efficiency, up to a maximum value in the highest gear (or overdrive). At still greater speeds, the efficiency decreases again, giving the relationship shown in the accompanying diagram. No figures are given for values of x

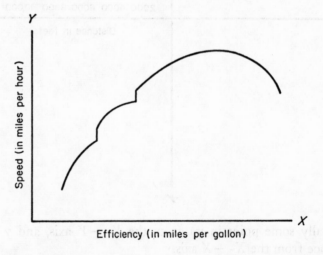

Efficiency (in miles per gallon)

and y because they will vary with the model of the engine, its condition, the gasoline used, and many other factors. Even the shape of the graph may vary considerably, and the effect of shifting from one gear ratio to another tends to produce abrupt changes of direction, or even breaks in the curve.

It is given here primarily to suggest the great range of applicability of rectangular Cartesian coordinates. Think of all the

other devices besides automobiles whose efficiency varies with
speed, e.g., engines, electric motors, pumps. Then think of all
the other properties of devices and materials which vary with
some other property.

Consider for example the most common substance in the
world—water. It can exist in three states, vapor, liquid and
solid (actually there are a number of solid forms, but only one
exists at ordinary pressures, so the others do not concern us
here). Our present purpose is to show how the pressure varies
with temperature in a system in which the vapor is always
present, and the liquid and solid are free to transform into each
other, or to undergo transformations with the vapor state. We
can show this system readily by a diagram in which the *x*-
coordinate represents temperature, and the *y*-coordinate, pressure. As you can see from the diagram, at pressures above

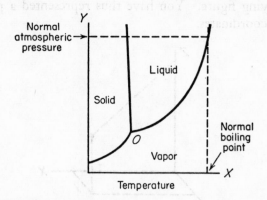

the triple point (*O* in the diagram), there are two branches,
one formed by the solid-liquid change (melting point or freezing point) at various pressures and the other by the liquid-vapor
change (which when called the boiling point without statement
of pressure means at normal atmospheric pressure). Note that
in order to show the various points clearly, this diagram is not
drawn to scale, since the triple point is at a temperature of
0.0098°C. and at a pressure of 4.6 mm. of mercury, while the
normal boiling point is at a temperature of 100°C. and a pressure of 760. mm. of mercury.

In order to describe fully the state properties of water, however, we need to consider another variable—the volume per unit mass. Therefore we need a coordinate system to show the relations between three variables—pressure, temperature and volume (per unit mass). How can we modify the x,y rectangular coordinate system to do that?

We can approach this question by returning briefly to the method of designating in x,y coordinates the location of your city address, as developed earlier in this chapter. Suppose your office is located on an upper story of the building. You can see that this information could be added to the previous diagram by adding a z coordinate axis, that is, perpendicular to the plane of the paper. Then you need only erect another perpendicular line at the point x,y and lay off on it a distance corresponding to the distance of your floor, as is shown isometrically in the accompanying figure. You have thus represented a point that has three coordinates.

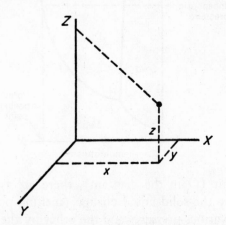

Now the graphical relationship between pressure, P, temperature, T, and volume per unit mass, v, consists of an indefinitely great number of such points defined by the three coordinates, which thus form a surface in space as shown in the next figure. Of course, in drawing it, only as many points were plotted as necessary to draw the parts of the surface smoothly and their lines of intersection accurately. Note that this three-dimensional representation gives much more informa-

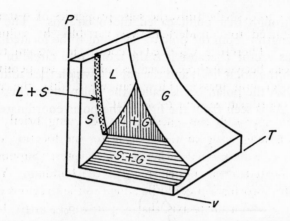

tion than the two-dimensional rectangular Cartesian system used
previously for the pressure-temperature relations, since it shows
not only the conditions under water can exist at equilibrium *
as only a solid, or a liquid or a gas (or vapor), but also the
conditions under which two states can coexist. Note also that
to avoid its crossing the surface of interest, the T axis has been
shown at the right of the diagram instead of its usual position
intersecting the other two axes.

Polar Coordinates in the Plane

While rectangular Cartesian coordinates have been shown as
convenient for use to designate a location in a city laid out so
the streets are parallel, the avenues are parallel, and the two
types intersect at right angles, there are also cities which have
been laid out in circles, or at any rate in circular arcs usually
called crescents. The position of a point in such a city can
then conveniently be described in relation to the center of town,
by means of a distance and an angle. This system is called that
of polar coordinates in the plane.

Its references consist of a fixed point, O, called the pole, and

---

* This is an equilibrium diagram. If pure water is slowly cooled, it can often
reach temperatures below the equilibrium freezing point without freezing—and
on heating it can similarly be raised above the equilibrium boiling point without
boiling. These conditions are called metastable, since they revert to the equilibrium conditions more or less readily.

a line through that point called the polar axis. The straight line of length r from the pole to the point to be located is called the radius vector (because it is the radius of a circle of position on which the point lies), and the angle θ which the radius vector makes with the polar axis is called the polar angle (or vectorial angle). As is seen from the figure, the polar coordinates of the

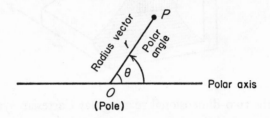

point P are r,θ. Note that the polar angle is measured, for positive values, in a counterclockwise direction from the polar axis.

Spherical Polar Coordinates

Just as rectangular Cartesian coordinates can be extended from the plane to space, so can polar coordinates in the plane be modified to represent the position of a point in space. We still have the fixed point, O, called the pole, from which the radius vector, r, extends to the point, P, and is one coordinate of it as before. We now have the polar axis ON through the point O, and our second coordinate is the angle θ, made as in plane polar coordinates, by OP (the radius vector) with ON (the polar axis). This angle is called the colatitude because it is the complementary angle * to the latitude. The third coordinate of P is the angle ϕ which is called the longitude and is the angle between the plane of θ and the plane NOA through the polar axis. This plane is called the initial meridional plane. Then a plane through O perpendicular to the plane AOP' will contain the point P' and the angle between the lines OP and OP' is the latitude. Note that the line NA which is the inter-

---

* The complementary angle to the angle θ is that angle which when added to θ makes a right angle.

section of the plane *NOA* with the surface of the sphere of radius *r* has been extended all around the sphere, being shown as a dashed line where not visible to the eye. Note also that this closed curve of intersection is a great circle, even though it does not appear so from a quick glance at the sketch. If you

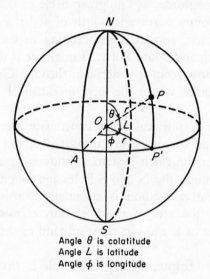

Angle θ is colatitude
Angle L is latitude
Angle ϕ is longitude

study the figure until you can recognize this closed curve as a circle, you will see the true three-dimensional positions of the angles θ, L, and ϕ.

One reason for the great importance of the spherical polar coordinate system is the fact the earth is close enough to a perfect sphere so that positions on its surface can be represented for most purposes by spherical polar coordinates. Since the radius of the earth is then taken as constant, only two angular coordinates are needed to fix a point on the surface of the earth. These coordinates are the well-known latitude and longitude, measured in the same way as already explained for general spherical polar coordinates, the difference in the two systems being that the former used colatitude, θ, as a coordinate, while the earth system uses latitude, which was denoted by L in the preceding diagram. Note that the initial meridian plane of the earth system is defined as the plane passing through the polar axis and Greenwich, England. Therefore the meridian (half great circle) cut by this plane on the surface of the earth from the North to the South Poles on the Atlantic Ocean side of the earth is called the meridian of Greenwich, England, and points on it have 0° longitude. (The great circle of 0° latitude is the Equator and points north and south of it have north latitude and south latitude, respectively, reaching maximum values of 90° at the North and South Poles. Longitude is measured along the earth's equator from the meridian through Greenwich west or east to the point where the local meridian of the point cuts the equator.

Note that in a spherical polar coordinate system the angles of colatitude and longitude are measured at the center of the sphere, while in the earth system latitude is measured along a great circle through the N and S Poles and longitude along the equator. The latter method is essentially consistent with the former because the arcs of the great circles measured are expressed in terms of the angles they subtend at the center of the earth.

An important feature of a great circle is that it represents the shortest distances between two points lying on it. Therefore to find the shortest trip between two points, you simply follow the great circle on which they lie. This is often impossible in planning the course of a ship, but can be approached more closely by an airplane. Thus planes flying between California and Scandinavia often follow a course that passes close to the North Pole.

Celestial Coordinates

Spherical coordinate systems are used not only to fix points on the surface of the earth, but also for objects distant from it, such as stars and planets. For such systems, however, another sphere than that of the earth itself is necessary as a reference. Since all the astronomical objects are at different distances from any fixed point, it would seem that no one sphere would do for all, or in fact for more than one. Mathematicians solved this problem by using the idea of the celestial sphere, defined as a sphere of infinite radius with its center within the solar system, against which the positions of the stars, planets, etc., are projected.

If the center of the celestial sphere is an arbitrary point on the surface of the earth, we have *apparent coordinates;* if it is the center of the earth, we have *geocentric coordinates,* and if it is the center of the Sun we have *heliocentric coordinates.* If the fundamental line of the system is the axis of the earth (line joining the North and South Poles) we have equatorial coordinates, so that there are apparent equatorial coordinates, geocentric equatorial coordinates, and heliocentric equatorial coordinates, depending on the point chosen as the center of the system.

In geocentric equatorial coordinates, the plane perpendicular to the fundamental line through the origin is the celestial equator. The fundamental direction in the system is the line of intersection of the celestial equator with the local meridian (the great circle passing through the poles of rotation and the zenith, which is the point where a plumb line extended upward from the observer's position intersects the celestial sphere). Instead of the local meridian, we may use the vernal equinox, which is the point of intersection, at the time * the Sun apparently passes from south to north of the earth's equator, of the earth's equator with the ecliptic, the latter being the great circle cut on the celestial sphere by the plane containing the orbit of the earth.

To locate an object in this system of coordinates, a plane is passed through the object and the line joining the poles of rotation, and this plane will cut out a great circle, known as an hour circle, on the celestial sphere perpendicular to the plane of the equator. The declination, δ, of an object is the angular distance

---

* Approximately March 21, the beginning of the Spring season in the Northern Hemisphere.

of the object north (+) or south (−) of the celestial equator measured in the plane of the hour circle through the object. The hour angle of the object is the angular distance measured in the plane of the equator from the point of intersection of the meridian above the horizon to the point of intersection of the hour circle through the object in the direction of apparent rotation (west) of the celestial sphere. The right ascension, *a*, of the object is the angular distance, measured in the plane of the equator from the vernal equinox, direction *T*, to the point of intersection of the hour circle in a direction (east) contrary to the direction of apparent rotation of the celestial sphere. For purpose of convenience both right ascension and hour angle are frequently expressed in units of hours, minutes and seconds of time, rather than the more common angular notation of degrees, minutes, and seconds or arc. These operations are shown in the accompanying figure. Note, however, that the

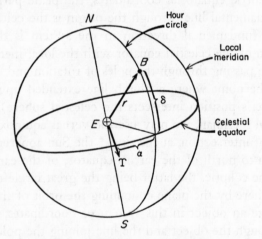

The geocentric equatorial coordinate system

radius of the sphere as drawn, *r*, has been taken as the distance of the object from the center of the earth.

As its name indicates, an ecliptic coordinate system uses the ecliptic plane as the reference plane. The geocentric ecliptic coordinates are called longitude and latitude, and are designated by the letters λ and β. The latitude, β, is counted positive if the body observed is north of the ecliptic plane, and negative if south of it. Note that the latitude in this system of celestial coordinates, used for locating celestial objects, is measured from the *ecliptic plane*, while the latitude of points on the earth's surface in the terrestrial coordinate system, discussed earlier in this chapter, and used in the navigation of ships and planes, is measured from the *equatorial plane*.

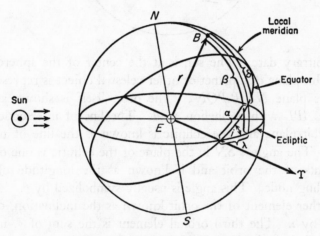

Geocentric equatorial and ecliptic coordinate system

In the heliocentric coordinate system, the central point is, as the name implies, the center of the sun. The fundamental reference plane is the ecliptic which is, as already stated, the plane of the earth's orbit about the sun, and the fundamental direction is that of the vernal equinox, also defined previously. The heliocentric system is generally used to describe the motions of the planets and other members of the Solar system with reference to the sun. To locate the position of such an object at any past or future time, seven so-called elements of the orbit of the object about the sun enter into the calculation.

The figure on the next page shows the celestial sphere, the plane of the ecliptic, and the vernal equinox, *V*, for

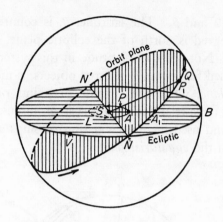

an arbitrary date. The sun is at the center of the sphere and
the orbit plane of a planet or other celestial object is represented
by the plane NA_1P_1PQN'. The orbit itself is shown as the
ellipse APL with perihelion at A. The line of intersection of
the orbit plane and the ecliptic is known as the line of nodes,
NN'. The angle VSN in the plane of the ecliptic is one of the
elements of the orbit and is known as the longitude of the
ascending node. This angle is usually symbolized by θ. A_1NB
is another element of the orbit known as the inclination, designated by i. The third orbital element is the sum of θ, in the
plane of the ecliptic, and NA_1 (which is designated by ω) in
the orbit plane. This sum, $\bar{\omega} = \theta + \omega$, is the longitude of perihelion. These three elements, θ, i, and $\bar{\omega}$ are three elements
of the orbit. The longitude of the nodes θ determines the
points N and N' on the celestial sphere at which the plane of
the orbit intersects the ecliptic. The angle i is the angle at
which the plane of the orbit is inclined to the plane of the
ecliptic. The longitude of perihelion, $\bar{\omega}$, determines the direction of the perihelion point.

Two other elements define the ellipse itself: ϵ is the eccen-
tricity of the orbit, and a is the semi-major axis of the ellipse,
usually expressed in astronomical units. Two more elements
are required to determine the position of the object in the orbit

at a given time. They are: P, the complete period of revolution about the ellipse, and μ, the mean daily motion, which is simply $360°/P$ in days.

In addition to the seven elements discussed above it is desirable to specify some starting time for the motion in the ellipse. The quantity used for this purpose is the mean longitude of the object as seen from the sun on some particular date called the epoch (E), e.g., January 1, 1960.

T is the precise time at which the planet was at perihelion.

The galactic coordinate system is a system of spherical coordinates having as its fundamental plane the plane of the milky way (or galaxy). The adopted position of the pole of this plane is 12^h40^m right ascension and $28°$ north declination. The plane of the milky way cuts the plane of the celestial equator at an angle of $62°$. Galactic latitude is measured perpendicular to the plane of the galaxy along great circles drawn through the galactic poles and hence perpendicular to the galactic plane. Galactic longitude is measured in the plane of the galaxy from the point where this plane cuts the plane of the equator in right ascension 18^h40^m to the point where the great circle perpendicular to the galactic plane through the object intersects the galactic plane.

Other Coordinate Systems

There are of course many coordinate systems based upon other geometric figures than circles and spheres. These other systems include ellipsoidal coordinates, paraboloidal coordinates, conical coordinates and cylindrical coordinates. There are even variants within these groups such as (circular) cylindrical coordinates, elliptic cylindrical coordinates and parabolic cylindrical coordinates. However, one of the mathematical inventions that has contributed very greatly to the solution of problems in theoretical mechanics and statistical mechanics is that of generalized coordinates. In order to specify the positions of a number of unrelated particles relative to a set of axes XYZ fixed in an inertial system, three times as many independent coordinates are needed as the number of particles. If, however, the coordinates of some of the particles are related, the number of independent coordinates required to specify their positions is reduced. In the case of a rigid body, where the distance between every pair of particles is invariable, the position of every particle in the body is completely specified by six independent coordinates, such as the three coordinate distances specifying the position of the center of mass and the three angles specifying the orientation of the body relative to the center of mass. By the number of degrees of freedom of a system of particles is meant the number of independent coordinates necessary to specify completely the position of every one of the particles. The coordinates employed, which may be distances or angles or quantities of quite different physical dimensions, are termed generalized coordinates and are usually designated by the letter q with an appropriate subscript.

Consider a system of particles of f degrees of freedom corresponding to the f generalized coordinates, q_1, q_2, q_3, $\cdots$ q_f. Then the rectangular coordinates x_i, y_i, z_i of the ith particle may be expressed as functions of the q's, that is,

$$x_i = x_i(q_1 \ldots q_f), \; y_i = y_i(q_1 \ldots q_f), \; z_i = z_i(q_1 \ldots q_f).$$

Use of Coordinate Systems

As emphasized throughout this chapter, the position of a point can be specified in any coordinate system (by definition), so that the choice of a particular one is a matter of convenience. For example, it is usually easier to calculate problems involving points on the surface of a sphere by using a spherical coordinate system. Cases often arise, however, in which later work is facilitated if a statement in one coordinate system can be expressed in another. For that reason we calculate interrelations between coordinates in various systems. A few such expressions are given below.

(1) Plane Polar to Rectangular Cartesian Coordinates

$$x = r \cos \theta$$
$$y = r \sin \theta$$

(For the trigonometric functions, see Chapter 26.)

(2) Spherical Polar to Rectangular Cartesian Coordinates

$$x = r \sin \theta \cos \phi$$
$$y = r \sin \theta \sin \phi$$
$$z = r \cos \theta$$

(3) Geocentric Ecliptic and Geocentric Equatorial Systems

$$\cos \beta \cos \lambda = \cos \delta \cos \alpha$$
$$\cos \beta \sin \lambda = \cos \delta \sin \alpha \cos \epsilon + \sin \delta \sin \epsilon$$
$$\sin \beta = \sin \delta \cos \epsilon - \cos \delta \sin \alpha \sin \epsilon$$

where α, δ, β and λ are shown in the figures illustrating the two systems, and ϵ is the inclination of the equatorial plane with respect to the ecliptic plane, the value of which is $23°26'59''$.

Staying in Orbit

Earth and space coordinates have been emphasized in this chapter because, in addition to their long-established use in navigation and astronomy, they have now found new uses in our trips away from the earth. We can begin the discussion, however, by using simply the geocentric distance, that is, the distance from the center of the earth, r, which for a satellite in circular orbit would be the sum of an average value of the radius of the earth and the height of the orbit above the surface of the earth, or

$$r = r_E + h$$

These relations are shown in the figure on page 722.

It also shows the method for calculating the velocity at

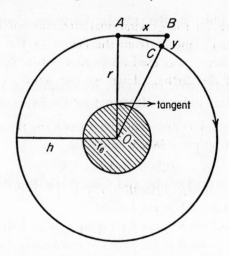

which a satellite must be placed into a circular orbit so that it will continue in that orbit. This velocity, which is called the injection velocity, is here symbolized by v_i and is taken as horizontal, that is, parallel at the point of injection, A, to a tangent to the surface of the earth at a point directly below. You will remember that a satellite is turned into this position before the rockets are fired that inject it into its orbit. Now let us compute v_i by a method widely used in applied mathematics, which is to calculate the result of a combination of two effects by calculating their separate results and combining them.

If the injection velocity were the sole factor in determining the motion of the satellite, it would follow the path AB and would cover a horizontal distance x, which is equal to the product of the injection velocity v_i by the time t. However, if the satellite is to stay in its orbit, at time t it must be at point C. It has therefore been moved a distance BC by the amount of gravitational attraction which the earth exerts along BC. Calling this gravitational acceleration a, we have

$$y = BC = \tfrac{1}{2} \, at^2$$

by the formula for the distance travelled by a body in time t under an acceleration a.

Let us represent the gravitational attraction of the earth for a satellite at a distance r from the center of the earth by the symbol g' (since g was used on page 638 for the attraction at the surface of the earth). Then we can write

$$y = BC = \tfrac{1}{2} g' t^2$$

Now let us solve the right triangle OAB, remembering the method given on page 384, whereby

$$(OB)^2 = (OA)^2 + (OC)^2$$

Since from the figure, $OB = r + y$, $OA = r$, and $AB = x$, we have

$$(r + y)^2 = r^2 + x^2$$

whence

$$r^2 + 2ry + y^2 = r^2 + x^2$$

or

$$2ry + y^2 = x^2$$

Now y is the distance of fall (in an interval of time t) that is very short in comparison with r, the distance of the satellite from the center of the earth. Therefore, the square of y can be dropped from the right-hand side of the above equation without introducing an inaccuracy that is serious for our purpose of obtaining an approximate value for the injection velocity of this orbit.

Dropping y^2 gives

$$x^2 = 2ry$$

Substituting this equation the value previously found for y, which was

$$y = \tfrac{1}{2} g' t^2,$$

we have

$$x^2 = 2r(\tfrac{1}{2} g' t^2) = rg' t^2$$

so that

$$x = t\sqrt{rg'}$$

Since velocity in a given direction is equal to the distance travelled divided by the time, we have for the injection velocity

$$v_i = x/t = (t\sqrt{rg'})/t = \sqrt{rg'}$$

In order to calculate v_i for a circular orbit of any given radius about the center of the earth, we need to calculate the value of g' at that distance. This is readily done, since by Newton's law of general gravitation (page 640) we know that gravitational attraction between two bodies varies inversely as the square of the distance between their centers of mass. We also know that at the surface of the earth, which has a radius, r_E, of about 4,000 miles, the gravitational attraction is 32 feet per second per second (page 638). Therefore we have the simple relation

$$g'/g = r_E^2/r^2$$

which gives

$$g' = g(r_E/r^2)$$

and on substituting 32 for g and 4,000 for r_E,

$$g' = \frac{(32)(4,000)^2}{(r \text{ in miles})^2} = \frac{5.12 \times 10^8}{(r \text{ in miles})^2} \text{ feet per second per second}$$

or in miles per second per second

$$g' = \frac{5.12 \times 10^8}{(5,280)(r \text{ in miles})^2} = \frac{9.7 \times 10^4}{(r \text{ in miles})^2} \text{ miles per second per second}$$

Substituting in the equation for v_i above

$$v_i = \sqrt{\frac{(9.7 \times 10^4)(r \text{ in miles})}{(r \text{ in miles})^2}} = \sqrt{\frac{9.7 \times 10^4}{r \text{ in miles}}}$$

Let us now compute values of v_i, the injection or orbital velocity for circular orbits at various distances above the earth, remembering that r is the distance from the center of the earth, and therefore is equal to the height above the earth plus the radius of the earth, taken here as 4,000 miles.

At 1,000 miles above the earth, we have

$$v_i = \sqrt{\frac{9.7 \times 10^4}{5,000}} = 4.40 \text{ miles per second}$$

At 2,500 miles above the earth, we have

$$v_i = \sqrt{\frac{9.7 \times 10^4}{6,500}} = 3.85 \text{ miles per second}$$

At 5,000 miles above the earth, we have

$$v_i = \sqrt{\frac{9.7 \times 10^4}{9.000}} = 3.28 \text{ miles per second}$$

Another computation of interest about satellites is the period, or length of time required to complete an orbit. Since r is the radius of a circular orbit, the distance it travels in one complete orbit is the circumference of the circle or $2\pi r$. Therefore, the time required is this distance divided by the velocity, or $P = 2\pi r/v_i$. For the orbits already computed the periods are:

For a satellite at 1,000 miles above the earth,

$$P = \frac{(2\pi)(5,000)}{4.40} = 7,140 \text{ seconds} = 1 \text{ hour } 59 \text{ minutes}$$

For a satellite at 2,500 miles above the earth,

$$P = \frac{(2\pi)(6,500)}{3.85} = 10.900 \text{ seconds} = 3 \text{ hours } 1 \text{ minute } 40 \text{ seconds}$$

For a satellite at 5,000 miles above the earth,

$$P = \frac{(2\pi)(9,000)}{3.28} = 17,320 \text{ seconds} = 4 \text{ hours } 48 \text{ minutes } 40 \text{ seconds}$$

An interesting related problem is the calculation of the orbit of a satellite for a given period. Since we have found that

$$v_i = \sqrt{\frac{9.7 \times 10^4}{r}}$$

and

$$P = 2\pi r/v_i$$

substitute for v_i in the second equation, obtaining

$$P = \frac{2\pi r}{\sqrt{\frac{9.7 \times 10^4}{r}}}$$

Squaring both sides, we have

$$P^2 = \frac{4\pi^2 r^2}{\dfrac{9.7 \times 10^4}{r}}$$

So

$$P^2 = \frac{4\pi^2 r^3}{9.7 \times 10^4}$$

Giving

$$P^2 = .000407\, r^3$$

or

$$r = \sqrt[3]{\frac{P^2}{.000407}}$$

An application of this equation that is of great interest is to find the orbit of a satellite that has the same period as the earth, that is, 24 hours. For if such a satellite were placed in an orbit vertically above the equator, and if its direction of rotation were the same as that of the earth, it would remain directly above a point on the equator. Such satellites are very useful as relay stations for communication systems, and are said to be earth-synchronous.

To calculate the radius of their orbits, we use the above formula, remembering that P must be given in seconds, since v_i was found in miles per second. Thus $P = 24$ hours $= 86,400$ seconds, and we have

$$r_{syn} = \sqrt[3]{\frac{(86,400)^2}{.000407}}$$

$$= \sqrt[3]{1.87 \times 10^{13}}$$

By logarithms

$$\log r_{syn} = \frac{1}{3} \log (1.87 \times 10^{13})$$

$$= \frac{1}{3} (13.272) = 4.418$$

and $r_{syn} = $ antilog $4.418 = 26,200$ miles.

Since the r values are radii about the earth's center, a synchronous satellite would be 22,200 miles above the earth.

It should be noted that the figures that we have calculated are approximate. We have been working with figures given to few decimal places. We have neglected the friction of the atmosphere, which is greater of course, for orbits close to the earth, where the atmosphere is more dense. Moreover, the earth is not a perfect sphere and its density is not uniform throughout, so that its gravitational attraction varies slightly in magnitude and direction. Finally, when a satellite is injected into its orbit, we cannot impart to it precisely the velocity calculated to put it into a circular orbit. Since velocities lower than those so calculated would cause the satellite to descend (on a curved path) to earth, injection velocities higher than those calculated for circular orbits are used (except for earth-synchronous satellites). Such higher injection velocities (up to $\sqrt{2}$ times the calculated values) put the satellites into the elliptical orbits with which we are familiar.

How Fast Must You Go?

Another question very important for space travellers is the velocity to which they must be accelerated to reach a desired distance above the earth and to put them or their satellites, into a circular orbit at that distance. An equation for this "characteristic velocity" can be derived by calculating the energy necessary to raise unit mass from the earth's surface to the given height, and to add its orbital energy for the corresponding orbital velocity. This equation simplifies to the form

$$v_{ch} = \sqrt{2\, g r_E{}^2 \left(\frac{1}{r_E} - \frac{1}{2r} \right)}$$

where v_{ch} is the characteristic velocity, g is the acceleration of gravity at the earth's surface, r_E is the radius of the earth, and

r is the radius of the orbit (from the center of the earth). Substituting the known values we have

$$v_{ch} = \sqrt{2\left(\frac{32}{5,280}\right)(4,000)^2\left(\frac{1}{4,000} - \frac{2}{r}\right)}$$

or

$$v_{ch} = \sqrt{193,940\left(\frac{1}{4,000} - \frac{1}{2r}\right)}$$

Therefore the characteristic velocities for the orbits already computed are as follows.

For a satellite 1,000 miles above the earth,

$$v_{ch} = \sqrt{193,940\left(\frac{1}{4,000} - \frac{1}{10,000}\right)} = 5.3 \text{ miles per second}$$

For a satellite 2,500 miles above the earth,

$$v_{ch} = \sqrt{193,940\left(\frac{1}{4,000} - \frac{1}{13,000}\right)} = 5.8 \text{ miles per second}$$

For a satellite 5,000 miles above the earth,

$$v_{ch} = \sqrt{193,940\left(\frac{1}{4,000} - \frac{1}{18,000}\right)} = 6.1 \text{ miles per second}$$

For a satellite at geosynchronous altitude,

$$v_{ch} = \sqrt{193,940\left(\frac{1}{4,000} - \frac{1}{52,400}\right)} = 6.7 \text{ miles per second}$$

Note that while the necessary increase in characteristic velocity in a satellite 5,000 miles above the earth over one 2,500 miles above, a difference of 2,500 miles, is 0.3 mile per second, the increase for a satellite 22,200 miles high, which is 17,200 miles higher than the 5,000 mile satellite is only $6.7 - 6.1 = 0.6$ mile per second. In other words, the value of the characteristic velocity may be approaching a limit. To find its value at that limit, let us take the radius of the orbit as approaching

infinity. In that case $1/2r$ approaches zero, and the expression
for v_{ch} becomes

$$v_{ch} \text{ (for } r = \infty) = \sqrt{193,940 \frac{1}{4,000}} = 6.95 \text{ miles per second}$$

This limiting value of v_{ch} has an interesting interpretation.
To understand it let us ask what is the geometrical significance
of a circle of infinite radius. The curvature of any curve is
the reciprocal of the radius of curvature, that is, unity divided
by the radius of curvature. Since the radius of curvature of a
circle at all points is its radius, it follows that the radius of
curvature of a circle of infinite radius is $(1/\infty) = 0$. But this
is a straight line, since it does not curve. Therefore the orbit
of an object having a characteristic velocity of 6.95 miles per
second or greater is a straight line. It will therefore escape
entirely from any earth orbit and travel into space. Any space
probe or manned spacecraft must acquire this velocity if it is
to travel to the moon, the planets, or other objects outside of
the earth's effective gravitational field.

As has been the case with other calculations, the computation of escape velocity from the earth has neglected certain
effects. One in particular is the rotation of the earth. Obviously if the object is launched in the same direction as the
rotation of the earth, that velocity will be additive, so the escape
velocity as measured with reference to a point on earth will be
somewhat reduced, while it will be correspondingly increased
if the launch in opposition to the direction of rotation of the
earth.

n 39 n

Playing to Win

In Chapter 20, we examined ways to calculate probabilities or, in the language of the gambler, how to "figure the odds." We dealt with many situations, some arising in games of chance and some in various other situations arising in the everyday world. But if you will read that chapter again, you will discover that a major factor was not considered—namely, your opponent. As if you were in the boxing ring, you must ask, what is the other fellow doing?

Now of course if you wanted to *know* to a certainty what he intended to do in one particular situation you would have to find a mind reader or a crystal ball that worked. However, you can make use of an extension of probability theory that takes in your opponent or any number of opponents. It is called the theory of games, and was formulated first more than twenty years ago by John von Neumann and Oskar Morgenstern.

Of course these men did not develop the theory to use in gambling. They were actuated by the much broader aim of studying competitive situations wherever they might occur, in business, in economics, in war, and even those in which the opponent was not a person or group of people but an impersonal entity, such as old Mother Nature herself. However, they found that the most convenient approach to the subject was in terms of games—the simpler, the better.

They began by classifying games into two major groups: zero-sum games and non-zero-sum games. In a zero-sum game the sum of the payments between the players as of the end of the game is zero, that is, one player's gain is a loss to the other or others. All games played for entertainment belong to this class, while competitive situations in business rarely do. The development of the theory of zero-sum games was found to provide methods of analysis which could be extended to the non-zero-sum ones.

Several fundamental questions arise in any discussion of game theory. These include the following: How does each player plan his strategy? How much information is available to each player throughout the game? How does each player modify his strategy from information about the other player's plan? In answering these questions we will begin by studying the zero-sum two-person game, in which each person may choose between two and only two distinct strategies.

Two-Person Zero-Sum Games

In introducing the methodology of game-theory analysis, it is well to begin with a very simple game. Consider, for example, that two players, A and B, are playing the game of matching pennies under rules whereby each player chooses the side of the penny he will show, and does not see, of course, the side shown by his opponent until the play is made. If the two faces match, Player A will win a unit sum from Player B; likewise if the two faces do not match, Player B will win a similar amount from Player A. This game may be represented by the following game matrix. This matrix is effective in summarizing

		Player B	
		Play #1 Heads	Play #2 Tails
Player A	Play #1 Heads	1	−1
	Play #2 Tails	−1	1

the results of the various plays in the game. Each row represents a play by Player A; each column a play by Player B; and the figures in the spaces formed by the intersection of rows and columns represent the payments for the plays. We use the convention that positive numbers indicate a gain for Player A and consequently a loss for Player B, and that negative numbers indicate a gain for Player B and consequently a loss for Player A.

A *pure strategy* is a play that is available to a participant in a game. In the above example each player has two pure strategies at his disposal (i.e., he may show either one face of the penny or the other). Pure strategies are mutually exclusive in that, when a player selects one, he automatically forfeits the right of employing another on that particular play of the game. A player's *grand strategy* is his method of selecting pure strategies for a series of plays in a given game. A player arrives at his grand strategy by calculating the odds that indicate the most favorable mixture of his pure strategies.

The game of matching pennies seems to be a "fair" game, but let us now establish the mathematical criterion for such a supposition. Our first step is to discover the odds that indicate the optimum grand strategy for each player. To do this we first subtract the second row from the first row in the game matrix and write the results, after interchanging them, directly below the figures in the second row. Then we subtract the second column from the first column and write the results, again after interchanging them, directly to the right of the figures in the second column. This gives us:

		Player B		
		1. Heads	2. Tails	
Player A	1. Heads	1	−1	−2
	2. Tails	−1	1	2
		−2	2	

Note that the -2 below the first column was obtained by disregarding the elements in the first column and by subtracting the elements in the second column as shown in the next diagram. The other differences were determined similarly by sub-

		Player B		
		1. Heads	2. Tails	
Player A	1. Heads		-1	$(-1) - (1) = (-2)$
	2. Tails		1	
		-2		

tracting the appropriate elements and interchanging the results. The absolute values (i.e., the numerical value without sign) of the four differences just obtained represent the odds or the ratio in which a player should mix his pure strategies. Thus Player A should select either of his two pure strategies at random, but all the while he must keep in mind that he should be using the two strategies in a $2:2$ (or $1:1$) ratio over a period of time.

Likewise, Player B should select his strategies at random but in accordance with the $1:1$ ratio. In other words, each player should decide by some device over which he has no control (such as flipping a coin) which pure strategy to select for a given play. By not using such a device, a player who seemingly makes an arbitrary decision for each play may be unconsciously following a system that can be interpreted by his opponent and used against him.

A "fair" game is defined as one whose value is zero. That is, if such a game is played over an extended length of time, neither player has a better chance than the other of reaping a profit. The value of a game can be found by selecting a row at random and multiplying each element through by the corresponding term of the odds affixed to the columns and then dividing the sum of the products thus obtained by the sum of the integers that represent the column odds. Similarly a column may be selected at random and the same value will be obtained by multiplying each element in it by the corresponding term from the set of row odds and dividing the sum of these products by the sum of the integers composing the set of row odds. Thus, in the example we have been using, if we select the first row, we obtain

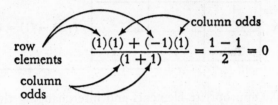

$$\frac{(1)(1) + (-1)(1)}{(1 + 1)} = \frac{1 - 1}{2} = 0$$

We will obtain the same result by selecting the remaining row or either column and conducting the appropriate operation. Here the result is zero, which proves that "matching pennies" is a fair game. In any case the value of a game can be thought of as the average payment over a period of time, taken from the point of view of one of the players involved. The applications of the operations just demonstrated will become more obvious when we now consider some games which possess values unequal to zero.

Saddle Points

Let us now investigate games in which the players must employ preferred strategies. An example of such a game is given in the following matrix, in which all the figures represent gains by A, and hence losses by B.

		Player B	
		1	2
Player A	1.	7	6
	2.	6	5

In this case, the numbers to the left of and above the matrix designate the pure strategies of Player A and Player B respectively. As stated above, all the numbers within the matrix itself are positive and therefore represent gains for A and losses for B. The main concern of Player A then is to find and adopt a grand strategy that will assure him of the maximum profit in spite of any grand strategy that Player B may adopt to thwart this purpose. Likewise, the main concern of Player B is to find and adopt a grand strategy that will minimize his losses in spite of any grand strategy that A may adopt.

To find his optimum grand strategy, Player A first examines the rows of the game matrix (his pure strategies) and then writes to the right of the last figure in each row the lowest figure in that row. These figures are called the *row minima* and represent the minimum gain available to Player A for each pure strategy at his disposal. Of these he naturally prefers the pure strategy with the greatest minimum return, e.g., row 1 in this case.

		Player B		
		1	2	
Player A	1	7	6	⑥
	2	6	5	5

Player B, on the other hand, examines the columns and lists below the last figure in each the largest figure in that column. These figures are called the *column maxima* and represent the maximum losses possible for Player B for each pure strategy at his disposal.

		Player B	
		1	2
Player A	1	7	6
	2	6	5
		7	⑥

Of these he favors the pure strategy which entails the least maximum loss, e.g., column 2 in this case. In this game we find that the maximum of the row minima (MAXMIN) is equal to the minimum of the column maxima (MINMAX).

	Player B		
	1	2	
Player A 1	7	*6	⑥
2	6	5	5
	7	⑥	

Whenever this occurs the game in question is said to have a *saddle point* (marked with an asterisk above) and in such a case it is to the advantage of each player to select only that pure strategy which contains the saddle point. Thus Player A will always play his first pure strategy, i.e., the first row in the game matrix, and Player B will always play his second pure strategy, i.e., the second column in the game matrix, and Player A will make a consistent profit of 6 units per play. Here we see several things. First, a player's grand strategy is simply a pure strategy when there is a saddle point. Second, from our preceding definition of the value of a game, we can see that, in a game which contains a saddle point, the value of the saddle point is invariably the value of the game. Thus the value of this game to Player A is 6. In other words the average payoff is 6 units to Player A and a loss of 6 units to Player B. This is obviously not a fair game, for the value of the game is not zero and the average payoff favors one player. Third, this game illustrates an important convention of game theory. The player who employs the row strategies is called the *maximizing player* and the player who employs the column strategies is called *minimizing player*. This terminology does not indicate any basic difference between the outlooks of the two players. Although Player A seems to be playing to maximize his winnings and Player B seems to be playing to minimize his losses, there is essentially no disparity between the goals of the two players. The introduction of these two terms is, in fact, simply a consequence of adopting the convention of using positive numbers to represent the winnings of Player A and negative numbers to represent the winnings of Player B.

The observations that we have just made were all obtained

by assuming that each player is intelligent and aware of the intelligence of his opposition. If either one of the above players selects the alternate pure strategy (the one not including the saddle point) he will only penalize himself in so doing. For example, if Player A decides to select his second pure strategy while B maintains his second pure strategy, A will find his winnings reduced from 6 to 5 on that particular play. Likewise, if Player B decides to select his first pure strategy while Player A maintains his first pure strategy, B will find his losses have increased from 6 to 7 on that particular play. So it is safe to say that in any game which has a saddle point, the optimum grand strategies for the two players involved consist of playing only those pure strategies that include the saddle point and neglecting the others. This brings us to the first rule for finding the value of any game: *Always seek to establish whether the game in question has a saddle point before employing any of the other methods. If it does, this value is also the value of the game.* Incidentally, the game in the above example could be considered fair if Player A were to make a side payment of 6 units to Player B before each play. Thus any game, whose value can be determined, may be made fair by having the player whom the game favors make a side payment equal to the value of the game to that player who is otherwise at a disadvantage.

Example 1. Find the saddle point in the game:

	Player B 1	Player B 2
Player A 1	8	4
Player A 2	1	2

First, we find the maximum of the row minima.

	Player B 1	Player B 2		
Player A 1	8	4	④	MAXMIN = 4
Player A 2	1	2	1	

Second, we find the minimum of the column maxima.

Player B

		1	2	
Player A	1	8	4	MINMAX = 4
	2	1	2	
		8	④	

Third, we see that the MAXMIN is equal to the MINMAX. Thus there is a saddle point, the number 4, and the value of this game is then 4. Furthermore, Player A will select his first pure strategy each time and Player B will select his second.

Mixed Strategies

Now let us turn our attention towards some games that require the use of definite mixed strategies on the part of the players. Consider the game:

Player B

		1	2
Player A	1	4	−5
	2	−3	5

When we examine for a saddle point, we find

Player B

		1	2		
	1	4	−5	−5	MAXMIN = −3
Player A					MINMAX = 4
	2	−3	5	(−3)	MAXMIN ≠ MINMAX
		④	5		∴ no saddle point.

The next step then is to find the odds that describe the optimum mixture of the pure strategies for each player. This we do by following the method outlined in our discussion of the game of matching pennies.

The odds relating B's pure strategies are found by subtracting the elements in the second row from the corresponding ones in the first and interchanging the results.

Player B				Player B				Player B	
1	2			1	2			1	2
·	−5			4	·			4	−5
·	5			−3	·			−3	5
−10				·	7			−10	7

Thus when we take the absolute values of these results we find that player B should play his first pure strategy 10 times for every 7 times he plays his second. His optimum grand strategy, therefore, is a 10:7 random mixture of his two pure strategies.

The odds relating A's pure strategies are found by subtracting the elements in the second column from those in the first and interchanging the results.

Player A $\begin{smallmatrix}1\\2\end{smallmatrix}$ $\begin{array}{|c|c|}\hline \cdot & \cdot \\\hline -3 & 5 \\\hline\end{array}$ $\begin{smallmatrix}-8\\ \cdot\end{smallmatrix}$ Player A $\begin{smallmatrix}1\\2\end{smallmatrix}$ $\begin{array}{|c|c|}\hline 4 & -5 \\\hline \cdot & \cdot \\\hline\end{array}$ $\begin{smallmatrix}\cdot\\9\end{smallmatrix}$ Player A $\begin{smallmatrix}1\\2\end{smallmatrix}$ $\begin{array}{|c|c|}\hline 4 & -5 \\\hline -3 & 5 \\\hline\end{array}$ $\begin{smallmatrix}-8\\9\end{smallmatrix}$

Taking the absolute values of these results, we find that Player A should play his first pure strategy 8 times for every 9 times he plays his second. Consequently, his optimum grand strategy is a 8:9 random mixture of his two pure strategies.

To find the value of this game we select any row or column, and proceed according to the following equations to crossmultiply, add, and divide:

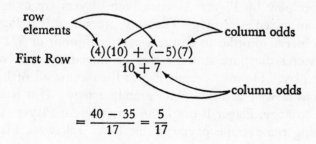

$$\text{First Row} \quad \frac{(4)(10) + (-5)(7)}{10 + 7}$$

$$= \frac{40 - 35}{17} = \frac{5}{17}$$

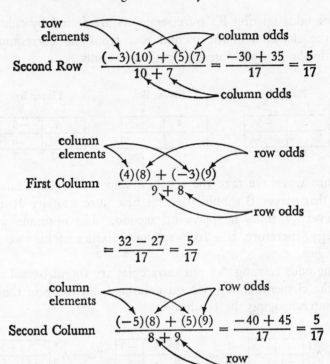

row elements → column odds

Second Row $\dfrac{(-3)(10) + (5)(7)}{10 + 7} = \dfrac{-30 + 35}{17} = \dfrac{5}{17}$

column odds

column elements → row odds

First Column $\dfrac{(4)(8) + (-3)(9)}{9 + 8}$

row odds

$= \dfrac{32 - 27}{17} = \dfrac{5}{17}$

column elements → row odds

Second Column $\dfrac{(-5)(8) + (5)(9)}{8 + 9} = \dfrac{-40 + 45}{17} = \dfrac{5}{17}$

row odds

Here we have worked out the values using each column and each row. In every instance we see that each element in a row or column was multiplied by the absolute value of corresponding integer from the set of column or row odds respectively, and then the sum of these products was divided by the sum of the integers representing the same odds. It is seen that the value of this game is 5/17, which represents the average amount won per play by Player A when both players are using their optimum mixed strategies. The only precaution that Player A must observe in order to ensure a continual profit of 5/17 is to keep secret the pure strategy that he intends to use on each future play. He may permit Player B to know all of his past decisions as well as to know his grand strategy. If it is a good grand strategy, Player B can in no way prevent Player A from obtaining the average payment due him. Likewise, Player B must maintain the same precautions or his losses will be greater.

The only foolproof method of deciding which pure strategy to employ on a given play is to let the decision rest entirely on some chance event. Thus a chance mechanism is an indispensable part of a good grand strategy. In the problem that we have just worked out, Player A might select his pure strategies by putting into a bowl 8 orange and 9 black marbles, all of the same size, shape, weight, and texture, and then selecting one of them with his eyes closed. If he should draw an orange marble, then he would play his first strategy; a black marble, his second strategy. Before drawing for each successive play, Player A must return the marble he drew for his present play so that the bowl always contains the same number of marbles in the same ratio. The best method, however, is to employ a table of random numbers such as the one shown on this page. For example, using this table to mix two strategies, *a* and *b*, in a 3:1 ratio, we would pick a starting point at random and then run down each column, playing strategy *a* for

NON-REPEATING RANDOM NUMBERS 1–200

41	185	107	1	13	52	151	115	134	194
167	73	81	68	120	146	70	64	31	118
125	147	21	183	27	172	193	72	76	65
197	162	140	93	144	98	139	37	131	33
181	36	8	123	106	178	90	30	35	200
133	159	4	165	160	117	53	198	92	116
3	108	32	85	7	135	173	86	42	132
49	58	169	109	124	5	82	62	168	95
112	129	96	78	67	84	138	128	195	15
149	113	148	142	45	186	10	155	40	34
14	110	69	54	164	163	174	24	189	6
66	48	12	25	190	60	114	75	158	71
199	19	136	44	170	157	122	121	111	18
126	192	103	184	127	99	153	187	9	191
87	104	188	150	38	171	56	154	89	101
137	97	51	88	166	91	28	17	23	29
50	161	63	119	74	55	105	175	57	182
180	39	130	77	83	61	11	16	176	177
59	47	80	152	22	196	79	179	46	43
94	102	143	20	26	145	2	100	141	156

all numbers between 1 and 150 and strategy b for all numbers between 150 and 200.

Returning for a moment to the game matrix, we find that the play of a game is not altered by adding a constant to each payoff or by multiplying each payoff by a positive constant. However, the value of the game is affected when either of these operations is performed. For the game that we analyzed previously in this section, we found the value to be $5/17$. Note the values obtained below first by adding 2 to each term (a) and then by multiplying each term by 3, (b).

(a)

6	−3
−1	7

$$\text{Value} = \frac{(6)(10) + (-3)(7)}{17} = \frac{39}{17} = 2\frac{5}{17} = 2 + \frac{5}{17}$$

(b)

12	−15
−9	16

$$\text{Value} = \frac{(12)(10) + (-15)(7)}{17} = \frac{120 - 105}{17} = \frac{15}{17} = 3\left(\frac{5}{17}\right)$$

Hence, when a constant is added to each element in the game matrix, the value of the game is also increased by that number. Similarly, when each element in the game matrix is multiplied by a positive constant, the value of the game is multiplied by the constant. In most cases the play as well as the value of a game would be influenced by multiplying each element in the game matrix by a negative constant.

Now let us examine two problems that will demonstrate how the techniques of game theory may be applied and how a stated problem may be translated into the notation of game theory.

Prob. 1. Recall the game of matching pennies. If strategy 1 for either player means that he shows heads and if strategy 2 means that he shows tails, which of the following game matrices illustrates the more advantageous set of payoffs for Player A?

I.

	Player B 1	Player B 2
Player A 1	3	0
Player A 2	−4	−1

II.

	Player B 1	Player B 2
Player A 1	−2	3
Player A 2	1	−2

To answer this question we must find the value of each of the above games. The game having the higher numerical value will be more advantageous to Player A. Let us examine matrix I first.

Our first step is always to check for a saddle point, so we begin by finding and comparing the maxmin and the minmax.

	Player B	
	1	2
1	3	0
2	−4	−1
	3	⓪

Ⓞ MAXMIN = MINMAX

−4 ∴ There is a saddle point at zero.

Thus we have already found the value of matrix I to be zero. Checking for a saddle point in matrix II we find

		Player B	
		1	2
Player A	1	−2	3
	2	1	−2
		①	3

⊖② MAXMIN ≠ MINMAX

⊖② ∴ no saddle point

Consequently we must compute the odds for the two sets of strategies before we can determine the value of the game.

		Player B		
		1	2	
Player A	1	−2	3	3
	2	1	−2	5 *
		5	3	

Selecting the first row, we find the value of matrix II.

$$\frac{(-2)(5) + (3)(3)}{(5 + 3)} = \frac{-10 + 9}{8} = -\frac{1}{8}$$

Thus Player A would experience an average loss of 1/8 unit per play if both players used their optimum grand strategies

---

* The minus signs preceding some of the terms in a set of odds are not necessary once the entire set has been determined.

(a mixture of 5:3 for A and 3:5 for B). This is worse than just breaking even; thus we have found that matrix I is more advantageous to Player A.

Prob. 2. A certain business buys and sells two commodities, commodity A and commodity B. In general, there are only two marketing conditions that it must consider: condition X and condition Y. It has no control over these conditions which may alternate at random, but it does know that under condition X, it can sell 60 items of commodity A per week, and under condition Y it can sell 10 items of commodity A and 100 items of commodity B per week. Commodity A costs the business concern $2 per item but it can be resold for $5. Commodity B costs $1 but can be resold for $2. The business concern is willing to invest $120 in goods at the beginning of each week, but at the end of the week, all the merchandise that has not been sold is considered a total loss, for both commodities are perishable. In what proportion should the business concern buy for condition X and for condition Y and what is its optimum average income per week?

We construct the following matrix

		Sells for	
		1.	**2.**
		Condition X	Condition Y
Purchase for	1. Condition X	180	−70
	2. Condition Y	−70	130

These figures represent the business concern's potential losses and gains under each given condition. For example, if it buys for condition X, it invests all of the $120 in commodity A. If, however, condition Y should then prevail, the concern is able to dispose of only 10 of the 60 items and thus experiences a loss of $70 (upper right-hand corner of matrix).

First we check for a saddle point and find that there is none. Then we must find the odds that will provide the concern with the optimum grand strategy. To simplify the calculations, we divide every element in the game matrix by 10 and then calculate the odds. This gives us:

		Sells for		
		1. X	2. Y	
Purchases for	1. X	18	−7	20
	2. Y	−7	13	25
		20	25	

Thus the concern should buy for condition X and condition Y according to the odds 4:5. The value of the game is

$$(10^*)\left[\frac{(18)(4) + (-7)(5)}{4 + 5}\right] = (10)\frac{37}{9} = \frac{370}{9} = \$41.11$$

As an alternative to playing the odds, the business concern could decide to invest 4/9 of the $120 in merchandise for condition X and 5/9 in merchandise for condition Y. It would then purchase $64.50 worth of commodity A and $55.50 worth of commodity B. This investment would ensure a steady profit of $42.11 in spite of the fluctuation in the prevailing condition. It is not always possible to form a synthesis of the strategies as we did here, for there are many cases that call for the selection of one and only one of a series of mutually exclusive pure strategies per play.

2 × N Games

Games in which one player has two strategies and the other has more than two are described as '2 × n' (two by n) games. Here the n may be replaced by any integer greater than two. As we shall soon see, only a few new techniques must be introduced to describe these games as an extension of the 2 × 2 games.

In every case a 2 × n game will have either a saddle point solution or an optimum mixed strategy based on only two pure

---

* Remember that previously we divided the game matrix through by 10.

strategies. Thus, *any 2 × n game may be reduced to an equivalent 2 × 2 game.*

As emphasized in the previous chapter, the first step in analyzing any game is to look for a saddle point. If there is one, the game is solved and some unnecessary calculation has been avoided. The technique for finding a saddle point for $2 \times n$ games is the same as that used for 2×2 games. We simply find and compare the maxmin and the minmax. Consider the following game.

		Player B 1	Player B 2	
	1	6	5	5
	2	5	5	5
Player A	3	6	4	4 row minima
	4	7	6	⑥
	5	2	4	2
column maxima		7	⑥	

MAXMIN = MINMAX = 6

Thus, this game does have a saddle point and we know immediately that Player A's optimum grand strategy is his fourth pure strategy and that Player B's optimum grand strategy is his second pure strategy. In other words, A plays his pure strategies according to the odds $0:0:0:1:0$ and B plays his pure strategies according to the odds $0:1$. The value of this game is obviously 6.

If, however, the given $2 \times n$ game does not contain a saddle point, the next step is to attempt to reduce it to a 2×2 matrix. When we study the choices of the player who has many strategies at his disposal, it may be obvious that some of them are inferior to others. In this case the superior strategies are said to *dominate* the inferior ones and the latter may be eliminated from the game. For our present purposes there are two types of dominance. When the values of all the elements in one pure strategy are greater than those of the corresponding elements of another, the situation is defined as *strict dominance*. However, when some of the values are equal, the situation is defined as *non-strict dominance*. It is always safe to eliminate a strategy on the basis of strict dominance. However, elimination of a strategy on the basis of non-strict dominance may cause a subtle alteration in a game that has more than one solution. Such games as these are of a higher order than we have yet discussed. The concept of dominance is an important one in game theory and will be elaborated on further in the subsequent sections of this chapter. Let us now consider another 2 × 5 game.

		Player B 1	Player B 2
	1	0	3
	2	2	1
Player A	3	1	4
	4	3	2
	5	2	1

If we check for a saddle point, we find that there is none. Our next step is to try to single out A's dominant pure strategies. Each element in A's fourth strategy is seen to be greater than the corresponding elements in his second and fifth strategies. Thus, we may eliminate both of these from the game matrix. This gives us:

		Player B 1	Player B 2
	1	0	3
Player A	3	1	4
	4	3	2

It is now evident that A's third strategy is dominant over his first strategy, so we eliminate the latter and obtain

		Player B 1	Player B 2
Player A	3	1	4
	4	3	2

This game may now be solved by the methods we have described for operations with 2×2 games. Thus, we find that A should play his third and fourth strategies according to the odds $1:3$ and that B should play his first and second strategies according to the odds $1:1$. The value of the 2×2 game, and consequently of the $2 \times n$ game, is 2.5. Player A may consider his set of odds for the original game to be $0:0:1:3:0$. The usefulness of dominance is quite evident in this example. It may also be applied to simple 2×2 games, but its occurrence in them indicates that the game must have a saddle point.

The next situation that must be discussed is the $2 \times n$ game that does not contain a saddle point and cannot be reduced by dominance to a 2×2 game. After we have examined a game and found it without a saddle point, it may still be possible to reduce the game somewhat by dominance. If A is the multistrategy player, we attempt to reduce the game by eliminating the *dominated* strategies. However, if B is the multistrategy player, we attempt to reduce the game by eliminating the *dominant* strategies. This follows, for A is striving to maximize his profits and B is striving to minimize his losses. After the game has been reduced as much as possible by dominance, the next step is to take one of the remaining 2×2 games, solve it, and test the solution in the original game. That is, first solve the 2×2 game and then, using the odds proposed for the two-strategy player, see how this player does against each of the strategies of the multistrategy player. If the two-strategy player does *as well or better* against the strategies not in the 2×2 subgame then the solution has been discovered. As we noted earlier, a player with a good grand strategy can win consistently against either of his opponents' pure strategies. This remark may now be extended. In the $2 \times n$ game, one can win the same amount against either of the strategies that form the opponent's best mix. However, one wins a greater amount against the opponent's remaining strategies. Occasionally the winnings are the same against the remaining strategies but this is the exception and not the rule. Consider this 2×6 game.

		Player B					Row
	1	**2**	**3**	**4**	**5**	**6**	**Min.**
Player A 1	−7	−2	0	3	3	2	−7
2	6	−3	5	2	−6	6	−6
Col. MAX.	6	−2	5	3	3	6	

$$\text{MAXMIN} = -6 \qquad \text{MINMAX} = -2$$

$$\text{MAXMIN} \neq \text{MINMAX}$$

∴ no saddle point.

Upon further investigation we discover that B's third, fourth, and sixth strategies dominate his second strategy so these may be eliminated to give us:

		Player B	
	1	**2**	**5**
Player A 1	−7	−2	3
2	6	−3	−6

There is no dominance among B's remaining three strategies. Consequently we must search for a 2×2 subgame within the 2×3 game which will satisfy the latter (thus automatically satisfying the original 2×6 game). We begin with

		Player B
	1	**2**
Player A 1	−7	−2
2	6	−3

and find that Player A should play according to the odds $9:5$ and Player B should play according to the odds $1:13$. Calculating the value of this subgame, we find

$$\frac{(9)(-7) + (5)(6)}{9 + 5} = \frac{-33}{14}$$

To see if this solution will satisfy the 2×3 game we must test A's $9:5$ strategy on B's remaining pure strategy (B-5). If the result is greater than or equal to $-22/14$, the 2×3 game is satisfied.

$$\frac{(9)(3) + (5)(-6)}{14} = \frac{-3}{14}$$

This result satisfies our criterion. Consequently the $9:5$ mixture is a good strategy for Player A and the $1:13:0:0:0:0$ mixture is a good strategy for Player B.

Let us compare these results with those we obtain by using another 2×2 subgame of the given 2×3 game.

		Player B 2	5
Player A	1	−2	3
	2	−3	−6

We find that this subgame has a saddle point at -2. Thus according to this matrix, A should always select his first strategy and B should always select his second. But now we must test A's $1:0$ mix on B's first strategy and we find that we obtain the value -7 which is considerably less than -2. Therefore, this subgame does not satisfy our criterion for a good strategy and its solution does not satisfy the 2×3 or 2×6 game matrix.

It is imperative to reduce a $2 \times n$ game as much as possible before starting the search for the 2×2 solution, for there are $n(n-1)/2$ games of the 2×2 variety contained within every $2 \times n$ game if we had not reduced the above 2×6 game, we would have been faced with the analysis of 15 possible 2×2 subgames.

Another very practical method of solving $2 \times n$ games consists of graphing the various strategies that are at the disposal of the multistrategy player. Recall the game matrix

		Player B 1	2	3	4	5	6
Player A	1	−7	−2	0	3	3	2
	2	6	−3	5	2	−6	6

This game may be graphed as shown in the figure by plotting the first element in each of B's pure strategies on one vertical axis and by plotting the second element in each B's pure strategies on a second vertical axis and by then connecting each of the six sets of corresponding points with straight lines. Next the line segments that bound the bottom portion of the graph (since B is the minimizing player) are marked with a heavier line. The highest point on this heavy line marks the intersection of the combination of pure strategies that will satisfy the original game. Here we see that the point lies on the intersection of the first and second pure strategies, which we have already proven correct by computation. This method of graphing provides a useful shortcut for determining which 2 × 2 subgame is the solution of a given 2 × n game. Once the desired subgame has been found, it is an easy matter to compute the odds and value attached to the original game.

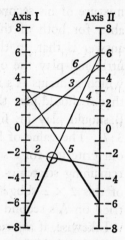

If the game in question provides Player A (the maximizing player) with the greater number of strategies, a similar graph may be drawn, but the line segments bounding the top rather than the bottom of the figure are now relevant and the lowest point on this broken line marks the intersection of the preferred mixture of strategies. Note the graphing of another 2 × 6 game.

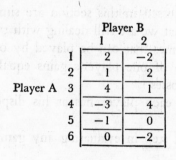

		Player B	
		1	2
	1	2	−2
	2	1	2
Player A	3	4	1
	4	−3	4
	5	−1	0
	6	0	−2

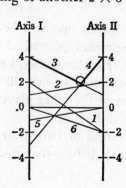

From this graph we can assume that A's best mixture of pure strategies consists of his third and fourth alternatives. This seems a little strange for his fourth strategy has the greatest loss potential of any of his pure strategies. Why wouldn't a mixture of his second and third pure strategies be more profitable, for both of these preclude the possibility of loss? The answer is that, in this case, it is more profitable to gamble a little and play the odds. First let us solve the 2×2 subgame which contains A's third and fourth pure strategies. We find that A should play these two strategies in the ratio $7:3$ and that B should play his first and second pure strategies in the ratio $3:7$. The value of his game for A is 1.9 and it conforms with our criterion for a solution; i.e., when B's odds are tried on A's remaining strategies, the result is invariably less than the value of this 2×2 subgame. For example, when B's $3:7$ odds are tried on A's second strategy, we obtain 1.7.

Likewise, if we solve the 2×2 subgame which contains A's second and third pure strategies, we find that A could best play these according to the ratio $3:1$ while B plays his first and second strategies according to the ratio $1:3$. However, the value of this game for A is merely 1.75. Thus, a little daring and a sound grand strategy will provide more of a profit in this case than will an untested section of the two strategies that contain no element of risk.

3 × 3 Games

The games that will be discussed in this section are similar to those already described in that we are still dealing with two-person zero-sum games, i.e., games that can be played by only two competitors with the sum of one player's gains equal to the sum of the other player's losses.

The difference here is that each player has at his disposal three instead of two strategies.

Note as before that the first step in evaluating any game is to determine the maxmin and minmax and look for a saddle point. Consider this 3×3 game.

		Player B			Row Min.
		1	2	3	
	1	2	1	0	⓪ MAXMIN = MINMAX = 0
Player A	2	−4	−3	−2	−4 ∴ There is a saddle point.
	3	3	4	−1	−1
Col. Max.		3	4	⓪	

Thus the game is immediately solved. The value is 0 and A's optimum grand strategy is $1:0:0$ while B's is $0:0:1$. If either player deviates from the saddle point strategy, he and he alone will suffer for it.

Just as the saddle point technique is seen to apply in the study of 3×3 games, so may the idea of dominance be extended in a similar manner. Consider the game

		Player B		
		1	2	3
	1	−3	1	−1
Player A	2	7	1	−2
	3	1	7	2

At once we see that A's third pure strategy dominates his first. The elimination of the latter reduces this matrix to a 2×3 game

		Player B		
		1	2	3
Player A	2	7	1	−2
	3	1	7	2

Next we notice that B's second strategy dominates his third. When the former is eliminated we obtain

		Player B	
		1	3
Player A	2	7	−2
	3	1	2

This 2×2 game, when solved, will provide the optimum grand strategies and the value for the original game. If we are confronted with 3×3 game that does not have a saddle point, the next step is to try to reduce it by dominance to a $2 \times n$ game, which can always be further reduced to a 2×2 game.

In the above game A should follow the grand strategy $0:1:9$ while B should follow a $2:0:3$ mixture. The value of the 2×2 game, and consequently of the 3×3 game, is 1.6.

Other Games

There are, of course, two-person 3×3 games, or games with an even greater number of strategies, which have neither saddle points nor dominant strategies. Even these can be solved for the optimum grand strategy by repeated subtraction of elements and computation of the various grand strategies of the resulting games.

Of particular interest are games involving more than two plays. Thus a three-person game introduces complications which do not arise in the two-person game. These complications stem from the possibility of coalitions, that is, a situation in which two of the players act in union to play against the third player. From game theory it follows that for players A, B, and C, there are four possible situations: (1) A three-person game between A, B and C; (2) a two-person game between A, B on one hand and C on the other; (3) a two-person game between the A-C combination and the player B; and (4) a two-person game between the B-C combination and the player A. Since the returns to the players will in all probability be different for all four of these games, the analysis of three-person games is far more complex than that of two-person games and the complexity increases, of course, with increasing numbers of players until that number reaches a size where the individual effect of each player is negligible.

The theory of games assumes that coalitions will be formed whenever they yield greater advantages of two of the players than they would obtain if each acted independently. Matrices for the three-person games can also be set up. Usually one of several simplifying assumptions is made, one of them being that gains for each individual player are possible only if he forms a coalition with another player. In such cases the entire objective of the game for each player is to form a coalition with another. The solutions of such games consist, therefore, in determining which of the three possible coalitions yields the greatest return to its two members. A further complication of such games, however, is the possibility of one of the members of the coalition dealing with the third player. For example, if A and B form a coalition whereby each profits by one unit at the expense of C who loses two units, then A might deal with C on the basis that C pays A 1 1/2 units in all, on condition of A's withdrawal from the coalition with B—in this manner C would reduce his potential loss to 1 1/2 units, while A would extend his gain from the one unit to be obtained from his coalition with B, to the 1 1/2 units he would obtain directly from C.

To deal with this situation the concept of dominance may be extended from two-person games to three-person games. Thus, one of the possible distributions of payments in a three-person game is said to dominate another if it is more advantageous to both the members of the coalition (in the above example to both A and B).

It is apparent at once, however, that the extension of the concept of dominance to three-person games does not exclude multiple solutions, that is, multiple distributions of payments which are of equal value. Assuming, for example, that the maximum payment which can be obtained by two players acting in coalition from the third player is the same whether the third player be A, B or C, then the theory of games obviously will not return a single answer as to which players should form the coalition. In cases of this sort, especially as they occur outside of the field of elementary games, in real games, or more particularly, in economics or other fields of human activity, there are often external conditions which limit the choices by the players to a smaller number than that mathematically possible. Thus, in the field of business there is specific legal prohibition of certain forms of cartel action. Moreover, the moral or social effect of this legal prohibition is to discourage even smaller businesses, to which it does not apply directly, from combining for the complete exploitation of a third enterprise. Their actions of this nature result far more frequently from the independent discovery by each in his own enterprise and from the results of his own operations, of a course of action which promises to yield the maximum profit, or the maxmin profit.

APPENDIX

1. SIGNS AND SYMBOLS USED IN THIS BOOK

$+$ *Plus*, the sign of addition. For example $2 + 3$.
This sign also denotes *a positive quantity*. For example $+4$, positive four.

$-$ *Minus*, the sign of subtraction. For example $5 - 3$.
This sign also denotes *a negative quantity*. For example -7, negative seven.

$\cdot$ The sign of multiplication. The dot is placed a little above the line. For example $3 \cdot 4$.

$.$ The decimal point. This dot is placed on the line. For example 3.5.

$\div$ The sign of division. For example $15 \div 3$.

$=$ The sign of equality. It reads *is equal to*. For example $2 + 3 = 5$.

$>$ The inequality sign which reads *is greater than*. For example $7 > 4$.

$<$ The inequality sign which reads *is less than*. For example $6 < 11$.

$\sqrt{}$ The radical. Also the square root. For example $\sqrt{16} = 4$.

$\sqrt[3]{}$ The cube root. For example $\sqrt[3]{27} = 3$.

$\sqrt[n]{}$ The n-th root.

a^2 The square, or the second power of a. $a^2 = a \cdot a$.

a^3 The cube, or the third power of a. $a^3 = a \cdot a \cdot a$.

a^n The n-th power of a.

$| \; |$ Two vertical bars denote the absolute value of a number. For example $|-5| = 5$.

∞ Infinity. For example $\dfrac{5}{0} = \infty$.

$(\;)$ Parentheses.

$[\;]$ Brackets.

$\{\;\}$ Figured brackets.

$\triangle$ Triangle. For example $\triangle ABC$.

$\angle$ Angle. For example $\angle A$.

$^\circ$ Degree, for denoting the measure of an angle. For example $45°$.
Also used for the purpose of denoting temperatures. For example $30°$.

$'$ Minute, for denoting the measure of an angle. For example $45° \, 12'$.

$''$ Second, for denoting the measure of an angle. For example $45° \, 12' \, 30''$.

π *Pi*, the multiplier used for the computation of circumferences
and areas of circles and of areas and volumes of spheres as
well as in many other instances. $\pi = 3.1416$, approximately.

sin The sine ratio of an angle.
cos The cosine ratio of an angle.
tan The tangent ratio of an angle.
log The logarithm of a number.

I. Algebra

2. ADDITION OF SIGNED NUMBERS

Example: $+ (+7) + (-6) - (+10) - (-8)$

Remove the parentheses. The same signs before and within
the parentheses result in a $+$ sign. Opposite signs before and
within the parentheses result in a $-$ sign.

$$+7 - 6 - 10 + 8$$

After the parentheses are removed add the absolute values of the
positive numbers and place a $+$ sign before the sum:

$$+7 + 8 = + 15$$

Add the absolute values of the negative numbers and place a $-$ sign
before the sum:

$$-6 - 10 = - 16$$

Find the difference between the two sums and place before this
difference the sign of the sum whose absolute value is the greatest:

$$-16 + 15 = - 1$$

3. MULTIPLICATION AND DIVISION OF SIGNED NUMBERS

When two signed numbers are multiplied (or divided) by each
other, the sign of the final result is $+$ if the signs of the two
numbers are the same (either both are $+$ or both are $-$), and the
sign of the result is $-$ if the signs of the two numbers are opposite
(one is $+$ and the other is $-$; the order in which these signs appear
is immaterial).
For example

$$(+ 9) \cdot (+7) = + 63, \qquad (- 9) \cdot (-7) = + 63$$
$$(+ 9) \cdot (-7) = - 63, \qquad (- 9) \cdot (+7) = - 63$$
$$(+54) \div (+9) = + 6, \qquad (-54) \div (-9) = + 6$$
$$(+54) \div (-9) = - 6, \qquad (-54) \div (+9) = - 6$$

If more than two signed numbers are to be multiplied or (and)
divided, the operations are performed on their absolute values.

The sign of the final result is $+$ if there is an even number of negative numbers involved. The sign of the final result is $-$ if there is an odd number of negative numbers involved.

For example

$$\frac{(+24)\cdot(-6)\cdot(+15)\cdot(-7)}{(-14)\cdot(+9)\cdot(-5)} = +\,24$$

$$\frac{(-24)\cdot(-6)\cdot(-15)\cdot(+7)}{(-14)\cdot(+9)\cdot(-5)} = -\,24$$

4. MULTIPLICATION OF POLYNOMIALS

When polynomials are multiplied every member of one polynomial is multiplied by every member of the other polynomial. The products thus obtained are then added.

For example

$$a(b+c) = ab + ac$$

$$(a+b)(c-d) = ac - ad + bc - bd$$

$$(a+b-c-d)(e-f+g) =$$

$$ae - af + ag + be - bf + bg - ce + cf - cg - de + df - dg$$

If the product contains similar terms (that is, terms that differ only in their coefficients), then these terms are added. For example

$$
\begin{array}{l}
2x^3 \quad + \quad 4x^2y \ - \ 5xy^2 - 2y^3 \\
\underline{\hspace{3.5cm} 2x^2 \quad - \ 3xy \ + \quad y^2} \\
2x^3y^2 + \quad 4x^2y^3 - 5xy^4 - 2y^5 \\
- 6x^4y - 12x^3y^2 + 15x^2y^3 + 6xy^4 \\
\underline{4x^5 + 8x^4y - 10x^3y^2 - \quad 4x^2y^3} \\
4x^5 + 2x^4y - 20x^3y^2 + 15x^2y^3 + \quad xy^4 - 2y^5
\end{array}
$$

5. DIVISION OF POLYNOMIALS BY A MONOMIAL

A monomial is divided by a monomial by writing the dividend over the divisor as a fraction, and the common factors are cancelled out. For example

$$24abcd \div 6bd = \frac{24a\cancel{b}c\cancel{d}}{6\cancel{b}\cancel{d}} = 4ac$$

When a polynomial is divided by a monomial every term of the polynomial is divided by the monomial. For example

$$(2a^2b^3 - 3ab^2 + 4b) \div ab = \frac{2a^2b^3}{ab} - \frac{3ab^2}{ab} + \frac{4b}{ab} = 2ab^2 - 3b + \frac{4}{a}$$

The division of each individual term of the polynomial is performed in the same manner as the division of a monomial by a monomial.

6. SOME FORMULAS FOR THE MULTIPLICATION OF POLYNOMIALS

The square of a sum of two numbers:

$$(a + b)^2 = a^2 + 2ab + b^2$$

The square of a difference of two numbers:

$$(a - b)^2 = a^2 - 2ab + b^2$$

The cube of a sum of two numbers:

$$(a + b)^3 = a^3 + 3a^2b + 3ab^2 + b^3$$

The cube of a difference of two numbers:

$$(a - b)^3 = a^3 - 3a^2b + 3ab^2 - b^3$$

The product of a sum and a difference of two numbers:

$$(a + b)(a - b) = a^2 - b^2$$

The sum of two cubes of numbers:

$$a^3 + b^3 = (a + b)(a^2 - ab + b^2)$$

The difference of two cubes of numbers:

$$a^3 - b^3 = (a - b)(a^2 + ab + b^2)$$

7. THE FUNDAMENTAL PROPERTY OF FRACTIONS

The magnitude of a fraction remains unchanged if the numerator and denominator of the fraction are multiplied (or are divided) by the same number. For example

$$\frac{A}{B} = \frac{Ac}{Bc}$$

$$\frac{A}{B} = \frac{\dfrac{A}{c}}{\dfrac{B}{c}}$$

The cancellation of factors in the numerator and denominator of a fraction as well as the bringing of several fractions to a common denominator are based on this fundamental property of fractions.

8. ADDITION AND SUBTRACTION OF FRACTIONS

When two (or more) fractions are to be added, they must be brought to a common denominator. Then the numerators of the transformed fractions are added. This sum is the numerator of the sum of the several fractions, and the common denominator is the denominator of the sum of the several fractions. For example

$$\frac{a}{b} + \frac{c}{d} = \frac{ad + bc}{bd}$$

$$\frac{a}{b} + \frac{c}{d} + \frac{e}{f} = \frac{adf + cbf + ebd}{bdf}$$

When the difference of two fractions is to be obtained, the two fractions must be brought to a common denominator. The difference of the two denominators of the transformed fractions is obtained. The difference thus obtained is the numerator of the difference of two fractions, and the common denominator is the denominator of the difference of the two fractions. For example

$$\frac{a}{b} - \frac{c}{d} = \frac{ad - bc}{bd}$$

9. MULTIPLICATION OF FRACTIONS

When two (or more) fractions are to be multiplied, the numerators of the fractions are multiplied separately, and the denominators of the fractions are multiplied separately. The product of the numerators is the numerator of the product of the fractions, and the product of the denominators is the denominator of the product of the fractions. For example

$$\frac{a}{d} \cdot \frac{b}{e} \cdot \frac{c}{f} = \frac{abc}{def}$$

10. DIVISION OF FRACTIONS

When two fractions are to be divided by one another, the numerator of the dividend is multiplied by the denominator of the divisor, and the product is the numerator of the quotient, and the denominator of the dividend is multiplied by the numerator of the divisor, and the product is the denominator of the quotient. For example

$$\frac{a}{b} \div \frac{c}{d} = \frac{ad}{bc}$$

Another simple rule for the division of two fractions is: Invert the divisor and multiply this inverted divisor by the dividend. Thus

$$\frac{a}{b} \div \frac{c}{d} = \frac{a}{b} \cdot \frac{d}{c} = \frac{ad}{bc}$$

11.   PROPORTION

If there are four magnitudes such that the ratio of two of them is equal to the ratio of the remaining two, then the equality of these two ratios is known as a proportion, and the four magnitudes are known as proportional.   Thus

$$\frac{a}{b} = \frac{c}{d}$$

is a proportion.

The fundamental property of a proportion is that, for a proportion

$$\frac{a}{b} = \frac{c}{d}$$

the product of the extreme terms of the proportion (ad) is equal to the product of the mean terms of the proportion (bc), that is,

$$ad = bc$$

12.   SOME RESULTS OF A PROPORTION

If we have a proportion

$$\frac{a}{b} = \frac{c}{d}$$

then the following proportions may be derived from it:

$$\frac{a+b}{b} = \frac{c+d}{d} \quad \text{and} \quad \frac{a-b}{b} = \frac{c-d}{d}$$

$$\frac{a+b}{a} = \frac{c+d}{c} \quad \text{and} \quad \frac{a-b}{a} = \frac{c-d}{c}$$

$$\frac{a+b}{a-b} = \frac{c+d}{c-d} \quad \text{and} \quad \frac{a-b}{a+b} = \frac{c-d}{c+d}$$

13.   THE ARITHMETIC MEAN

The arithmetic mean of two quantities is equal to one half the sum of these quantities, that is,

$$\frac{a+b}{2}$$

is the arithmetic mean of these two quantities.

The arithmetic mean of several quantities is equal to the sum of these quantities divided by the number of these quantities, that is,

$$\frac{a+b+c+d+e}{5}$$

is the arithmetic mean of a, b, c, d, and e.

14. RAISING TO A POWER

A number multiplied by itself several times is known as the power of this number. If the number is repeated as a factor n times, then the product is known as the n-th power of this number. If the number is a, then the product of n a's is denoted by the symbol a^n. The finding of the n-th power of a number is called raising to a power.

For example

$$3^4 = 3 \cdot 3 \cdot 3 \cdot 3 = 81$$

The number a which repeated several times as a factor is called *the base* of the power. The number n which indicates the number of times a is repeated as a factor is called *the exponent* of the power. Thus, in the above example ($3^4 = 81$) the number 3 is the base, and the number 4 is the exponent.

The second power is known as *the square* of a number. Thus a^2 is the square of a, and it is read *a squared*. The third power of a is known as *the cube* of a, and it is read *a cubed*.

15. EXTRACTION OF ROOTS

The extraction of roots is an operation inverse to the raising to a power. When a power of some number (the base) and the exponent of this power are given, the finding of the number that was raised to the power indicated by the exponent) is known as the extraction of roots. If $3^4 = 81$, then the extraction of the 4-th root of 81 will result in the base 3. In other words, the power (81) and the exponent (4) are given, and the base (3) is obtained.

The operation of the extraction of a root is indicated by the symbol $\sqrt{}$ which is known as *the radical* or the root sign, and the operation of the extraction of a particular root is indicated by writing under the radical the number from which the root is to be extracted and above the radical, on the left, the exponent of the base. This exponent of the base is known in the case of the extraction of roots as *the exponent of the root*. Thus, the extraction of the 4-th root of 81 is written as $\sqrt[4]{81}$.

The root of the second power of a ($\sqrt[2]{a}$) is known as *the square root* of a. Instead of $\sqrt[2]{a}$ we write $\sqrt{a}$. The root of the third power of a ($\sqrt[3]{a}$) is known as *the cube root* of a.

16. THE SIGN OF THE ROOT

When the exponent of the root is odd, the sign of the root (after the extraction is completed) is the same as the sign of the number under the radical sign (that is, the number from which it is to be extracted). For example

$$\sqrt[5]{243} = 3, \quad \text{and} \quad \sqrt[5]{-243} = -3$$

That this is correct may be checked by reversing the process of the extraction of roots, that is, by raising to a power. We then have

$$3^5 = 243, \quad \text{and} \quad (-3)^5 = -243$$

When the exponent of the root is even, and the number under the radical sign is positive (we shall not be concerned with negative numbers under such radicals) there are two roots whose absolute values are equal but the signs are opposite. For example

$$\sqrt{25} = +5, \quad \text{and} \quad \sqrt{25} = -5$$

because $5^2 = 25$, and $(-5)^2 = 25$.

17. SPECIAL PROPERTIES OF POWERS AND ROOTS

A number raised to the first power is equal to itself, that is,

$$a^1 = a \qquad (4^1 = 4)$$

A number raised to the zero power is equal to 1, that is,

$$a^0 = 1 \qquad (5^0 = 1)$$

A number raised to a negative power is equal to a fraction whose numerator is 1, and whose denominator is the same number raised to the same, but positive, power, that is,

$$a^{-n} = \frac{1}{a^n} \qquad \left(7^{-2} = \frac{1}{7^2}\right)$$

A root of a number may be expressed as the number whose exponent is a fraction; the numerator of this fraction is 1, and the denominator of this fraction is the exponent of the root, that is,

$$\sqrt[n]{a} = a^{\frac{1}{n}} \qquad (\sqrt[3]{5} = 5^{\frac{1}{3}})$$

As a consequence of the above we have the following properties:

$$a^{\frac{m}{n}} = \sqrt[rn]{a^m}$$

$$a^{-\frac{m}{n}} = \frac{1}{\sqrt[n]{a^m}}$$

18. OPERATIONS WITH POWERS AND ROOTS

When a product is raised to a power, each factor is raised to this power, that is,

$$(a \cdot b \cdot c \cdot \ldots \cdot k)^n = a^n b^n c^n \ldots k^n$$

When a fraction is raised to a power, the numerator and denominator of this fraction are raised to this power, that is

$$\left(\frac{a}{b}\right)^n = \frac{a^n}{b^r}$$

The converse of the above two also holds, that is,

$$a^n b^n c^n \ldots k^n = (a \cdot b \cdot c \cdot \ldots \cdot k)^n$$

and

$$\frac{a^n}{b^n} = \left(\frac{a}{b}\right)^n$$

When two powers with equal bases are multiplied, then the exponents of the powers are added, that is,

$$a^m a^n = a^{m+n}$$

When two powers with equal bases are divided by one another, the exponent of the divisor is subtracted from the exponent of the dividend, that is,

$$a^m \div a^n = \frac{a^m}{a^n} = a^{m-n}$$

When a power is raised to a power, the exponents are multiplied by one another, that is,

$$(a^m)^n = a^{mn}$$

When a root is extracted from a product, the root may be extracted from each factor, and the product of the extracted roots is the root of the product, that is,

$$\sqrt[n]{a \cdot b \cdot c \cdot \ldots \cdot k} = \sqrt[n]{a} \cdot \sqrt[n]{b} \cdot \sqrt[n]{c} \cdot \ldots \cdot \sqrt[n]{k}$$

When a root is extracted from a fraction, it may be extracted from the numerator and denominator separately, that is,

$$\sqrt[n]{\frac{a}{b}} = \frac{\sqrt[n]{a}}{\sqrt[n]{b}}$$

The converses of the above two also hold, that is,

$$\sqrt[n]{a} \cdot \sqrt[n]{b} \cdot \sqrt[n]{c} \cdot \ldots \cdot \sqrt[n]{k} = \sqrt[n]{a \cdot b \cdot c \cdot \ldots \cdot k}$$

and

$$\frac{\sqrt[n]{a}}{\sqrt[n]{b}} = \sqrt[n]{\frac{a}{b}}$$

When a root is raised to a power, then the number under the radical is raised to this power, that is,

$$\left(\sqrt[n]{a}\right)^m = \sqrt[n]{a^m}$$

When a root is to be extracted from a root, the exponents of the roots must be multiplied by one another, that is,

$$\sqrt[m]{\sqrt[n]{a}} = \sqrt[mn]{a}$$

19. EXTRACTION OF SQUARE ROOTS OF NUMBERS

The extraction of square roots of numbers is performed as follows:

Extract the square root of 544644.

First step: Group the digits of the numbers by pairs from right to left

$$54 \quad 46 \quad 44$$

Second step: Obtain the nearest whole square root of 54 (whose square does not exceed 54) and write it to the right of 54 46 44. This square root is 7

$$54 \quad 46 \quad 44 \qquad 7$$

Third step: Square 7 and write it under 54 and subtract 49 from 54

$$\begin{array}{ccc} 54 & 46 & 44 \qquad 7 \\ 49 \\ \hline 5 \end{array}$$

Fourth step: Bring down the next pair of digits and write them to the right of 5. Double the 7 and write it to the left of 546 but leave a free space to the right of 14. Then divide 54 by 14, and write (3) the whole quotient in three places:

   a. To the right of the 14,
   b. To the right of the 7,
   c. Just below itself, where it was written to the right of 14.

Multiply 143 by 3 and write the product below 546. We then have:

$$\begin{array}{ccc} 54 & 46 & 44 \qquad 73 \\ 49 \end{array}$$

$$143 \begin{array}{|l} 546 \\ 429 \end{array} \quad 3$$

Fifth step: Subtract 429 from 546. Bring down the next pair of digits and write them to the right of the difference. Then follow the same procedure as above

$$\sqrt{54 \quad 46 \quad 44} = 738$$

$$\begin{array}{r|l} & 49 \\ 143 & 546 \\ 3 & 429 \\ \hline 1468 & 11744 \\ 8 & 11744 \\ \hline & 0 \end{array}$$

Thus 738 is the square root of 544644.   Generally, not all numbers
are perfect squares.   When a number is not a perfect square, the
extraction of the square root may be continued after the extraction
from the whole (integral) part of the number is completed by bringing down two zeros at a time, and the extraction is continued into
the decimals.   For example

$$\sqrt{46\ 73} = 68.35$$

	36
128	1073
8	1024
1363	4900
3	4089
13666	81100
6	81996

If the number from which a square root is to be extracted has an
integral as well as a decimal part, only the digits in the integral part
are grouped by pairs.   For example

$$\sqrt{3\ 47.6739} = 18.646$$

	1
28	247
8	224
366	2367
6	2196
3724	17139
4	14896
37286	224300
6	223716

20.   ARITHMETIC PROGRESSIONS

A sequence of numbers such that the difference between any two
successive pairs of them is the same, is known as an arithmetic
progression.   This difference is obtained by subtracting the preceding term from the one that follows it.   For example

$$4, \ 7, \ 10, \ 13, \ \ldots$$

is an arithmetic progression.   Also

$$29, \quad 22, \quad 15, \quad 8, \quad 1, \quad -6, \quad -13, \quad \ldots$$

is an arithmetic progression.

If the first term of an arithmetic progression is a, the difference
between two successive terms is d, and the number of terms is n,
then the n-th term of the arithmetic progression is

$$a + (n - 1)d$$

The sum of the n terms of an arithmetic progression is

$$S = \frac{[2a + (n-1)d]n}{2}$$

or

$$S = \frac{(\text{first term} + \text{last term}) \cdot \text{number of terms}}{2}$$

21. GEOMETRIC PROGRESSION

A sequence of numbers such that the ratio of every two successive pairs of them (one term is always divided by that preceding it) is always the same, is known as a geometric progression. For example

$$2, \quad 6, \quad 18, \quad 54, \quad 162, \quad \ldots$$

is a geometric progression. Also

$$24, \quad 6, \quad \tfrac{3}{2}, \quad \tfrac{3}{8}, \quad \tfrac{3}{32}, \quad \ldots$$

is a geometric progression.

If the first term of a geometric progression is a, and the ratio is r, and the number of terms is n, then the n-th term is

$$ar^{n-1}$$

The sum of n terms of a geometric progression is

$$S = \frac{ar^n - a}{r - 1} = \frac{a - ar^n}{1 - r}$$

If the absolute value of r is less than 1, that is, if r is either a positive or negative fraction, the sum of n terms of a geometric progression, when n is infinite, is

$$S = \frac{a}{1 - r}$$

For example, the sum

$$1 + \tfrac{1}{2} + \tfrac{1}{4} + \tfrac{1}{8} + \ldots$$

when the number of the terms becomes infinite, is

$$\frac{1}{1 - \tfrac{1}{2}} = 2$$

The sum

$$1 - \tfrac{1}{2} + \tfrac{1}{4} - \tfrac{1}{8} + \tfrac{1}{16} - \ldots$$

when the number of the terms becomes infinite, is

$$\frac{1}{1 + \tfrac{1}{2}} = \tfrac{2}{3}$$

22. LOGARITHMS

By means of logarithms we can obtain the exponent of the power to which a given base is raised when the power is also given.

For example, if the power is 243, and the base is 3, then the logarithm of 243 to the base 3 is 5. The number 3 is known as the base of the logarithms in this case, and 5 is the logarithm of 243 to this base.

Thus, if

$$a^b = N$$

we have two other relationships, that is,

$$\sqrt[b]{N} = a, \quad \text{and} \quad \log_a N = b$$

For practical computations we use logarithms to the base 10. For methods and their illustrations of computations with logarithms see Tables.

The logarithm of a product is equal to the sum of the logarithms of the factors:

$$\log (ab) = \log a + \log b$$

The logarithm of a quotient is equal to the difference between the logarithm of the dividend and the divisor:

$$\log (a \div b) = \log a - \log b$$

The logarithm of a power: $\log a^n = n \log a$

The logarithm of a root: $\log \sqrt[n]{a} = \dfrac{1}{n} \log a$

Note: All the logarithms indicated in the above relationships are to be taken to the same base.

23. RAISING OF A BINOMIAL TO A POWER

The raising of a binomial to a power may be performed by means of a formula. This formula is known as Newton's Binomial Expansion.

$$(a + b)^n = a^n + na^{n-1}b + \frac{n(n-1)}{1 \cdot 2} a^{n-2}b^2$$
$$+ \frac{n(n-1)(n-2)}{1 \cdot 2 \cdot 3} a^{n-3}b^3 + \ldots$$
$$\ldots + \frac{n(n-1)(n-2) \ldots (n-k+1)}{1 \cdot 2 \cdot 3 \cdot \ldots \cdot k} a^{n-k}b^k + \ldots + nab^{n-1} + b^n$$

The Binomial Expansion is a polynomial so arranged that the exponents of the powers of one term (a) decrease in magnitude, while exponents of the powers of the second term (b) increase in magnitude.

If the exponent of the binomial is n, then:

 a. The polynomial contains $(n + 1)$ terms.
 b. The exponents of a decrease from n to zero.
 c. The exponents of b increase from zero to n.
 d. The coefficients of the terms of the expansion increase in magnitude until the middle term (or middle two terms) is reached, and then they decrease in magnitude. If n is even there is one middle term. If n is odd there are two middle terms with equal coefficients.
 e. The coefficients of terms equidistant from the middle term (or middle two terms) are equal.

When the binomial is a difference of two terms, the even numbered terms of the expansion are negative, that is,

$$(a - b)^n = a^n - na^{n-1}b + \frac{n(n - 1)}{1 \cdot 2}a^{n-2}b^2 - \ldots\ldots$$

24. EQUATIONS OF THE FIRST DEGREE IN ONE UNKNOWN

Equations of the first degree in one unknown are solved as illustrated below.

Equation	Solution
$\dfrac{16x + 4}{4} + \dfrac{3x - 7}{5} = 4x + 2$	
$(16x + 4)5 + (3x - 7)4 = (4x + 2)20$	Bring both sides of the equation to a common denominator thus freeing the equation of fractions.
$80x + 20 + 12x - 28 = 80x + 40$	Remove the parentheses.
$80x + 12x - 80x = -20 + 28 + 40$	Collect the terms with the unknown on the left side of the equation and the remaining terms on the right side of the equation.
$12x = 48$	Perform the indicated operations.
$x = \frac{48}{12} = 4$	Divide both sides of the equation by the coefficient of the unknown.

The value of the unknown x is known as the solution of the equation or its *root*. When this value is substituted in the original equation, the equation becomes an identity. Thus

$$\frac{16 \cdot 4 + 4}{4} + \frac{3 \cdot 4 - 7}{5} = 4 \cdot 4 + 2$$

$$\frac{68}{4} + \frac{5}{5} = 18$$

$$17 + 1 = 18$$

All the equations of the first degree in one unknown can be reduced to the form

$$ax = b$$

In order to reduce an equation to this form certain operations (leading to transformations) must be performed. Whenever a certain operation is performed on one side of the equation it must also be performed on the other side of the equation. The following transformations are usually performed:

    a. The same quantity may be added to each side of the equation, or the same quantity may be subtracted from each side of the equation. This transformation is equivalent to the transposition of a term from one side of the equation to the other with its sign changed. For example,

$$
\begin{array}{rcl}
3x + 2 &=& 7x - 3 \\
-7x - 2 &=& -7x - 2 \\
\hline
-4x &=& -5 \\
3x + 2 &=& 7x - 3 \\
3x - 7x &=& -3 - 2
\end{array}
$$

    b. Both sides of the equation may be multiplied or divided by the same quantity (except the division by zero). For example

$$\frac{2x - 9}{3} = 3x + 2$$

$$\frac{3(2x - 9)}{3} = 3(3x + 2)$$

$$2x - 9 = 3(3x + 2)$$

Also

$$5x + 15 = 20x - 75$$

$$\frac{5x + 15}{5} = \frac{20x - 75}{5}$$

$$x + 3 = 4x - 15$$

c. Both sides of the equation may be raised to the same power or the same root may be extracted from both sides of the equation. For example

$$\sqrt[4]{2x - 5} = 3$$
$$(\sqrt[4]{2x - 5})^4 = 3^4$$
$$2x - 5 = 81$$
$$2x = 86$$
$$x = 43$$

Also

$$x^3 = 64$$
$$\sqrt[3]{x^3} = \sqrt[3]{64}$$
$$x = 4$$

d. A logarithm of both sides of the equation may be taken. For example

$$3^x = 243$$
$$x \log 3 = \log 243$$
$$x = \frac{\log 243}{\log 3}$$
$$x = \frac{2.3856}{0.4771} = 5$$

25. RULES FOR THE SOLUTION OF EQUATIONS OF THE FIRST DEGREE IN ONE UNKNOWN

The above transformations that can be performed on equations of the first degree in one unknown lead to the following rules for the solution of these equations:

Rule 1. If the equation contains several terms which have the unknown (generally denoted by one of the letters, x, y, or z), then it is necessary to transpose the terms with the unknowns to one side of the equation (appropriately changing their signs when necessary), and at the same time terms free from the unknown should be transposed to the opposite side of the equation. Then the indicated operations should be performed. For example

$$5x - 3(10 + 2x) - 3x = 15 - 13x + 4(5 - x)$$
$$5x - 30 - 6x - 3x = 15 - 13x + 20 - 4x$$
$$5x - 6x - 3x + 13x + 4x = 15 + 20 + 30$$
$$13x = 65$$
$$x = 5$$

Rule 2.   If the unknown is in the denominator, it is necessary to free the equation from this denominator. Thus both sides of the equation should be multiplied by this denominator. If the equation contains fractions whose denominators do not contain the unknown, it is not absolutely necessary to multiply both sides of the equation by the least common denominator. However, the multiplication of both sides of the equation by the least common denominator will simplify the work. For example

$$\frac{4}{x+2} - \frac{5}{2(x+2)} = \frac{1}{2} + \frac{9}{2(x+2)}$$

$$2 \cdot 4 - 5 = x + 2 + 9$$

$$x = 8 - 5 - 9 - 2$$

$$x = -8$$

Rule 3.   If the unknown of the equation is a part of an expression from which a root is extracted, this expression should be isolated, and then both sides of the equation should be raised to the power indicated by the exponent of the root. For example

$$\sqrt[3]{5x - 3} + 6 = 9$$

$$\sqrt[3]{5x - 3} = 3$$

$$5x - 3 = 27$$

$$5x = 30$$

$$x = 6$$

Rule 4.   If the unknown of the equation is a part of an expression that is raised to some power, this expression should be isolated, and a root indicated by the exponent of the power should be extracted from both sides of the equation. For example

$$(x - 5)^3 + 5 = 69$$

$$(x - 5)^3 = 64$$

$$x - 5 = 4$$

$$x = 9$$

Rule 5.   If the unknown of the equation is a part of the exponent of some power, then this power must be isolated and the logarithm of both sides of the equation should be taken. For example

$$4 + 3^{x+5} = 31$$

$$3^{x+5} = 27$$

$$(x + 5) \log 3 = \log 27$$

$$x + 5 = \frac{\log 27}{\log 3}$$

$$x + 5 = \frac{1.4314}{0.4771} = 3$$

$$x = -2$$

Note: Only when the bases of the powers are equal can the equation of the first degree in one unknown be solved according to the above rule. If the bases are not equal, as for example

$$2^x + 3^x = 7$$

the solution of such equations at times becomes very difficult. Such equations are known as exponential equations.

26. SYSTEMS OF EQUATIONS OF THE FIRST DEGREE IN TWO UNKNOWNS

Every equation of the first degree in two unknowns can be reduced to the form

$$ax + by = c$$

For example

$$\frac{x + 3}{y} + 2 = 5$$

$$x + 3 + 2y = 5y$$

$$x - 3y = -3$$

One equation with two unknowns does not have determinate solutions. Two equations with two unknowns generally have solutions, and the solution of such equations consists of finding such values of x and y (known as the roots of these equations) which, if substituted in the two equations, will transform the equations into identities.

Systems of two equations with two unknowns in the first degree are solved by two methods:

a. The method of equalization of coefficients,
and b. The method of substitution.

The same methods are applied to the solution of systems of equations with several unknowns in the first degree.

a. *The Method of Equalization of Coefficients*

$$15x - 4y = 37$$
$$9x + 6y = 39$$

Solution

Multiply the first equation by 3 and the second equation by 2. We thus equalize the coefficients of y.

$$
\begin{array}{rcl|c}
15x - 4y &=& 37 & 3 \\
9x + 6y &=& 39 & 2 \\
\end{array}
$$

$$45x - 12y = 111$$
$$18x + 12y = 78$$

$$
\begin{array}{rcl}
45x - 12y &=& 111 \\
18x + 12y &=& 78 \\
\hline
63x \quad\quad &=& 189
\end{array}
$$

$$x = \frac{189}{63} = 3$$

We equalize the coefficients of some unknown. In order to do this we obtain the least common multiple of the coefficients of that unknown. This least common multiple is the smallest number such that contains these coefficients as factors. Thus, if we wish to equalize the coefficients of y the least common multiple is 12.

We add the two equations term by term (or, when the signs of the equalized coefficients are the same we subtract one equation from the other) and thus one unknown is eliminated.

We solve the resultant equation with one unknown.

Substitute $x = 3$ in the first equation and solve for y.

$$15 \cdot 3 - 4y = 37$$
$$4y = 45 - 37 = 8$$
$$y = 2$$

We substitute the value of unknown obtained in the previous step in one of the equations and we solve the equation for the second unknown.

Thus the solution of the system of equations is

$$x = 3 \quad \text{and} \quad y = 2$$

b. *The Method of Substitution*

$$15x - 4y = 37$$
$$9x + 6y = 39$$

Solution

Solve the first equation for x in terms of y.

$$x = \frac{37 + 4y}{15}$$

We solve one of the equations for one of the unknowns in terms of the other unknown, assuming for the time being that this unknown is known to us.

Substitute the expression for x in the second equation.

$$\frac{9(37 + 4y)}{15} + 6y = 39$$

Solve the above equation for y.

$$\frac{3(37 + 4y)}{5} + 6y = 39$$

$$111 + 12y + 30y = 195$$

$$42y = 84$$

$$y = 2$$

The expression for the unknown just obtained, we substitute in the other equation, and thus we eliminate from it the unknown for which the first equation was solved.

We solve the equation obtained after the substitution was made for the remaining unknown.

Substitute $y = 2$ in the expression

$$x = \frac{37 + 4y}{15}$$

$$x = \frac{37 + 4 \cdot 2}{15}$$

$$x = \frac{45}{15} = 3$$

Substitute the value of the unknown obtained in the expression for the other unknown obtained in terms of the first unknown (see the first step).

Thus the solution of the system is

$$x = 3 \quad \text{and} \quad y = 2$$

27. QUADRATIC EQUATIONS

Quadratic equations in one unknown may be reduced to the form

$$ax^2 + bx + c = 0$$

or to the form

$$x^2 + px + q = 0$$

If the coefficient b or the coefficient c (also known as *the free term*) is equal to zero, the quadratic equation is known as *incomplete*. Thus we may have two forms of incomplete quadratic equations, that is,

$$ax^2 + c = 0$$

or

$$ax^2 + bx = 0$$

The values of x that would, when substituted into the equation, make the equation an identity, are known as *the solutions* or *the roots* of the equation. A quadratic equation has two solutions or roots.

28. FORMULAS FOR THE ROOTS OF QUADRATIC EQUATIONS

a. The complete quadratic equation $ax^2 + bx + c = 0$

$$x_{1,2} = \frac{-b \pm \sqrt{b^2 - 4ac}}{2a}$$

or (when b is even)

$$x_{1,2} = \frac{-\left(\dfrac{b}{2}\right) \pm \sqrt{\left(\dfrac{b}{2}\right)^2 - ac}}{a}$$

b. The complete quadratic equation $x^2 + px + q = 0$

$$x_{1,2} = -\left(\frac{p}{2}\right) \pm \sqrt{\left(\frac{p}{2}\right)^2 - q}$$

c. The incomplete quadratic equation $ax^2 + bx = 0$

$$x_1 = 0, \quad x_2 = -\left(\frac{b}{a}\right)$$

d. The incomplete quadratic equation $ax^2 + c = 0$

$$x_{1,2} = \pm \sqrt{-\left(\frac{c}{a}\right)}$$

29. THE TEST FOR THE ROOTS OF A QUADRATIC EQUATION

a. For a complete quadratic equation $ax^2 + bx + c = 0$

If $b^2 - 4ac > 0$ the quadratic equation has two real and unequal roots (that is, the roots do not contain negative numbers under the radicals).

Example, $x^2 + 5x + 6 = 0$

$$x_{1,2} = \frac{-5 \pm \sqrt{25 - 24}}{2} = \frac{-5 \pm 1}{2}$$

$$x_1 = -2, \quad x_2 = -3$$

If $b^2 - 4ac = 0$ the quadratic equation has two equal roots.

Example, $x^2 - 8x + 16 = 0$

$$x_{1,2} = \frac{8 \pm \sqrt{64 - 64}}{2} = 8$$

If $b^2 - 4ac < 0$, that is, $b^2 - 4ac$ is negative the quadratic equation has two roots known as imaginary. They are associated with the square root of a negative number.

Example, $5x^2 + 4x + 1 = 0$

$$x_{1,2} = \frac{-4 \pm \sqrt{16 - 20}}{10} = \frac{-4 \pm \sqrt{-4}}{10} = \frac{-4 \pm 2\sqrt{-1}}{10}$$

$$x_{1,2} = \frac{-2 \pm \sqrt{-1}}{5}$$

b. For the incomplete quadratic equation $ax^2 + c = 0$
If the signs of a and c are different, the roots are real.

Example, $9x^2 - 16 = 0$

$$x_{1,2} = \pm \sqrt{\frac{16}{9}}, \quad x_{1,2} = \pm \left(\frac{4}{3}\right)$$

If the signs of a and c are the same, the roots are not real (they are called *imaginary*).

Example, $9x^2 + 16 = 0$

$$x_{1,2} = \pm \sqrt{-\left(\frac{16}{9}\right)}, \quad x_{1,2} = \pm \left(\frac{4}{3}\right)\sqrt{-1}$$

c. The incomplete quadratic equation $ax^2 + bx = 0$ always has two real solutions. One of them is zero, and the other is $-\left(\dfrac{b}{a}\right)$.

Example, $3x^2 - 7x = 0$

$$x_1 = 0, \quad \text{and} \quad x_2 = \tfrac{7}{3}$$

30. THE PROPERTIES OF THE ROOTS OF A QUADRATIC EQUATION

If the roots of a quadratic equation $ax^2 + bx + c = 0$ are x_1 and x_2, then

$$x_1 + x_2 = -\left(\frac{b}{a}\right)$$

and

$$x_1 x_2 = \frac{c}{a}$$

For the equation $x^2 + px + q = 0$ we have that

$$x_1 + x_2 = -p$$

and

$$x_1 x_2 = q$$

These properties are useful for the purpose of checking the

solution of a quadratic equation as well as for the construction of the quadratic equation when the roots are given. For example,

$$x^2 - (x_1 + x_2)x + x_1x_2 = 0, \quad \text{or,} \quad x^2 - x_1x - x_2x + x_1x_2 = 0$$

and

$$(x - x_1)(x - x_2) = 0$$

II. Geometry

31. LINES AND ANGLES

A trace of a moving point represents a generated line.

There are two kinds of lines, straight and curved.

The definition of a straight line is impossible. It may be stated, however, that the distance between two points is measured along a straight line. A straight line has no width (or breadth).

A straight line may be extended in either direction indefinitely.

A straight line, limited in length is known as *a straight line segment*. A straight line segment has two end points.

A line composed of several straight line segments is known as a broken straight line.

A curved line cannot be defined in general. Specifically it may be defined in terms of its specific properties, such as a circle, ellipse, parabola, etc.

Straight line

Broken straight line

Curved line

Two intersecting straight lines form an angle.

An angle is measured in degrees and parts of a degree, minutes and seconds (one degree, 1°, is one 360th part of an angle around a point, also one 360th part of a circle; there are 60 minutes in a degree, and 60 seconds in a minute).

Two straight lines forming an angle of 90° (also known as a right angle) are perpendicular to one another (and conversely, perpendicular straight lines form a right angle).

Two right angles are equal to a straight angle, that is, an angle about a point to one side of a straight line.

When two straight lines intersect they form four angles which are equal in pairs (except when the straight lines are perpendicular to one another, and they are all equal). The equal angles are known as vertical. Thus, vertical angles are equal.

The kinds of angles that can be made by two intersecting straight lines are shown below.

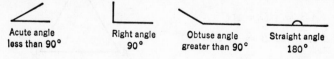

Acute angle
less than 90°

Right angle
90°

Obtuse angle
greater than 90°

Straight angle
180°

32. TRIANGLES

The vertices of a triangle are denoted by the letters, A, B, and C.

The angles of a triangle are denoted by $\angle A$ (or $\angle BAC$), $\angle B$ (or $\angle ABC$), and $\angle C$ (or $\angle ACB$).

The sides of a triangle are AB (or c, which is opposite $\angle C$), AC (or b, which is opposite $\angle B$), and BC (or a, which is opposite $\angle A$).

The sum of the sides of a triangle, that is, $a + b + c = 2p$. This is also known as *the perimeter* of the triangle.

The sum of the angles of any triangle is equal to 180°, that is,

$$\angle A + \angle B + \angle C = 180°.$$

Kinds of triangles	Examples

Acute

(all the angles are less than 90° each)

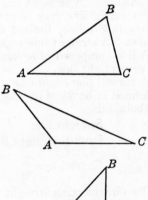

Obtuse

(one of the angles, $\angle A$, is greater than 90°)

Right

(One of the angles, $\angle C$, is 90°, and the angles $\angle A$ and $\angle B$ are acute)
The side c (or AB) is known as *the hypotenuse*

Isosceles

(two sides are equal)

$$AB = BC$$

and $\qquad \angle A = \angle C$

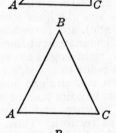

Equilateral

(three sides are equal)

$$AB = BC = AC$$

and $\quad \angle A = \angle B = \angle C = 60°$

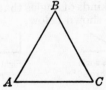

33. PARALLEL LINES

Two straight lines that are equidistant from one another (that is, the distance between them is always the same) are parallel to one another.   Parallel straight lines do not intersect, however far they may be extended.

The shortest distance from a point outside a straight line to the straight line is measured along a perpendicular drawn from the point to the straight line.

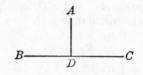

Parallel straight lines

When two or more parallel straight lines are cut by a third straight line, the *transversal*, equal angles are formed as indicated by the numbers in the diagram.

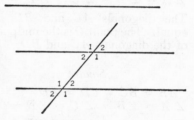

34.   QUADRANGLES

A quadrangle is a closed geometric figure consisting of four sides. It has four angles.

The sum of the angles of any quadrangle is 360°.

If two sides of a quadrangle are parallel, the quadrangle is a trapezoid.   If the opposite sides of a quadrangle are parallel, then the quadrangle is a parallelogram.   If in a parallelogram all the sides are equal it is either a rhombus or a square (in the square all the sides are perpendicular to one another).   If the sides of a parallelogram are perpendicular to one another, then the quadrangle is a rectangle.   Thus, a square is rectangle all of whose sides are equal.

Kind of quadrangles	Examples
The general quadrangle	

No special properties, except that $\angle A + \angle B + \angle C + \angle D = 360°$.

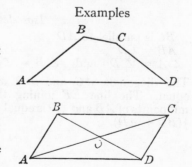

Parallelogram

AB is parallel to CD, $AB = CD$
BC is parallel to AD, $BC = AD$
The point O is the midpoint of the diagonals AC and BD

Rhombus

$AB = BC = CD = AD$
AB is parallel to CD
BC is parallel to AD

The point O is the midpoint of the diagonals AC and BD, and AC is perpendicular to BD.

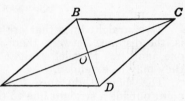

Rectangle

AB is parallel to CD, $AB = CD$
BC is parallel to AD, $BC = AD$
$\angle A = \angle B = \angle C = \angle D = 90°$

The diagonals AC and BD are equal. The point O is the midpoint of the diagonals AC and BD.

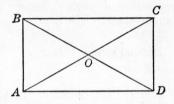

Square

$AB = BC = CD = AD$
$\angle A = \angle B = \angle C = \angle D = 90°$

The diagonals AC and BD equal and perpendicular to one another. The point O is the midpoint of the diagonals AC and BD.

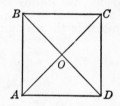

Trapezoid

BC is parallel to AD
$\angle A + \angle B = \angle C + \angle D = 180°$

The diagonals AC and BD are unequal. The line EF joining the midpoints of AB and CD is equal to $\frac{1}{2}(BC + AD)$.

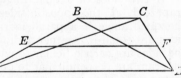

Isosceles trapezoid

BC is parallel to AD
$AB = CD$
$\angle A = \angle D$ and $\angle B = \angle C$

The diagonals AC and BD are equal. The line EF joining the midpoints of AB and CD is equal to $\frac{1}{2}(BC + AD)$.

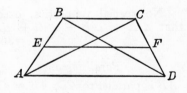

35. THE ALTITUDE, THE ANGLE BISECTOR AND THE MEDIAN OF A TRIANGLE

The straight line drawn from a vertex of a triangle perpendicular to the opposite base is the altitude of the triangle. A triangle has three altitudes. If the triangle is acute the altitudes fall within

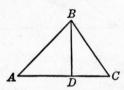
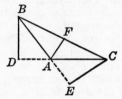

the triangle. If the triangle is obtuse, two of the altitudes will fall outside the triangle and will intersect the extensions of the sides to which they are drawn.

The straight line bisecting an angle of a triangle is the angle bisector of the triangle. A triangle has three angle bisectors. The angle bisectors of a triangle all fall within the triangle. An angle bisector of a triangle cuts the side it meets into two segments proportional to the other two sides. Thus,

$$AD : DC = AB : BC$$

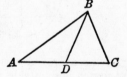

A line drawn from one vertex of a triangle to the midpoint of the opposite side in the median of the triangle.

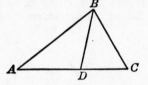

36. FOUR REMARKABLE POINTS IN A TRIANGLE

The three altitudes of a triangle intersect in one point. This point is known as *the orthocenter* of the triangle. When the triangle

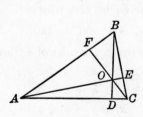
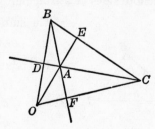

is acute the orthocenter lies within the triangle. When the triangle is obtuse the orthocenter lies outside the triangle.

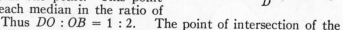

The three angle bisectors of a triangle intersect in a point. This point is the center of the circle inscribed in the triangle, and it is known as *the incenter* of the triangle.

The three medians of a triangle intersect in one point. This point divides each median in the ratio of 1 : 2. Thus $DO : OB = 1 : 2.$ The point of intersection of the three medians is also known as *the center of gravity of the triangle.* If a triangle is placed on a needle so that point O is resting on the point of the needle, the triangle will be in balance.

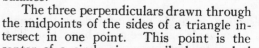

The three perpendiculars drawn through the midpoints of the sides of a triangle intersect in one point. This point is the center of a circle circumscribed around the triangle. It is also known as *the excenter* of the triangle. If the triangle is acute

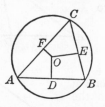

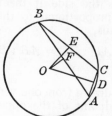

the excenter lies within the triangle; if the triangle is obtuse, the excenter lies outside the triangle.

37.   FORMULAS ASSOCIATED WITH TRIANGLES

In the following formulas A, B, and C denote angles, and a, b, and c denote sides of a triangle.

The sum of the angles of a triangle

$$\angle A + \angle B + \angle C = 180°$$

The relation between the sides of a triangle

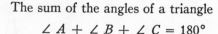

$$a + b > c, \quad a - b < c$$
$$a + c > b, \quad a - c < b$$
$$b + c > a, \quad b - c < a$$

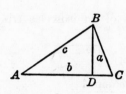

The Pythagorean relation for a right triangle

$$a^2 + b^2 = c^2$$

The generalized Pythagorean relation for an acute triangle.

$$a^2 = b^2 + c^2 - 2b \cdot AD$$

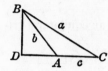

The Pythagorean relation for the side opposite the obtuse angle of a triangle.

$$a^2 = b^2 + c^2 + 2b \cdot AD$$

38. FORMULAS FOR THE AREAS OF POLYGONS

The area of a square.

$$\mathbf{A} = a^2$$

$$\mathbf{A} = \frac{d^2}{2}$$

The area of a rectangle.

$$\mathbf{A} = ab$$

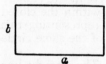

The area of a parallelogram.

$$\mathbf{A} = ah$$

$$\mathbf{A} = ab \sin A$$

The area of a rhombus.

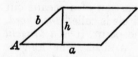

$$\mathbf{A} = ah$$

$$\mathbf{A} = a^2 \sin A$$

$$\mathbf{A} = \frac{AC \cdot BD}{2}$$

The area of a triangle.

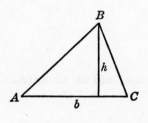

$$\mathbf{A} = \frac{bh}{2}$$

$$\mathbf{A} = \frac{ab \sin A}{2}$$

$$\mathbf{A} = \sqrt{p(p-a)(p-b)(p-c)},$$

$$p = \frac{a+b+c}{2}$$

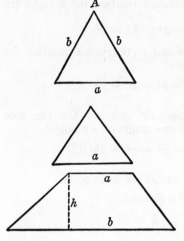

The area of an isosceles triangle.

$$A = \frac{a}{4}\sqrt{4b^2 - a^2}$$

$$A = \frac{b^2 \sin A}{2}$$

The area of an equilateral triangle.

$$A = \frac{a^2}{4}\sqrt{3}$$

The area of a trapezoid.

$$A = \frac{h}{2}(a + b)$$

39. THE CIRCLE

A closed plane curved line such that all of its points are equally distant from a point within the same plane (and within the closed curve) is a circle, and the straight line segment representing this distance is *the radius* of this circle. All the radii of the same circle are equal.

A straight line cuts the circle in two points. The straight line cutting the circle is called *the secant*. The portion of a secant cut off by the circle and lying wholly within the circle is called *the chord*. When a secant touches the circle at only one point, it is *a tangent to the circle*. The chords of a circle vary in size. The longest chord in a circle is that which passes though the center of the circle, and it is known as *the diameter*. The farther away a chord is from the center of a circle the shorter it is in length.

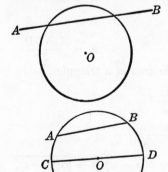

A circle and a secant.

A chord and the diameter.

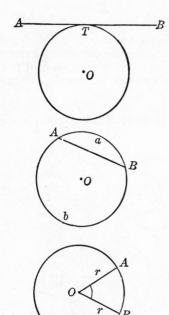

A tangent to the circle.

A portion of the circumference of a circle cut off by a secant is called *the arc* of the circle. The smaller arc (AaB) is called *the minor arc*. The larger arc (AbB) is called *the major arc*.

An angle formed by two radii of the circle is called *the central angle*. It is measured by the number of degrees in this arc, and, if it contains some portion of a degree, the portion of the degree is measured in minutes and seconds.

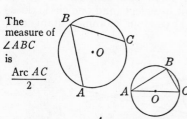

The measure of $\angle ABC$ is

$$\frac{\text{Arc } AC}{2}$$

An angle formed by two chords whose intersection in on the circumference of the circle is called *the inscribed angle*. It is measured by one half of the arc it subtends, that is, by one half the arc AC. A right angle subtends one half the circumference of one circle.

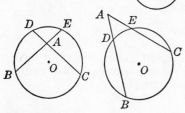

The measure of $\angle BAC$ is

$$\frac{\text{Arc } DE + \text{Arc } BC}{2}$$

The measure of $\angle BAC$ is

$$\frac{\text{Arc } BC - \text{Arc } DE}{2}$$

An angle formed by two intersecting chords is measured by one half the sum of the two arcs the angle subtends (when the point of intersection of the two chords lies within the circle), and it is measured by one half the difference of the two arcs the angle subtends (when the point of intersection of the two chords lies outside the circle).

40. TWO CIRCLES

The relative positions of two circles are shown in the drawing below. When the centers of two circles coincide, the circles are known as *concentric* (Figure a). Two circles may be tangent to one another internally (Figure c), and they may be tangent externally (Figure f).

When two circles are tangent to one another (either internally or externally), their common tangent is perpendicular to the straight line joining their centers.

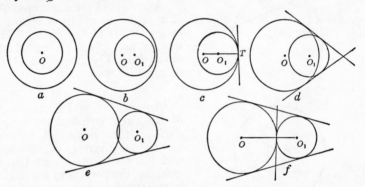

When two circles intersect they have two common tangents (Figures d and e). When they do not intersect (and one circle does not lie within the other), they have four common tangents

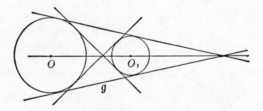

(Figure g). When two circles are tangent externally, they have three common tangents, and one of them is perpendicular to the straight line joining the centers of the circle (Figure f).

41. THE CIRCUMFERENCE AND AREA OF A CIRCLE

The circumference of a circle is obtained as the product of the numerical value of the diameter of the circle and the number π. The approximate value of π is 3.14159 .... .

Below are the formulas stating the expression for the circumference and the area of a circle, as well as certain parts of the circle.

The radius of the circle is denoted by r, and the diameter of the circle is denoted by $d = 2r$.

	Formula
The circumference of a circle.	$C = \pi d = 2\pi r$
The length of an arc subtended by an angle of $A°$.	$L = \dfrac{\pi d \cdot A}{360} = \dfrac{\pi r \cdot A}{180}$

The area of a circle. The portion of a circle enclosed by two radii and an arc is called *the sector*.	$A = \dfrac{\pi d^2}{4} = \pi r^2$
The area of a sector with a central angle $A°$.	$A = \dfrac{\pi r^2 A}{360}$

The portion of a circle enclosed by a chord and the arc this chord subtends is called *the segment*.

The central angle between the radii is $A°$.

The area of the segment is obtained as the difference between the area of the sector and the area of the isosceles triangle formed by the two radii and the chord.

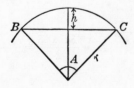

The length of chord BC.

Chord $BC = 2r \sin \dfrac{A}{2}$

The length of the arc BC.

Arc $BC = \dfrac{\pi r A}{180}$

The height of the segment is h.

$$h = r\left(1 - \cos \dfrac{A}{2}\right).$$

42. REGULAR POLYGONS

A polygon (a many sided closed plane geometric figure, all of whose sides are straight lines) all of whose sides are equal, and all of whose angles are equal is called *a regular polygon.*

A regular polygon may be inscribed in a circle, and a circle may be inscribed in a regular polygon.

In the following formulas it is assumed that a regular polygon is inscribed in a circle whose radius is r. This is equivalent to the statement that a circle is circumscribed around a regular polygon.

Regular polygon	Length of side	Area

Equilateral triangle

$$a = r\sqrt{3}$$

$$A = \frac{a^2\sqrt{3}}{4} = \frac{3r^2\sqrt{3}}{4}$$

Square $a = r\sqrt{2}$ $A = a^2 = 2r^2$

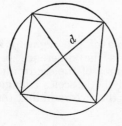

Diagonal

$$d = a\sqrt{2} = 2r$$

Regular six-sided polygon (called a *hexagon*).

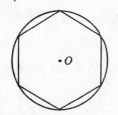

$$a = r$$

$$A = \frac{3a^2\sqrt{3}}{2} = \frac{3r^2\sqrt{3}}{2}$$

Regular polygon	Length of side	Area

Regular n-sided polygon

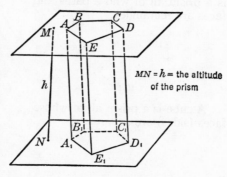

$$a = 2r \cos \frac{A}{2} \qquad \mathbf{A} = \frac{nr^2 \sin A}{2}$$

The sum of the angles of an n-sided regular polygon is $(n-2)\,180°$.

The angle between two sides of such a polygon is

$$A = \frac{(n-2)\,180°}{n}$$

43.   POLYHEDRA

A polyhedron is a solid (three dimensional) geometric figure whose faces are polygons.

Prism

A prism is a solid geometric figure whose bases are equal polygons of any number of sides, and whose faces are parallelograms.

The bases of a prism are parallel to one another.

All the edges of a prism (they are also the sides of the parallelograms) are parallel to one another.

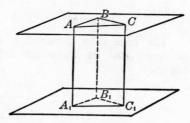

$MN = h =$ the altitude of the prism

Right prism

The faces of a right prism are rectangles. The edges of a right prism are all equal and perpendicular to the bases. The altitude of a right prism is equal to the edge of the prism.

Regular prism

A regular prism is a right prism whose bases are regular polygons.

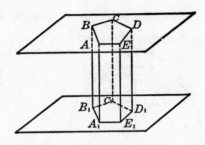

Parallelopiped

A parallelopiped is a prism all of whose bases and faces are parallelograms.

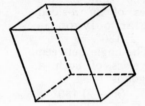

Rectangular parallelopiped

A rectangular parallelopiped is a prism all of whose bases and faces are rectangles.

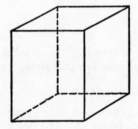

Cube

A cube is a prism all of whose faces (sides) are squares.

Pyramid

The base of a pyramid is a polygon, and its faces are triangles.

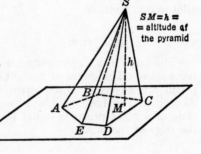

$SM = h =$ = altitude of the pyramid

Regular pyramid

A regular pyramid is a solid geometric figure whose base is a regular polygon and whose sides (faces) are isosceles triangles. The altitude of a regular pyramid is the line joining the vertex S of the pyramid with the center O of the circle circumscribed around the regular polygon.

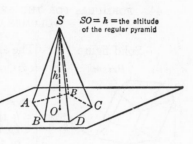

$SO = h =$ the altitude of the regular pyramid

Right circular cylinder

A right circular cylinder is a solid geometric figure whose bases are equal circles and whose altitude is the line joining the centers of the circles.

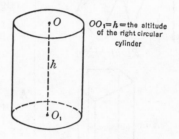

$OO_1 = h =$ the altitude of the right circular cylinder

Right circular cone

A right circular cone is a solid geometric figure whose base is a circle and whose vertex is a point. The altitude of the right circular cone joins the vertex of the cone and the center of the circle.

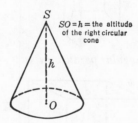

$SO = h =$ the altitude of the right circular cone

Sphere

A sphere is a solid geometric figure all of whose points (located on its surface) are equally distant from a point located within this figure, known as the center of the sphere.

The distance from a point on the surface of the sphere to the center is the radius of the sphere.

The diameter of the sphere is twice the radius.

The intersection of the sphere and a plane is a circle.

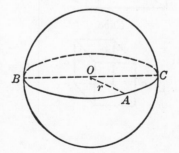

$OA = r =$ radius of the sphere
$BC = d = 2r =$ diameter of the sphere

44. FORMULAS FOR THE AREAS OF THE SURFACES AND THE VOLUMES OF POLYHEDRA

Solid figure	The area of the surface	Volume
Prism 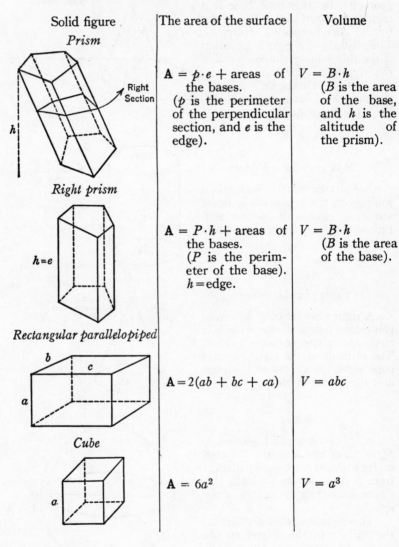	$A = p \cdot e$ + areas of the bases. (p is the perimeter of the perpendicular section, and e is the edge).	$V = B \cdot h$ (B is the area of the base, and h is the altitude of the prism).
Right prism	$A = P \cdot h$ + areas of the bases. (P is the perimeter of the base). h = edge.	$V = B \cdot h$ (B is the area of the base).
Rectangular parallelopiped	$A = 2(ab + bc + ca)$	$V = abc$
Cube	$A = 6a^2$	$V = a^3$

Solid figure	The area of the surface	Volume
Pyramid 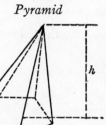	$\mathbf{A} = $ area of base $+$ areas of the triangles forming the faces.	$V = \dfrac{B \cdot h}{3}$ (B is the area of the base, and h the altitude of the pyramid).
Regular pyramid 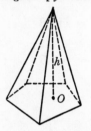	$\mathbf{A} = \dfrac{P \cdot H}{2} + $ area of base. (P is the perimeter of the base, and H is the altitude of one of the triangles drawn from the vertex of the pyramid).	$V = \dfrac{B \cdot h}{3}$ (B is the area of the base, and h altitude of the pyramid).
Right circular cylinder	$\mathbf{A} = 2\pi rh + 2\pi r^2$ (r is the radius of the base, and h is the altitude of the cylinder).	$V = \pi r^2 h$
Right circular cone 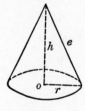	$\mathbf{A} = \pi re + \pi r^2$ (r is the radius of the base, and e is the edge, or the generating line as it is called).	$V = \dfrac{\pi r^2 h}{3}$ (h is the altitude of the cone).
Sphere 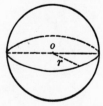	$\mathbf{A} = \pi d^2 = 4\pi r^2$ (r is the radius of the sphere, and $d = 2r$).	$V = \dfrac{\pi d^3}{6} = \dfrac{4\pi r^3}{3}$

III. Trigonometry

45. TRIGONOMETRIC RATIOS OF AN ACUTE ANGLE

From the right triangle ABC ($\angle C = 90°$) we have the following ratios.

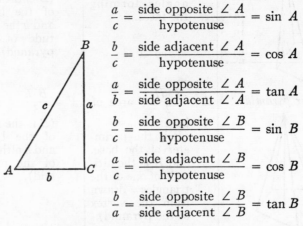

$$\frac{a}{c} = \frac{\text{side opposite } \angle A}{\text{hypotenuse}} = \sin A$$

$$\frac{b}{c} = \frac{\text{side adjacent } \angle A}{\text{hypotenuse}} = \cos A$$

$$\frac{a}{b} = \frac{\text{side opposite } \angle A}{\text{side adjacent } \angle A} = \tan A$$

$$\frac{b}{c} = \frac{\text{side opposite } \angle B}{\text{hypotenuse}} = \sin B$$

$$\frac{a}{c} = \frac{\text{side adjacent } \angle B}{\text{hypotenuse}} = \cos B$$

$$\frac{b}{a} = \frac{\text{side opposite } \angle B}{\text{side adjacent } \angle B} = \tan B$$

But $\angle A + \angle B = 90°$, then $\angle B = 90° - \angle A$.

Then we have that

$$\sin A = \cos B = \cos (90° - A)$$

$$\cos A = \sin B = \sin (90° - A)$$

and

$$\tan A = \frac{1}{\tan B} = \frac{1}{\tan (90° - A)}$$

46. SOME SPECIAL VALUES OF TRIGONOMETRIC RATIOS

Angle	Sine	Cosine	Tangent
0°	0	1	0
30°	$\frac{1}{2}$	$\frac{\sqrt{3}}{2}$	$\frac{\sqrt{3}}{3}$
45°	$\frac{\sqrt{2}}{2}$	$\frac{\sqrt{2}}{2}$	1
60°	$\frac{\sqrt{3}}{3}$	$\frac{1}{2}$	$\sqrt{3}$
90°	1	0	∞

47.   FORMULAS FOR THE SOLUTION OF RIGHT TRIANGLES

The fundamental formulas for the solution of right triangle are:

$$\angle A + \angle B = 90°$$

$$a^2 + b^2 = c^2$$

$$a = c \sin A, \quad b = c \cos A, \quad \text{and} \quad a = b \tan A$$

$$b = c \sin B, \quad a = c \cos B, \quad \text{and} \quad b = a \tan B$$

The solutions of right triangles may be performed according to the following scheme:

Given	Solution

Given   Solution

$c, \ A$ $B = 90° - A, \quad a = c \sin A, \quad b = c \cos A$

also $a = c \cos B, \quad b = c \sin B$

$a, \ A$ $B = 90° - A, \quad b = a \tan B, \quad c = \dfrac{a}{\sin A}$

also $b = \dfrac{a}{\tan A}, \quad c = \sqrt{a^2 + b^2}$

$c, \ a$ $\sin A = \dfrac{a}{c}, \quad B = 90° - A, \quad b = c \cos A$

also $b = a \tan B.$

$a, \ b$ $\tan A = \dfrac{a}{b}, \quad B = 90° - A, \quad c = \sqrt{a^2 + b^2}$

also $c = \dfrac{a}{\sin A}.$

48.   FUNDAMENTAL FORMULAS OF TRIGONOMETRY

If the angle is greater than 90°, but less than 360°, its sine, cosine, and tangent ratios are determined according to the following rules:

a. Find the difference between this angle and 180° or 360° (whichever happens to be the nearest to this angle).   Pay no attention to the sign, and find the value of the respective ratio in the table of values of trigonometric ratios.

b. The sign of the ratio obtained from the table should be in accordance with the following table of signs, considering the original value of the angle.

Ratio	First quadrant	Second quadrant	Third quadrant	Fourth quadrant
	0° to 90°	90° to 180°	180° to 270°	270° to 360°
Sine........	+	+	−	−
Cosine......	+	−	−	+
Tangent.....	+	−	+	−

Examples.

$$\cos 300° = + \cos 60° = + 0.5000, \quad (360° - 300° = 60°)$$

$$\sin 240° = - \sin 60° = - 0.8660, \quad (240° - 180° = 60°)$$

$$\tan 210° = + \tan 30° = + 0.5774, \quad (210° - 180° = 30°)$$

If the angle is greater than 360°, it is necessary to subtract from it an integral multiple of 360°, and only an angle less than 360° is considered. For example

$$\sin 780° = \sin (780° - 720°) = \sin 60° = 0.8660$$

The fundamental relations in trigonometry are:

$$\sin^2 A + \cos^2 A = 1, \quad \text{and} \quad \tan A = \frac{\sin A}{\cos A}$$

$$\sin (90° - A) = \cos A, \quad \text{and} \quad \cos (90° - A) = \sin A$$

$$\sin (A + B) = \sin A \cdot \cos B + \cos A \cdot \sin B$$

$$\sin (A - B) = \sin A \cdot \cos B - \cos A \cdot \sin B$$

$$\cos (A + B) = \cos A \cdot \cos B - \sin A \cdot \sin B$$

$$\cos (A - B) = \cos A \cdot \cos B + \sin A \cdot \sin B$$

$$\tan (A + B) = \frac{\tan A + \tan B}{1 - \tan A \cdot \tan B}$$

$$\tan (A - B) = \frac{\tan A - \tan B}{1 + \tan A \cdot \tan B}$$

$$\sin 2A = 2 \sin A \cdot \cos A$$

$$\cos 2A = \cos^2 A - \sin^2 A$$

$$\cos 2A = 1 - 2 \sin^2 A = 2 \cos^2 A - 1$$

$$\tan 2A = \frac{2 \tan A}{1 - \tan^2 A}$$

49. SOLUTION OF TRIANGLES

The fundamental relations used in the solution of triangles are:

a. The sine law

$$\frac{a}{\sin A} = \frac{b}{\sin B} = \frac{c}{\sin C}$$

b. The cosine law

$$\cos A = \frac{b^2+c^2-a^2}{2bc}, \quad \cos B = \frac{a^2+c^2-b^2}{2ac}, \quad \cos C = \frac{a^2+b^2-c^2}{2ab}$$

c. The tangent law

$$\frac{a+b}{a-b} = \frac{\tan \dfrac{A+B}{2}}{\tan \dfrac{A-B}{2}}, \quad \frac{a+c}{a-c} = \frac{\tan \dfrac{A+C}{2}}{\tan \dfrac{A-C}{2}}, \quad \frac{b+c}{b-c} = \frac{\tan \dfrac{B+C}{2}}{\tan \dfrac{B-C}{2}}$$

The solution of triangles may be performed according to the following scheme:

Given	Solution
$a, b,$ and c	$\cos A = \dfrac{b^2+c^2-a^2}{2bc}, \quad \sin B = \dfrac{b \sin A}{a},$
	$C = 180° - (A+B)$
$a, b,$ and C	$\dfrac{A+B}{2} = 90° - \dfrac{C}{2}, \quad \tan \dfrac{A-B}{2} = \dfrac{a-b}{a+b} \tan \dfrac{A+B}{2}$

If $\dfrac{A+B}{2}$ and $\dfrac{A-B}{2}$ are known, the values of A and B are obtained as the solution of the equations

$$A + B = 2k$$

and

$$A - B = 2m$$

$$c = \frac{a \sin C}{\sin A}.$$

$a, B,$ and C	$A = 180° - (B+C)$
	$b = \dfrac{a \sin B}{\sin A}, \quad c = \dfrac{a \sin C}{\sin A}$
$a, b,$ and A	$C = 180° - (A+B)$
	$\sin B = \dfrac{b \sin A}{a}, \quad c = \dfrac{a \sin C}{\sin A}$

IV. Tables

All the tables given below contain values stated generally to four significant places. On the other hand, the numbers, for which the corresponding tabular values of the various relationships are listed, are stated to three places only. The tables are so arranged, however, that it is possible to calculate a tabular value corresponding to a four-place number. The method for the calculation of such values will be described presently.

All the tables given in this book may be used for computations with numbers containing one, two, three, and four places. If a number is given to more than four places, it is necessary to round it to four places before any computations by means of the tables are performed.

The rules for rounding numbers are as follows:

a. If the first digit that is to be dropped is less than 5 (that is, it is one of the following: 0, 1, 2, 3, or 4), then the last digit (counting from the left) on the extreme right of the number, that is to be retained, should be left unchanged. For example, 124.6345 is rounded to *124.6*. Here the first digit that is dropped is 3.

b. If the first digit that is to be dropped is 5 or greater than 5 (that is, it is one of the following: 5, 6, 7, 8, or 9), then the last digit (counting from the left) on the extreme right of the number, that is to be retained, should be increased by 1. For example, 78.4689 is rounded to 78.47. Here the first digit that is dropped is 8.

c. If the digits that are dropped are in the decimal part of the number, nothing is written in their places, after the undesirable digits are dropped. If the digits that are dropped are in the integral (whole) part of the number, zeros are written in their places, after the undesirable digits are dropped.

For example,   49.98634 is rounded to *49.99*,

  5273498 is rounded to 5273000.

If a number is given to four places the calculation of a tabular value that corresponds to it is computed as follows.

Each table is arranged so that the first two digits of a number are given in the first column (printed in heavy type). To the right of this first column there are several columns (for squares, square roots, and logarithms ten columns, and for trigonometric ratios ten columns also) each of these columns is headed by a number printed in heavy type. This number is the third digit of the number for which a corresponding tabular value is to be found. Thus, a number 473 will be located as follows: 43 is found in the first column, and 7 is found in the column denoted **7**.

When a number has four digits, the tabular value that corresponds to this number is calculated as follows.

The required tabular value cannot be found directly in the table, because the table lists the tabular values that correspond to three-place numbers. But when a number is given to four places its value may be considered as located between two values. For example, suppose that we wish to calculate $\sqrt{17.35}$. We note that 17.35 is located between 17.3 and 17.4. The square roots of 17.3 and of 17.4 can be located in the table. They are found at the intersection of the row denoted **17** and the columns denoted **3** and **4** respectively. We have then

$$\sqrt{17.3} = 4.159 \quad \text{and} \quad \sqrt{17.4} = 4.171$$

On the right of the table there are nine columns of numbers known as *Corrections*. We locate in the place where the row denoted **17** intersects with the column denoted **5** the number *6*. This correction *6* is added to the last place on the right of the value of $\sqrt{17.3} = 4.159$, and the sum thus obtained is the required square root

$$\sqrt{17.35} = 4.159 + 0.006 = 4.165$$

We may check this result. We have that

$$(4.165)^2 = 17.347225,$$

which, when rounded to four places is 17.35.

In the case of tables of trigonometric ratios, the procedure is exactly the same. See Section D.

A. TABLE OF LOGARITHMS OF NUMBERS

This table gives the values of *the mantissas* of the logarithms of numbers, that is, of the decimal portions of the logarithms.

The integral (whole) portion of a logarithm of a number, which is known as *the characteristic*, is found according to the following rules.

    a. If the number has an integral (whole) part, then count the number of the digits there are in this whole part, that is, *the number of digits to the left of the decimal point.* Subtract 1 (one) from this number of digits. The difference thus obtained is the characteristic of the logarithm.

    b. If the number is a pure decimal, then count the number of zeros there are in the decimal part, that is, *to the right of the decimal point.* Add 1 (one) to this number of zeros. The sum thus obtained is the characteristic of the logarithm of the number. It should be remembered that the logarithm of a positive fraction less than 1 is negative. The representation of any fraction may be as follows. It may be represented as the product of a number with a negative power of 10. For example, $0.5 = 5 \cdot 10^{-1}$. This property is used for the purpose of writing of logarithms of decimal fraction. We write the mantissa as obtained from the table, and we write the characteristic as a negative number. This last is written with a bar over it, in order to indicate that it is negative. Thus, the characteristic of the logarithm of 45.67 is $2 - 1 = 1$. The characteristic of 0.3269 is obtained as $0 + 1 = 1$; since it is -1, it is written as $\bar{1}$. The characteristic of 0.0006489 is written as $\bar{4}$.

The table of logarithms (that is, of the mantissas of the logarithms) is arranged so that the first two digits of a number are found in the first column (whose heading is N), and the third digit of a number is found in one of the ten columns immediately to the right of N. Thus this table contains the mantissas of all three-place numbers. These mantissas are found as follows:

Locate the line in the first column that corresponds to the first two digits of the number. Then locate the intersection of the column whose heading is the third digit with the row that corresponds to the first two digits. At the intersection the mantissa of the logarithm of the three place number is found.

For example, the logarithm of 723 is found at the intersection of the row numbered **72** and the column numbered **3**. Then log 723 = 2.8591.

The logarithm of a four-place number is found by locating the characteristic that corresponds to the first three digits (counting from the left) of the number and adding to this the mantissa of the correction that corresponds to the fourth digit. This correction is found in the columns on the right of the table with such computed *Corrections.* The values of the corrections given in the table are in terms of the last place on the right of the mantissa. Thus, if the correction is stated as 7, its value is 0.0007, if the correction is stated as 13, its value is 0.0013.

For example, the logarithm of 54.38 is calculated as follows:

$$\log 54.3 \ = 1.7348$$

the correction for

$$0.08 = 0.0006$$

$$\log 54.38 = 1.7354$$

The logarithm of 0.02846 is calculated as follows:

$$\log 0.0284 \ = \bar{2}.4533$$

the correction for

$$0.00006 = 0.0006$$

$$\log 0.02846 = \bar{2}.4539$$

By means of the table of logarithms it is possible to calculate the number when its logarithm is given. The process of calculation of the number by means of its logarithm is the reverse of the process of calculating the logarithm.

Suppose that 2.7087 is the logarithm of some number. We find in the table that there is no listing for the mantissa 7087. But there is a listing for the mantissa 7084. Thus the number whose logarithm is 2.7087 is greater than the number whose logarithm is 2.7084. Moreover, the number whose logarithm is 2.7087 is less than the number whose logarithm is 2.7093 (the listing next to the mantissa 7087). In other words, the number whose logarithm is 2.7087 is greater than 511, but it is less than 512. The difference between 0.7087 and 0.7084 is 0.0003. In the columns for the corrections we find that 3 corresponds to the headings **3** and **4.** Thus the required number is either 511.3 or 511.4. But, on the other hand the difference between 0.7093 and 0.7087 is 0.0006, and the correction for 6 is given by the heading **7.** Thus, the required number is $512.0 - 0.7 = 511.3$. The actual calculation is performed as follows:

$$2.7087$$

$$2.7084 = \log 511$$

Difference   3   0.3   correction

$$2.7087 = \log 511.3$$

It should be understood that the results of the computations with logarithms generally can be stated only approximately. Only in exceptional cases may the results be obtained exactly.

The logarithm of a product is equal to the sum of the logarithms of the individual factors. For example, the product $(3.789 \cdot 6.115 \cdot 78.09)$ is computed as follows:

$$\log 3.789 = 0.5785$$
$$\log 6.115 = 0.7864$$
$$\log 78.09 = 1.8926$$

logarithm of product = 3.2575
and the product is 180.9 (approximately).

The logarithm of a quotient is equal to the difference between the logarithm of the dividend and the logarithm of the divisor. For example, the logarithm of $(17.82 \div 0.4638)$ is obtained as follows:

$$\log 17.82 \; = 1.2509$$
$$\log 0.4638 = \bar{1}.6663$$

logarithm of the quotient = 1.5846

(the subtraction is performed with due regard to the characteristic of the logarithm of the divisor; when $\bar{1}$ is subtracted it becomes $+1$).
The quotient is then 38.83.

When a larger logarithm is subtracted from a smaller logarithm, the subtraction of the characteristic should be so performed that it is recorded with the proper sign. For example,

$$\begin{array}{r} 1.0009 \\ -1.1119 \\ \hline \overline{1}.8890 \end{array}$$

In this subtraction 0.1119 is subtracted from 1.0009, and this leads to a positive mantissa. Then, the characteristic is $\overline{1}$.

The logarithm of a power is equal to the product of the logarithm of the base and the exponent of the power. For example, the logarithm of $(2.473)^8$ is obtained as follows:

$$\log 2.473 = 0.3932.$$

$$8 \log 2.473 = 8 \cdot 0.3932 = 3.1456$$

and $(2.473)^8 = 1398$ (approximately).

If the base is a fraction, the products of the mantissa and the characteristic (which is negative) are obtained separately. For example, $(0.05863)^7$ is computed as follows:

$$\log 0.05863 = \overline{2}.7681$$

$$7 \log 0.05863 = 7 \cdot \overline{2} + 7 \cdot 07861 = \overline{14} + 5.5027 = \overline{9}.5027$$

and $(0.05863)^7 = 0.000000003182$ (approximately).

The logarithm of a root is equal to the logarithm of the number under the radical divided by the exponent of the root. For example, $\sqrt[15]{18.65}$ is computed as follows:

$$\log 18.65 = 1.2707$$

$$\frac{\log 18.65}{15} = \frac{1.2707}{15} = 0.0847$$

and $\sqrt[15]{18.65} = 1.215$ (approximately).

If the number under the radical sign is a fraction, that is, if the logarithm of the number has a negative characteristic, the division is performed as follows: Suppose that the $\sqrt[12]{0.05474}$ is to be computed. We have then

$$\log 0.05474 = \overline{2}.7383$$

$$\frac{\log 0.05474}{12} = \frac{\overline{2}.7383}{12}$$

Since the logarithm of the fraction consists of two parts, one negative and the other positive it becomes necessary to perform the division separately. But, in order to divide the negative part, that is, $\bar{2}$, we shall subtract 10 from it, and thus make it divisible by 12, and in order to compensate for this, we shall add 10 to the positive part. Then the division is performed as follows:

$$\frac{\bar{2}.7383}{12} = \frac{\overline{12} + 10.7383}{12} = \bar{1}.8949$$

and $\sqrt[12]{0.05474} = 0.785$ (approximately).

B. TABLE OF SQUARES OF NUMBERS

In order to square a number given to three places it is necessary to locate the first two digits of the number in the first column on the left, and the third digit among the ten columns located to the left of the first column. Where the row, indicated by the first two digits, and the column indicated by the third digit, intersect, there is a listing of the required square of the number. However, two facts must be kept in mind.

a. Only the squares listed under the heading O are exact. All other listings are approximate.
b. The reader should note that the numbers in the column N are given with one digit to the left of the decimal place. In order to facilitate computation it is then necessary to reduce to this form a number whose square is to be obtained. That is, if we have a number 643, it should be written as $6.43 \cdot 10^2$, and the square of 643 is then $41.22 \cdot 10^4 = 412200$ (approximately). If we have a number 0.00563, then it must be written as $5.63 \cdot 10^{-3}$, and its square is $31.58 \cdot 10^{-6} = 0.00003158$ (approximately).

If a number is given to four places, the first three places enable us to locate a value of a square to which a correction for the fourth place must be added, and this correction is obtained in the columns on the right of the table containing the *Corrections*.
For example,

$(56.93)^2 = (5.693 \cdot 10)^2 = 10^2(32.38 + 0.10) = 10^2 \cdot 32.48 = 3248$
  (approximately).

$(0.009834)^2 = (10^{-3} \cdot 9.834)^2 = 10^{-6} \cdot 96.71 = 0.00009671$
  (approximately).

LOGARITHMS OF NUMBERS

	0	1	2	3	4	5	6	7	8	9	1	2	3	4	5	6	7	8	9
10	0000	0043	0086	0128	0170	0212	0253	0294	0334	0374									
11	0414	0453	0492	0531	0569	0607	0645	0682	0719	0755	4	8	11	15	19	23	26	30	34
12	0792	0828	0864	0899	0934	0969	1004	1038	1072	1106	3	7	10	14	17	21	24	28	31
13	1139	1173	1206	1239	1271	1303	1335	1367	1399	1430	3	6	10	13	16	19	23	26	29
14	1461	1492	1523	1553	1584	1614	1644	1673	1703	1732	3	6	9	12	15	18	21	24	27
15	1761	1790	1818	1847	1875	1903	1931	1959	1987	2014	3	6	8	11	14	17	20	22	25
16	2041	2068	2095	2122	2148	2175	2201	2227	2253	2279	3	5	8	11	13	16	18	21	24
17	2304	2330	2355	2380	2405	2430	2455	2480	2504	2529	2	5	7	10	12	15	17	20	22
18	2553	2577	2601	2625	2648	2672	2695	2718	2742	2765	2	5	7	9	12	14	16	19	21
19	2788	2810	2833	2856	2878	2900	2923	2945	2967	2989	2	4	7	9	11	13	16	18	20
20	3010	3032	3054	3075	3096	3118	3139	3160	3181	3201	2	4	6	8	11	13	15	17	19
21	3222	3243	3263	3284	3304	3324	3345	3365	3385	3404	2	4	6	8	10	12	14	16	18
22	3424	3444	3464	3483	3502	3522	3541	3560	3579	3598	2	4	6	8	10	12	14	15	17
23	3617	3636	3655	3674	3692	3711	3729	3747	3766	3784	2	4	6	7	9	11	13	15	17
24	3802	3820	3838	3856	3874	3892	3909	3927	3945	3962	2	4	5	7	9	11	12	14	16
25	3979	3997	4014	4031	4048	4065	4082	4099	4116	4133	2	3	5	7	9	10	12	14	15
26	4150	4166	4183	4200	4216	4232	4249	4265	4281	4298	2	3	5	7	8	10	11	13	15
27	4314	4330	4346	4362	4378	4393	4409	4425	4440	4456	2	3	5	6	8	9	11	13	14
28	4472	4487	4502	4518	4533	4548	4564	4579	4594	4609	2	3	5	6	8	9	11	12	14
29	4624	4639	4654	4669	4683	4698	4713	4728	4742	4757	1	3	4	6	7	9	10	12	13
30	4771	4786	4800	4814	4829	4843	4857	4871	4886	4900	1	3	4	6	7	9	10	11	13
31	4914	4928	4942	4955	4969	4983	4997	5011	5024	5038	1	3	4	6	7	8	10	11	12
32	5051	5065	5079	5092	5105	5119	5132	5145	5159	5172	1	3	4	5	7	8	9	11	12
33	5185	5198	5211	5224	5237	5250	5263	5276	5289	5302	1	3	4	5	6	8	9	10	12
34	5315	5328	5340	5353	5366	5378	5391	5403	5416	5428	1	3	4	5	6	8	9	10	11
35	5441	5453	5465	5478	5490	5502	5514	5527	5539	5551	1	2	4	5	6	7	9	10	11
36	5563	5575	5587	5599	5611	5623	5635	5647	5658	5670	1	2	4	5	6	7	8	10	11
37	5682	5694	5705	5717	5729	5740	5752	5763	5775	5786	1	2	3	5	6	7	8	9	10
38	5798	5809	5821	5832	5843	5855	5866	5877	5888	5899	1	2	3	5	6	7	8	9	10
39	5911	5922	5933	5944	5955	5966	5977	5988	5999	6010	1	2	3	4	5	7	8	9	10
40	6021	6031	6042	6053	6064	6075	6085	6096	6107	6117	1	2	3	4	5	6	8	9	10
41	6128	6138	6149	6160	6170	6180	6191	6201	6212	6222	1	2	3	4	5	6	7	8	9
42	6232	6243	6253	6263	6274	6284	6294	6304	6314	6325	1	2	3	4	5	6	7	8	9
43	6335	6345	6355	6365	6375	6385	6395	6405	6415	6425	1	2	3	4	5	6	7	8	9
44	6435	6444	6454	6464	6474	6484	6493	6503	6513	6522	1	2	3	4	5	6	7	8	9
45	6532	6542	6551	6561	6571	6580	6590	6599	6609	6618	1	2	3	4	5	6	7	8	9
46	6628	6637	6646	6656	6665	6675	6684	6693	6702	6712	1	2	3	4	5	6	7	7	8
47	6721	6730	6739	6749	6758	6767	6776	6785	6794	6803	1	2	3	4	5	5	6	7	8
48	6812	6821	6830	6839	6848	6857	6866	6875	6884	6893	1	2	3	4	4	5	6	7	8
49	6902	6911	6920	6928	6937	6946	6955	6964	6972	6981	1	2	3	4	4	5	6	7	8
50	6990	6998	7007	7016	7024	7033	7042	7050	7059	7067	1	2	3	3	4	5	6	7	8
51	7076	7084	7093	7101	7110	7118	7126	7135	7143	7152	1	2	3	3	4	5	6	7	8
52	7160	7168	7177	7185	7193	7202	7210	7218	7226	7235	1	2	2	3	4	5	6	7	7
53	7243	7251	7259	7267	7275	7284	7292	7300	7308	7316	1	2	2	3	4	5	6	6	7
54	7324	7332	7340	7348	7356	7364	7372	7380	7388	7396	1	2	2	3	4	5	6	6	7

LOGARITHMS OF NUMBERS

	0	1	2	3	4	5	6	7	8	9	1 2 3	4 5 6	7 8 9
55	7404	7412	7419	7427	7435	7443	7451	7459	7466	7474	1 2 2	3 4 5	5 6 7
56	7482	7490	7497	7505	7513	7520	7528	7536	7543	7551	1 2 2	3 4 5	5 6 7
57	7559	7566	7574	7582	7589	7597	7604	7612	7619	7627	1 2 2	3 4 5	5 6 7
58	7634	7642	7649	7657	7664	7672	7679	7686	7694	7701	1 1 2	3 4 4	5 6 7
59	7709	7716	7723	7731	7738	7745	7752	7760	7767	7774	1 1 2	3 4 4	5 6 7
60	7782	7789	7796	7803	7810	7818	7825	7832	7839	7846	1 1 2	3 4 4	5 6 6
61	7853	7860	7868	7875	7882	7889	7896	7903	7910	7917	1 1 2	3 4 4	5 6 6
62	7924	7931	7938	7945	7952	7959	7966	7973	7980	7987	1 1 2	3 3 4	5 6 6
63	7993	8000	8007	8014	8021	8028	8035	8041	8048	8055	1 1 2	3 3 4	5 5 6
64	8062	8069	8075	8082	8089	8096	8102	8109	8116	8122	1 1 2	3 3 4	5 5 6
65	8129	8136	8142	8149	8156	8162	8169	8176	8182	8189	1 1 2	3 3 4	5 5 6
66	8195	8202	8209	8215	8222	8228	8235	8241	8248	8254	1 1 2	3 3 4	5 5 6
67	8261	8267	8274	8280	8287	8293	8299	8306	8312	8319	1 1 2	3 3 4	5 5 6
68	8325	8331	8338	8344	8351	8357	8363	8370	8376	8382	1 1 2	3 3 4	4 5 6
69	8388	8395	8401	8407	8414	8420	8426	8432	8439	8445	1 1 2	2 3 4	4 5 6
70	8451	8457	8463	8470	8476	8482	8488	8494	8500	8506	1 1 2	2 3 4	4 5 6
71	8513	8519	8525	8531	8537	8543	8549	8555	8561	8567	1 1 2	2 3 4	4 5 5
72	8573	8579	8585	8591	8597	8603	8609	8615	8621	8627	1 1 2	2 3 4	4 5 5
73	8633	8639	8645	8651	8657	8663	8669	8675	8681	8686	1 1 2	2 3 4	4 5 5
74	8692	8698	8704	8710	8716	8722	8727	8733	8739	8745	1 1 2	2 3 4	4 5 5
75	8751	8756	8762	8768	8774	8779	8785	8791	8797	8802	1 1 2	2 3 3	4 5 5
76	8808	8814	8820	8825	8831	8837	8842	8848	8854	8859	1 1 2	2 3 3	4 5 5
77	8865	8871	8876	8882	8887	8893	8899	8904	8910	8915	1 1 2	2 3 3	4 4 5
78	8921	8927	8932	8938	8943	8949	8954	8960	8965	8971	1 1 2	2 3 3	4 4 5
79	8976	8982	8987	8993	8998	9004	9009	9015	9020	9025	1 1 2	2 3 3	4 4 5
80	9031	9036	9042	9047	9053	9058	9063	9069	9074	9079	1 1 2	2 3 3	4 4 5
81	9085	9090	9096	9101	9106	9112	9117	9122	9128	9133	1 1 2	2 3 3	4 4 5
82	9138	9143	9149	9154	9159	9165	9170	9175	9180	9186	1 1 2	2 3 3	4 4 5
83	9191	9196	9201	9206	9212	9217	9222	9227	9232	9238	1 1 2	2 3 3	4 4 5
84	9243	9248	9253	9258	9263	9269	9274	9279	9284	9289	1 1 2	2 3 3	4 4 5
85	9294	9299	9304	9309	9315	9320	9325	9330	9335	9340	1 1 2	2 3 3	4 4 5
86	9345	9350	9355	9360	9365	9370	9375	9380	9385	9390	1 1 2	2 3 3	4 4 5
87	9395	9400	9405	9410	9415	9420	9425	9430	9435	9440	0 1 1	2 2 3	3 4 4
88	9445	9450	9455	9460	9465	9469	9474	9479	9484	9489	0 1 1	2 2 3	3 4 4
89	9494	9499	9504	9509	9513	9518	9523	9528	9533	9538	0 1 1	2 2 3	3 4 4
90	9542	9547	9552	9557	9562	9566	9571	9576	9581	9586	0 1 1	2 2 3	3 4 4
91	9590	9595	9600	9605	9609	9614	9619	9624	9628	9633	0 1 1	2 2 3	3 4 4
92	9638	9643	9647	9652	9657	9661	9666	9671	9675	9680	0 1 1	2 2 3	3 4 4
93	9685	9689	9694	9699	9703	9708	9713	9717	9722	9727	0 1 1	2 2 3	3 4 4
94	9731	9736	9741	9745	9750	9754	9759	9763	9768	9773	0 1 1	2 2 3	3 4 4
95	9777	9782	9786	9791	9795	9800	9805	9809	9814	9818	0 1 1	2 2 3	3 4 4
96	9823	9827	9832	9836	9841	9845	9850	9854	9859	9863	0 1 1	2 2 3	3 4 4
97	9868	9872	9877	9881	9886	9890	9894	9899	9903	9908	0 1 1	2 2 3	3 4 4
98	9912	9917	9921	9926	9930	9934	9939	9943	9948	9952	0 1 1	2 2 3	3 4 4
99	9956	9961	9965	9969	9974	9978	9983	9987	9991	9996	0 1 1	2 2 3	3 3 4

SQUARES OF NUMBERS

N	0	1	2	3	4	5	6	7	8	9	1	2	3	4	5	6	7	8	9
1.0	1.000	1.020	1.040	1.061	1.082	1.103	1.124	1.145	1.166	1.188	2	4	6	8	10	13	15	17	19
1.1	1.210	1.232	1.254	1.277	1.300	1.323	1.346	1.369	1.392	1.416	2	5	7	9	11	14	16	18	21
1.2	1.440	1.464	1.488	1.513	1.538	1.563	1.588	1.613	1.638	1.664	2	5	7	10	12	15	17	20	22
1.3	1.690	1.716	1.742	1.769	1.796	1.823	1.850	1.877	1.904	1.932	3	5	8	12	13	16	19	22	24
1.4	1.960	1.988	2.016	2.045	2.074	2.103	2.132	2.161	2.190	2.220	3	6	9	12	14	17	20	23	26
1.5	2.250	2.280	2.310	2.341	2.372	2.403	2.434	2.465	2.496	2.528	3	6	9	12	15	19	22	25	28
1.6	2.560	2.592	2.624	2.657	2.690	2.723	2.756	2.789	2.822	2.856	3	7	10	13	16	20	23	26	30
1.7	2.890	2.924	2.958	2.993	3.028	3.063	3.098	3.133	3.168	3.204	3	7	10	14	17	21	24	28	31
1.8	3.240	3.276	3.312	3.349	3.386	3.423	3.460	3.497	3.534	3.572	4	7	11	15	18	22	26	30	33
1.9	3.610	3.648	3.686	3.725	3.764	3.803	3.842	3.881	3.920	3.960	4	8	12	16	19	23	27	31	35
2.0	4.000	4.040	4.080	4.121	4.162	4.203	4.244	4.285	4.326	4.368	4	8	12	16	20	25	29	33	37
2.1	4.410	4.452	4.494	4.537	4.580	4.623	4.666	4.709	4.752	4.796	4	9	13	17	21	26	30	34	39
2.2	4.840	4.884	4.928	4.973	5.018	5.063	5.108	5.153	5.198	5.244	4	9	13	18	22	27	31	36	40
2.3	5.290	5.336	5.382	5.429	5.476	5.523	5.570	5.617	5.664	5.712	5	9	14	19	23	28	33	38	42
2.4	5.760	5.808	5.856	5.905	5.954	6.003	6.052	6.101	6.150	6.200	5	10	15	20	24	29	34	39	44
2.5	6.250	6.300	6.350	6.401	6.452	6.503	6.554	6.605	6.656	6.708	5	10	15	20	25	31	36	41	46
2.6	6.760	6.812	6.864	6.917	6.970	7.023	7.076	7.129	7.182	7.236	5	11	16	21	26	32	37	42	48
2.7	7.290	7.344	7.398	7.453	7.508	7.563	7.618	7.673	7.728	7.784	5	11	16	22	27	33	38	44	49
2.8	7.840	7.896	7.952	8.009	8.066	8.123	8.180	8.237	8.294	8.352	6	11	17	23	28	34	40	46	51
2.9	8.410	8.468	8.526	8.585	8.644	8.703	8.762	8.821	8.880	8.940	6	12	18	24	29	35	41	47	53
3.0	9.000	9.060	9.120	9.181	9.242	9.303	9.364	9.425	9.486	9.548	6	12	18	24	30	37	43	49	55
3.1	9.610	9.672	9.734	9.797	9.860	9.923	9.986				6	13	19	25	31	38	44	50	56
3.1								10.05	10.11	10.18	1	1	2	3	4	5	5	6	
3.2	10.24	10.30	10.37	10.43	10.50	10.56	10.63	10.69	10.76	10.82	1	1	2	3	3	4	5	5	6
3.3	10.89	10.96	11.02	11.09	11.16	11.22	11.29	11.36	11.42	11.49	1	1	2	3	3	4	5	5	6
3.4	11.56	11.63	11.70	11.76	11.83	11.90	11.97	12.04	12.11	12.18	1	1	2	3	3	4	5	6	6
3.5	12.25	12.32	12.39	12.46	12.53	12.60	12.67	12.74	12.82	12.89	1	1	2	3	4	4	5	6	6
3.6	12.96	13.03	13.10	13.18	13.25	13.32	13.40	13.47	13.54	13.62	1	1	2	3	4	4	5	6	7
3.7	13.69	13.76	13.84	13.91	13.99	14.06	14.14	14.21	14.29	14.36	1	2	2	3	4	5	5	6	7
3.8	14.44	14.52	14.59	14.67	14.75	14.82	14.90	14.98	15.05	15.13	1	2	2	3	4	5	5	6	7
3.9	15.21	15.29	15.37	15.44	15.52	15.60	15.68	15.76	15.84	15.92	1	2	2	3	4	5	5	6	7
4.0	16.00	16.08	16.16	16.24	16.32	16.40	16.48	16.56	16.65	16.73	1	2	2	3	4	5	6	6	7
4.1	16.81	16.89	16.97	17.06	17.14	17.22	17.31	17.39	17.47	17.56	1	2	2	3	5	5	6	7	7
4.2	17.64	17.72	17.81	17.89	17.98	18.06	18.15	18.23	18.32	18.40	1	2	3	3	4	5	6	7	8
4.3	18.49	18.58	18.66	18.75	18.84	18.92	19.01	19.10	19.18	19.27	1	2	3	3	4	5	7	7	8
4.4	19.36	19.45	19.54	19.62	19.71	19.80	19.89	19.98	20.07	20.16	1	2	3	4	5	5	6	7	8
4.5	20.25	20.34	20.43	20.52	20.61	20.70	20.79	20.88	20.98	21.07	1	2	3	4	5	5	6	7	8
4.6	21.16	21.25	21.34	21.44	21.53	21.62	21.72	21.81	21.90	22.00	1	2	3	4	5	6	7	7	8
4.7	22.09	22.18	22.28	22.37	22.47	22.56	22.66	22.75	22.85	22.94	1	2	3	4	5	6	7	8	9
4.8	23.04	23.14	23.23	23.33	23.43	23.52	23.62	23.72	23.81	23.91	1	2	3	4	5	6	7	8	9
4.9	24.01	24.11	24.21	24.30	24.40	24.50	24.60	24.70	24.80	24.90	1	2	3	4	5	6	7	8	9
5.0	25.00	25.10	25.20	25.30	25.40	25.50	25.60	25.70	25.81	25.91	1	2	3	4	5	6	7	8	9
5.1	26.01	26.11	26.21	26.32	26.42	26.52	26.63	26.73	26.83	26.94	1	2	3	4	5	6	7	8	9
5.2	27.04	27.14	27.25	27.35	27.46	27.56	27.67	27.77	27.88	27.98	1	2	3	4	5	6	7	8	9
5.3	28.09	28.20	28.30	28.41	28.52	28.62	28.73	28.84	28.94	29.05	1	2	3	4	5	6	7	9	10
5.4	29.16	29.27	29.38	29.48	29.59	29.70	29.81	29.92	30.03	30.14	1	2	3	4	6	7	8	9	10
5.5	30.25	30.36	30.47	30.58	30.69	30.80	30.91	31.02	31.14	31.25	1	2	3	4	6	7	8	9	10
5.6	31.36	31.47	31.58	31.70	31.81	31.92	32.04	32.15	32.26	32.38	1	2	3	5	6	7	8	9	10
5.7	32.49	32.60	32.72	32.83	32.95	33.06	33.18	33.29	33.41	33.52	1	2	3	5	6	7	8	9	10
5.8	33.64	33.76	33.87	33.99	34.11	34.22	34.34	34.46	34.57	34.69	1	2	3	5	6	7	8	9	11
5.9	34.81	34.93	35.05	35.16	35.28	35.40	35.52	35.64	35.76	35.88	1	2	4	5	6	7	8	10	11
6.0	36.00	36.12	36.24	36.36	36.48	36.60	36.72	36.84	36.97	37.09	1	2	4	5	6	7	9	10	11
6.1	37.21	37.33	37.45	37.58	37.70	37.82	37.95	38.07	38.19	38.32	1	2	4	5	6	7	9	10	11
N	0	1	2	3	4	5	6	7	8	9	1	2	3	4	5	6	7	8	9

SQUARES OF NUMBERS

N	0	1	2	3	4	5	6	7	8	9	1	2	3	4	5	6	7	8	9
6.2	38.44	38.56	38.69	38.81	38.94	39.06	39.19	39.31	39.44	39.56	1	3	4	5	6	8	9	10	11
6.3	39.69	39.82	39.94	40.07	40.20	40.32	40.45	40.58	40.70	40.83	1	3	4	5	6	8	9	10	11
6.4	40.96	41.09	41.22	41.34	41.47	41.60	41.73	41.86	41.99	42.12	1	3	4	5	6	8	9	10	12
6.5	42.25	42.38	42.51	42.64	42.77	42.90	43.03	43.16	43.30	43.43	1	3	4	5	7	8	9	10	12
6.6	43.56	43.69	43.82	43.96	44.09	44.22	44.36	44.49	44.62	44.76	1	3	4	5	7	8	9	11	12
6.7	44.89	45.02	45.16	45.29	45.43	45.56	45.70	45.83	45.97	46.10	1	3	4	5	7	8	9	11	12
6.8	46.24	46.38	46.51	46.65	46.79	46.92	47.06	47.20	47.33	47.47	1	3	4	5	7	8	10	11	12
6.9	47.61	47.75	47.89	48.02	48.16	48.30	48.44	48.58	48.72	48.86	1	3	4	6	7	8	10	11	13
7.0	49.00	49.14	49.28	49.42	49.56	49.70	49.84	49.98	50.13	50.27	1	3	4	6	7	8	10	11	13
7.1	50.41	50.55	50.69	50.84	50.98	51.12	51.27	51.41	51.55	51.70	1	3	4	6	7	9	10	11	13
7.2	51.84	51.98	52.13	52.27	52.42	52.56	52.71	52.85	53.00	53.14	1	3	4	6	7	9	10	12	13
7.3	53.29	53.44	53.58	53.73	53.88	54.02	54.17	54.32	54.46	54.61	1	3	4	6	7	9	10	12	13
7.4	54.76	54.91	55.06	55.20	55.35	55.50	55.65	55.80	55.95	56.10	1	3	4	6	7	9	10	12	13
7.5	56.25	56.40	56.55	56.70	56.85	57.00	57.15	57.30	57.46	57.61	2	3	5	6	8	9	11	12	14
7.6	57.76	57.91	58.06	58.22	58.37	58.52	58.68	58.83	58.98	59.14	2	3	5	6	8	9	11	12	14
7.7	59.29	59.44	59.60	59.75	59.91	60.06	60.22	60.37	60.53	60.68	2	3	5	6	8	9	11	12	14
7.8	60.84	61.00	61.15	61.31	61.47	61.62	61.78	61.94	62.09	62.25	2	3	5	6	8	9	11	13	14
7.9	62.41	62.57	62.73	62.88	63.04	63.20	63.36	63.52	63.68	63.84	2	3	5	6	8	10	11	13	14
8.0	64.00	64.16	64.32	64.48	64.64	64.80	64.96	65.12	65.29	65.45	2	3	5	6	8	10	11	13	14
8.1	65.61	65.77	65.93	66.10	66.26	66.42	66.59	66.75	66.91	67.08	2	3	5	7	8	10	11	13	15
8.2	67.24	67.40	67.57	67.73	67.90	68.06	68.23	68.39	68.56	68.72	2	3	5	7	8	10	12	13	15
8.3	68.89	69.06	69.22	69.39	69.56	69.72	69.89	70.06	70.22	70.39	2	3	5	7	8	10	12	13	15
8.4	70.56	70.73	70.90	71.06	71.23	71.40	71.57	71.74	71.91	72.08	2	3	5	7	8	10	12	14	15
8.5	72.25	72.42	72.59	72.76	72.93	73.10	73.27	73.44	73.62	73.79	2	3	5	7	9	10	12	14	15
8.6	73.96	74.13	74.30	74.48	74.65	74.82	75.00	75.17	75.34	75.52	2	3	5	7	9	10	12	14	16
8.7	75.69	75.86	76.04	76.21	76.39	76.56	76.74	76.91	77.09	77.26	2	4	5	7	9	11	12	14	16
8.8	77.44	77.62	77.79	77.97	78.15	78.32	78.50	78.68	78.85	79.03	2	4	5	7	9	11	12	14	16
8.9	79.21	79.39	79.57	79.74	79.92	80.10	80.28	80.46	80.64	80.82	2	4	5	7	9	11	13	14	16
9.0	81.00	81.18	81.36	81.54	81.72	81.90	82.08	82.26	82.45	82.63	2	4	5	7	9	11	13	14	16
9.1	82.81	82.99	83.17	83.36	83.54	83.72	83.91	84.09	84.27	84.46	2	4	5	7	9	11	13	15	16
9.2	84.64	84.82	85.01	85.19	85.38	85.56	85.75	85.93	86.12	86.30	2	4	6	7	9	11	13	15	17
9.3	86.49	86.68	86.86	87.05	87.24	87.42	87.61	87.80	87.98	88.17	2	4	6	7	9	11	13	15	17
9.4	88.36	88.55	88.74	88.92	89.11	89.30	89.49	89.68	89.87	90.06	2	4	6	8	9	11	13	15	17
9.5	90.25	90.44	90.63	90.82	91.01	91.20	91.39	91.58	91.78	91.97	2	4	6	8	10	11	13	15	17
9.6	92.16	92.35	92.54	92.74	92.93	93.12	93.32	93.51	93.70	93.90	2	4	6	8	10	12	14	15	17
9.7	94.09	94.28	94.48	94.67	94.87	95.06	95.26	95.45	95.65	95.84	2	4	6	8	10	12	14	16	18
9.8	96.04	96.24	96.43	96.63	96.83	97.02	97.22	97.42	97.61	97.81	2	4	6	8	10	12	14	16	18
9.9	98.01	98.21	98.41	98.60	98.80	99.00	99.20	99.40	99.60	99.80	2	4	6	8	10	12	14	16	18
N	0	1	2	3	4	5	6	7	8	9	1	2	3	4	5	6	7	8	9

When the decimal point in N is moved 1, 2, 3, 4, ... places the decimal point in N^2 is moved in the same direction 2, 4, 6, 8 ... places. For example, $24.3^2 = 590.5$.

C. TABLE OF SQUARE ROOTS OF NUMBERS

In order to obtain a square root of a number given to three places it is necessary to locate the first two digits of the number in the first column on the left, and the third digit among the ten columns located to the left of the first column. Where the row, indicated by the first two digits, and the column, indicated by the third digit, intersect, there is a listing of the required square root. However, two facts must be kept in mind.

a. Only a few square roots (of those numbers that are perfect squares, such as 4, 16, 49, etc.) are exact. All other listings are approximate.

b. The reader should note that the numbers in the column **N** are first given with one digit to the left of the decimal place, and then with two digits to the left of the decimal place.

In order to facilitate the computation of the square roots, it is necessary to reduce the number under the radical sign either to the form with one digit to the left of the decimal place or with two digits to the left of the decimal place.

The selection of one of these two forms is not arbitrary, but it depends on the exponent of 10 when the number is reduced to one of these forms. The exponent of 10 must always be even, because when the square root of some power of 10 is computed, the exponent of 10 must be divided by 2.

For example, 89300 is transformed into $8.93 \cdot 10^4$, and 643000 is transformed into $64.3 \cdot 10^4$, 0.145 is transformed into $14.5 \cdot 10^{-2}$, and 0.000647 is transformed into $6.47 \cdot 10^{-4}$, and 0.0000856 is transformed into $85.6 \cdot 10^{-6}$.

The rule for these transformations is as follows:

If the number has no decimal part, or if it has an odd number of digits, one digit should be to the left of the decimal place. If the number of digits is even, two digits should be to left of the decimal place.

If the number has no integral (whole) part, that is, it is a pure decimal, and if it has an odd number of zeros immediately to the right of the decimal point, the transformed number should have one digit to the left of the decimal point.

If a number is given to four places, the first three places enable us to locate a value of a square root to which a correction for the fourth place must be added, and this correction is obtained in the column with the *Corrections*. These corrections are given in terms of the last unit of the listed value of the square root.

SQUARE ROOTS OF NUMBERS

N	0	1	2	3	4	5	6	7	8	9	1	2	3	4	5	6	7	8	9
1.0	1.000	1.005	1.010	1.015	1.020	1.025	1.030	1.034	1.039	1.044	0	1	1	2	2	3	3	4	4
1.1	1.049	1.054	1.058	1.063	1.068	1.072	1.077	1.082	1.086	1.091	0	1	1	2	2	3	3	4	4
1.2	1.095	1.100	1.105	1.109	1.114	1.118	1.122	1.127	1.131	1.136	0	1	1	2	2	3	3	4	4
1.3	1.140	1.145	1.149	1.153	1.158	1.162	1.166	1.170	1.175	1.179	0	1	1	2	2	3	3	3	4
1.4	1.183	1.187	1.192	1.196	1.200	1.204	1.208	1.212	1.217	1.221	0	1	1	2	2	2	3	3	4
1.5	1.225	1.229	1.233	1.237	1.241	1.245	1.249	1.253	1.257	1.261	0	1	1	2	2	2	3	3	3
1.6	1.265	1.269	1.273	1.277	1.281	1.285	1.288	1.292	1.296	1.300	0	1	1	2	2	2	3	3	3
1.7	1.304	1.308	1.311	1.315	1.319	1.323	1.327	1.330	1.334	1.338	0	1	1	2	2	2	3	3	3
1.8	1.342	1.345	1.349	1.353	1.356	1.360	1.364	1.367	1.371	1.375	0	1	1	1	2	2	3	3	3
1.9	1.378	1.382	1.386	1.389	1.393	1.396	1.400	1.404	1.407	1.411	0	1	1	1	2	2	3	3	3
2.0	1.414	1.418	1.421	1.425	1.428	1.432	1.435	1.439	1.442	1.446	0	1	1	1	2	2	2	3	3
2.1	1.449	1.453	1.456	1.459	1.463	1.466	1.470	1.473	1.476	1.480	0	1	1	1	2	2	2	3	3
2.2	1.483	1.487	1.490	1.493	1.497	1.500	1.503	1.507	1.510	1.513	0	1	1	1	2	2	2	3	3
2.3	1.517	1.520	1.523	1.526	1.530	1.533	1.536	1.539	1.543	1.546	0	1	1	1	2	2	2	3	3
2.4	1.549	1.552	1.556	1.559	1.562	1.565	1.568	1.572	1.575	1.578	0	1	1	1	2	2	2	3	3
2.5	1.581	1.584	1.587	1.591	1.594	1.597	1.600	1.603	1.606	1.609	0	1	1	1	2	2	2	3	3
2.6	1.612	1.616	1.619	1.622	1.625	1.628	1.631	1.634	1.637	1.640	0	1	1	1	2	2	2	2	3
2.7	1.643	1.646	1.649	1.652	1.655	1.658	1.661	1.664	1.667	1.670	0	1	1	1	2	2	2	2	3
2.8	1.673	1.676	1.679	1.682	1.685	1.688	1.691	1.694	1.697	1.700	0	1	1	1	2	2	2	2	3
2.9	1.703	1.706	1.709	1.712	1.715	1.718	1.720	1.723	1.726	1.729	0	1	1	1	1	2	2	2	3
3.0	1.732	1.735	1.738	1.741	1.744	1.746	1.749	1.752	1.755	1.758	0	1	1	1	1	2	2	2	3
3.1	1.761	1.764	1.766	1.769	1.772	1.775	1.778	1.780	1.783	1.786	0	1	1	1	1	2	2	2	3
3.2	1.789	1.792	1.794	1.797	1.800	1.803	1.806	1.808	1.811	1.814	0	1	1	1	1	2	2	2	2
3.3	1.817	1.819	1.822	1.825	1.828	1.830	1.833	1.836	1.838	1.841	0	1	1	1	1	2	2	2	2
3.4	1.844	1.847	1.849	1.852	1.855	1.857	1.860	1.863	1.865	1.868	0	1	1	1	1	2	2	2	2
3.5	1.871	1.873	1.876	1.879	1.881	1.884	1.887	1.889	1.892	1.895	0	1	1	1	1	2	2	2	2
3.6	1.897	1.900	1.903	1.905	1.908	1.910	1.913	1.916	1.918	1.921	0	1	1	1	1	2	2	2	2
3.7	1.924	1.926	1.929	1.931	1.934	1.936	1.939	1.942	1.944	1.947	0	1	1	1	1	2	2	2	2
3.8	1.949	1.952	1.954	1.957	1.960	1.962	1.965	1.967	1.970	1.972	0	1	1	1	1	2	2	2	2
3.9	1.975	1.977	1.980	1.982	1.985	1.987	1.990	1.992	1.995	1.997	0	1	1	1	1	2	2	2	2
4.0	2.000	2.002	2.005	2.007	2.010	2.012	2.015	2.017	2.020	2.022	0	0	1	1	1	1	2	2	2
4.1	2.025	2.027	2.030	2.032	2.035	2.037	2.040	2.042	2.045	2.047	0	0	1	1	1	1	2	2	2
4.2	2.049	2.052	2.054	2.057	2.059	2.062	2.064	2.066	2.069	2.071	0	0	1	1	1	1	2	2	2
4.3	2.074	2.076	2.078	2.081	2.083	2.086	2.088	2.090	2.093	2.095	0	0	1	1	1	1	2	2	2
4.4	2.098	2.100	2.102	2.105	2.107	2.110	2.112	2.114	2.117	2.119	0	0	1	1	1	1	2	2	2
4.5	2.121	2.124	2.126	2.128	2.131	2.133	2.135	2.138	2.140	2.142	0	0	1	1	1	1	2	2	2
4.6	2.145	2.147	2.149	2.152	2.154	2.156	2.159	2.161	2.163	2.166	0	0	1	1	1	1	2	2	2
4.7	2.168	2.170	2.173	2.175	2.177	2.179	2.182	2.184	2.186	2.189	0	0	1	1	1	1	2	2	2
4.8	2.191	2.193	2.195	2.198	2.200	2.202	2.205	2.207	2.209	2.211	0	0	1	1	1	1	2	2	2
4.9	2.214	2.216	2.218	2.220	2.223	2.225	2.227	2.229	2.232	2.234	0	0	1	1	1	1	2	2	2
5.0	2.236	2.238	2.241	2.243	2.245	2.247	2.249	2.252	2.254	2.256	0	0	1	1	1	1	2	2	2
5.1	2.258	2.261	2.263	2.265	2.267	2.269	2.272	2.274	2.276	2.278	0	0	1	1	1	1	2	2	2
5.2	2.280	2.283	2.285	2.287	2.289	2.291	2.293	2.296	2.298	2.300	0	0	1	1	1	1	2	2	2
5.3	2.302	2.304	2.307	2.309	2.311	2.313	2.315	2.317	2.319	2.322	0	0	1	1	1	1	2	2	2
5.4	2.324	2.326	2.328	2.330	2.332	2.335	2.337	2.339	2.341	2.343	0	0	1	1	1	1	1	2	2
5.5	2.345	2.347	2.349	2.352	2.354	2.356	2.358	2.360	2.362	2.364	0	0	1	1	1	1	1	2	2
5.6	2.366	2.369	2.371	2.373	2.375	2.377	2.379	2.381	2.383	2.385	0	0	1	1	1	1	1	2	2
5.7	2.387	2.390	2.392	2.394	2.396	2.398	2.400	2.402	2.404	2.406	0	0	1	1	1	1	1	2	2
5.8	2.408	2.410	2.412	2.415	2.417	2.419	2.421	2.423	2.425	2.427	0	0	1	1	1	1	1	2	2
5.9	2.429	2.431	2.433	2.435	2.437	2.439	2.441	2.443	2.445	2.447	0	0	1	1	1	1	1	2	2
6.0	2.449	2.452	2.454	2.456	2.458	2.460	2.462	2.464	2.466	2.468	0	0	1	1	1	1	1	2	2
6.1	2.470	2.472	2.474	2.476	2.478	2.480	2.482	2.484	2.486	2.488	0	0	1	1	1	1	1	2	2
N	0	1	2	3	4	5	6	7	8	9	1	2	3	4	5	6	7	8	9

SQUARE ROOTS OF NUMBERS

N	0	1	2	3	4	5	6	7	8	9	1	2	3	4	5	6	7	8	9
6.2	2.490	2.492	2.494	2.496	2.498	2.500	2.502	2.504	2.506	2.508	0	0	1	1	1	1	1	2	2
6.3	2.510	2.512	2.514	2.516	2.518	2.520	2.522	2.524	2.526	2.528	0	0	1	1	1	1	1	2	2
6.4	2.530	2.532	2.534	2.536	2.538	2.540	2.542	2.544	2.546	2.548	0	0	1	1	1	1	1	2	2
6.5	2.550	2.551	2.553	2.555	2.557	2.559	2.561	2.563	2.565	2.567	0	0	1	1	1	1	1	2	2
6.6	2.569	2.571	2.573	2.575	2.577	2.579	2.581	2.583	2.585	2.587	0	0	1	1	1	1	1	2	2
6.7	2.588	2.590	2.592	2.594	2.596	2.598	2.600	2.602	2.604	2.606	0	0	1	1	1	1	1	2	2
6.8	2.608	2.610	2.612	2.613	2.615	2.617	2.619	2.621	2.623	2.625	0	0	1	1	1	1	1	2	2
6.9	2.627	2.629	2.631	2.632	2.634	2.636	2.638	2.640	2.642	2.644	0	0	1	1	1	1	1	2	2
7,0	2.646	2.648	2.650	2.651	2.653	2.655	2.657	2.659	2.661	2.663	0	0	1	1	1	1	1	2	2
7.1	2.665	2.666	2.668	2.670	2.672	2.674	2.676	2.678	2.680	2.681	0	0	1	1	1	1	1	1	2
7.2	2.683	2.685	2.687	2.689	2.691	2.693	2.694	2.696	2.698	2.700	0	0	1	1	1	1	1	1	2
7.3	2.702	2.704	2.706	2.707	2.709	2.711	2.713	2.715	2.717	2.718	0	0	1	1	1	1	1	1	2
7.4	2.720	2.722	2.724	2.726	2.728	2.729	2.731	2.733	2.735	2.737	0	0	1	1	1	1	1	1	2
7.5	2.739	2.740	2.742	2.744	2.746	2.748	2.750	2.751	2.753	2.755	0	0	1	1	1	1	1	1	2
7.6	2.757	2.759	2.760	2.762	2.764	2.766	2.768	2.769	2.771	2.773	0	0	1	1	1	1	1	1	2
7.7	2.775	2.777	2.778	2.780	2.782	2.784	2.786	2.787	2.789	2.791	0	0	1	1	1	1	1	1	2
7.8	2.793	2.795	2.796	2.798	2.800	2.802	2.804	2.805	2.807	2.809	0	0	1	1	1	1	1	1	2
7.9	2.811	2.812	2.814	2.816	2.818	2.820	2.821	2.823	2.825	2.827	0	0	1	1	1	1	1	1	2
8.0	2.828	2.830	2.832	2.834	2.835	2.837	2.839	2.841	2.843	2.844	0	0	1	1	1	1	1	1	2
8.1	2.846	2.848	2.850	2.851	2.853	2.855	2.857	2.858	2.860	2.862	0	0	1	1	1	1	1	1	2
8.2	2.864	2.865	2.867	2.869	2.871	2.872	2.874	2.876	2.877	2.879	0	0	1	1	1	1	1	1	2
8.3	2.881	2.883	2.884	2.886	2.888	2.890	2.891	2.893	2.895	2.897	0	0	1	1	1	1	1	1	2
8.4	2.898	2.900	2.902	2.903	2.905	2.907	2.909	2.910	2.912	2.914	0	0	1	1	1	1	1	1	2
8.5	2.915	2.917	2.919	2.921	2.922	2.924	2.926	2.927	2.929	2.931	0	0	1	1	1	1	1	1	2
8.6	2.933	2.934	2.936	2.938	2.939	2.941	2.943	2.944	2.946	2.948	0	0	1	1	1	1	1	1	2
8.7	2.950	2.951	2.953	2.955	2.956	2.958	2.960	2.961	2.963	2.965	0	0	1	1	1	1	1	1	2
8.8	2.966	2.968	2.970	2.972	2.973	2.975	2.977	2.978	2.980	2.982	0	0	1	1	1	1	1	1	2
8.9	2.983	2.985	2.987	2.988	2.990	2.992	2.993	2.995	2.997	2.998	0	0	1	1	1	1	1	1	2
9.0	3.000	3.002	3.003	3.005	3.007	3.008	3.010	3.012	3.013	3.015	0	0	0	1	1	1	1	1	1
9.1	3.017	3.018	3.020	3.022	3.023	3.025	3.027	3.028	3.030	3.032	0	0	0	1	1	1	1	1	1
9.2	3.033	3.035	3.036	3.038	3.040	3.041	3.043	3.045	3.046	3.048	0	0	0	1	1	1	1	1	1
9.3	3.050	3.051	3.053	3.055	3.056	3.058	3.059	3.061	3.063	3.064	0	0	0	1	1	1	1	1	1
9.4	3.066	3.068	3.069	3.071	3.072	3.074	3.076	3.077	3.079	3.081	0	0	0	1	1	1	1	1	1
9.5	3.082	3.084	3.085	3.087	3.089	3.090	3.092	3.094	3.095	3.097	0	0	0	1	1	1	1	1	1
9.6	3.098	3.100	3.102	3.103	3.105	3.106	3.108	3.110	3.111	3.113	0	0	0	1	1	1	1	1	1
9.7	3.114	3.116	3.118	3.119	3.121	3.122	3.124	3.126	3.127	3.129	0	0	0	1	1	1	1	1	1
9.8	3.130	3.132	3.134	3.135	3.137	3.138	3.140	3.142	3.143	3.145	0	0	0	1	1	1	1	1	1
9.9	3.146	3.148	3.150	3.151	3.153	3.154	3.156	3.158	3.159	3.161	0	0	0	1	1	1	1	1	1
10.	3.162	3.178	3.194	3.209	3.225	3.240	3.256	3.271	3.286	3.302	1	3	5	6	8	9	11	12	14
11.	3.317	3.332	3.347	3.362	3.376	3.391	3.406	3.421	3.435	3.450	1	3	4	6	7	9	10	12	13
12.	3.464	3.479	3.493	3.507	3.521	3.536	3.550	3.564	3.578	3.592	1	3	4	6	7	8	10	11	13
13.	3.606	3.619	3.633	3.647	3.661	3.674	3.688	3.701	3.715	3.728	1	3	4	5	7	8	10	11	12
14.	3.742	3.755	3.768	3.782	3.795	3.808	3.821	3.834	3.847	3.860	1	3	4	5	7	8	9	11	12
15.	3.873	3.886	3.899	3.912	3.924	3.937	3.950	3.962	3.975	3.987	1	3	4	5	6	8	9	10	11
16.	4.000	4.012	4.025	4.037	4.050	4.062	4.074	4.087	4.099	4.111	1	2	4	5	6	7	9	10	11
17.	4.123	4.135	4.147	4.159	4.171	4.183	4.195	4.207	4.219	4.231	1	2	4	5	6	7	8	10	11
18.	4.243	4.254	4.266	4.278	4.290	4.301	4.313	4.324	4.336	4.347	1	2	3	5	6	7	8	9	10
19.	4.359	4.370	4.382	4.393	4.405	4.416	4.427	4.438	4.450	4.461	1	2	3	5	6	7	8	9	10
20.	4.472	4.483	4.494	4.506	4.517	4.528	4.539	4.550	4.561	4.572	1	2	3	4	6	7	8	9	10
21.	4.583	4.593	4.604	4.615	4.626	4.637	4.648	4.658	4.669	4.680	1	2	3	4	5	6	8	9	10
22.	4.690	4.701	4.712	4.722	4.733	4.743	4.754	4.764	4.775	4.785	1	2	3	4	5	6	7	8	9
23.	4.796	4.806	4.817	4.827	4.837	4.848	4.858	4.868	4.879	4.889	1	2	3	4	5	6	7	8	9
24.	4.899	4.909	4.919	4.930	4.940	4.950	4.960	4.970	4.980	4.990	1	2	3	4	5	6	7	8	9
25.	5.000	5.010	5.020	5.030	5.040	5.050	5.060	5.070	5.079	5.089	1	2	3	4	5	6	7	8	9
N	0	1	2	3	4	5	6	7	8	9	1	2	3	4	5	6	7	8	9

SQUARE ROOTS OF NUMBERS

N	0	1	2	3	4	5	6	7	8	9	1	2	3	4	5	6	7	8	9
26.	5.099	5.109	5.119	5.128	5.138	5.148	5.158	5.167	5.177	5.187	1	2	3	4	5	6	7	8	9
27.	5.196	5.206	5.215	5.225	5.235	5.244	5.254	5.263	5.273	5.282	1	2	3	4	5	6	7	8	9
28.	5.292	5.301	5.310	5.320	5.329	5.339	5.348	5.357	5.367	5.376	1	2	3	4	5	6	7	7	8
29.	5.385	5.394	5.404	5.413	5.422	5.431	5.441	5.450	5.459	5.468	1	2	3	4	5	5	6	7	8
30.	5.477	5.486	5.495	5.505	5.514	5.523	5.532	5.541	5.550	5.559	1	2	3	4	4	5	6	7	8
31.	5.568	5.577	5.586	5.595	5.604	5.612	5.621	5.630	5.639	5.648	1	2	3	3	4	5	6	7	8
32.	5.657	5.666	5.675	5.683	5.692	5.701	5.710	5.718	5.727	5.736	1	2	3	3	4	5	6	7	8
33.	5.745	5.753	5.762	5.771	5.779	5.788	5.797	5.805	5.814	5.822	1	2	3	3	4	5	6	7	8
34.	5.831	5.840	5.848	5.857	5.865	5.874	5.882	5.891	5.899	5.908	1	2	3	3	4	5	6	7	8
35.	5.916	5.925	5.933	5.941	5.950	5.958	5.967	5.975	5.983	5.992	1	2	2	3	4	5	6	7	8
36.	6.000	6.008	6.017	6.025	6.033	6.042	6.050	6.058	6.066	6.075	1	2	2	3	4	5	6	7	7
37.	6.083	6.091	6.099	6.107	6.116	6.124	6.132	6.140	6.148	6.156	1	2	2	3	4	5	6	7	7
38.	6.164	6.173	6.181	6.189	6.197	6.205	6.213	6.221	6.229	6.237	1	2	2	3	4	5	6	6	7
39.	6.245	6.253	6.261	6.269	6.277	6.285	6.293	6.301	6.309	6.317	1	2	2	3	4	5	6	6	7
40.	6.325	6.332	6.340	6.348	6.356	6.364	6.372	6.380	6.387	6.395	1	2	2	3	4	5	6	6	7
41.	6.403	6.411	6.419	6.427	6.434	6.442	6.450	6.458	6.465	6.473	1	2	2	3	4	5	5	6	7
42.	6.481	6.488	6.496	6.504	6.512	6.519	6.527	6.535	6.542	6.550	1	2	2	3	4	5	5	6	7
43.	6.557	6.565	6.573	6.580	6.588	6.595	6.603	6.611	6.618	6.626	1	2	2	3	4	5	5	6	7
44.	6.633	6.641	6.648	6.656	6.663	6.671	6.678	6.686	6.693	6.701	1	2	2	3	4	5	6	6	7
45.	6.708	6.716	6.723	6.731	6.738	6.745	6.753	6.760	6.768	6.775	1	1	2	3	4	4	5	6	7
46.	6.782	6.790	6.797	6.804	6.812	6.819	6.826	6.834	6.841	6.848	1	1	2	3	4	4	5	6	7
47.	6.856	6.863	6.870	6.877	6.885	6.892	6.899	6.907	6.914	6.921	1	1	2	3	4	4	5	6	7
48.	6.928	6.935	6.943	6.950	6.957	6.964	6.971	6.979	6.986	6.993	1	1	2	3	4	4	5	6	6
49.	7.000	7.007	7.014	7.021	7.029	7.036	7.043	7.050	7.057	7.064	1	1	2	3	4	4	5	6	6
50.	7.071	7.078	7.085	7.092	7.099	7.106	7.113	7.120	7.127	7.134	1	1	2	3	4	4	5	6	6
51.	7.141	7.148	7.155	7.162	7.169	7.176	7.183	7.190	7.197	7.204	1	1	2	3	4	4	5	6	6
52.	7.211	7.218	7.225	7.232	7.239	7.246	7.253	7.259	7.266	7.273	1	1	2	3	4	4	5	6	6
53.	7.280	7.287	7.294	7.301	7.308	7.314	7.321	7.328	7.335	7.342	1	1	2	3	3	4	5	5	6
54.	7.348	7.355	7.362	7.369	7.376	7.382	7.389	7.396	7.403	7.409	1	1	2	3	4	4	5	5	6
55.	7.416	7.423	7.430	7.436	7.443	7.450	7.457	7.463	7.470	7.477	1	1	2	3	4	4	5	5	6
56.	7.483	7.490	7.497	7.503	7.510	7.517	7.523	7.530	7.537	7.543	1	1	2	3	3	4	5	5	6
57.	7.550	7.556	7.563	7.570	7.576	7.583	7.589	7.596	7.603	7.609	1	1	2	3	3	4	5	5	6
58.	7.616	7.622	7.629	7.635	7.642	7.649	7.655	7.662	7.668	7.675	1	1	2	3	3	4	5	5	6
59.	7.681	7.688	7.694	7.701	7.707	7.714	7.720	7.727	7.733	7.740	1	1	2	3	3	4	4	5	6
60.	7.746	7.752	7.759	7.765	7.772	7.778	7.785	7.791	7.797	7.804	1	1	2	3	3	4	4	5	6
61.	7.810	7.817	7.823	7.829	7.836	7.842	7.849	7.855	7.861	7.868	1	1	2	3	3	4	4	5	6
62.	7.874	7.880	7.887	7.893	7.899	7.906	7.912	7.918	7.925	7.931	1	1	2	3	3	4	4	5	6
63.	7.937	7.944	7.950	7.956	7.962	7.969	7.975	7.981	7.987	7.994	1	1	2	3	3	4	4	5	6
64.	8.000	8.006	8.012	8.019	8.025	8.031	8.037	8.044	8.050	8.056	1	1	2	2	3	4	4	5	6
65.	8.062	8.068	8.075	8.081	8.087	8.093	8.099	8.106	8.112	8.118	1	1	2	2	3	4	4	5	6
66.	8.124	8.130	8.136	8.142	8.149	8.155	8.161	8.167	8.173	8.179	1	1	2	2	3	4	4	5	5
67.	8.185	8.191	8.198	8.204	8.210	8.216	8.222	8.228	8.234	8.240	1	1	2	2	3	4	4	5	5
68.	8.246	8.252	8.258	8.264	8.270	8.276	8.283	8.289	8.295	8.301	1	1	2	2	3	4	4	5	5
69.	8.307	8.313	8.319	8.325	8.331	8.337	8.343	8.349	8.355	8.361	1	1	2	2	3	4	4	5	5
70.	8.367	8.373	8.379	8.385	8.390	8.396	8.402	8.408	8.414	8.420	1	1	2	2	3	4	4	5	5
71.	8.426	8.432	8.438	8.444	8.450	8.456	8.462	8.468	8.473	8.479	1	1	2	2	3	4	4	5	5
72.	8.485	8.491	8.497	8.503	8.509	8.515	8.521	8.526	8.532	8.538	1	1	2	2	3	3	4	5	5
73.	8.544	8.550	8.556	8.562	8.567	8.573	8.579	8.585	8.591	8.597	1	1	2	2	3	4	4	5	5
74.	8.602	8.608	8.614	8.620	8.626	8.631	8.637	8.643	8.649	8.654	1	1	2	2	3	3	4	5	5
75.	8.660	8.666	8.672	8.678	8.683	8.689	8.695	8.701	8.706	8.712	1	1	2	2	3	3	4	5	5
76.	8.718	8.724	8.729	8.735	8.741	8.746	8.752	8.758	8.764	8.769	1	1	2	2	3	3	4	4	5
77.	8.775	8.781	8.786	8.792	8.798	8.803	8.809	8.815	8.820	8.826	1	1	2	2	3	3	4	4	5
N	0	1	2	3	4	5	6	7	8	9	1	2	3	4	5	6	7	8	9

SQUARE ROOTS OF NUMBERS

N	0	1	2	3	4	5	6	7	8	9	1	2	3	4	5	6	7	8	9
78.	8.832	8.837	8.843	8.849	8.854	8.860	8.866	8.871	8.877	8.883	1	1	2	2	3	3	4	4	5
79.	8.888	8.894	8.899	8.905	8.911	8.916	8.922	8.927	8.933	8.939	1	1	2	2	3	3	4	4	5
80.	8.944	8.950	8.955	8.961	8.967	8.972	8.978	8.983	8.989	8.994	1	1	2	2	3	3	4	4	5
81.	9.000	9.006	9.011	9.017	9.022	9.028	9.033	9.039	9.044	9.050	1	1	2	2	3	3	4	4	5
82.	9.055	9.061	9.066	9.072	9.077	9.083	9.088	9.094	9.099	9.105	1	1	2	2	3	3	4	4	5
83.	9.110	9.116	9.121	9.127	9.132	9.138	9.143	9.149	9.154	9.160	1	1	2	2	3	3	4	4	5
84.	9.165	9.171	9.176	9.182	9.187	9.192	9.198	9.203	9.209	9.214	1	1	2	2	3	3	4	4	5
85.	9.220	9.225	9.230	9.236	9.241	9.247	9.252	9.257	9.263	9.268	1	1	2	2	3	3	4	4	5
86.	9.274	9.279	9.284	9.290	9.295	9.301	9.306	9.311	9.317	9.322	1	1	2	2	3	3	4	4	5
87.	9.327	9.333	9.338	9.343	9.349	9.354	9.359	9.365	9.370	9.375	1	1	2	2	3	3	4	4	5
88.	9.381	9.386	9.391	9.397	9.402	9.407	9.413	9.418	9.423	9.429	1	1	2	2	3	3	4	4	5
89.	9.434	9.439	9.445	9.450	9.455	9.460	9.466	9.471	9.476	9.482	1	1	2	2	3	3	4	4	5
90.	9.487	9.492	9.497	9.503	9.508	9.513	9.518	9.524	9.529	9.534	1	1	2	2	3	3	4	4	5
91.	9.539	9.545	9.550	9.555	9.560	9.566	9.571	9.576	9.581	9.586	1	1	2	2	3	3	4	4	5
92.	9.592	9.597	9.602	9.607	9.612	9.618	9.623	9.628	9.633	0.638	1	1	2	2	3	3	4	4	5
93.	9.644	9.649	9.654	9.659	9.664	9.670	9.675	9.680	9.685	9.690	1	1	2	2	3	3	4	4	5
94.	9.695	9.701	9.706	9.711	9.716	9.721	9.726	9.731	9.737	9.742	1	1	2	2	3	3	4	4	5
95.	9.747	9.752	9.757	9.762	9.767	9.772	9.778	9.783	9.788	9.793	1	1	2	2	3	3	4	4	5
96.	9.798	9.803	9.808	9.813	9.818	9.823	9.829	9.834	9.839	9.844	1	1	2	2	3	3	4	4	5
97.	9.849	9.854	9.859	9.864	9.869	9.874	9.879	9.884	9.889	9.894	1	1	2	2	3	3	4	4	5
98.	9.899	9.905	9.910	9.915	9.920	9.925	9.930	9.935	9.940	9.945	0	1	1	2	2	3	3	4	4
99.	9.950	9.955	9.960	9.965	9.970	9.975	9.980	9.985	9.990	9.995	0	1	1	2	2	3	3	4	4
100.	10.00																		
N	0	1	2	3	4	5	6	7	8	9	1	2	3	4	5	6	7	8	9

When the decimal point in N is moved 2, 4, 6, 8, ... places the decimal point in $\sqrt{N}$ is moved in the same direction 1, 2, 3, 4, ... places. For example, $\sqrt{0.262} = 0.5119$, $\sqrt{812} = 28.50$.

For example,

$$\sqrt{3894000} = \sqrt{3.894 \cdot 10^6} = 10^3(1.972 + 0.001) = 10^3 \cdot 1.973$$
$$= 1973 \text{ (approximately)}.$$

$$\sqrt{657800} = \sqrt{65.78 \cdot 10^4} = 10^2(8.106 + 0.005) = 10^2 \cdot 8.111$$
$$= 811.1 \text{ (approximately)}.$$

$$\sqrt{0.0005478} = \sqrt{5.478 \cdot 10^{-4}} = 10^{-2}(2.339 + 0.002)$$
$$= 10^{-2} \cdot 2.341 = 0.02341.$$

$$\sqrt{0.00004892} = \sqrt{48.92 \cdot 10^{-6}} = 10^{-3}(6.993 + 0.001)$$
$$= 10^{-3} \cdot 6.994 = 0.006994.$$

D. TABLES OF TRIGONOMETRIC RATIOS

The tables of trigonometric ratios (sine, cosine, and tangent) are so arranged that they contain the values of the ratios listed for every six minutes. For intermediate values corrections are provided in the three columns on the extreme right with the *Corrections*.

Since the step from one listing to the next one is only six minutes, the corrections are provided for one, two, three, four and five minutes.

For example, sin 34° 27' is computed as follows

$$
\begin{array}{ll}
& \sin 34° 24' = 0.5050 \\
\text{correction for} & \underline{ 3' = 0.0007} \\
& \sin 34° 27' = 0.5057
\end{array}
$$

The values of the cosine ratios are obtained by reading the table of cosines. Moreover, since the cosine ratio of 0° is 1, and the cosine ratio of 90° is 0, the cosine ratio decreases. Therefore, all the corrections for one, two, three, four, and five minutes are subtracted from the listed value.

For example, cos 24° 20' is computed as follows

$$
\begin{array}{ll}
& \cos 24° 18' = 0.9114 \\
\text{subtract correction for} & \underline{ 2' = 0.0002} \\
& \cos 24° 20' = 0.9112
\end{array}
$$

cos 56° 40' is computed as follows:

$$
\begin{array}{ll}
& \cos 56° 42' = 0.5490 \\
\text{add correction for} & \underline{ 2' = 0.0005} \\
& \cos 56° 40' = 0.5495
\end{array}
$$

The table of the tangent ratios has the same properties as the table of the sine ratios, and the computation of the tangent ratios is performed in the same manner as the computation of the sine ratios.

The reverse process of computation with these tables (that is, when the value of the ratio is given and the angle is to be computed) is performed in the same manner as the reverse process of computation with logarithms. For example, if the sine ratio is 0.6631, then

$$
\begin{array}{ll}
& 0.6626 = \sin 41° 30', \\
\text{add the correction which is} & \underline{0.0005 \text{ and add} \quad 2'} \\
& 0.6631 = \sin 41° 32'
\end{array}
$$

If 0.7853 is the cosine ratio then $\quad 0.7859 = \cos 38° 6'$
subtract the correction which is $\underline{0.0006 \text{ and add} \quad 3'}$
$$0.7853 = \cos 38° 9'$$

SINE RATIO

	0'	6'	12'	18'	24'	30'	36'	42'	48'	54'	1	2	3	4	5
0°	0000	0017	0035	0052	0070	0087	0105	0122	0140	0157	3	6	9	12	15
1	0175	0192	0209	0227	0244	0262	0279	0297	0314	0332	3	6	9	12	15
2	0349	0366	0384	0401	0419	0436	0454	0471	0488	0506	3	6	9	12	15
3	0523	0541	0558	0576	0593	0610	0628	0645	0663	0680	3	6	9	12	15
4	0698	0715	0732	0750	0767	0785	0802	0819	0837	0854	3	6	9	12	15
5	0872	0889	0906	0924	0941	0958	0976	0993	1011	1028	3	6	9	12	14
6	1045	1063	1080	1097	1115	1132	1149	1167	1184	1201	3	6	9	12	14
7	1219	1236	1253	1271	1288	1305	1323	1340	1357	1374	3	6	9	12	14
8	1392	1409	1426	1444	1461	1478	1495	1513	1530	1547	3	6	9	12	14
9	1564	1582	1599	1616	1633	1650	1668	1685	1702	1719	3	6	9	12	14
10	1736	1754	1771	1788	1805	1822	1840	1857	1874	1891	3	6	9	12	14
11	1908	1925	1942	1959	1977	1994	2011	2028	2045	2062	3	6	9	11	14
12	2079	2096	2113	2130	2147	2164	2181	2198	2215	2232	3	6	9	11	14
13	2250	2267	2284	2300	2317	2334	2351	2368	2385	2402	3	6	8	11	14
14	2419	2436	2453	2470	2487	2504	2521	2538	2554	2571	3	6	8	11	14
15	2588	2605	2622	2639	2656	2672	2689	2706	2723	2740	3	6	8	11	14
16	2756	2773	2790	2807	2823	2840	2857	2874	2890	2907	3	6	8	11	14
17	2924	2940	2957	2974	2990	3007	3024	3040	3057	3074	3	6	8	11	14
18	3090	3107	3123	3140	3156	3173	3190	3206	3223	3239	3	6	8	11	14
19	3256	3272	3289	3305	3322	3338	3355	3371	3387	3404	3	5	8	11	14
20	3420	3437	3453	3469	3486	3502	3518	3535	3551	3567	3	5	8	11	14
21	3584	3600	3616	3633	3649	3665	3681	3697	3714	3730	3	5	8	11	14
22	3746	3762	3778	3795	3811	3827	3843	3859	3875	3891	3	5	8	11	14
23	3907	3923	3939	3955	3971	3987	4003	4019	4035	4051	3	5	8	11	14
24	4067	4083	4099	4115	4131	4147	4163	4179	4195	4210	3	5	8	11	13
25	4226	4242	4258	4274	4289	4305	4321	4337	4352	4368	3	5	8	11	13
26	4384	4399	4415	4431	4446	4462	4478	4493	4509	4524	3	5	8	10	13
27	4540	4555	4571	4586	4602	4617	4633	4648	4664	4679	3	5	8	10	13
28	4695	4710	4726	4741	4756	4772	4787	4802	4818	4833	3	5	8	10	13
29	4848	4863	4879	4894	4909	4924	4939	4955	4970	4985	3	5	8	10	13
30	5000	5015	5030	5045	5060	5075	5090	5105	5120	5135	3	5	8	10	13
31	5150	5165	5180	5195	5210	5225	5240	5255	5270	5284	2	5	7	10	12
32	5299	5314	5329	5344	5358	5373	5388	5402	5417	5432	2	5	7	10	12
33	5446	5461	5476	5490	5505	5519	5534	5548	5563	5577	2	5	7	10	12
34	5592	5606	5621	5635	5650	5664	5678	5693	5707	5721	2	5	7	10	12
35	5736	5750	5764	5779	5793	5807	5821	5835	5850	5864	2	5	7	10	12
36	5878	5892	5906	5920	5934	5948	5962	5976	5990	6004	2	5	7	9	12
37	6018	6032	6046	6060	6074	6088	6101	6115	6129	6143	2	5	7	9	12
38	6157	6170	6184	6198	6211	6225	6239	6252	6266	6280	2	5	7	9	11
39	6293	6307	6320	6334	6347	6361	6374	6388	6401	6414	2	4	7	9	11
40	6428	6441	6455	6468	6481	6494	6508	6521	6534	6547	2	4	7	9	11
41	6561	6574	6587	6600	6613	6626	6639	6652	6665	6678	2	4	7	9	11
42	6691	6704	6717	6730	6743	6756	6769	6782	6794	6807	2	4	6	9	11
43	6820	6833	6845	6858	6871	6884	6896	6909	6921	6934	2	4	6	8	11
44	6947	6959	6972	6984	6997	7009	7022	7034	7046	7059	2	4	6	8	10

SINE RATIO

	0'	6'	12'	18'	24'	30'	36'	42'	48'	54'	1	2	3	4	5
45°	7071	7083	7096	7108	7120	7133	7145	7157	7169	7181	2	4	6	8	10
46	7193	7206	7218	7230	7242	7254	7266	7278	7290	7302	2	4	6	8	10
47	7314	7325	7337	7349	7361	7373	7385	7396	7408	7420	2	4	6	8	10
48	7431	7443	7455	7466	7478	7490	7501	7513	7524	7536	2	4	6	8	10
49	7547	7558	7570	7581	7593	7604	7615	7627	7638	7649	2	4	6	8	9
50	7660	7672	7683	7694	7705	7716	7727	7738	7749	7760	2	4	6	7	9
51	7771	7782	7793	7804	7815	7826	7837	7848	7859	7869	2	4	5	7	9
52	7880	7891	7902	7912	7923	7934	7944	7955	7965	7976	2	4	5	7	9
53	7986	7997	8007	8018	8028	8039	8049	8059	8070	8080	2	3	5	7	9
54	8090	8100	8111	8121	8131	8141	8151	8161	8171	8181	2	3	5	7	8
55	8192	8202	8211	8221	8231	8241	8251	8261	8271	8281	2	3	5	7	8
56	8290	8300	8310	8320	8329	8339	8348	8358	8368	8377	2	3	5	6	8
57	8387	8396	8406	8415	8425	8434	8443	8453	8462	8471	2	3	5	6	8
58	8480	8490	8499	8508	8517	8526	8536	8545	8554	8563	2	3	5	6	8
59	8572	8581	8590	8599	8607	8616	8625	8634	8643	8652	1	3	4	6	7
60	8660	8669	8678	8686	8695	8704	8712	8721	8729	8738	1	3	4	6	7
61	8746	8755	8763	8771	8780	8788	8796	8805	8813	8821	1	3	4	6	7
62	8829	8838	8846	8854	8862	8870	8878	8886	8894	8902	1	3	4	5	7
63	8910	8918	8926	8934	8942	8949	8957	8965	8973	8980	1	3	4	5	6
64	8988	8996	9003	9011	9018	9026	9033	9041	9048	9056	1	3	4	5	6
65	9063	9070	9078	9085	9092	9100	9107	9114	9121	9128	1	2	4	5	6
66	9135	9143	9150	9157	9164	9171	9178	9184	9191	9198	1	2	3	5	6
67	9205	9212	9219	9225	9232	9239	9245	9252	9259	9265	1	2	3	4	6
68	9272	9278	9285	9291	9298	9304	9311	9317	9323	9330	1	2	3	4	5
69	9336	9342	9348	9354	9361	9367	9373	9379	9385	9391	1	2	3	4	5
70	9397	9403	9409	9415	9421	9426	9432	9438	9444	9449	1	2	3	4	5
71	9455	9461	9466	9472	9478	9483	9489	9494	9500	9505	1	2	3	4	5
72	9511	9516	9521	9527	9532	9537	9542	9548	9553	9558	1	2	3	4	4
73	9563	9568	9573	9578	9583	9588	9593	9598	9603	9608	1	2	2	3	4
74	9613	9617	9622	9627	9632	9636	9641	9646	9650	9655	1	2	2	3	4
75	9659	9664	9668	9673	9677	9681	9686	9690	9694	9699	1	1	2	3	4
76	9703	9707	9711	9715	9720	9724	9728	9732	9736	9740	1	1	2	3	3
77	9744	9748	9751	9755	9759	9763	9767	9770	9774	9778	1	1	2	3	3
78	9781	9785	9789	9792	9796	9799	9803	9806	9810	9813	1	1	2	2	3
79	9816	9820	9823	9826	9829	9833	9836	9839	9842	9845	1	1	2	2	3
80	9848	9851	9854	9857	9860	9863	9866	9869	9871	9874	0	1	1	2	2
81	9877	9880	9882	9885	9888	9890	9893	9895	9898	9900	0	1	1	2	2
82	9903	9905	9907	9910	9912	9914	9917	9919	9921	9923	0	1	1	2	2
83	9925	9928	9930	9932	9934	9936	9938	9940	9942	9943	0	1	1	1	2
84	9945	9947	9949	9951	9952	9954	9956	9957	9959	9960	0	1	1	1	1
85	9962	9963	9965	9966	9968	9969	9971	9972	9973	9974	0	0	1	1	1
86	9976	9977	9978	9979	9980	9981	9982	9983	9984	9985	0	0	1	1	1
87	9986	9987	9988	9989	9990	9990	9991	9992	9993	9993	0	0	0	1	1
88	9994	9995	9995	9996	9996	9997	9997	9997	9998	9998	0	0	0	0	0
89	9998	9999	9999	9999	9999	1.000 nearly	1.000 nearly	1.000 nearly	1.000 nearly	1.000 nearly	0	0	0	0	0

COSINE RATIO

	0'	6'	12'	18'	24'	30'	36'	42'	48'	54'	1	2	3	4	5
0°	1.000	1.000 nearly	1.000 nearly	1.000 nearly	1.000 nearly	9999	9999	9999	9999	9999	0 0 0			0	0
1	9998	9998	9998	9997	9997	9997	9996	9996	9995	9995	0 0 0			0	0
2	9994	9993	9993	9992	9991	9990	9990	9989	9988	9987	0 0 0			1	1
3	9986	9985	9984	9983	9982	9981	9980	9979	9978	9977	0 0 1			1	1
4	9976	9974	9973	9972	9971	9969	9968	9966	9965	9963	0 0 1			1	1
5	9962	9960	9959	9957	9956	9954	9952	9951	9949	9947	0 1 1			1	2
6	9945	9943	9942	9940	9938	9936	9934	9932	9930	9928	0 1 1			1	2
7	9925	9923	9921	9919	9917	9914	9912	9910	9907	9905	0 1 1			2	2
8	9903	9900	9898	9895	9893	9890	9888	9885	9882	9880	0 1 1			2	2
9	9877	9874	9871	9869	9866	9863	9860	9857	9854	9851	0 1 1			2	2
10	9848	9845	9842	9839	9836	9833	9829	9826	9823	9820	1 1 2			2	3
11	9816	9813	9810	9806	9803	9799	9796	9792	9789	9785	1 1 2			2	3
12	9781	9778	9774	9770	9767	9763	9759	9755	9751	9748	1 1 2			3	3
13	9744	9740	9736	9732	9728	9724	9720	9715	9711	9707	1 1 2			3	3
14	9703	9699	9694	9690	9686	9681	9677	9673	9668	9664	1 1 2			3	4
15	9659	9655	9650	9646	9641	9636	9632	9627	9622	9617	1 2 2			3	4
16	9613	9608	9603	9598	9593	9588	9583	9578	9573	9568	1 2 2			3	4
17	9563	9558	9553	9548	9542	9537	9532	9527	9521	9516	1 2 3			4	4
18	9511	9505	9500	9494	9489	9483	9478	9472	9466	9461	1 2 3			4	5
19	9455	9449	9444	9438	9432	9426	9421	9415	9409	9403	1 2 3			4	5
20	9397	9391	9385	9379	9373	9367	9361	9354	9348	9342	1 2 3			4	5
21	9336	9330	9323	9317	9311	9304	9298	9291	9285	9278	1 2 3			4	5
22	9272	9265	9259	9252	9245	9239	9232	9225	9219	9212	1 2 3			4	6
23	9205	9198	9191	9184	9178	9171	9164	9157	9150	9143	1 2 3			5	6
24	9135	9128	9121	9114	9107	9100	9092	9085	9078	9070	1 2 4			5	6
25	9063	9056	9048	9041	9033	9026	9018	9011	9003	8996	1 3 4			5	6
26	8988	8980	8973	8965	8957	8949	8942	8934	8926	8918	1 3 4			5	6
27	8910	8902	8894	8886	8878	8870	8862	8854	8846	8838	1 3 4			5	7
28	8829	8821	8813	8805	8796	8788	8780	8771	8763	8755	1 3 4			6	7
29	8746	8738	8729	8721	8712	8704	8695	8686	8678	8669	1 3 4			6	7
30	8660	8652	8643	8634	8625	8616	8607	8599	8590	8581	1 3 4			6	7
31	8572	8563	8554	8545	8536	8526	8517	8508	8499	8490	2 3 5			6	8
32	8480	8471	8462	8453	8443	8434	8425	8415	8406	8396	2 3 5			6	8
33	8387	8377	8368	8358	8348	8339	8329	8320	8310	8300	2 3 5			6	8
34	8290	8281	8271	8261	8251	8241	8231	8221	8211	8202	2 3 5			7	8
35	8192	8181	8171	8161	8151	8141	8131	8121	8111	8100	2 3 5			7	8
36	8090	8080	8070	8059	8049	8039	8028	8018	8007	7997	2 3 5			7	9
37	7986	7976	7965	7955	7944	7934	7923	7912	7902	7891	2 4 5			7	9
38	7880	7869	7859	7848	7837	7826	7815	7804	7793	7782	2 4 5			7	9
39	7771	7760	7749	7738	7727	7716	7705	7694	7683	7672	2 4 6			7	9
40	7660	7649	7638	7627	7615	7604	7593	7581	7570	7559	2 4 6			8	9
41	7547	7536	7524	7513	7501	7490	7478	7466	7455	7443	2 4 6			8	10
42	7431	7420	7408	7396	7385	7373	7361	7349	7337	7325	2 4 6			8	10
43	7314	7302	7290	7278	7266	7254	7242	7230	7218	7206	2 4 6			8	10
44	7193	7181	7169	7157	7145	7133	7120	7108	7096	7083	2 4 6			8	10

COSINE RATIO

N	0'	6'	12'	18'	24'	30'	36'	42'	48'	54'	1	2	3	4	5
45°	7071	7059	7046	7034	7022	7009	6997	6984	6972	6959	2	4	6	8	10
46	6947	6934	6921	6909	6896	6884	6871	6858	6845	6833	2	4	6	8	11
47	6820	6807	6794	6782	6769	6756	6743	6730	6717	6704	2	4	6	9	11
48	6691	6678	6665	6652	6639	6626	6613	6600	6587	6574	2	4	7	9	11
49	6561	6547	6534	6521	6508	6494	6481	6468	6455	6441	2	4	7	9	11
50	6428	6414	6401	6388	6374	6361	6347	6334	6320	6307	2	4	7	9	11
51	6293	6280	6266	6252	6239	6225	6211	6198	6184	6170	2	5	7	9	11
52	6157	6143	6129	6115	6101	6088	6074	6060	6046	6032	2	5	7	9	12
53	6018	6004	5990	5976	5962	5948	5934	5920	5906	5892	2	5	7	9	12
54	5878	5864	5850	5835	5821	5807	5793	5779	5764	5750	2	5	7	9	12
55	5736	5721	5707	5693	5678	5664	5650	5635	5621	5606	2	5	7	10	12
56	5592	5577	5563	5548	5534	5519	5505	5490	5476	5461	2	5	7	10	12
57	5446	5432	5417	5402	5388	5373	5358	5344	5329	5314	2	5	7	10	12
58	5299	5284	5270	5255	5240	5225	5210	5195	5180	5165	2	5	7	10	12
59	5150	5135	5120	5105	5090	5075	5060	5045	5030	5015	3	5	8	10	13
60	5000	4985	4970	4955	4939	4924	4909	4894	4879	4863	3	5	8	10	13
61	4848	4833	4818	4802	4787	4772	4756	4741	4726	4710	3	5	8	10	13
62	4695	4679	4664	4648	4633	4617	4602	4586	4571	4555	3	5	8	10	13
63	4540	4524	4509	4493	4478	4462	4446	4431	4415	4399	3	5	8	10	13
64	4384	4368	4352	4337	4321	4305	4289	4274	4258	4242	3	5	8	11	13
65	4226	4210	4195	4179	4163	4147	4131	4115	4099	4083	3	5	8	11	13
66	4067	4051	4035	4019	4003	3987	3971	3955	3939	3923	3	5	8	11	14
67	3907	3891	3875	3859	3843	3827	3811	3795	3778	3762	3	5	8	11	14
68	3746	3730	3714	3697	3681	3665	3649	3633	3616	3600	3	5	8	11	14
69	3584	3567	3551	3535	3518	3502	3486	3469	3453	3437	3	5	8	11	14
70	3420	3404	3387	3371	3355	3338	3322	3305	3289	3272	3	5	8	11	14
71	3256	3239	3223	3206	3190	3173	3156	3140	3123	3107	3	6	8	11	14
72	3090	3074	3057	3040	3024	3007	2990	2974	2957	2940	3	6	8	11	14
73	2924	2907	2890	2874	2857	2840	2823	2807	2790	2773	3	6	8	11	14
74	2756	2740	2723	2706	2689	2672	2656	2639	2622	2605	3	6	8	11	14
75	2588	2571	2554	2538	2521	2504	2487	2470	2453	2436	3	6	8	11	14
76	2419	2402	2385	2368	2351	2334	2317	2300	2284	2267	3	6	8	11	14
77	2250	2233	2215	2198	2181	2164	2147	2130	2113	2096	3	6	9	11	14
78	2079	2062	2045	2028	2011	1994	1977	1959	1942	1925	3	6	9	11	14
79	1908	1891	1874	1857	1840	1822	1805	1788	1771	1754	3	6	9	12	14
80	1736	1719	1702	1685	1668	1650	1633	1616	1599	1582	3	6	9	12	14
81	1564	1547	1530	1513	1495	1478	1461	1444	1426	1409	3	6	9	12	14
82	1392	1374	1357	1340	1323	1305	1288	1271	1253	1236	3	6	9	12	14
83	1219	1201	1184	1167	1149	1132	1115	1097	1080	1063	3	6	9	12	14
84	1045	1028	1011	0993	0976	0958	0941	0924	0906	0889	3	6	9	12	14
85	0872	0854	0837	0819	0802	0785	0767	0750	0732	0715	3	6	9	12	15
86	0698	0680	0663	0645	0628	0610	0593	0576	0558	0541	3	6	9	12	15
87	0523	0506	0488	0471	0454	0436	0419	0401	0384	0366	3	6	9	12	15
88	0349	0332	0314	0297	0279	0262	0244	0227	0209	0192	3	6	9	12	15
89	0175	0157	0140	0122	0105	0087	0070	0052	0035	0017	3	6	9	12	15

TANGENT RATIO

	0'	6'	12'	18'	24'	30'	36'	42'	48'	54'	1	2	3	4	5
0°	.0000	0017	0035	0052	0070	0087	0105	0122	0140	0157	3	6	9	12	14
1	.0175	0192	0209	0227	0244	0262	0279	0297	0314	0332	3	6	9	12	15
2	.0349	0367	0384	0402	0419	0437	0454	0472	0489	0507	3	6	9	12	15
3	.0524	0542	0559	0577	0594	0612	0629	0647	0664	0682	3	6	9	12	15
4	.0699	0717	0734	0752	0769	0787	0805	0822	0840	0857	3	6	9	12	15
5	.0875	0892	0910	0928	0945	0963	0981	0998	1016	1033	3	6	9	12	15
6	.1051	1069	1086	1104	1122	1139	1157	1175	1192	1210	3	6	9	12	15
7	.1228	1246	1263	1281	1299	1317	1334	1352	1370	1388	3	6	9	12	15
8	.1405	1423	1441	1459	1477	1495	1512	1530	1548	1566	3	6	9	12	15
9	.1584	1602	1620	1638	1655	1673	1691	1709	1727	1745	3	6	9	12	15
10	.1763	1781	1799	1817	1835	1853	1871	1890	1908	1926	3	6	9	12	15
11	.1944	1962	1980	1998	2016	2035	2053	2071	2089	2107	3	6	9	12	15
12	.2126	2144	2162	2180	2199	2217	2235	2254	2272	2290	3	6	9	12	15
13	.2309	2327	2345	2364	2382	2401	2419	2438	2456	2475	3	6	9	12	15
14	.2493	2512	2530	2549	2568	2586	2605	2623	2642	2661	3	6	9	12	16
15	.2679	2698	2717	2736	2754	2773	2792	2811	2830	2849	3	6	9	13	16
16	.2867	2886	2905	2924	2943	2962	2981	3000	3019	3038	3	6	9	13	16
17	.3057	3076	3096	3115	3134	3153	3172	3191	3211	3230	3	6	10	13	16
18	.3249	3269	3288	3307	3327	3346	3365	3385	3404	3424	3	6	10	13	16
19	.3443	3463	3482	3502	3522	3541	3561	3581	3600	3620	3	6	10	13	17
20	.3640	3659	3679	3699	3719	3739	3759	3779	3799	3819	3	7	10	13	17
21	.3839	3859	3879	3899	3919	3939	3959	3978	4000	4020	3	7	10	13	17
22	.4040	4061	4081	4101	4122	4142	4163	4183	4204	4224	3	7	10	14	17
23	.4245	4265	4286	4307	4327	4348	4369	4390	4411	4431	3	7	10	14	17
24	.4452	4473	4494	4515	4536	4557	4578	4599	4621	4642	4	7	10	14	18
25	.4663	4684	4706	4727	4748	4770	4791	4813	4834	4856	4	7	11	14	18
26	.4877	4899	4921	4942	4964	4986	5008	5029	5051	5073	4	7	11	15	18
27	.5095	5117	5139	5161	5184	5206	5228	5250	5272	5295	4	7	11	15	18
28	.5317	5340	5362	5384	5407	5430	5452	5475	5498	5520	4	8	11	15	19
29	.5543	5566	5589	5612	5635	5658	5681	5704	5727	5750	4	8	12	15	19
30	.5774	5797	5820	5844	5867	5890	5914	5938	5961	5985	4	8	12	16	20
31	.6009	6032	6056	6080	6104	6128	6152	6176	6200	6224	4	8	12	16	20
32	.6249	6273	6297	6322	6346	6371	6395	6420	6445	6469	4	8	12	16	20
33	.6494	6519	6544	6569	6594	6619	6644	6669	6694	6720	4	8	13	17	21
34	.6745	6771	6796	6822	6847	6873	6899	6924	6950	6976	4	9	13	17	21
35	.7002	7028	7054	7080	7107	7133	7159	7186	7212	7239	4	9	13	18	22
36	.7265	7292	7319	7346	7373	7400	7427	7454	7481	7508	5	9	14	18	23
37	.7536	7563	7590	7618	7646	7673	7701	7729	7757	7785	5	9	14	18	23
38	.7813	7841	7869	7898	7926	7954	7983	8012	8040	8069	5	10	14	19	24
39	.8098	8127	8156	8185	8214	8243	8273	8302	8332	8361	5	10	15	20	24
40	.8391	8421	8451	8481	8511	8541	8571	8601	8632	8662	5	10	15	20	25
41	.8693	8724	8754	8785	8816	8847	8878	8910	8941	8972	5	10	16	21	26
42	.9004	9036	9067	9099	9131	9163	9195	9228	9260	9293	5	11	16	21	27
43	.9325	9358	9391	9424	9457	9490	9523	9556	9590	9623	6	11	17	22	28
44	.9657	9691	9725	9759	9793	9827	9861	9896	9930	9965	6	11	17	23	29

TANGENT RATIO

	0'	6'	12'	18'	24'	30'	36'	42'	48'	54'	1	2	3	4	5
45°	1.0000	0035	0070	0105	0141	0176	0212	0247	0283	0319	6	12	18	24	30
46	1.0355	0392	0428	0464	0501	0538	0575	0612	0649	0686	6	12	18	25	31
47	1.0724	0761	0799	0837	0875	0913	0951	0990	1028	1067	6	13	19	25	32
48	1.1106	1145	1184	1224	1263	1303	1343	1383	1423	1463	7	13	20	26	33
49	1.1504	1544	1585	1626	1667	1708	1750	1792	1833	1875	7	14	21	28	34
50	1.1918	1960	2002	2045	2088	2131	2174	2218	2261	2305	7	14	22	29	36
51	1.2349	2393	2437	2482	2527	2572	2617	2662	2708	2753	8	15	23	30	38
52	1.2799	2846	2892	2938	2985	3032	3079	3127	3175	3222	8	16	23	31	39
53	1.3270	3319	3367	3416	3465	3514	3564	3613	3663	3713	8	16	25	33	41
54	1.3764	3814	3865	3916	3968	4019	4071	4124	4176	4229	9	17	26	34	43
55	1.4281	4335	4388	4442	4496	4550	4605	4659	4715	4770	9	18	27	36	45
56	1.4826	4882	4938	4994	5051	5108	5166	5224	5282	5340	10	19	29	38	48
57	1.5399	5458	5517	5577	5637	5697	5757	5818	5880	5941	10	20	30	40	50
58	1.6003	6066	6128	6191	6255	6319	6383	6447	6512	6577	11	21	32	43	53
59	1.6643	6709	6775	6842	6909	6977	7045	7113	7182	7251	11	23	34	45	56
60	1.7321	7391	7461	7532	7603	7675	7747	7820	7893	7966	12	24	36	48	60
61	1.8040	8115	8190	8265	8341	8418	8495	8572	8650	8728	13	26	38	51	64
62	1.8807	8887	8967	9047	9128	9210	9292	9375	9458	9542	14	27	41	55	68
63	1.9626	9711	9797	9883	9970	0057	0145	0233	0323	0413	15	29	44	58	73
64	2.0503	0594	0686	0778	0872	0965	1060	1155	1251	1348	16	31	47	63	78
65	2.1445	1543	1642	1742	1842	1943	2045	2148	2251	2355	17	34	51	68	85
66	2.2460	2566	2673	2781	2889	2998	3109	3220	3332	3445	18	37	55	74	92
67	2.3559	3673	3789	3906	4023	4142	4262	4383	4504	4627	20	40	60	79	99
68	2.4751	4876	5002	5129	5257	5386	5517	5649	5782	5916	22	43	65	87	108
69	2.6051	6187	6325	6464	6605	6746	6889	7034	7179	7326	24	47	71	95	118
70	2.7475	7625	7776	7929	8083	8239	8397	8556	8716	8878	26	52	78	104	130
71	2.9042	9208	9375	9544	9714	9887	0061	0237	0415	0595	29	58	87	115	144
72	3.0777	0961	1146	1334	1524	1716	1910	2106	2305	2506	32	64	96	129	161
73	3.2709	2914	3122	3332	3544	3759	3977	4197	4420	4646	36	72	108	144	180
74	3.4874	5105	5339	5576	5816	6059	6305	6554	6806	7062	41	82	122	162	203
75	3.7321	7583	7848	8118	8391	8667	8947	9232	9520	9812	46	94	139	186	232
76	4.0108	0408	0713	1022	1335	1653	1976	2303	2635	2972	53	107	160	214	267
77	4.3315	3662	4015	4374	4737	5107	5483	5864	6252	6646	62	124	186	248	310
78	4.7046	7453	7867	8288	8716	9152	9594	0045	0504	0970	73	146	219	292	365
79	5.1446	1929	2422	2924	3435	3955	4486	5026	5578	6140	87	175	262	350	437
80	5.6713	7297	7894	8502	9124	9758	0405	1066	1742	2432					
81	6.3138	3859	4596	5350	6122	6912	7920	8548	9395	0264					
82	7.1154	2066	3002	3962	4947	5958	6996	8062	9158	0285					
83	8.1443	2636	3863	5126	6427	7769	9152	0579	2052	3572					
84	9.5144	9.677	9.845	10.02	10.20	10.39	10.58	10.78	10.99	11.20					
85	11.43	11.66	11.91	12.16	12.43	12.71	13.00	13.30	13.62	13.95					
86	14.30	14.67	15.06	15.46	15.89	16.35	16.83	17.34	17.89	18.46					
87	19.08	19.74	20.45	21.20	22.02	22.90	23.86	24.90	26.03	27.27					
88	28.64	30.14	31.82	33.69	35.80	38.19	40.92	44.07	47.74	52.08					
89	57.29	63.66	71.62	81.85	95.49	114.6	143.2	191.0	286.5	573.0					

col- umns cease to be useful, owing to the rapidity with which the value of the tangent changes.

V.   Approximate Formulas for Simplified Computation

If a is either positive or negative, and it is less than one in absolute value, then the following approximate relations may be satisfactorily used for computation purposes. However, it should be understood that an error of about a^2 or less is thereby introduced.

	Approximate value	Error
$(1 + a)^2 = 1 + 2a$	$1.001^2 = 1.002$	0.000001
$(1 - a)^2 = 1 - 2a$	$0.998^2 = 0.996$	0.000004
$\dfrac{1}{1 + a} = 1 - a$	$\dfrac{1}{1.0003} = 0.9997$	0.00000009
$\dfrac{1}{1 - a} = 1 + a$	$\dfrac{1}{0.9998} = 1.0002$	0.00000002
$(1 + a)^n = 1 + na$		
$(1 - a)^n = 1 - na$		
$\dfrac{1}{(1 + a)^n} = 1 - na$		
$\dfrac{1}{(1 - a)^n} = 1 + na$		
$\sqrt{1 + a} = 1 + \dfrac{a}{2}$	$\sqrt{1.0004} = 1.0002$	0.00000002
$\sqrt{1 - a} = 1 - \dfrac{a}{2}$	$\sqrt{0.9998} = 0.9999$	0.000000005
$\dfrac{1}{\sqrt{1 + a}} = 1 - \dfrac{a}{2}$	$\dfrac{1}{\sqrt{1.00002}} = 0.99999$	0.0000000001
$\dfrac{1}{\sqrt{1 - a}} = 1 + \dfrac{a}{2}$	$\dfrac{1}{\sqrt{0.99996}} = 0.99998$	0.0000000004
$\sqrt[n]{1 + a} = 1 + \dfrac{a}{n}$	$\dfrac{1}{\sqrt[n]{1 + a}} = 1 - \dfrac{a}{n}$	
$\sqrt[n]{1 - a} = 1 - \dfrac{a}{n}$	$\dfrac{1}{\sqrt[n]{1 - a}} = 1 + \dfrac{a}{n}$	

ANSWERS TO PROBLEMS

Chapter 2

1. The seven-system. **2.** The nine-system. **3.** The six-system. **4.** The five-system. **5.** In the two-system 111,011,001; the three-system 122,112; the four-system 13,121; the five-system 3,343; the six-system 2,105; the seven-system 1,244; the eight-system 731; the nine-system 575; the eleven-system $3t0$; the twelve-system 335. **6.** (a) In the five-system 4,493; the six-system 10,533; the seven-system 21,829; the eight-system 41,243; the nine-system 72,525; the eleven-system 190,853; the twelve-system 290,919. (b) In the six-system this number is odd; in the seven-system this number is odd. (c) No.

Chapter 3

1. $888 + 88 + 8 + 8 + 8 = 1,000.$ **2.** $8 + 8 + 8 = 24.$ **3.** $3^3 - 3 = 24.$ **4.** $5 \cdot 5 + 5 = 30.$ **5.** $1 \cdot 9 + 8 \cdot 2 - 7 \cdot 3 + 6 - 5 - 4 = 1$; $\frac{148}{296} + \frac{35}{70} = 1.$ **6.** $\frac{99}{99} + 9 = 10$; $\frac{99}{9} - \frac{9}{9} = 10.$ **7.** $111 - 11 = 100$; $33 \cdot 3 + \frac{3}{3} = 100$; $5 \cdot 5 \cdot 5 - 5 \cdot 5 = 100$; $(5 + 5 + 5 + 5)5 = 100.$ **8.** $99 + \frac{9}{9} = 100.$

Chapter 4

1. 109,500,000 trucks. **2.** 14,000,000 trucks. **3.** 63.13, or about 64 days. **4.** 50,000 days, or about 137 years. **5.** 160 cups. **6.** About 800,000,000 pints. **7.** About 23.7 miles. The hour number will be about 10,417 feet long. **8.** The mosquito will be about 5.92 (almost 6) miles long. **9.** 1,000 kilograms, or 1 metric ton $=$ 2,204.6 pounds. **10.** About 39.5 miles. **11.** About 47.4 miles. **12.** About 23,674 miles. The hour number will be about 197 miles long. **13.** Weight varies as the cube of the linear dimensions. A pair of shoes will weigh about 750,000,000,000,000,000,000,000 tons. **14.** About 158,000 miles long. **15.** 7,500,000,000 pounds. **16.** 6,300,000,000 pounds of water. **17.** About $898,000,000. **18.** About $366 \cdot 10^9$ gallons. **19.** About 49,000 gallons. **20.** About $73.5 \cdot 10^{11}$ gallons. **21.** 10^{myriad} is greater than myriad[10]. **22.** 10^{80000}. **23.** About 2,759,400,000 heartbeats. **24.** About 10^{16} tons. **25.** It will take sound about $\frac{250}{1100} = \frac{25}{110}$ second to reach the opposite wall of the concert hall. It will take a radio wave about $\frac{3000}{186000} = \frac{1}{62}$ second to reach Los Angeles. Thus the man in Los Angeles will hear the performance first. **26.** About $3 \cdot 10^{12}$ miles. **27.** About $3 \cdot 10^{18}$ miles. **28.** About 818,400,000 seconds, or 25 years 357 days 5 hours and 2 minutes.

Chapter 5

1. The diminished radius of the earth would be about 83.3 times larger than the breadth of a hair. **2.** About 23,000 times larger.

3. About one millionth part. **4.** About $\dfrac{1}{5\cdot10^9}$ part. **5.** About one millionth part. **6.** One molecule for every $1.78\cdot10^{21}$ cubic miles. **7.** About $14\cdot10^{36}$ molecules. **8.** The water in a cubic mile will weigh approximately 10^{13} gram. **9.** The number of red corpuscles will be about $13\cdot10^{10}$. **10.** About $5\cdot10^{25}$ cubic miles for one red blood corpuscle. **11.** The space allotted to one electron will be approximately $9\cdot10^{-18}$ cubic mile, or approximately 0.0023 cubic inch. **12.** About $111\cdot10^{15}$ electrons. **13.** Approximately one billionth of a gram. **14.** 10^{9900} googols. **15.** (1) A googol^{googol} is larger than a myriad^{myriad}; (2) A googol^{googol} is larger than 9^{9^9}; (3) Googol^{googolplex} is larger than googolplex^{googol}. **16.** (1) $10^{10^{102}-4\cdot10^4}$ times; (2) $\dfrac{\text{googol}^{\text{googol}}}{9^{9^9}}$ times; (3) $10^{10^2+10^{100}-10^{200}}$ times.

17. $(10^{\text{googol}})^{10^{\text{googol}}} = 10^{\text{googol}\,\cdot\,\text{googolplex}} = 10^{10^{100}\cdot10^{10^{100}}} = 10^{10^{10^2}\,\cdot\,10^{10^2}}$.
18. The length of one wave is approximately $2.95\cdot10^{-5}$ inch.
19. $4.07\cdot10^5$, or 407,000 waves. **20.** Approximately $26\cdot10^{29}$ waves.

CHAPTER 7

1. 3.142. **2.** 365.22. **3.** 1570. **4.** 288 feet. **5.** 922.25. **6.** 58 feet. **7.** 41,000 square feet. **8.** 2.3 times. **9.** 13.4. **10.** 10.5.

CHAPTER 10

1.		or		or		2.		or	
	4632		.2051		.4367		2051		4367
	8632		.3051		.2367		3051		2367
	13264		.5102		0.6734		5102		6734

3.		4.		5.		6.		7.	
	41052		93467		5927		4623		5349 and other
	31052		83467		3402		99145		24588 solutions
	72104		176934		9329		103768		64259
									94196

8.		9.		10.		11.		12.	
	9427		2413		5352		1615		349
	64983		92476		413		815		62
	972492		889235		4939		800		698
	1046902		9763421						2094
			10747545						21638

13. 762
485
3810
6096
3048
369570

14. 2774545 | 643
2572   4315
2025
1929
964
643
3215
3215

CHAPTER 12

1. $+374°$ C. 2. $180°$ F. 3. $1°$ F. $= \frac{5}{9}°$ C. 4. $44.4°$ C. 5. $161.6°$ F.
6. $-461.2°$ F. 7. $-49°$ F. 8. $-52.78°$ C. 9. $-172.2°$ C.
10. $-153.4°$ F.

CHAPTER 13

1. $243 \cdot 10^{13}$ grains. 2. $127 \cdot 10^{7} = 1,270,000,000$ passengers.
3. About 2 cents. 4. About 375 acres. 5. About \$27.
6. $123456789^{0} = 1$. 7. $2^{2^{2}}$. 8. $5^{5^{5}}$. 9. $2^{3^{4^{1}}}$. 10. $6^{7^{9}}$.
11. $5.68 \cdot 10^{7}$ grams, or about 56.8 metric tons. 12. Approximately
3.64 grams. 13. $19 \cdot 10^{26}$ tons. 14. About $2 \cdot 10^{59}$ times. 15. 1
mile $= 16 \cdot 10^{4}$ centimeters. The radius of the universe is then
$6 \cdot 10^{12} \cdot 16 \cdot 10^{4} \cdot 10^{9}$ centimeters. About 28 electrons. 16. About
$5 \cdot 10^{47}$ electrons. 17. About 0.00000000000000000001 cent.
18. About $7.4 \cdot 10^{33}$ cubic centimeters for one electron. 19. About
0.034 pound. 20. About 0.00000542 cent. 21. In about $2^{87.4}$
seconds. This number has 27 digits. 22. In about $(\frac{1}{2})^{40}$ of a
second. 23. At $520°$ C. 24. At $630°$ C. 25. In about $(\frac{1}{2})^{540}$ of
a second. 26. The radius of an electron is about $7.5 \cdot 10^{-12}$ cm.
The radius of the sun is about $5 \cdot 10^{10}$ cm. The volume of an
electron is $4.18 (7.5 \cdot 10^{-12})^{3}$ cubic cm. The volume of the sun is
$4.18(5 \cdot 10^{10})^{3}$ cubic cm. Then the volume of the sun is

$$\frac{(5 \cdot 10^{10})^{3}}{(7.5 \cdot 10^{-12})^{3}}$$

times larger than the volume of an electron. Performing the computations we have this number approximately equal to $3 \cdot 10^{65}$. We
agreed that $10^{3} = 2^{10}$ approximately. We have then $3 \cdot 10^{65} =$
$300 \cdot 10^{63} = 300(2^{10})^{21} = 300 \cdot 2^{210}$. Replace 300 by $256 = 2^{8}$. We
have then $2^{210} \cdot 2^{8} = 2^{218}$. This gives the answer: 218 times.
27. Approximately 199 times. 28. Approximately 40 times.
29. Approximately 6 times. 30. $2^{63} = 9,223,372,036,854,775,808$
grains. 31. 2^{46}. 32. 3^{57}. 33. 5^{79}. 34. $5^{6^{7^{8^{9}}}}$.

CHAPTER 14

1. He sold 208 tires during June and July, that is, in 61 days.
Suppose that during x days he sold motorcycle tire sets (two to a
set). Then during $(61 - x)$ days he sold automobile tires, that is,
4 tires to a set. Then, he sold $[2x + 4(61 - x)] = 208$ tires. Solving this equation, we find that he sold 36 motorcycle tires and 172
automobile tires.

2. Suppose that she ordered x one cent stamps, then she ordered
$2x$ two cent stamps, and $15x$ three cent stamps. Then

$$x + 4x + 45x = 500.$$

Solving the equation, we find that she bought 10 one cent stamps,
20 two cent stamps, and 150 three cent stamps.

3. Suppose that there were x customers. Then $\frac{x}{2}$ ordered minestrone, $\frac{x}{3}$ **ordered fried chicken,** $\frac{3}{4}\left(\frac{x}{2}+\frac{x}{3}\right)$ ordered macaroni.

The sum of these orders is equal to 70. Solving the equation, we find that there were 48 customers in Caprini's restaurant, and from this we obtain that there were 24 orders of minestrone, 16 orders of fried chicken, and 30 orders of macaroni.

4. Suppose that Mr. Collins contributed x dollars. Then the total collection was $(x + 100)$ dollars. The average contribution was then

$$\frac{x + 100}{11}$$

and from this we have that

$$x - \frac{x + 100}{11} = 20$$

Solving this equation we find that Mr. Collins contributed $32.

5. Suppose that Mr. Collins had $(2n + 1)$ five-dollar bills. Then he offered to contribute $5n$ dollars. The solution of this problem follows the method of the solution of Problem 4. Mr. Cashbox had $135 in his wallet.

6. Suppose that Mr. Collins had x dollars in his wallet. Then

the first received $\frac{x}{2} + 1$ dollars

the second received $\frac{1}{2}\left(\frac{x}{2} - 1\right) + 1$ dollars

the third received $\frac{1}{2}\left(\frac{x}{4} - \frac{3}{2}\right) + 1$ dollars

and the fourth received $\frac{x}{8} - \frac{7}{4}$ dollars

and from this we set up the proper equation as indicated in the problem. Solving this equation we find that Mr. Collins distributed $30 as follows:

the first received $16

the second received $8

the third received $4

and   the fourth received $2

7. Suppose that there were x men in Elmville. Then there were $(1349 - x)$ women, and only $\dfrac{1349 - x}{2}$ women voted. Then Mr. Collins paid out

$$7.5x + \frac{15(1349 - x)}{2} = 7.5x + 15 \cdot 1349 - 7.5x = 15 \cdot 1349 = 20235$$

dollars.

8. Let the total prize money be x dollars.   Then

the first prize is $\dfrac{x}{3} + 5$ dollars

the second prize is $\dfrac{x}{6} + \dfrac{15}{4}$ dollars

the third prize is $\dfrac{x}{10} + \dfrac{13}{4}$ dollars

and   the fourth prize is $\dfrac{2x}{5} - 12$ dollars

Since the sum of the first three prizes is twice as large as the fourth prize, the fourth prize is equal to one third of the total prize money. We have then the equation

$$\frac{2x}{5} - 12 = \frac{x}{3}$$

Solving this equation we find that the total prize money was \$180 which was distributed as follows: the first prize \$65, the second prize \$33.75, the third prize \$21.25, and the fourth prize \$60.

9. Suppose that the amount paid for the automobile was x dollars.   Then the cost of the garage was $\dfrac{x}{8} + 50$ dollars, or $\dfrac{3x}{4} - 575$ dollars.   Equating these two expressions, and solving the equation we find that Mr. Collins paid \$680 for the automobile, and the garage cost \$175 to construct.

10. We have the following table of values

Ages of	Then	Now	7 years later
Student.......	$\dfrac{x}{9}$	x	$x + 7$
Professor......	x	$78 - x$	$85 - x$

From this we obtain the equation

$$x - \frac{x}{9} = 78 - x - x$$

and solving it we find that the student is 27 years old, and the Professor is 51 years old.

11. We have the following table of values

Ages	Then	Now	Later
Eddie.........	0	x	$2x$
Professor......	$x + 13$	$3x$	$4x$

From this we obtain the equation

$$x - 0 = 3x - x - 13$$

and solving it we find that Eddie is 13 years old, and Professor is 39 years old.

12. The professor is 47 years old, and his wife is 41 years old.

13. One son is 9 years old, and the other is 15 years old.

14. Suppose that there were x animals and $x - 15$ birds. Then the number of legs is

animals: $4x$, birds: $2(x - 15)$, and the total: $6x - 30$.

If the number of animals and birds were reversed, the number of legs would be

animals: $4(x - 15)$, birds: $2x$, and the total: $6x - 60$.

We have then the equation

$$\frac{2}{3} \cdot (6x - 30) = 6x - 60$$

Solving this equation we find that there were 20 animals and that there were 5 birds.

15. Suppose that x members left the meeting. Then

$$\frac{5}{2} \cdot (x + 2) = 3(x - 3)$$

Thus 28 members left the meeting, and there were 75 members in the club.

16. Suppose that x tickets were sold. Then the women sold $\frac{2x}{3}$ tickets, and the men sold $\frac{x}{3}$ tickets. If the men sold twice as many tickets as the women sold, they would have sold $\frac{4x}{3}$ tickets, and the extra $150 would constitute the price of 300 tickets. Thus $x = 300$, and the women sold 200 tickets.

17. The $400 rent was to run for 18 years, and the $600 rent was to run for 24 years. The total rent would then be $21,600. Thus the club would pay $600 more under the terms proposed by Mr. Collins.

18. 150 men and 80 women.

19. The slower typist can copy one page in 6 minutes, and the faster typist can copy one page in 4 minutes. Thus, in 72 minutes each typist copied 12 and 18 pages respectively, or 30 pages together, and this was the number of the pages in the manuscript.

20. Mr. Collins engaged the three painters. John could complete $\frac{1}{5}$ of the job in a day, Jim could complete $\frac{1}{6}$ of the job in a day, and Jack could complete $\frac{1}{7}$ of the job in one day. Then in one day

$$\frac{1}{5} + \frac{1}{6} + \frac{1}{7} = \frac{107}{210} \text{ th}$$

part of the job could be completed, and in a trifle less than two days the work could be done. The $214 were divided as follows: John received $84, Jim received $70, and Jack received $60.

21. In one hour the larger candle will burn $\frac{1}{6}$ of its length, and the smaller candle will burn $\frac{1}{4}$ of its length. Suppose that the two candles burned x hours. Then

$$1 - \frac{x}{6} = 2\left(1 - \frac{x}{4}\right)$$

Solving this equation we find that the two candles burned 3 hours.

22. Johnson figured that his average speed was

$$\frac{\dfrac{180}{2.5} + \dfrac{180}{5}}{2} = \frac{72 + 36}{2} = 54$$

miles per hour, and at this speed it would take him 3 hours and 2 minutes to reach Squirrel Bluffs. However, this computation was wrong. His average speed was to be computed as follows:

$$\frac{2}{x} = \frac{1}{72} + \frac{1}{36} = \frac{36 + 72}{72 \cdot 36} = \frac{1}{24}$$

and $x = 48$ miles per hour. At this speed it should take him seven and a half hours for the round trip.

23. The clue to the solution of this problem is the statement concerning the ten additional miles which would have saved ten minutes. Thus, the original speed was 60 miles per hour. Suppose that the distance from the Professor's home to Canarsie University was x miles. Then, had he gone at the original rate from the time he fixed the flat tire, it would have taken him $\dfrac{x - 60}{60}$ hours to complete the trip. But he proceeded at 48 miles an hour, and this trip took him $\dfrac{x - 60}{48}$ hours to complete. He spent 10 minutes fixing the flat tire and he was 30 minutes late, that is, he travelled 20 more minutes, or $\frac{1}{3}$ of an hour. We then have the equation

$$\frac{x - 60}{60} + \frac{1}{3} = \frac{x - 60}{48}$$

Solving this equation, we find that the required distance was 140 miles.

24. Stone's share in the gasoline expense was one half of the total cost of the trip.

25. If the original cost of a sandwich was x cents, then the 300 sandwiches cost $300x$ cents, and the 3 cents rise in price would have offset the loss, that is,

$$300x = 240(x + 3)$$

and from this we obtain $x = 12$ cents.

Suppose that the first sandwich was to be sold for y cents, and the second sandwich was to be sold for $\frac{y}{2}$ cents. Then

$$120y + \frac{120y}{2} = 3600$$

From this we obtain $y = 20$ cents, and $\frac{y}{2} = 10$ cents.

26. Suppose that the bat cost x cents and the baseball cost $\frac{2x}{5}$. A 25 percent profit on the bat would have brought its selling price to $\frac{5x}{4}$, and a 25 percent loss on the baseball would have made its selling price $\frac{2}{5} \cdot \frac{3}{4}x$. We then have the equation

$$\frac{5x}{4} + \frac{3x}{10} = 155$$

From this equation we find that $x = 100$, and this is the cost of the bat to Eddie. The cost of the baseball to him was 40 cents. Thus he made a profit of 15 cents.

27. The total investment in the bus company including Brown's share was $3500. In the new set-up Stone's share was $700, a gain of $300, and Parker's share was $1000, a gain of $400. Thus, Stone gained $300 on a $400 share, while Parker gained $400 on a $600 share.

28. Let the required time be x. Then the squadron will cover $26x$ miles in this time, and the destroyer will cover $35x$ miles. The total trip of the destroyer will be 80 miles. Then

$$35x + 26x = 80$$

or $x = 1$ hour and 20 minutes (approximately).

29. Suppose that the destroyer will turn back after x hours. In this time it will move ahead of the squadron

$$35x - 26x = 9x \text{ miles}$$

On the return trip the destroyer and the squadron will travel $(7 - x)$ hours until they meet, and they will both cover

$$35(7 - x) + 26(7 - x) = 9x \text{ miles}$$

From this we find that $x = 6$ hours 6 minutes. After this time has elapsed the destroyer must turn back.

30. Suppose that the distance to be covered is x miles. Then at 45 miles an hour the trip will take $\frac{x}{45}$ hours, and he would be 30 minutes late,

at 50 miles an hour the trip will take $\frac{x}{50}$ hours, and he would be 20 minutes early.

Then

$$\frac{x}{45} - \frac{x}{50} = \frac{5}{6} \left(30 + 20 = 50 \text{ minutes} = \frac{5}{6} \text{ hour} \right)$$

From this we find that $x = 375$ miles.

At 45 miles an hour the trip will take $\frac{375}{45} = 8$ hours 20 minutes, and since this would be 30 minutes too late, the trip should take 7 hours 50 minutes, or $\frac{47}{6}$ hours. Then the correct speed should be about 48 miles an hour. $\left(375 \div \frac{47}{6} = 47.87. \right)$

31. The method for the solution of this problem is similar to the one illustrated in this chapter. The third pasture will suffice 18 weeks for 36 bulls.

32. Suppose that farmer Jones had x chickens. Also suppose that the feed he bought is F. Then one chicken will be given

$$\frac{F}{15x}$$

and $\frac{2}{3}$ of this is

$$\frac{2F}{45x}$$

If there were 21 more chickens, then the total number of chickens would be $(21 + x)$, and since the food would last only 12 days, each chicken would receive

$$\frac{F}{12(21 + x)}$$

Equating these two values we have, after cancelling out the F's,

$$24(21 + x) = 45x$$

Solving the equation, we find that $x = 24$ chickens.

CHAPTER 16

1. $20.10. **2.** About 17%. **3.** About 21.3%. On the weekly plan the yearly rate of interest is about 95.28%. **4.** About 22.5% on the monthly plan, and about 26.5% on the weekly plan. **5.** About 30.25%.

CHAPTER 17

1. a. 18,446,744,073,709,551,615; **b.** 1,229,782 cubic kilometers, or about 295,060 cubic miles; **c.** About 576,460,752,304 years. **2.** About $2 \cdot 10^{13}$ rats. **3.** About $2,115. **4.** 88,572. **5.** $\frac{4}{9}$.

CHAPTER 21

1. 10^{20}. The population of the earth is about 2,000,000,000. Thus, an exact double is impossible. **2.** $100^5 = 10,000,000,000$ combinations. **3.** 3,750. **4.** 1,320. **5.** 10,000. **6.** 30,000. **7.** 20. **8.** 48,000 dinners.

CHAPTER 23

1. 25. **2.** 41. **3.** 13. **4.** 37. **5.** 29.

CHAPTER 24

1. $x^2 + y^2 = 1$. **2.** $x^2 + (y + 3)^2 = 6$. **3.** $(x + 2)^2 + y^2 = 49$. **4.** $x^2 + y^2 = 1$. **5.** $(x + 5)^2 + y^2 = 50$. **6.** $(x + 3)^2 + (y + 5)^2 = 8$. **7.** $(x - 2)^2 + (y + 3)^2 = 50$. **8.** $(x - 2)^2 + (y + 4)^2 = r^2$. This is a circle. **9.** Suppose that the sum of the distances is $2a$. Then

the equation is $\dfrac{x^3}{a^2} + \dfrac{y^2}{a^2 - \frac{1}{2}} = 1$.

10. $\dfrac{x^2}{a^2} - \dfrac{y^2}{b^2} = 1$. This curve is known as the hyperbola.

11. $4y^2 = -3x^2 - 12x$, or $\dfrac{(x + 2)^2}{4} + \dfrac{y^2}{3} = 1$.

12. $(x + \frac{3}{8})^2 + (y - \frac{27}{8})^2 = \frac{81}{32}$. **13.** $x + y = 3$. This is a straight line.

CHAPTER 27

1. 151,000,000 miles. **2.** 1,110 miles per minute. **3.** 0.623 mile per second, or 3,290 feet per second. **4.** 25,000 miles. **5.** 0.291 mile per second, or about 1,540 feet per second. **6.** No, the difference will be the same. **7.** Yes, yes. **8.** 5,654 feet in a day, 7.49 miles in a week, about 225 miles in a month, about 2.735 miles in a year.

Chapter 28

1. 974.5 feet. **2.** About 20,600 feet. **3.** About 1° 55′. **4.** About 110 feet. **5.** About 20,600 feet. **6.** About 0.6 of normal. **7.** About 0.8 of normal. **8.** About 22 feet. **9.** At a distance slightly less than 2,160 feet. **10.** About 0.29 of normal.

Chapter 29

1. About 1.5 miles. **2.** About 2.0 miles. **3.** About 0.9 mile. **4.** About 0.3 mile. **5.** About 3.7 miles (the correction of 1.06 was introduced in this result). **6.** 1.03 of normal. **7.** Normal vision. **8.** 0.92 of normal. **9.** 0.98 of normal. **10.** Almost normal (about 1.02 of normal). In the following problems the correction of 1.06 was introduced. **11.** About 17.4 miles. **12.** About 1.6 miles. **13.** About 30 miles. **14.** About 2.13 miles. **15.** About 212 miles. **16.** About 413 feet. **17.** About 72.2 feet. **18.** About 1.16 miles.

Chapter 31

1. 75 in.² **2.** 25 $\sqrt{3}$ = 43.25 in.² **3.** 28.6 in.² **4.** 250 in.² **5.** 200 in.²

Chapter 32

1. The volumes of similar solids are to one another as the cubes of the linear measures. If the linear measure of a Lilliputian was 1, then the linear measure of Gulliver was 12, and 12^3 = 1728.

2. The calculations of Gulliver were wrong. An English barrel contains 672 half-pints, and an American barrel contains 512 half-pints. Thus, the Lilliputian barrel as described by Gulliver was too large.

3. No. This mattress was one third as thick as a usual mattress. In order to make up a usual mattress, 12 layers would be required.

4. An average apple weighs about $\frac{1}{4}$ of a pound. In the land of the Brobdingnags such an apple would weigh 1728 times as much, that is, 432 pounds. Since all the objects (and this included trees) were 12 times larger in their linear dimensions, the apple (which would have fallen from the height of about 10 feet under normal conditions) must have fallen from the height of 120 feet in the land of the Brobdingnags. An object weighing 432 pounds and falling from the height of 120 feet would kill a man if it struck him.

5. The diameter of an average ring is about $\frac{5}{8}$ in. Then the diameter of the ring that the Queen of the Brobdingnags gave to Gulliver was about 7.5 in. If an average ring weighs about $\frac{1}{3}$ of an ounce then the ring of the Queen of the Brobdingnags weighed about 36 lbs.

Index

Absolute temperature, 159-160
Absolute value of a number, 159, 161
Acceleration, 623, 629, 633, 635, 637
  centripetal, 629, 637, 680, 683, 694
  negative, 695
Addition
  in various systems of numeration, 19-20, 25-27, 29
  of approximate numbers, 109-110
  of fractions, 709
  of signed numbers, 161, 706
  restoration of missing numerals, 143-144
After, coordinate of, 612
Aiming at a target, 646-649, 667-669, 677
American Experience Mortality Table, 347
Amount of motion, 634-635, 646
Angle,
  central, 735
  dihedral, 587
  exterior of a triangle, 592, 602
  inscribed in a circle, 735
  measure of, 402-403
  of elevation of gun, 669-676
  of vision, 470
  right, 398
  straight, 398
Angles, 727
  vertical, 495
Angular magnitude, 470, 472
Applications of mathematics to
  Astronomy, 289-292, 630-640
  Athletics, 689-692
  Automobile accidents, 699-700
  Aviation, 316-320
  Ballistics, 641-677
  Banking and Savings, 260-263, 283-285, 295-305
  Business, 201-202, 281-283, 292-294, 306-313
  Circus stunts, 685-689, 692-694, 696-699

Applications of mathematics to—*Cont*
  Code writing, 79-101
  Instalment buying, 224-246
  Life insurance, 345-349
  Mechanics, 609-640, 678-704
  Mortgages, 243-245
  Motoring, 694-696
  Music, 285-287
  Physics, 285-292, 316, 324, 609-640, 678-704
  Small loans, 240-243
  Surveying, 420-455
  Warfare, 475, 487-488, 641-677
Approximate formulas, 220-223, 771
  for division, 221, 771
  for extraction of roots, 223, 533, 771
  for raising to a power, 771
Approximate numbers, 103-104, 106, 108-112
  nature of, 107
  rounding, 109, 111
  rules for operations with
    addition, 109-110
    division, 110
    multiplication, 108, 110-111
    subtraction, 110-111
  significant digits, 108-110
Archimedes, 59-60, 513, 559
  calculation of pi (π), 513
  number of sands in the universe, 59, 559
Area, concept of, 524-525
Area, unit of measure, 525
Area of
  circle, 531-534
  parallelogram, rule for computation, 527
  polygons, 733-734
  rectangle, computation of, 108
    rule for computation, 526
  rhombus, 733
  square, 384
  surface of the earth, 249
  trapezoid, 530
  triangle, 531

Areas of similar figures, 549-550, 558
Arithmetic mean, 579-580, 710
Arithmetic progression, 224-245, 715
  any term, 234, 715
  sum of, 235, 716
Astronomy, 289-292, 630-640
Axioms, 371
Axis of cylinder, 598

Ballistics, 641-677
Banking and Savings, 260-263, 283-285,
  295-305
Before, coordinate of, 612
Big numbers, 57-58, 60-65, 73-75, 172-
  185
  comparison of, 61-65
  problems with, 172, 173, 175, 177-179
Billion, 54-56, 58
Billion times, 56
Binomial expansion, 337-339, 717-718
  coefficients of, 339
Blood corpuscle, red, dimensions of,
  68
Boring of gun barrel, 665

Calculating machines, 117-124
  Napier's rods, 117-121
  Schoty, 121-122
  Soroban, 121
  Suan-pan, 123-124
Centigrade, 138
Centrifugal force, 629, 684
Centripetal acceleration, 629, 637, 680,
  683, 694
Certainty, 330-332
Chord of a circle, 471
Circle, 394-396, 406, 409, 416-419, 457,
  459, 471, 628, 734-737
  arc, 737
  area, 531-534, 737
  chord, 471
  circumference, 457, 459, 737
  diameter, 471
  equation of, 395-396, 406, 409, 416-
    419
  motion along, 628
  radius, 394
  sector, 737
  segment, 737
  tangent to, 736
Circles, walking in, 465-468
Classification, method of, 7-8, 508-511
  in libraries, 7-8
  in mathematics, 508-510
  in other fields, 510-511

Code writing, 79-101
  grille, 89-98
  substitution, 98-101
  systems of numeration, 88-89
  transposition, 78-85
  transposition of columns, 85-89
  two-system of numeration, 94-96
Coincidence, probability of, 333, 337,
  342-343, 348-349
Collision of objects, 696-700
Combinations, 354-364
  locks, 356-359
Component velocity, 685
Compound interest, 260-262, 295-299
  accumulation of capital, 261-262,
    283-285
  savings with regular deposits, 261-
    262
Compound interest computed, 295-299
  annually, 295, 296
  daily, 299
  monthly, 299
  quarterly, 298-299
  semiannually, 296-298
Cone, 552, 582-584, 601
  generator of, 601
  volume, 552
Congruence of triangles, 421, 426
Coordinate geometry, plane, 365-376,
  378-380, 386-387, 392-411, 413-419
Coordinate of after, 612
Coordinate of before, 612
Coordinate of here, 612
Coordinate of time, 612
Coordinates, 368-374, 379, 392-393, 521,
  612
  in four dimensions, 374
  in six dimensions, 521
  in three dimensions, 373
  in two dimensions, 368-371
  origin, 379
  moving of origin, 392-393
Copernicus, 630
Cosine law, 747
Cosine ratio, 403, 744
Cosine ratios, table, 766-767
Counting, 1-2
Cube, five-dimensional, 562
  volume of, 543
Cubes, number of in volume of, 561-
  562
  three-dimensional cube, 561
  four-dimensional cube (cuboid), 561
  five-dimensional cube, 562

Cubed unit, 541
Cuboid, four-dimensional cube, 562
  number in a five-dimensional cube,
    562
Curve of death, 313-316
Curve of growth, 313-316
Cylinder, 545-546, 566, 594, 598
  axis of, 598
  generator of, 594
  volume, 545-546, 566

Decimal system of numeration, 9-10,
    32
Depreciation, 292-294, 306-313
  rate of continuous, 311-313
Diameter of a circle, 471
Diameter of the earth, 104
Difference as a method of comparison,
    423
Dihedral angle, 587
Directed numbers, 158-163, 706
Distance formula for
  four dimensions, 388-391
  line-world, 380
  six dimensions, 521
  three dimensions, 387-388, 390
  two dimensions, 386-387, 390
Distance from earth to moon, 638, 702
Distance from earth to sun, 71, 104, 250
Distance of target, 663
Distance of vision, 476, 479, 486-490
Distance, result of motion, 621-625, 635
  shortest, 583-608
Distance to island universe, 71
Division
  in various systems of numeration,
    23-24, 30
  of approximate numbers, 110
  of fractions, 709
  of polynomials, 707
  of signed numbers, 706
  restoration of missing numerals, 146

e, 295-328
  applications of, 303-311, 316-328
  barometric pressure and elevation,
    316-320
  calculation of, 299, 301
  cooling, 320-324
  long distance telephoning, 327
  parachute jumping, 326
  slowing down of speeds, 324, 327
  suspension bridges, 328
  value of, 301

Earth, diameter, 104
Electron, weight, 179, 181
Electrons, number in the universe,
    73
Elevation above ground, 489-490
Elevation of gun, angle, 669-676
Ellipse, 406-411, 515, 518
  drawing of, 410
  equation of, 406-409
  foci, 411
  relation to circle, 411, 515, 518
Ellipsoid, equation of four-dimen-
    sional, 413
  equation of three-dimensional, 413
English system of measures, lengths,
    68
Equation of a curve, method of writ-
    ing, 394-396, 407-409, 414-417
Equations, 186-220, 718-727
  fractional, 196-198
  in one unknown, 186-193, 195, 201-
    208, 218-220, 718-722
  in two unknowns, 193-194, 722-724
  quadratic, 674-675, 724-727
Event, coordinates of, 612
Exponents, laws, 173-177, 266-269, 712-
    713
  method of writing numbers, 66-67
Extraction of roots, 218-221, 282, 385-
    386, 711, 714-715
  approximate method, 218-221
  concept of square roots, 385-386
  method of logarithms, 282
  numerical extraction, 714-715
Eyesight, measure of, 475

Faces, number of, in
  five-dimensional cube, 562
  four-dimensional cube (cuboid),
    562
  square, 561
  three-dimensional cube, 561
Fahrenheit, 138, 158-160, 320-324
Finger counting, 113
Finger multiplication, 114-116
Five-system of numeration, 9-10, 18,
    25
Flatland, description of, 371-372, 380-
    383
  properties of, 380-383, 389-390
Force, 629, 634-635, 684, 696-697
  centrifugal, 629, 684
  of collision, 696-697

Formula
  circumference of circle, 459
  elevation above ground, 489
  guessing ages and numbers, 155, 157
  horizon distance, 483
  instalments and interest, 238, 240
  sum of arithmetic progression, 235,
    716
  sum of geometric progression, 254,
    716
  sum of interior angles of a polygon,
    514, 515
Formulas for areas
  circle, 534
  parallelogram, 528
  rectangle, 528
  rhombus, 733
  square, 528
  trapezoid, 531
  trapezoidal rule, 535
  triangle, 528
Formulas for volumes
  circular cone, 552
  cube, 543
  prism, 544, 545
  pyramid, 552
  rectangular prism, 542-543
  right circular cylinder, 545
  right elliptical cylinder, 546
  sphere, 547
  trapezoidal rule, 543
Four dimensions, 389
Fractions
  addition, 708
  division, 709
  fundamental property, 708
  in various systems of numeration, 29
  in the twelve-system, 33
  multiplication, 709
  subtraction, 708
Future, representation of, 613

Galileo, 633
  law of falling bodies, 633, 651, 659
Generation of one-dimensional world,
    522
Generation of three-dimensional
    world, 523, 538
Generation of two-dimensional world,
    522
Generator of a cone, 601
Generator of a cylinder, 594
Geodesics, 585-608

Geometric progression, 246-263, 716
  any term, 253, 716
  sum of, 254, 716
  sum of decreasing terms, 255-260, 716
Geometry, coordinate, plane, 365-376,
    378-380, 386-387, 392-411, 413-419
  plane, 420-430, 456-460, 468, 493-537
  solid, 538-563, 585-608
Googol, 73-75, 401
Googolplex, 74, 112
Gravitation, 638, 640, 679, 684-685, 690-
    691, 701
  force of, 679, 684-685, 690-691, 701
  force of, for various latitudes, 690-
    691
  law, of universal, 640
Great circle, 605-608
Great Pyramid, 102-103
Grille, 89-98
Gyroscope, 664

Helix, 603
Here, coordinate of, 612
Horizon, 481-483
Horizon distance, formula for, 483
Horsepower, 645
Hyperbola, equation of, 418-419
  relation to circle, 515, 519

Impulse, 634-635, 646
Inequalities, method of, 568-570, 572
Infinity, 402, 515, 517
  graphical representation of, 515, 517
Instalment buying, 224-240
  formula for instalments and interest,
    238, 240
  of a house, 236-240
  periodical payments, 230-232
Instruments for surveying, 429-445, 450
Interest, compound, 260-262, 283-285,
    295-299
  simple, 228-229, 240-245
  on mortgages, 243-245
  on small loans, 240-243
Inverse operation, 385

Kasner, E., see googol and googol-
    plex, 73
Kepler, 630
Kepler's laws, 631

Law of cosines, 747
Law of falling bodies, 633, 651, 659

Law of sines, 747
Law of tangents, 747
Law of universal gravitation, 640
Laws of exponents, 173-177, 266-269, 712-713
Laws of Kepler, 631
Length of year, 103-104
Length, units of measure, 68
Life expectancy, 345-349
Light, speed of, 71, 76, 78
Linear equations, 186-220, 718-724
   in one unknown, 186-193, 195, 201-208, 218-220, 718-722
   rules for solution, 720-722
   systems in two unknowns, 722-724
Line-world, 378
Locks, see combinations, 356-359
Logarithms, 264-294, 717, 749-755
   at the base, 2, 269-271
   at the base 10, common, 271-280
   calculation of, 275-278
   characteristic, 280
   mantissa, 281
   of fractions, negative, 273, 280
   rules for operations with, 274-275, 282, 749-753
   tables, 749-755
Logarithms, applications of, to, 281-294
   Compound interest, 283-285
   Depreciation. 292-294
   Magnitude of starlight, 289-292
   Measurement of noise, 287-289
   Music, tempered scale, 285-287
   Price mark-up, 281-283

Magnification of angle of vision, 477
Mass, 633, 635
Mathematical expectation, 349-350
Maximum, 574, 577, 579, 581, 582
Mean, arithmetic, 579-580, 710
Measure of
   angle, 402-403
   area, unit of, 525
   eyesight, 475
   volume, unit of, 541
Mechanics, 609-640, 678-704
Metric system, lengths, 68
Million, 51-52
Million times, 53, 69
Minimum, 573, 579, 581-582
Missing numerals, problems with, 142-149
Molecule, dimensions of, 69-70

Mortgages, 243-245
Motion, accelerated, 622
Motion along a circle, 628
Motion, amount of, 634-635, 646
Motion uniform, 615, 621
   equation of, 621
Motion, uniformly accelerated, 622-626
   equation of, 625
Multiplication, 22-23, 25-27, 29, 108, 110-111, 127-133, 145, 163-166, 209-223, 707-709
   by complements, 130-132, 165, 209-223
   in various systems of numeration, 22-23, 25-27
   of approximate numbers, 108, 110-111
   of fractions, 709
   of polynomials, 707-708
   of signed numbers, 163, 706
   rapid, 127-133, 164-166, 209-223
   restoration of missing numerals, 145
Music, 285-287
Myriad, see Archimedes, 59-60, 74

Napier, John, 119, 265-266, 269, 272
Napier's rods, 117-121
   calculating machine, 120
   multiplication with, 118
Negative exponents, 67, 176
Negative numbers, 158-163
Newton, 628, 640
Newton's law of universal gravitation, 640
Normal vision, 475, 485
Notch, 1, 2, 11
Now, coordinate of, 612
Number
   absolute value, 159, 161
   negative, 158-163
   of electrons in the universe, 73
   positive, 158-163
Number curiosities, 39-45, 48-50, 166-170
   analyzed, 40-42, 166-170
Number, property of, 31-47
   2,   31
   5,   31
   9,   31
   12, 32-33
   99, 34
   365, 34
   999, 35
   1,001, 36

Number, 9,999, 38
  10,001, 37
  10,101, 37
  99,999, 38
  111,111, 38
  142,857, 45-47
  999,999, 38
Number scale, directed, 161, 516-517
Number system of Archimedes, 59-60
Number tricks, 150-157
Numbers, approximate, 103-104, 106, 108-112
Numbers, directed, 158-163, 706
  operations with, 706
Numbers, memorization of, 126-127
Numbers with repeated digits, 43-45
Numerals, 3-7
  Babylonian, 4
  Chinese, 5-6
  Egyptian, 4
  Greek, 7
  Hebrew, 7
  letter, 6-7, 127, 134-137
  missing and restoration of, 142-149
  Roman, 4-5
  Tatar, 3
Numeration, systems of, 9-33, 94-96, 137-142
  decimal, 9-10, 32
  five, 9-10, 18, 25
  three, 16-17, 25
    weight problems, 141-142
  twelve, 18, 27, 32-33
  two, 12-14, 25
    Chinese, Je-Kim, 15
    code writing, application to, 94-96
    puzzles and tricks, 137-141
  unitary, 11

Octade, see Archimedes, 60-61
Odds, 343-345
One dimension, 378
Orbit, 626-628
Origin of coordinates, 379, 392-393
  moving of, 393

Paper folding, 429-430
Parabola, 413-415, 419, 515, 519, 625-626
  equation of, 414
  graph of, 419
  relation to circle, 515, 519
  time line, 625-626
Parallel lines, 495, 500, 503, 518, 591, 729
  and infinity, 518
  transversal to, 591

Parallelogram, 505, **527**
  area, 527
Past, representation of, 613
Path of projectile, 650, 653, 656, 660, 685
Percent, 225-228
Percentage, three cases of, 226-227
Perpendicular lines, 398, 500
Physical relations, table, 635
Physics, 609-640, 678-704
Pi (π), 352, 458-459, 468, 513-**514**
  calculation of, 513
  in probability, 352
Plane, properties of, 522
Point-world, 377
Polygons, regular, 738-739
Polyhedra, 739-743
  areas of surfaces, 742-743
  descriptions of, 739-741
  volumes, 742-743
Power, 635
Powers, see exponents, 712-**713**
  operations with, 712-713
Present, representation of, 613
Prism, volume of, 542, 544-**545**
Probability, 329-353
  addition, 340-342
  coincidence, 333, 337, **342-343**, 348-349
  dice, 342-343
  measure of, 330-333
  multiplication of, 335-336
  odds, 343-345
  Needle problem of Count Buffon, see pi (π), 350-353
Problems with missing numerals, 134-137
Proportion, 424-426, 549-550, 555-558, 710
Protractor, 430
Pyramid, volume, 552
Pythagoras, theorem of, 383-385, 496-498, 733
  generalization, 497-498

Quadrangle, 500, 729-730, 733
Quadratics equations, 674-675, 724-727
  roots, 724-727
Quadrilateral, see quadrangle, 500

Radius of circle, 394
Railroad timetable, graph of, 613
Raising to a power, see exponents, 173-177, 266-269, 711

Rate of compounded growth, 303-305
Rate of continuous depreciation, 311-313
Rate, problems in, 199-201, 203-207
Ratio, 423, 425
Recoil of gun, 646-648
Rectangle, 108, 501-502, 526
  area, 108, 526
  diagonals, 502
Reflection of light, property of, 437
Restoration of missing numerals, 142-149
  addition, 143, 144
  construction of problems, 147-149
  division, 146
  multiplication, 145
  subtraction, 144
Rhombus, 502, 733
  area, 733
  diagonals, 502
Rifling of the gun barrel, 665
Roots, 218-221, 282, 385-386, 711-715
  extraction of (see extraction of roots)
  operations with, 712-713
  signs of, 711-712
Rule for creating worlds of any number of dimensions, 523
Rules for signs in operations with directed numbers, 161-163

Screw curve on a cylinder, 598, 600
Secant of circle, 603
Shortest distances, 585-608
Sides, number of, in
  five-dimensional cube, 562
  four-dimensional cube (cuboid), 562
  square, 561
  straight line, 560
  three-dimensional cube, 561
Signed numbers, 158-163, 706
  operations with, 706
Significant digits, 108-110
Signs, 705
Similarity of triangles, 422, 424-425, 548-549
Sine law, 747
Sine ratio, 403, 744
Sine ratios, table, 764-765
Small loans, interest on, 240-243
Small numbers, 65-67
Solid geometry, 538-563, 585-608
Solution of triangles, 453-455, 745, 747
Speed, 620

Speed of light, 71, 73
Sphere, 412, 546-547, 554, 605-608, 743
  area of surface, 554
  equation of four-dimensional, 412
  equation of ten-dimensional, 412
  equation of three-dimensional, 412
  great circle, 605
  shortest route on, 606-608
  volume, 546-547
Spinning top, see gyroscope, 664
Spiral screw, 603
Square, 384, 501
  area, 384
  diagonals, 501
  properties of, 384
Square root, 218-221, 385-386, 714-715
  concept of, 385-386
  extraction of, approximate methods, 218-221
  numerical extraction, 714-715
Square roots of numbers, table, 758-762
Square unit of measure, 525
Squares of numbers, table, 753, 756-757
Straight line
  equation of, 374-376
  graph of, 375
  properties of, 378
  shortest distance, along a, 586
Subtraction
  in various systems of numeration, 20-21, 29
  of approximate numbers, 110-111
  of fractions, 709
  of signed numbers, 161, 706
  restoration of missing numerals, 144
Sum of interior angles of a
  polygon, 514-515
  quadrangle, 503
  triangle, 421, 514
Symbols, 705

Tables of
  Addition for various systems of numeration, 24-27
  American Experience Mortality, 347
  Logarithms of numbers, 749-755
  Multiplication for various systems of numeration, 24-27
  Physical relations, 635
  Squares of numbers, 753, 756-757
  Square roots of numbers, 758-762
  Trigonometric ratios (sine, cosine, and tangent), 763-769
Tabulation, 1-2

Tangent law, 747
Tangent ratio, 399-405, 744
Tangent ratios, table, 768-769
Tangent to circle, 481, 603, 736
Tangent to sphere, 481, 604
Target distance, 663
Temperature
    absolute, 159-160, 702
    Centigrade, 158-160, 180-181
    Fahrenheit, 138, 158-160, 320-324
Test for odd and even numbers, 28-30
Three dimensions, 387-388
Three-system of numeration, 16-17, 25
Time, 609, 635
Time coordinate, 610
Time line, motion along a straight line
    accelerated motion, 623
    uniform motion, 618
    uniformly accelerated motion, 626
Time line, motion in plane, 625-628
Trajectory, see path of projectile, 650,
        653, 656, 660, 685
    equation of, 660, 662, 669, 674
Trapezoid, properties of, 506
    area, 530
Trapezoidal rule for
    areas, 534-536
    volumes, 543
Triangle
    area, 531
    equilateral, 426
    exterior angle, 592, 602
    isosceles, 427, 496
    properties of, 421
    right, 384, 496
    sum of interior angles, 421, 514
Triangles, 728, 731-734
    congruent, 421, 426
    similar, 422, 424-425, 493, 548-549
Trigonometric ratios, 446-450, 452-455,
        460-465
    calculation of, 460-465
    tables, 763-769

Trigonometry, fundamental relations,
        744-747
    fundamental formulas, 745-746
    solution of right triangles, 745
    solution of triangles, 747
Twelve-system of numeration, 18, 27,
        32-33
Two dimensions, 380-383, 389-390
Two-system of numeration, 12-14, 25

Unit of area, 525
Unit of volume, 541

Veering effect of a projectile, 668
Velocity, 620, 634
    component, 627, 659, 661
Velocity of escape from earth, 701-704
Vertices, number of, in
    five-dimensional cube, 562
    four-dimensional cube (cuboid), 562
    square, 561
    straight line, 560
    three-dimensional cube, 561
Vision, normal, 474, 485
Volume
    concept of, 539
    of rectangular prism, rule for com-
        putation, 542
    of sphere, 546-547
    unit of measure, 541
Volumes of
    polyhedra, 742-743
    similar solids, 556, 558, 564, 567

Walking in circle, 465-468
Wave length, 77
Weight, 633, 645
Work, 635, 644
Work problems, 196-198

Zero dimensions, 377
Zero point of coordinates, see origin
        of coordinates, 379